Symbol	Meaning	Section(s)
$\hat{g}(x)$, $\hat{L}(X)$	Least square solutions	5.1B, 5.1C
I, I_n	Identity matrix	3.1E
IVP	Initial value problem	8.1A
$(\text{IVP})_x$	IVP associated with $(\text{BVP})_2$	8.5A
$(\lambda, \mathbf{v})$	Eigenpair for an $n \times n$ matrix A	9.1A
$L_j(x)$	jth Lagrange polynomial	6.1B
$L\backslash U$, $\hat{L}\backslash\hat{U}$	Compact form of LU-factorization of A, $\hat{A}$	3.3B, 3.3C
$[\hat{L}\backslash\hat{U} : \hat{\mathbf{b}} : \overline{\mathbf{c}} : \overline{\mathbf{x}}]$	Forback matrix for solving $\hat{A}\mathbf{x} = \hat{\mathbf{b}}$	3.3B, 3.3E
m_k	Slope for a slope method formula	2.2A
$\|\ \|$	Norm of a vector or matrix	3.5E, 4.2C
NR	Newton–Raphson method	2.2B, 4.6B
O, O_{mxn}	Zero matrix	3.1B
$O(h^n)$	nth order convergence to zero as $h \to 0$	7.1A
PEP	Partial Extended Precision	4.1D
$p_{k,k+m}(x)$	Interpolating polynomial for $P_k, \ldots, P_{k+m}$	6.1B
$P_n(x)$	nth Taylor polynomial	5.4A
Q	Quantity (exact) approximated by $F[h]$	7.1A
$\rho_i \rightleftarrows \rho_j$	Interchange rows i and j of a matrix	3.3G, 3.4A
ρ_x	Relative error of X	1.6A
$\rho[h]$	Roundoff error when using formula $F[h]$	7.1C
$R(g)$	Determination index of $g(x)$	5.3D
$R_{ij}(\theta)$	Rotation matrix	9.3B
RK4	Fourth-order Runge–Kutta method	8.2C
RKF4	Fourth-order Runge–Kutta–Fehlberg method	2.2C
$R_n(x)$	nth Taylor remainder	1.5D, 5.4A
σ_k	Variable for $s''(x_k)$; s is a cubic spline	6.4C
s	Significant digit accuracy (e.g., $4s$)	1.4A
SEC	Secant Method	2.2E
$S[h]$	Composite Simpson's rule	7.4A
SPP	Scaled Partial Pivoting strategy	4.1B
$\tau[h]$	Truncation error	7.1A
$T[h]$	Composite Trapezoidal Rule	7.4A
$T_k(\xi)$	kth Chebyshev polynomial	5.4C
trid $(\mathbf{a}, \mathbf{b}, \mathbf{c})$	Tridiagonal matrix	3.4D
$\overline{x}$	Solution of a nonlinear equation	2.1B
$\overline{\mathbf{x}}$	Solution of a system of equations	3.2A, 4.6A
$y(t)$	Exact solution of a differential equation	8.1A
$y_x(t)$	Exact solution of $(\text{IVP})_x$	8.5A

Numerical Analysis: A Practical Approach

Numerical Analysis:

A Practical Approach

Melvin J. Maron
University of Louisville

Macmillan Publishing Co., Inc.
New York

Collier Macmillan Publishers
London

Macmillan Publishing Co., Inc.
866 Third Avenue, New York, New York 10022

Collier Macmillan Canada, Inc.

ISBN: 0-02-475670-9

Printing: 3 4 5 6 7 8   Year: 4 5 6 7 8 9

ISBN   0-02-475670-9

To the memory of my mentor and friend,
Norman Molomut

Preface

Numerical analysis is concerned with methods for generating numerical answers when analytic procedures are either computationally difficult or nonexistent. The primary purpose of this text is to produce intelligent users of the practical methods of numerical analysis.

An intelligent user of a particular method should possess:

- A sound intuitive grasp of the mathematical basis for the method.
- An understanding of how the method proceeds when it is working well.
- An awareness of the conditions under which the method can fail.
- The ability to recognize failure from the progression of the method.

The topics covered in this book are standard for an introductory sophomore-senior-level numerical analysis or numerical methods course. Generally, only one or two methods for each type of problem are presented in detail. The methods selected are those considered closest to the current "state of the art," which can be presented clearly using only calculus and the concepts introduced in this book.

Much emphasis is put on practical techniques for assessing whether a method works successfully. Simple indicators such as the *pivot condition number* (for an ill-conditioned matrix—Section 4.2B) and the *index of determination* (for good least square fit—Section 5.3D) are described and illustrated in greater detail than in most texts. Also, formulas that allow the user to form improved estimates from available approximations, for example, the formulas of *Aitken* (Section 2.3B) and *Richardson* (Section 7.1D), are used extensively.

Most of the sections that present new methods proceed in the following order.

A. A thorough description of each method covered, including:
   1. *The mathematical basis for the method.* This is presented in a way that offers the best intuitive and/or geometric insight into why the method should work. Proofs or derivations are given at this point only if they are short and can help the reader gain this insight.
   2. *A pseudoprogram describing the algorithm for the method.* This is given in a structured form suitable for easy translation to a computer program.
   3. *Numerical examples illustrating how the method generates numbers.* For the sake of comparison, all methods for a particular problem are illustrated using the same example(s). Rates of convergence are observed empirically at this time.
B. Examples illustrating what can go wrong. Where appropriate, simple procedures for recognizing, avoiding, and dealing with troublesome situations are given at this time.
C. Practical considerations of implementation.
D. Deferred proofs and derivations, and more sophisticated error analyses. These are given after the reader has had experience with the method.

In any section, the (A) and (B) materials alone are designed to give the reader a sound understanding of how and why the methods covered work. The instructor is then free to use his or her individual approach to these methods by covering some, all, or none of the computational (C) material and the mathematical (D) material. Suggestions for exercising this flexibility are described in an Instructor's Manual, available upon request from the publisher.

Throughout, an attempt is made to defer consideration of any concept until just before it can be reinforced by being used as a tool. Thus, although roundoff error is considered from the outset, truncation error is not discussed systematically until Chapter 7, from which point it is used extensively. The chapters are ordered so that each one is either an extension or application of the preceding one. As a result:

- Curve fitting (Chapter 5) is presented earlier than in most texts because it provides a particularly useful application of the material in Chapters 3 and 4. However, it can be deferred until later, if desired, without disrupting the continuity of the presentation.
- Interpolation (Chapter 6) appears just after the related material on curve fitting and just before Chapter 7, where it is used as a tool for obtaining formulas for derivatives and integrals. However, it can be covered earlier (even before Chapter 1) if desired.
- Matrix eigenvalues are covered in the first part of Chapter 9, where their role in solving linear differential equations can be used for motivation. However, this material can be covered right after Section 4.2.

The reader is assumed to be familiar with the calculus concepts summarized in Appendix II. Self-contained presentations of the relevant material from introductory courses in linear algebra, differential equations, and computer science are given in the text itself.

Specifically, there are introductory discussions of the following material:

- The way digital devices store numbers and the kinds of roundoff errors that this storage can produce (Sections 1.1 through 1.5).
- The basic properties of matrices (Section 3.1), determinants (Section 3.5), and eigenvalues (Section 9.1).
- The existence and uniqueness of solutions of first-order initial value problems (Sections 8.1A and 8.4F).

This material appears just before it is needed, where it can serve as a handy reference for all readers. Readers familiar with the linear algebra and differential equation material are urged to peruse the introductory discussions to become familiar with the notation (which is for the most part standard). Readers familiar with the kinds of roundoff error that occur when using fixed precision arithmetic can go right to Section 1.6.

Most of the algorithms are presented as pseudoprograms as described in Section 1.7B and Appendix I. A list of algorithms is given inside the back cover. The pseudoprograms are designed to be read and understood by anyone having some experience with any programming language. "Slick" programming devices for improving the efficiency of either computer storage or execution time are generally *not* incorporated in the pseudocode. They are, however, included in the "implementation" discussion later in the section.

Some representative, nontrivial subroutines have been included to illustrate the translation from pseudocode to actual code and to give the reader some familiarity with the use of "canned" software. These subroutines are in ANSI FORTRAN,† not because of any desirable characteristics of the language itself, but rather because of the likelihood that it will be familiar to the reader. They are intended to exemplify general purpose code that is reliable, accurate, and, to the extent allowed by the language, well structured. No attempt was made to use features peculiar to FORTRAN to improve the efficiency of these programs.

Although computer programs are given for only a few selected methods, numerous runs of actual computer programs are given and discussed critically. These were all performed on the University of Louisville's DEC-1090 system.

The reader interested in using available software is urged to examine the extensive IMSL (International Mathematical and Statistical Library) package. Other commercially available software will be noted as appropriate.

The exercises at the end of each chapter have evolved over the two years that various drafts of this book were class-tested. Most of them can be done using a hand calculator although readers who wish to write their own programs to solve them are encouraged to do so. Each chapter's exercises are given by section, followed by "Computer and Programming Exercises." The exercises that require writing a program can be done in any language, not necessarily in FORTRAN.

† Two deviations from ANSI FORTRAN have been incorporated consistently to improve readability: Input (from read device IR) is made using an unformatted READ(IR, *); and output of character strings (to write device IW) is indicated using single quotes rather than the standard Hollerith format. These I/O statements may have to be changed to run on some computers.

Every attempt was made to choose notation that provides the most precision with the least clutter. In particular, the simultaneous use of sub- and superscripts, for example, $x_n^{(k)}$, is avoided whereas suggestive notation such as $[\leftarrow]_L$ ("look left in L"), $L\backslash U$ (the compact form of a triangular factorization), and Δ (divided difference) is used extensively. For the reader's convenience, a glossary of symbols is given inside the front cover.

I wish to thank R. Leonard Brown (Drexel University), John Hoff (TimeWare, Palo Alto, California), Larry R. Nyhoff (Calvin College), Stanley Preiser (Polytechnic Institute of New York), and George E. Witter (Western Washington University) for their constructive reviews; and Jeanette Myers (Georgia Institute of Technology) for her critical review of the programs and pseudoprograms. I am also grateful for the assistance of Greg Darnley, who helped prepare the FORTRAN programs; Sam Jensen and Scott Miller, who checked answers to the exercises; Jan Maclaughlin, Sherri Breeze, and especially Wendy Dickson who typed various drafts of the manuscript; the many students who offered criticisms and corrections of the class notes that became the manuscript; and the Dean's Office of the Speed Scientific School for the computing resources and secretarial assistance it generously provided.

I also wish to express my appreciation for the assistance provided by Wayne Yuhasz, Senior Editor, and the very competent production staff of the Macmillan Publishing Co., Inc., especially my production editor, Elaine Wetterau. Finally, my thanks to my wife Anne for her support and forbearance during the last three years.

M. J. M.

Contents

2   Numerical Methods for Finding Roots and Solving Equations   43

3 Solving Linear Systems Exactly Using Direct Methods

7 Numerical Methods for Differentiation and Integration   273

8 Numerical Methods for Ordinary Differential Equations   333

9 Eigenvalues   391

APPENDIXES

Numerical Analysis: A Practical Approach

1

Computers, Errors, and Algorithms

Introduction   1.0

This book deals with the use of digital devices (calculators and computers) to obtain numerical answers to certain mathematical problems. All digital devices have one thing in common: They are incapable of recognizing *all* real numbers. However, the "recognizable" numbers differ from device to device and affect the *accuracy* that it is capable of achieving. Digital devices also differ with regard to *speed* (computers are generally faster than calculators), *expense* (calculators are generally cheaper to buy and use than computers), *storage capability* and *input/out* (usually better on computers), and capability of being *programmed* (usually better on computers).

The purpose of this chapter is to describe how both programmable and nonprogrammable digital devices perform arithmetic operations, and to develop the mathematical tools for assessing the accuracy of these operations. This understanding is then incorporated in a discussion of *iterative algorithms*.

What Is a Numerical Method?   1.1

In elementary calculus one learns how to use differentiation and integration to get *exact* answers to a remarkably diverse range of realistic problems that could not be solved by purely algebraic methods. Unfortunately, from a practical point of view, the techniques of elementary (or even advanced) calculus alone are not adequate for solving calculus-type problems such as:

1

Problem 1. Find the maximum and minimum values on the interval [0, 1] of

$$F(x) = x^6 + 5x^4 - 9x + 1$$

This requires solving the fifth-degree polynomial equation

$$F'(x) = 6x^5 + 20x^3 - 9 = 0$$

Problem 2. Evaluate $\int_0^b e^{-x^2}\, dx$ and $\int_0^b \frac{\sin x}{x}\, dx$ for a given $b > 0$.

Problem 3. Find $y = y(t)$ that satisfies the differential equation

$$\frac{dy}{dt} = y^2 + t^2, \quad y(0) = 1 \qquad (\text{i.e., } y = 1 \text{ at } t = 0)$$

Problem 4. Find the local extrema of the two-variable function†

$$f(x, y) = xe^y - \ln(2x^2 + y^2)$$

This requires solving simultaneously the equations

$$\frac{\partial f}{\partial x} = e^y - \frac{4x}{2x^2 + y^2} = 0 \qquad \text{and} \qquad \frac{\partial f}{\partial y} = xe^y - \frac{2y}{2x^2 + y^2} = 0$$

The reader is invited to try to solve problems 1–4 but is warned against trying too hard because it is impossible to get explicit formulas to "plug into" to obtain exact answers to any of them!

Fortunately, one rarely needs *exact* answers. Indeed, in the "real world" the problems themselves are usually inexact because they are generally posed in terms of parameters that are *measured,* hence only approximate. What one is likely to require in a realistic situation is not an exact answer but rather one having a prescribed accuracy.

1.1A NUMERICAL METHODS AND TERMINATION TESTS

The word **algorithm** is used to describe a step-by-step procedure that requires a finite number of steps. A **numerical method** is an algorithm for finding a numerical quantity to a prescribed accuracy.

EXAMPLE
a. Describe a general numerical method for finding the derivative of a given function f at a prescribed point x to four-decimal-place accuracy.‡

---

† Throughout the text, ln will be used for $\log_e$, the *natural logarithm.*
‡ When we say that "X approximates x to d decimal places," we mean that X and x differ by less than $\frac{1}{2}$ unit in the dth place, that is, $|X - x| < \frac{1}{2} \cdot 10^{-d}$.

b. Use this method to approximate

$$\frac{d}{dx}(\sin x)\bigg|_{x=0}$$

to four-decimal-place accuracy.

Solution

a. In the absence of a universal differentiation formula we must go back to the definition of the derivative of f at x, namely

$$f'(x) = \lim_{h \to 0} \frac{\Delta f(x)}{h} \qquad \text{(if it exists)} \tag{1a}$$

where

$$\frac{\Delta f(x)}{h} = \frac{f(x+h) - f(x)}{h}, \qquad \text{the \textbf{difference quotient} of } f \text{ at } x \tag{1b}$$

The natural approach to this problem is to

$$\text{approximate } f'(x) \text{ by } \frac{\Delta f(x)}{h} \text{ for a suitably small } h \tag{2}$$

The values of h that are small enough to ensure that $\Delta f(x)/h$ approximates $f'(x)$ to four-place accuracy depend upon the given function f and the (fixed) specified point x. To help determine a suitable h, we can simply

$$\text{evaluate } \frac{\Delta f(x)}{h} \text{ for a sequence of decreasing } h\text{'s} \tag{3}$$

stopping when

$$E[h] = f'(x) - \frac{\Delta f(x)}{h} = \text{the error of the approximation} \tag{4}$$

is sufficiently close to zero. Although this strategy sounds simple enough, it is confounded by the fact that we cannot presume to know what $f'(x)$ is. (If we did, we would not need a numerical method!) So we shall simply continue (3) until the calculated difference quotients appear to be "close enough."

Since we must repeat the same calculation [of $\Delta f(x)/h$] for several h's, we shall implement strategy (3) in the FORTRAN program DERIV shown in Figure 1.1-1. To use it, we must specify an *initial h*, a *shrinking ratio r*, and *the number of desired repetitions* of the following steps:

$$\begin{aligned} &\text{Calculate and print } h \text{ and } \Delta f(x)/h. \\ &h \leftarrow h/r \text{ \{replace } h \text{ by (current } h)/r\} \end{aligned} \tag{5}$$

```
00100    C * * * * * * * * * * *    DERIV    * * * * * * * * * * * * *
00200    C APPROXIMATE F'(X) BY DQ[H], H=HO, HO/R, ... , HO/R**(NREPS-1)
00300    C
00400    C SET IW=WRITE DEVICE #, IR=READ DEVICE # (COMPUTER DEPENDENT)
00500            DATA IW, IR /5, 5/
00600    C
00700            F(X) = SIN(X)
00800    C
00900    C GET PARAMETER VALUES AND PRINT HEADING
01000            WRITE(IW,1)
01100          1 FORMAT('0ENTER X, HO, SHRINKING RATIO, # REPETITIONS')
01200            READ(IR,*) X, H, R, NREPS
01300            WRITE(IW,2)
01400          2 FORMAT('0        H', 11X, 'DQ[H]')
01500    C
01600    C ITERATE
01700            DO 10 N=1, NREPS
01800              DQ = (F(X+H) - F(X))/H
01900              WRITE (5,3) H, DQ
02000          3   FORMAT(E13.5, 2X, F11.6)
02100              H = H/R
02200         10 CONTINUE
02300            STOP
02400            END
```

FIGURE 1.1-1   DERIV: A FORTRAN PROGRAM FOR ESTIMATING $f'(x)$.

These steps are done in lines† 1700–2200 using the function specified in line 700.

b. We are faced with the problem of finding an h that is sufficiently small to make $\Delta f(x)/h$ approximate $f'(x)$ when $f(x) = \sin x$ and $x = 0$. Let us arbitrarily choose

$$H_{\text{initial}} = 1, \ R = \text{shrinking ratio} = 4, \text{ and NREPS} = 8 \tag{6}$$

A run of DERIV using these values is shown in Figure 1.1-2.‡ In this case we know that the exact value of $f'(x)$ (x in radians) is

$$f'(x) = \frac{d}{dx}(\sin x)\bigg|_{x=0} = \cos 0 = 1 \tag{7}$$

So we have added an E[H] column to display the error for each of the calculated values of $\Delta f(x)/h$ shown in the DQ[H] column. It can be seen from Figure 1.1-2 that

$$h = \tfrac{1}{16} = 0.0625 \quad \Rightarrow \text{DQ}[h] = 0.9993 \qquad \text{(rounded to four decimal places)} \tag{8a}$$

$$h = \tfrac{1}{64} = 0.015625 \Rightarrow \text{DQ}[h] = 1.0000 \qquad \text{(rounded to four decimal places)} \tag{8b}$$

So $h = \tfrac{1}{64}$ is sufficiently small to ensure that $\Delta f(x)/h$ approximates $\sin'(0)$ to four-place accuracy. Notice that §

$$\text{DQ}[\tfrac{1}{64}] - \text{DQ}[\tfrac{1}{16}] = 0.999959 - 0.999349 = 0.000610 \approx \text{E}[\tfrac{1}{16}] \tag{9a}$$

$$\text{DQ}[\tfrac{1}{256}] - \text{DQ}[\tfrac{1}{64}] = 0.999997 - 0.999959 = 0.000038 \approx \text{E}[\tfrac{1}{64}] \tag{9b}$$

† The **line numbers** (to the left of the program listing in Figure 1.1-1) are included for ease of reference. *They are not part of the FORTRAN program.* It is important not to confuse them with the **statement numbers** (e.g., 1 in line 1100 and 2 in line 1400) that are part of the program.

‡ The underlined numbers indicate input values entered from a terminal.

§ The symbol "$\approx$" should be read as "is approximately to."

```
          ENTER X, HO, SHRINKING RATIO, # REPETITIONS
          0, 1, 4, 8


               H             DQ[H]        E[H]=F'(X)-DQ[H]
          0.10000E+01      0.841471          0.158529
          0.25000E+00      0.989616          0.010384
          0.62500E-01      0.999349          0.000651
          0.15625E-01      0.999959          0.000041
          0.39063E-02      0.999997          0.000003
          0.97656E-03      1.000000          0.000000
          0.24414E-03      1.000000          0.000000
          0.61035E-04      1.000000          0.000000
```

FIGURE 1.1-2   USING DERIV TO GET $\dfrac{d}{dx} (\sin x) \mid_{x=0}$ TO FOUR-PLACE ACCURACY.

More generally, the difference between two successive estimates, that is,

$$\Delta DQ = DQ[h] - DQ[\text{preceding } h] \tag{10}$$

is a number that can be *evaluated without knowing $f'(x)$* and *used to approximate the error of DQ[preceding h]*. Consequently, rather than perform all NREPS repetitions, we could have discontinued the repetitions when the magnitude of ΔDQ is sufficiently small. A suitable condition for four-place accuracy is

$$|\Delta DQ| < 10^{-4} \tag{11}$$

In view of (9), this **termination test** would have stopped the iterations after printing H = $\frac{1}{256}$ and DQ = 0.999997.

1.1B WHY USE A PROGRAMMABLE DEVICE FOR NUMERICAL METHODS?

The preceding discussion illustrates three characteristics of programmable devices (i.e., computers or programmable calculators) that make them well suited for numerical methods.

1. *Flexibility.* Notice how easy it is to change the function F in line 700 of DERIV. Once this program is stored, the derivative of any $f(x)$ can be approximated numerically at any point x to any (reasonable) prescribed number of decimal places by simply modifying this line and then entering the necessary values of H, R, and NREPS during execution.
2. *Efficiency.* The algorithm coded in DERIV is typical of many numerical algorithms in the sense that a single procedure (calculate the next DQ, output H and DQ, then "shrink" H) is repeated until a termination criterion is satisfied. Such algorithms are called **iterative**. An iterative algorithm can be programmed very efficiently using a **loop**. The loop in Figure 1.1-1 requires only six FORTRAN statements (lines 1700–2200), but they can be repeated as many times as necessary.

3. *Speed and reliability.* Once a program is debugged and given the necessary input data, it will step through the programmed algorithm *faster* and *more reliably* than any human being could hope to.

It is no accident that we used the word *reliably* rather than the word *accurately* as the reader might have expected. The reasons for this are discussed in the next section.

1.2   Do Digital Devices Make Mistakes?

Calculators and computers do what they are designed to do almost flawlessly. In fact, modern computers typically can perform billions of operations without making a single "mistake." Nevertheless, *digital devices often give erroneous answers!*

All too frequently, incorrect answers are the result of **human error.** The blame for these errors can usually be traced to the programmer (logical error in the program), the keypuncher (typographical error in either the program or in the input data), or the user (incorrect input data, formula, or method). *There is only one remedy for such errors: Find them and make the appropriate corrections.* In all of our discussions of numerical output we shall presume that both input and programs are logically correct and accurately keyed in. However, *the reader should always be alert for the possibility that human error is the cause of unreasonable computer or calculator answers.*

A second source of digital errors is a bit more subtle. There are legitimate mathematical procedures that yield the correct answer when carried out *analytically* (i.e., using analysis with real numbers) but that yield erroneous answers when carried out *numerically* (i.e., on a computer or calculator).

1.2A   AN EXAMPLE OF DIGITAL DEVICE ERRORS

Let A and B be defined by

$$A = \frac{1 - \cos x}{x^2} \quad \text{and} \quad B = \frac{\sin^2 x}{x^2 \, (1 + \cos x)} \tag{1}$$

Upon multiplying A by $(1 + \cos x)/(1 + \cos x)$, we see that A and B are equal for all nonzero values of x for which $\cos x \neq -1$. In particular,

If $x = 0 + 0.1$,   then $A = B = 0.499583$; if $x = \pi + 0.1$,   then $A = B = 0.189857$
If $x = 0 + 0.01$,   then $A = B = 0.499996$; if $x = \pi + 0.01$,   then $A = B = 0.201353$
If $x = 0 + 0.001$,   then $A = B = 0.500000$; if $x = \pi + 0.001$,   then $A = B = 0.202513$
If $x = 0 + 0.0001$,   then $A = B = 0.500000$; if $x = \pi + 0.0001$,   then $A = B = 0.202629$
If $x = 0 + 0.00001$, then $A = B = 0.500000$; if $x = \pi + 0.00001$, then $A = B = 0.202641$

The common values of A and B shown have been rounded to six decimal places. A computer program for computing A and B for these 10 values of x is shown in Figure

```
00100    C  * * * * * * * *  ERROR  * * * * * * * * * * * * *
00200    C  THIS PROGRAM DEMONSTRATES DIGITAL DEVICE ERRORS
00300    C
00400          DATA  IW, IR  /5, 5/
00500          WRITE(IW,1)
00600        1 FORMAT('0ENTER THE LIMITING VALUE OF X')
00700          READ(IR,*) XLIMIT
00800    C
00900          H = 0.1
01000          DO 10 K=1, 5
01100             X = XLIMIT + H
01200    C
01300             A = (1 - COS(X))/X**2
01400             B = (SIN(X)/X)**2/(1 + COS(X))
01500    C
01600             WRITE (IW,2) X, A, B
01700        2    FORMAT(' IF X=',F9.6,'  THEN    A=',E13.6,
01800        &             '  AND    B=',E13.6)
01900             H = H/10
02000       10 CONTINUE
02100          STOP
02200          END

ENTER THE LIMITING VALUE OF X
0

IF X= 0.100000  THEN    A= 0.499584E+00    AND    B= 0.499583E+00
IF X= 0.010000  THEN    A= 0.500008E+00    AND    B= 0.499996E+00
IF X= 0.001000  THEN    A= 0.506639E+00    AND    B= 0.500000E+00
IF X= 0.000100  THEN    A= 0.745058E+00    AND    B= 0.500000E+00
IF X= 0.000010  THEN    A= 0.000000E+00    AND    B= 0.500000E+00

ENTER THE LIMITING VALUE OF X
3.14159265

IF X= 3.241593  THEN    A= 0.189857E+00    AND    B= 0.189857E+00
IF X= 3.151593  THEN    A= 0.201353E+00    AND    B= 0.201346E+00
IF X= 3.142593  THEN    A= 0.202513E+00    AND    B= 0.199852E+00
IF X= 3.141693  THEN    A= 0.202629E+00    AND    B= 0.135837E+00
%FRSAPR Floating divide check    PC= 235

IF X= 3.141603  THEN    A= 0.202641E+00    AND    B= 0.170141E+39
```

FIGURE 1.2-1   A FORTRAN PROGRAM TO CALCULATE A AND B NEAR 0 AND π.

1.2-1. Digits that would be incorrect *after rounding* were underlined for clarity in the output of the two runs shown below the program.

Evidently, a computer can calculate B accurately near 0, and A accurately near π, but produces complete garbage upon "correctly" calculating A near 0 or B near π. So computers are certainly capable of giving wrong answers!

As it turned out in Figure 1.2-1, a warning was given to indicate that something was going amiss in calculating B for x near π. What is really troublesome about Figure 1.2-1 is the first run (x near 0), which shows that:

Computers make no judgment about the correctness of the values they produce; they will display nonsensical answers as neatly and authoritatively as correct ones.

Indeed, we could find ourselves in serious trouble if we believed A to be zero when $x = 0.00001$ just because a computer said so.

1.2B ERRORS IN USING THE QUADRATIC FORMULA

The two roots of the general quadratic equation

$$ax^2 + bx + c = 0 \qquad (a \neq 0) \tag{2}$$

can be expressed in terms of the normalized values

```
00100   C * * * * * * * * * * * *   QUAD   * * * * * * * * * * * * * *
00200   C THIS PROGRAM DEMONSTRATES ERRORS THAT CAN OCCUR WHEN USING
00300   C THE QUADRATIC FORMULA TO FIND THE REAL ROOTS OF A*X**2+B*X+C
00400   C
00500         DATA IW, IR /5, 5/
00600         WRITE(IW,1)
00700       1 FORMAT('0FOR REAL ROOTS OF AX**2+BX+C, INPUT A, B, C')
00800         READ(IR,*) A, B, C
00900   C
01000         B1 = -0.5*B/A
01100         C1 = C/A
01200         DISC = B1*B1 - C1
01300         IF (DISC .GE. 0.) GOTO 20
01400           WRITE(IW,2)
01500       2   FORMAT(' ROOTS ARE COMPLEX')
01600           STOP
01700   C
01800   C     REAL ROOTS: FIND THEM AS R(+), C1/R(+) AND AS R(-), C1/R(-)
01900      20 D1 = SQRT(DISC)
02000         RPLUS  = B1 + D1
02100         RMINU  = B1 - D1
02200         R2PLUS = C1/RPLUS
02300         R2MINU = C1/RMINU
02400   C
02500         WRITE(IW,3) RPLUS, RMINU, R2PLUS, R2MINU
02600       3 FORMAT(' ROOTS:      R(+) = ',E13.6,5X,'   R(-) = ',E13.6,
02700      &       /'      C1/R(+) = ',E13.6,5X,'C1/R(-) = ',E13.6)
02800         STOP
02900         END
```

```
FOR REAL ROOTS OF AX**2+BX+C, INPUT A, B, C
2, 9, -5

ROOTS:      R(+) =  0.500000E+00        R(-) = -0.500000E+01
        C1/R(+) = -0.500000E+01    C1/R(-) =  0.500000E+00

FOR REAL ROOTS OF AX**2+BX+C, INPUT A, B, C
1, -100.01, 1

ROOTS:      R(+) =  0.100000E+03        R(-) =  0.100002E-01
        C1/R(+) =  0.100000E-01    C1/R(-) =  0.999977E+02

FOR REAL ROOTS OF AX**2+BX+C, INPUT A, B, C
1, +100.01, 1

ROOTS:      R(+) = -0.100002E-01        R(-) = -0.100000E+03
        C1/R(+) = -0.999977E+02    C1/R(-) = -0.100000E-01
```

FIGURE 1.2-2 A FORTRAN PROGRAM TO COMPUTE $r(+)$, $r(-)$, $c_1/r(+)$, AND $c_1/r(-)$.

$$b_1 = \frac{-b}{2a}, \qquad c_1 = \frac{c}{a}, \qquad \text{and} \qquad d_1 = \sqrt{b_1^2 - c_1} \tag{3a}$$

using the following form of the quadratic formula:

$$r(+) = b_1 + d_1 \qquad \text{and} \qquad r(-) = b_1 - d_1 \tag{3b}$$

It follows from (3b) and (3a) that $r(+)r(-) = b_1^2 - d_1^2 = c_1$ so that

$$\frac{c_1}{r(+)} = r(-) \qquad \text{and} \qquad \frac{c_1}{r(-)} = r(+) \tag{3c}$$

provided that we do not divide by zero.

The computer program of Figure 1.2-2 was used to calculate $r(+)$, $r(-)$, $c_1/r(+)$, and $c_1/r(-)$ for three quadratics. For the first, all four were correct to the accuracy shown. However, for the second, only $r(+)$ and $c_1/r(+)$ were accurate, whereas for the third only $r(-)$ and $c_1/r(-)$ were accurate. As in Section 1.2A, whether one formula for calculating a given quantity is more accurate than another depends upon the numbers involved.

It is important to realize that *the errors in Figures 1.2-1 and 1.2-2 are not unique to computers. They also occur when using a hand calculator,* as will be seen in doing the exercises. Fortunately, such errors can often be avoided or at least minimized once we understand *why* they occur. This in turn requires an examination of the way in which computers and calculators store real numbers and perform mathematical operations on them. We do this next.

How Do Computers Store Real Numbers?   **1.3**

We begin by reviewing the binary (base 2) representation of numbers.

1.3A   BINARY NUMBERS

A **binary number** is a real number X that can be expressed as

$$\boxed{X = \pm[(b_n 2^n + b_{n-1} 2^{n-1} + \cdots + b_1 2^1 + b_0)] + [(b_{-1} 2^{-1} + b_{-2} 2^{-2} + \cdots + b_{-k} 2^{-k})]} \tag{1a}$$

$$\underbrace{\qquad\qquad\qquad\quad}_{\text{integer part of } X} \qquad \underbrace{\qquad\qquad\qquad}_{\text{fractional part of } X}$$

where the coefficients b_i, which we shall call **bits,**† are 0 or 1. The expression on the right in (1a) is called the **binary** (or **base 2**) **expansion** of X; it is usually abbreviated as the **binary representation**

---

† The word *bit* is an abbreviation for *binary digit.*

$$X = \pm(b_n b_{n-1} \cdots b_1 b_0 . b_{-1} b_{-2} \cdots b_{-k})_2, \qquad \text{all } b_i\text{'s are 0 or 1} \tag{1b}$$

The period in front of b_{-1} is the **binary point.** The real number X is an $(n+1)$-**bit integer** if it can be represented (possibly with leading 0's) as $\pm(b_n b_{n-1} \cdots b_1 b_0)_2$, and a k-**bit fraction** if it can be represented (possibly with trailing 0's) as $\pm(0.b_{-1}b_{-2} \cdots b_{-k})_2$. For example, 5.25 is a binary number because it can be expressed as follows:

$$5.25 = 5\tfrac{1}{4} = +[(1 \cdot 2^2 + 0 \cdot 2^1 + 1) + (0 \cdot 2^{-1} + 1 \cdot 2^{-2})] = \qquad +(101.01)_2 \tag{2}$$

$$\underbrace{\phantom{5.25 = 5\tfrac{1}{4} = +[(1 \cdot 2^2 + 0 \cdot 2^1 + 1) + (0 \cdot 2^{-1} + 1 \cdot 2^{-2})] =}}_{\text{binary expansion}} \qquad \underbrace{}_{\text{binary representation}}$$

Also, $9 = (01001)_2$ and $-31 = -(11111)_2$ are five-bit integers, but $34 = (100010)_2$ is not. Similarly, $-\tfrac{13}{32} = -(0.01101)_2$ and $\tfrac{1}{2} = (0.10000)_2$ are five-bit fractions, but $\tfrac{3}{64} = (0.000011)_2$ is not.

It follows from (1a) that *binary numbers are precisely those rational numbers* that can be written as $\pm m/2^k$, *where m and k are nonnegative integers.* So there are infinitely many real numbers that are *not* binary numbers (e.g., $\tfrac{4}{3}$, 0.1, $-\pi$, $\sqrt{2}$, etc.). It is also easy to show that

$$(\underbrace{1 \quad 1 \quad \cdots \quad 1 \quad 1}_{m \text{ 1's}})_2 = 2^m - 1 \text{ is the largest } m\text{-bit integer} \tag{3}$$

and

$$(\underbrace{0.1 \quad 1 \quad \cdots \quad 1 \quad 1}_{k \text{ 1's}})_2 = 1 - 2^{-k} \text{ is the largest } k\text{-bit fraction} \tag{4}$$

For example, $(11111)_2 = 2^5 - 1 = 31$ is the largest five-bit integer, and $(0.111)_2 = 1 - 2^{-3} = \tfrac{7}{8}$ is the largest three-bit fraction.

1.3B   STORING INTEGERS

Digital devices use a string of bits called a **word** to store a number. The size of a word is fixed for a particular device; it can be as small as 8 bits (in early microcomputer systems) or as large as 60 bits (in the CDC 7600 computer). A 32-bit word can be thought of as boxes numbered 0 to 31, as shown in Figure 1.3-1. Also shown is the way INTEGER variables are stored in FORTRAN, Pascal, or PL/I. For example, if the bits not shown are all 0's, then the integer stored would be

$$+(2^{28} + 2^{26} + 2^{25} + 2^{22} + 1) = 373{,}293{,}057$$

It follows from (3) that an integer X can be stored in a 32-bit word only if it satisfies $|X| \leq (2^{31} - 1) = 2{,}147{,}483{,}647$; an attempt to store an integer of larger magnitude will produce **integer overflow.**

BIT NO. 31 30 29 28 27 26 25 24 23 22 21 20 . . . 3 2 1 0

| 0 | 0 | 0 | 1 | 0 | 1 | 1 | 0 | 0 | 1 | 0 | 0 | · · · | 0 | 0 | 0 | 1 |

|←————— 31 bits for the integer's binary representation ——————→|

—Sign bit (0 for +, 1 for −)

FIGURE 1.3-1 STORING A 31-BIT INTEGER IN A 32-BIT WORD.

The arithmetic calculations used in science and engineering require numbers with a more extensive range than ±2,147,483,647, and certainly with closer spacing than the integers. This is accomplished with remarkable efficiency by using exponential notation as described next.

1.3C STORING FLOATING-POINT REPRESENTATIONS OF BINARY NUMBERS

The effect of multiplying a nonzero binary fraction M by 2^c is to move its binary point c bits to the right or left according as the integer c is positive or negative. It follows that every nonzero binary number X can be expressed as

$$X = \pm M \cdot 2^c, \qquad \text{where } M = +(0.1b_{-2}b_{-3}\cdots b_{-k})_2 \text{ and } c \text{ is an integer} \qquad (5)$$

This is called the **normalized floating-point (binary) representation** of X. Some examples of normalized floating-point representations are given in Table 1.3-1.

TABLE 1.3-1 NORMALIZED FLOATING-POINT REPRESENTATIONS.

X	Binary Representation	Normalized Floating-Point Binary Representation
-3.5	$-(11.1)_2$	$-(0.111)_2 \cdot 2^2$, that is, $M = (0.111)_2$ and $c = 2$
$\frac{7}{8}$	$(0.111)_2$	$(0.111)_2 \cdot 2^0$, that is, $M = (0.111)_2$ again, but $c = 0$
$\frac{1}{16}$	$(0.0001)_2$	$(0.1)_2 \cdot 2^{-3}$, that is, $M = (0.1)_2$, and $c = -3$

"Normalized" refers to the fact that the positive k-bit fraction M, called the **mantissa** of X, has $b_{-1} = 1$, hence satisfies $M \geq \frac{1}{2}$. "Floating point" refers to the fact that the integer c, called the **characteristic** or **exponent** of X, is adjusted to "float" the binary point just to the left of the leading nonzero bit in the binary representation of X (i.e., to make $b_{-1} = 1$).

All digital devices store mantissas normalized. This ensures that as many bits of M as possible are used to store *significant* bits of X. For example,

$$\tfrac{1}{5} = 0.2 = (0.0011001100110011...)_2 \qquad (6)$$

could be stored as follows in a six-bit mantissa device†

† We are assuming that the device *chops* (i.e., simply ignores all bits to the right of the sixth) rather than rounds to six bits. Most computers do this.

Not normalized: $(0.001100)_2 \cdot 2^0 = \frac{1}{8} + \frac{1}{16} = \frac{3}{16}$ $(\text{error} = \frac{1}{5} - \frac{3}{16} = \frac{1}{80})$

Normalized: $(0.110011)_2 \cdot 2^{-2} = (\frac{1}{2} + \frac{1}{4} + \frac{1}{32} + \frac{1}{64}) \cdot \frac{1}{4} = \frac{51}{256}$ $(\text{error} = \frac{1}{5} - \frac{51}{256} = \frac{1}{1280})$

The normalized representation is 16 times more accurate because it does not "waste" two bits by storing (nonsignificant) leading zeros of M.

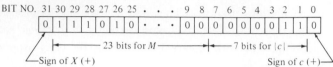

FIGURE **1.3-2** STORING A FLOATING POINT BINARY REPRESENTATION IN A 32-BIT WORD.

If we take $k = 23$ and $|c| \leqslant (1111111)_2 = 127$, then $X = \pm M \cdot 2^c$ can be stored in a 32-bit word as shown in Figure 1.3-2. If the bits not shown are 0's, the binary number X stored there has $c = +(0000011)_2 = +3$ and $M = (0.11101)_2$. Since the sign bit (number 31) for X is 0 (for +),

$$X = +(0.11101)_2 \cdot 2^3 = +(111.01)_2 = 7\tfrac{1}{4}$$

1.3D WHAT NUMBERS CAN BE STORED ON A 23-BIT MANTISSA DEVICE?

Let us call a nonzero binary number X **representable** if it can be stored as in Figure 1.3-2, that is, if

$$X = \pm M \cdot 2^c, \qquad \text{where } M \text{ is a normalized 23-bit fraction and } |c| \leqslant 127 \qquad (7)$$

For each $c = -127, -126, \ldots, +127$ in (7) there are 2^{22} normalized mantissas M (remember: b_{-1} must be 1). These correspond to 2^{22} equally spaced X's in each of the intervals $[2^{c-1}, 2^c)$ and $(-2^c, -2^{c-1}]$ because

$$\tfrac{1}{2} = (0.10\ldots0)_2 \leqslant M \leqslant (0.11\ldots1)_2 = 1 - 2^{-23}; \qquad \text{hence } \tfrac{1}{2}2^c \leqslant M \cdot 2^c = |X| < 1 \cdot 2^c$$

(Figure 1.3-3). Since increasing c by 1 doubles the length of both $[2^{c-1}, 2^c)$ and $(-2^c, -2^{c-1}]$, we see that *the representable X's are densely spaced near 0 and sparsely spaced away from 0*. And since $-127 \leqslant c \leqslant 127$ and $\tfrac{1}{2} \leqslant M \leqslant 1 - 2^{-23}$,

$$s = \tfrac{1}{2} \cdot 2^{-127} = 2^{-128} = 2.938736\ldots \cdot 10^{-39} \text{ is the smallest representable } X > 0 \quad (8)$$
$$L = (1 - 2^{-23}) \cdot 2^{127} = 1.70141\ldots \cdot 10^{38} \text{ is the largest representable } X \quad (9)$$

Any attempt to store an X satisfying $|X| > L$ will produce **floating-point overflow**; when this occurs, the computer used in Section 1.2 stores L and then resumes execution

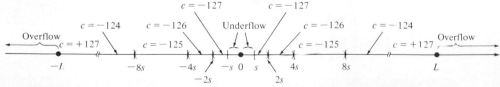

FIGURE **1.3-3** INTERVALS CORRESPONDING TO VARIOUS CHARACTERISTICS c.

(see the last output value of B in Figure 1.2-1). Similarly, an attempt to store an X satisfying $0 < |X| < s$ will produce **floating-point underflow.**

Using more bits for M increases the density (on the real line) of the representable X's; using more bits for c increases the range of the representable X's (i.e., the size of the interval $[s, L]$). Different computers make the tradeoff between the sizes of M and c in different ways (see Section 1.3F).†

1.3E INHERENT ERROR

Most real numbers x cannot be stored exactly on a k-bit mantissa device. The best such a device can do is to store a representable approximation $X = \pm M \cdot 2^c$ which may be in error in the least significant bit of M (i.e., b_{-k}). We shall refer to this error as the **inherent error** of storing x; it is less than 2^{-k}. In particular,

$$k = 23 \quad \Rightarrow \quad M \text{ is in error by less than } 2^{-23} \approx 1.2 \cdot 10^{-7} \qquad \textbf{(10)}$$

Thus *a 23-bit mantissa device stores most x's with about seven accurate significant digits.* For example,

$$x = 0.1 = 0.8 \cdot 2^{-3} \text{ is stored as } X = M \cdot 2^{-3} \qquad \textbf{(11a)}$$

where [see Exercise 1-7(c)]

$$M = (0.11001100110011001100110)_2 = \frac{6,710,886}{8,388,608} = 0.7999999523 \dots \qquad \textbf{(11b)}$$

So the "nice" decimal number $x = 0.1$ is stored as the smaller number

$$X = (0.7999999523 \dots) \cdot \tfrac{1}{8} = 0.09999999404 \dots \qquad \textbf{(11c)}$$

This X is in error when rounded to the seventh significant digit (i.e., the eighth decimal place).

To minimize inherent roundoff, variables x that are input as decimals should be entered rounded to as many significant digits as can possibly be stored on the device used.

We did this in the second run of Figure 1.2-1 when 3.14159265 was used to set XLIMIT to π on a device that can store 8^+ significant digits. And we chose H = 1 and R = 4 (= 2^2) in Figure 1.1-2 to ensure that the H values 1, $\tfrac{1}{4}$, $\tfrac{1}{16}$, . . . were *binary* numbers, hence could be stored without inherent error.

When using any computer, a computation similar to (10) should be made to determine how many significant digits should be used to enter input values.

---

† The use of a sign bit of c is wasteful because it allows $c = \pm 0$. What some computers do instead is to use all bits of c (say all eight in Figure 1.3-2) to store $\hat{c} = c + 2^{8-1}$. Then $c = 0$ corresponds to only $\hat{c} = 128$. Since $\hat{c}$ can vary from $(00000000)_2 = 0$ to $(11111111)_2 = 2^8 - 1 = 255$, $c = \hat{c} - 128$ can vary from -128 to $+127$ (rather than -127 to $+127$).

1.3F BASES OTHER THAN 2

Many computers store **octal** (base 8) or **hexadecimal** (base 16) representations of real numbers. Most calculators store **binary-coded decimal** (base 10) representations. With only minor modifications, our discussion of binary (base 2) representation carries over to these other bases.

The accuracy of a computer calculation depends on the size of the mantissa and, to a lesser extent, the arithmetic base, but *not* the programming language used. (See Table 1.3-2.) As a general rule, when the base is 2^e, increasing e improves the speed of arithmetic operations but makes normalizing less efficient, hence worsens inherent roundoff.

Note: The runs of Sections 1.1 and 1.2 (and elsewhere in the text) were all performed on a 36-bit word computer (Device 1 of Table 1.3-2).

TABLE 1.3-2 REPRESENTATION OF $X = \pm \left(\dfrac{d_1}{\beta} + \dfrac{d_2}{\beta^2} + \cdots + \dfrac{d_k}{\beta^k} \right) \cdot \beta^c$ WHERE $0 \leq d_i \leq \beta - 1,\ d_1 \neq 0.$

Device	Word Size	β = Base	Range of c	k	β^{-k}	Precision
1. DEC-1090	36 bits	8	$-128 \leq c \leq 127$	9	$0.75 \cdot 10^{-8}$	$\approx 8s$
2. IBM 370	32 bits	16	$-64 \leq c \leq 63$	6	$0.59 \cdot 10^{-7}$	$\approx 7s$
3. CDC 6600	60 bits	2	$-976 \leq c \leq 1{,}071$	48	$0.36 \cdot 10^{-14}$	$\approx 14s$
4. PDP-11	32 bits	2	$-128 \leq c \leq 127$	23	$0.12 \cdot 10^{-6}$	$\approx 6s$
5. Apple II	40 bits	2	$-128 \leq c \leq 127$	31	$0.47 \cdot 10^{-9}$	$\approx 9s$
6. TI-58	15 digits[a]	10	$-98 \leq c \leq 100$	12	$0.10 \cdot 10^{-12}$	$\approx 12s$
7. HP 45	15 digits[a]	10	$-98 \leq c \leq 100$	12	$0.10 \cdot 10^{-12}$	$\approx 12s$

[a] These devices display 10 digits, but store a 13 digit mantissa (with 3 "guard digits").

1.4 Errors in Fixed-Precision Arithmetic

We are now prepared to describe the errors produced when calculations are performed on a digital device.

1.4A DECIMAL-PLACE VERSUS SIGNIFICANT-DIGIT ACCURACY

The leading significant digit of a decimal number is the leftmost *nonzero* digit. Thus

$$-0.00666667 \text{ approximates } -\tfrac{1}{150}$$

to only six accurate significant digits, although it is accurately rounded to the eighth decimal place. We abbreviate this as either

$$-\tfrac{1}{150} = -0.00666667 \ (6s) \qquad \text{or} \qquad -\tfrac{1}{150} = -0.00666667 \ (8d)$$

In the fractional part of a decimal representation, zeros following the leading significant digit are significant. Thus

$$4\tfrac{1}{90} = 4.010101 \ldots = 4.01 \ (2d \text{ or } 3s) \qquad \text{and} \qquad 4\tfrac{1}{90} = 4.010 \ (3d \text{ or } 4s)$$

We use the special symbol "$\doteq$" to indicate that an approximation is accurate (rounded) to all digits shown. For example, the preceding approximations can be written as simply

$$-\tfrac{1}{150} \doteq -0.00666667, \qquad 4\tfrac{1}{90} \doteq 4.01, \qquad \text{and} \qquad 4\tfrac{1}{90} \doteq 4.010$$

Every digital device has a *fixed precision* that can be described in terms of the number of significant digits that it can accurately store in one word. For example, a 23-bit mantissa device can store about seven accurately rounded digits; such a device will therefore be referred to as a **7s device**. See Table 1.3-2.

In this section we consistently use lowercase letters x, y, z, . . . for real numbers, and uppercase letters, X, Y, Z, . . . for their representable approximations stored in a digital device. Thus, for a 7s device, x = X (7s).

1.4B   FIXED-PRECISION ARITHMETIC

We wish to illustrate the way both calculators and computers do arithmetic. Toward this end, let us consider a 4s, base 10 device (e.g., a really cheap calculator) that rounds a real number x to 4s and stores this representable approximation X as

$$X = \pm M \cdot 10^c, \qquad \text{where} \begin{cases} M = +0.d_1 d_2 d_3 d_4 & (d_1 \neq 0 \text{ if } X \neq 0) \\ c \text{ is an integer between } -9 \text{ and } +9 \end{cases} \tag{1}$$

that is, as its normalized floating-point (decimal) representation. Thus

$$x = -\tfrac{1}{150} \text{ is stored as } X = -0.6667 \cdot 10^{-2} \qquad (M = +0.6667 \text{ and } c = -2)$$
$$y = \quad 4\tfrac{1}{9} \text{ is stored as } Y = 0.4010 \cdot 10^1 \qquad (M = +0.4010 \text{ and } c = 1)$$

The smallest and largest representable positive numbers are, respectively,

$$s = 0.1000 \cdot 10^{-9} = 10^{-10} \qquad \text{and} \qquad L = 0.9999 \cdot 10^9 = 999,900,000$$

Let "$\circ$" denote one of the four arithmetic operations $+$, $-$, $*$, and $/$. Rather than perform $x \circ y$ exactly, the best our 4s device can do is to produce the number $X \,\hat{\circ}\, Y$ where

$$X \,\hat{\circ}\, Y \text{ means: Find } X \circ Y \text{ to at least 5s, then round to 4s} \tag{2}$$

We now show how this perfectly reasonable procedure, which we call **4s arithmetic**, can result in a variety of errors.

1.4C ERRORS IN FIXED-PRECISION ARITHMETIC

The five numbers

$$x = 8846.4, \quad y = 0.0012495, \quad z = 0.40366, \quad w = 0.4037681, \quad u = 50$$

are stored in our hypothetical 4s device as

$$X = 0.8846 \cdot 10^4, \quad Y = 0.1250 \cdot 10^{-2}, \quad Z = 0.4037, \quad W = 0.4038, \quad U = 0.5000 \cdot 10^2$$

Some illustrations of the errors that can result from (2) are

$$x + y = 8846.4012495 \neq x, \qquad \text{but } X \hat{+} Y = 8846 = X \tag{3}$$
$$z + w = 0.8074281 \doteq 0.8074, \qquad \text{but } Z \hat{+} W = Z + W = 0.8075 \tag{4}$$
$$z - y = 0.4024105 \doteq 0.4024, \qquad \text{but } Z \hat{-} Y = 0.4025 \tag{5}$$
$$x^2 = 78,258,793 \ (8s) \doteq 0.7826 \cdot 10^8, \text{ but } X \hat{*} X = 0.7825 \cdot 10^8 \tag{6}$$
$$u/y = 40016.0 \ (6s) \doteq 0.4002 \cdot 10^5, \qquad \text{but } U \hat{/} Y = 0.4000 \cdot 10^5 \tag{7}$$
$$z - w = -0.0001081 \doteq -0.1081 \cdot 10^{-3}, \text{ but } Z \hat{-} W = -0.0001 = -0.1000 \cdot 10^{-3} \tag{8}$$

Equations (3)–(7) illustrate how *inexactness in X or Y (either inherent roundoff or as a result of errors of previous arithmetic calculations) can produce worsened inexactness in* $X \hat{\circ} Y$; we shall refer to this phenomenon as **propagated roundoff error.**

In words, (3) shows that *the sum of a number and a much larger (or smaller) number is the larger number;* we shall call this **negligible addition.** And (4)–(7) show that *even if X and Y are correctly rounded to s significant digits,* $X \hat{\circ} Y$ *can have an error in the* sth *significant digit.* This is why digital devices usually store more digits than they display.† When, all stored digits are output, the last one (and possibly more if numerous calculations are performed) should *not* be taken as accurate.

The calculations shown in (6) and (7) illustrate how *errors are magnified when multiplying by a large number or dividing by a small number.* Although the differences

$$X \hat{*} X - x^2 = -8793 \qquad \text{and} \qquad U \hat{/} Y - u/y = -16 \tag{9}$$

represent only minor inaccuracy in the least significant digit, *they are rather large numbers.* Consequently, this kind of propagated error, which we shall call **error magnification,** can be serious in certain situations.

The error illustrated in (8) occurs when *subtracting two nearly equal numbers.* **It is very serious.** In (8), when *W* was subtracted from *Z,* the three leading significant digits canceled; consequently, the leading significant digit of $Z - W$ came from the least (i.e., fourth) significant digit of *Z* and *W.* We have just seen how easy it is for this least significant digit to be in error. So *the result of subtracting two nearly equal numbers can be a number with an erroneous leading digit and completely meaningless following digits.* For this reason this most insidious of roundoff errors is called **loss of significance**

---

† To ensure a desired accuracy (say 4s) when using a hand calculator with limited storage, critical intermediate values that cannot be stored should be recorded with one or two extra *guard digits* (e.g., to 6s). Only the final answer(s) should be rounded to the desired accuracy.

or **catastrophic cancellation.** It is important to remember these names because they will appear frequently.

Let us summarize the errors considered so far.

1. **Underflow/overflow.** Performing an operation that produces a number whose magnitude is too small or large to be stored on the device.
2. **Roundoff error.** The general name given to errors produced when calculations are performed on a (fixed precision) digital device. Roundoff error results from the combined effects of:
   a. *Inherent roundoff.* The error introduced by storing a binary number that only approximates a real number.
   b. *Propagated roundoff.* The errors caused by performing fixed precision arithmetic on the stored numbers. The three types of propagated roundoff errors are
      (1) *Negligible addition.* Adding or subtracting a number from a much smaller or much larger number.
      (2) *Error magnification.* Multiplying by a large number or dividing by a small one.
      (3) *Loss of significance.* Subtracting two nearly equal numbers.

The error inherent in a particular approximation formula in the absence of roundoff error is called **truncation error.** Truncation error will be discussed in detail in Chapter 7 after we have had some experience using numerical methods.

1.4D   INTERNAL FUNCTIONS

On both calculators and computers, built-in functions such as sin, cos, and exp, and ln generally produce more propagated roundoff than is produced by a single arithmetic operation $+$, $-$, $*$, or $/$. In particular, the internal subroutine for computing x^y for any real exponent y uses the formula

$$x^y = e^{y \ln x} \qquad \text{provided that the base } x \text{ is positive} \qquad \textbf{(10)}$$

This is the calculation performed when executing $X ** Y$ in FORTRAN, $X \uparrow Y$ in BASIC, and x^y on calculators. If Y is a positive integer, then (10) is generally less accurate than $X * X * \cdots * X$ (Y times); for such Y (say $2 \leq Y \leq 4$), propagated roundoff can be reduced by programming x^y as $X * X * \cdots * X$ unless you know that the computer, in executing (10), does this automatically.

Avoiding Roundoff Error   **1.5**

The purpose of this section is to give some general rules for avoiding, or at least minimizing, roundoff error when executing a numerical method on a calculator or computer.

1.5A RULES FOR REDUCING ROUNDOFF ERRORS

Rule 1. *To minimize inherent error, always input real data using as many significant digits as the device can store (see Section 1.3E).*

Rule 2. *To minimize the possibility of overflow or underflow, try to keep the value of all intermediate calculations close to* ±1 *(i.e., keep the characteristic close to zero).*

For example, if the magnitudes of x, y, z are known, then the expression xy/z should be calculated as

$(xy)/z$ if one of $|x|$ or $|y|$ is large and the other is small

$x(y/z)$ if $|y|$ and $|z|$ are both large or both small

$(x/z)y$ if $|x|$ and $|z|$ are both large or both small

On most 32-bit word computers, overflow (underflow) will occur when calculating e^x for $x > 40$ ($x < -40$). This makes it especially important to *keep the argument of the exponential function as close to zero as possible.* For example, if it is known that $x \gg 0$, $y \gg 0$, and $n > 1$, then one should calculate (or program)

$$\frac{e^x}{e^y} \text{ as } e^{x-y} \quad \text{and} \quad \frac{y^n}{e^{nx}} \text{ as } \left(\frac{y}{e^x}\right)^n$$

Rule 3. *To help minimize propagated roundoff, put mathematical expressions in a form requiring the fewest arithmetic operations.*

Rule 3 was used when B was programmed as $(\sin x/x)^2/(1 + \cos x)$ in line 1400 of Figure 1.2-1. (This requires one less multiplication than $\sin^2 x/[x^2(1 + \cos x)]$.) A more general application of Rule 3 is the

Nested Multiplication Rule. *A polynomial whose* **exponential form** *is*

$$p_{\text{exp}}(x) = a_1 x^5 + a_2 x^4 + a_3 x^3 + a_4 x^2 + a_5 x + a_6 \tag{1}$$

should be evaluated in the equivalent **nested form**

$$p_{\text{nest}}(x) = ((((a_1 x + a_2)x + a_3)x + a_4)x + a_5)x + a_6 \tag{2}$$

Notice that both $p_{\text{exp}}(x)$ and $p_{\text{nest}}(x)$ require five addition/subtractions and five multiplications; but $p_{\text{exp}}(x)$ requires four additional uses of the slower and possibly less accurate x^y subroutine. Moreover, $p_{\text{exp}}(x)$ may be impossible to evaluate on a digital device when x is negative [see (10) of Section 1.4D].

Table 1.5-1 shows the accuracy achieved by a 27-bit mantissa device when evaluating the following alternative forms of a fourth-degree polynomial:

$$p_{\text{exp}}(x) = x^4 - 9.5x^3 + 28.49x^2 - 28.417x + 2.5662 \tag{3a}$$
$$p_{\text{nest}}(x) = (((x - 9.5)x + 28.49)x - 28.417)x + 2.5662 \tag{3b}$$

TABLE 1.5-1   COMPARING THE ACCURACY OF $p_{exp}(x)$ AND $p_{nest}(x)$.

x	Calculated $p_{exp}(x)$	Calculated $p_{nest}(x)$	Exact Value
2.4	0.317401*	0.317399	0.3174
2.5	0.211199	0.211200*	0.2112
2.7	−0.312001	−0.312000*	−0.3120
2.8	−0.718201	−0.718200*	−0.7182
2.9	−1.209599*	−1.209601	−1.2096
3.1	−2.399997	−2.400001*	−2.4000
3.2	−3.069001	−3.068999*	−3.0690
3.3	−3.763199	−3.763200*	−3.7632
3.5	−5.140801	−5.140800*	−5.1408
3.6	−5.775004	−5.775001*	−5.7750
3.7	−6.335999	−6.336001*	−6.3360
3.8	−6.793202	−6.793201*	−6.7932
3.9	−7.113601*	−7.113602	−7.1136
4.3	−6.283200*	−6.283197	−6.2832
4.4	−5.340597	−5.340602*	−5.3406
4.6	−2.250000*	−2.249999	−2.2500
4.7	0.000010	0.000001*	0.0000
4.8	2.791805	2.791802*	2.7918
4.9	6.182398	6.182401*	6.1824

The x values shown are those among 0.0, 0.1, . . . 4.9, 5.0 for which

$$|p_{nest}(x) - p_{exp}(x)| > 10^{-6}$$

An asterisk (*) is placed to the right of the more accurate value.

To help interpret Table 1.5-1, we note that the roots of the evaluated polynomial are 0.1, 2.1, 2.6, and 4.7 so that

$$p_{exp}(x) = p_{nest}(x) = (x - 0.1)(x - 2.1)(x - 2.6)(x - 4.7) \qquad \textbf{(3c)}$$

It can thus be seen from the table that:

1. In most instances $p_{nest}(x)$ is at least as accurate as $p_{exp}(x)$.
2. Both $p_{exp}(x)$ and $p_{nest}(x)$ are in error near the largest root of the polynomial (i.e., near $x = 4.7$). In fact, the computer appears not to recognize $x = 4.7$ as an exact root! This is because for x's near 4.7, subtraction of rather large and nearly equal numbers (i.e., loss of significance) must occur in both $p_{exp}(x)$ and $p_{nest}(x)$ in order to get $p(x) \approx 0$.

More generally, even if nesting is used, *the nth-degree polynomial*

$$p(x) = a_1 x^n + a_2 x^{n-1} + \cdots + a_n x + a_{n+1} \quad (a_1 \neq 0) \tag{4}$$

will be difficult to evaluate accurately near real roots of large magnitude, especially if some of the coefficients are large (causing error magnification) or the slope near the root is close to zero. This unfortunate manifestation of roundoff gets worse as n is increased.

Figure 1.5-1(a) describes the **Synthetic Division** algorithm **(Horner's method)** for evaluating polynomials in nested form. Figure 1.5-1(b) shows how the algorithm proceeds for a particular x. The reader who has seen Synthetic Division before may recognize it in this form. Figure 1.5-1(c) shows a FORTRAN subprogram POLVAL implementing the algorithm.

Our final, and perhaps most important rule is

Rule 4. *Introduce program logic to avoid any anticipated loss of significance that might occur when adding or subtracting.*

Three illustrations of this rule are given next. Study them carefully.

(a) **Algorithm: Synthetic Division (Horner's Method)**

Purpose: To evaluate $PolValue = a_1 x^n + a_2 x^{n-1} + \cdots + a_n x + a_{n+1}$

```
GET n, a₁, a₂, . . . , aₙ₊₁, x
PolValue ← 0
DO FOR i = 1 TO n + 1
    PolValue ← PolValue * x + aᵢ
```

(b) Find $p(x) = (((1x - 9.5)x + 28.49)x - 28.417)x + 2.5662$ when $x = -2$.

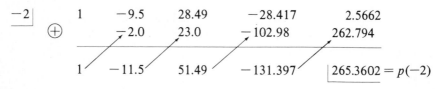

Note 1: Diagonal arrows indicate multiplication by $x = -2$.

Note 2: $\dfrac{p(x)}{x - (-2)} = x^3 - 11.5x^2 + 51.49x - 131.397 + \dfrac{265.3602}{x - (-2)}$.

```
(c)  00100              FUNCTION POLVAL(X, NP1, A)
     00200              DIMENSION A(NP1)
     00300      C - - - - - - - - - - - - - - - - - - - - C
     00400      C  POLVAL = A(1)*X**N + ... + A(N)*X + A(NP1)  C
     00500      C  WHERE   N = DEGREE OF POLYNOMIAL          C
     00600      C         NP1 = NUMBER OF COEFFICIENTS = N+1  C
     00700      C - - - - - - - - - - - - - - - - - - - - C
     00800              POLVAL = 0.0
     00900              DO 1 I=1, NP1
     01000        1       POLVAL = POLVAL*X + A(I)
     01100              RETURN
     01200              END
```

FIGURE 1.5-1   (a) SYNTHETIC DIVISION ALGORITHM FOR EVALUATING $p(x)$; (b) EVALU-
ATING $p(-2)$; (c) FORTRAN SUBPROGRAM POLVAL.

1.5B   USING TRIGONOMETRIC REARRANGEMENT TO AVOID LOSS OF SIGNIFICANCE

PROBLEM Describe how to compute $f(x) = \dfrac{1 - \cos x}{x^2}$ accurately for all $x \neq 0$.

Solution. We saw in Section 1.2A that the calculated values of†

$$A = \frac{1 - \cos x}{x^2} \text{ became very inaccurate for } x \approx 0$$

The reason is simple: Since $\cos x \approx 1$ for $x \approx 0$, the numerator of A will suffer loss of significance, which gets magnified when divided by the small denominator x^2. On the other hand,

$$B = \left(\frac{\sin x}{x}\right)^2 \frac{1}{1 + \cos x} \text{ became very inaccurate for } x \approx \pi$$

because $\cos x \approx -1$ for $x \approx \pi$, causing the denominator of B to lose significance while itself getting small. (In the last lines of the runs of Figure 1.2-1, the computer used could not distinguish the subtracted numbers and calculated their difference as zero. This produced the absurd results seen there.)

Once understood, the problem is easy to avoid. Simply calculate $f(x)$ as

$$f(x) = \begin{cases} B & \text{whenever } 1 - \cos x \approx 0 \text{ (say, } |1 - \cos x| \leqslant 0.01) \\ A & \text{otherwise } (|1 - \cos x| > 0.01) \end{cases} \tag{5}$$

It is not always possible to anticipate when loss of significance may occur; but when it is, the kind of "programming for avoidance" suggested in Rule 4 can more than repay the effort, as we now see.

---

† Unlike "$\doteq$" discussed in Section 1.4A, the "approximately equal to" symbol "$\approx$" does *not* indicate how accurate the approximation is.

1.5C   USING ALGEBRAIC REARRANGEMENT TO AVOID LOSS OF SIGNIFICANCE

If $b_1^2 \gg |c_1|$,† then $b_1^2 - c_1$ will not differ much from b_1^2, hence

$$r(-) = b_1 - \sqrt{b_1^2 - c_1} \text{ will suffer loss of significance if } b_1 > 0$$

and

$$r(+) = b_1 + \sqrt{b_1^2 - c_1} \text{ will suffer loss of significance if } b_1 < 0$$

(This is what we saw in Section 1.2B.) So the real roots of the quadratic

$$ax^2 + bx + c = 0 \qquad (a \neq 0)$$

can be calculated without loss of significance using the formula

$$\text{root}_1 = (\pm)(|b_1| + \sqrt{b_1^2 - c_1}) \qquad \text{and} \qquad \text{root}_2 = \frac{c_1}{\text{root}_1} \tag{6a}$$

where

$$b_1 = -\frac{b}{2a}, \quad c_1 = \frac{c}{a}, \quad \text{and} \quad (\pm) \text{ is } (+) \text{ unless } b_1 < 0 \tag{6b}$$

```
00100          SUBROUTINE QROOTS(A, B, C, ROOT1, ROOT2, COMPLX, IW, PRINT)
00200          LOGICAL PRINT, COMPLX
00300   C - - - - - - - - - - - - - - - - - - - - - - - - - - - - - - - C
00400   C THIS SUBROUTINE FINDS THE TWO ROOTS OF THE QUADRATIC         C
00500   C           AX**2 + BX + C                                     C
00600   C IF PRINT = TRUE, IT PRINTS THEM ON OUTPUT DEVICE IW.         C
00700   C REAL ROOTS (COMPLX=FALSE) ARE RETURNED AS ROOT1 AND ROOT2,   C
00800   C AND COMPLEX ROOTS (COMPLX=TRUE) AS ROOT1 +OR- I*ROOT2.       C
00900   C - - - - - - - - - - - - - - - VERSION 1  5/1/81  - - - - - C
01000          B1 = -0.5*B/A
01100          C1 = C/A
01200          DISCR = B1*B1 - C1
01300          IF (DISCR .LT. 0.) GOTO 10
01400   C
01500   C    REAL ROOTS:  ROOT1 AND ROOT2
01600          COMPLX = .FALSE.
01700          ROOT1 = ABS(B1) + SQRT(DISCR)
01800          IF (B1 .LT. 0.) ROOT1 = -ROOT1
01900          ROOT2 = 0.0
02000          IF (ROOT1 .NE. 0.) ROOT2 = C1/ROOT1
02100   C
02200          IF (PRINT) WRITE(IW,1) ROOT1, ROOT2
02300   1      FORMAT(' REAL ROOTS:  ',E14.7,'  AND ',E14.7)
02400          RETURN
02500   C
02600   C    COMPLEX CONJUGATE ROOTS:  ROOT1  +OR-  I*ROOT2
02700   10     COMPLX = .TRUE.
02800          ROOT1 = B1
02900          ROOT2 = SQRT(-DISCR)
03000   C
03100          IF (PRINT) WRITE(IW,2) ROOT1, ROOT2
03200   2      FORMAT(' COMPLEX ROOTS:',E15.7,'  +OR-  I*(',E14.7,')')
03300          RETURN
03400   C
03500          END
```

FIGURE 1.5-2   QROOTS: A FORTRAN SUBROUTINE TO GET ROOTS OF A QUADRATIC.

† "$b_1^2 \gg |c_1|$" should be read as "b_1^2 is much larger than $|c_1|$."

These formulas are implemented in the FORTRAN subroutine QROOTS shown in Figure 1.5-2. In Figure 1.5-3 (run on the same computer used in Figure 1.2-2), the real roots of the equations $x^2 \pm 100.01x + 1 = 0$ and the complex roots of the equation $x^2 - 2x + 3 = 0$ were all calculated accurately to at least the seven digits shown.

```
00100    C  * * * * * * * * *  TESTQR  * * * * * * * * * * * * * *
00200    C INTERACTIVE PROGRAM TO TEST SUBROUTINE QROOTS (IW = 5)
00300          LOGICAL COMPLX
00400    C
00500          WRITE (5,1)
00600        1 FORMAT('0TO FIND ROOTS OF AX**2+BX+C, INPUT A, B, C')
00700          READ (5,*) A, B, C
00800    C
00900          CALL QROOTS (A, B, C, R1, R2, COMPLX, 5, .TRUE.)
01000    C
01100          STOP
01200          END
```

```
TO FIND ROOTS OF AX**2+BX+C, INPUT A, B, C
1, -100.01, 1

REAL ROOTS:   0.1000000E+03  AND   0.1000000E-01


TO FIND ROOTS OF AX**2+BX+C, INPUT A, B, C
1, +100.01, 1

REAL ROOTS:  -0.1000000E+03  AND  -0.1000000E-01


TO FIND ROOTS OF AX**2+BX+C, INPUT A, B, C
1, -2, 3

COMPLEX ROOTS:  0.1000000E+01  +OR-  I*( 0.1414214E+01)
```

FIGURE 1.5-3   AN INTERACTIVE PROGRAM TO EXERCISE QROOTS.

1.5D   USING MACLAURIN SERIES TO AVOID LOSS OF SIGNIFICANCE

PROBLEM   Compute $f(x) = \dfrac{e^x - 1}{x}$ accurately for all $x \neq 0$.

Solution. Since $e^x \to 1$ as $x \to 0$, the numerator of $f(x)$ suffers loss of significance that gets magnified by the small denominator when $x \approx 0$. Unlike the $f(x)$ of Section 1.5B, this $f(x)$ has no equivalent expression that avoids the problem. In such situations one should try to use an appropriate Maclaurin series. For the problem at hand, the Maclaurin series for e^x [see Appendix II.2B] gives

$$f(x) = \frac{1}{x}\left\{\left[1 + x + \frac{x^2}{2!} + \frac{x^3}{3!} + R_3(x)\right] - 1\right\} = 1 + \frac{x}{2!} + \frac{x^2}{3!} + \frac{R_3(x)}{x} \qquad (7a)$$

where $R_3(x)$ is the *Lagrange form of the remainder* given by

$$R_3(x) = \frac{e^\xi}{4!}\,x^4, \qquad \text{where } \xi \text{ lies between 0 and } x \qquad \text{(7b)}$$

If $|x| < 0.01$, then $R_3(x)/x$, which is the *truncation error* of approximating $f(x)$ by $1 + x/2! + x^2/3!$, satisfies

$$\left| \frac{R_3(x)}{x} \right| = \frac{e^\xi |x|^3}{24} < \frac{e^{0.01}(0.01)^3}{24} < 0.00000005$$

This assures us that

$$1 + \frac{x}{2!} + \frac{x^2}{3!} \text{ approximates } \frac{e^x - 1}{x} \text{ to seven decimal places if } |x| < 0.01$$

So if we evaluate $f(x)$ as

$$f(x) = \begin{cases} \dfrac{1}{x}(e^x - 1) & \text{if } |x| \geqslant 0.01 \\[2mm] 1 + \dfrac{1}{2}\,x\left(1 + \dfrac{1}{3}\,x\right) & \text{if } |x| < 0.01 \end{cases} \qquad \text{(8)}$$

then $f(x)$ will be calculated to the accuracy of the device for $|x| \geqslant 0.01$, and to seven-place accuracy for $|x| < 0.01$.

1.5E   EXTENDED PRECISION

There are situations when the roundoff error in obtaining a numerical solution is so great that the accuracy of the answer is questionable even if Rules 1–4 of Section 1.5A are followed. One such situation, that of evaluating polynomials of high degree near certain zeros, arose in our discussion of Rule 3. In such situations the bit size of the mantissa is simply too small to store the number of significant digits needed to achieve the desired accuracy. To remedy this, programming languages that were designed for scientific computation (e.g., FORTRAN, PL/I, and some versions of BASIC) have the capability of storing real numbers in **extended precision.**

When a FORTRAN variable is declared to be DOUBLE PRECISION, it is stored in what can be thought of as two words in tandem, with most or all of the additional word used for the mantissa. In this way, the number of significant digits that can be stored is generally at least doubled.

The execution of a mathematical operation takes about twice as long in double precision as it does in single precision. So in a realistic context where computer time must be paid for, *Rules 1–4 of Section 1.5A should be used to make the most efficient use of single precision.* However, extended precision should be used if it appears that the desired accuracy may not be assured even with the use of these rules. Such situations will be noted as they arise in our discussions.

Errors, Accuracy, and Tests for Closeness   **1.6**

In this brief section we introduce terminology for describing errors and use it to develop criteria for imposing a desired accuracy.

1.6A   ABSOLUTE, RELATIVE, AND PERCENT ERROR

If X is an approximation of the real number x, then the difference

$$\boxed{\epsilon_X = x - X = (\text{exact value}) - (\text{approximate value})} \qquad (1)$$

is the **absolute error,** or simply the **error,** of the approximation. Thus

$$x = X + \epsilon_X \qquad (2)$$

so that ϵ_X *is what must be added to the approximation X to get the exact value x.*† If $x \neq 0$, the ratio

$$\boxed{\rho_X = \frac{\epsilon_X}{x} = \frac{x - X}{x} \text{ is the \textbf{relative error} of approximating } x \text{ by } X} \qquad (3)$$

In situations where ρ_X is known, the absolute error can be found as

$$\epsilon_X = x \cdot \rho_X \qquad (4)$$

The relative error ρ_X tells what fractional part of x is in error. It is closely related to the idea of percent error. For example, if it is known that $|\rho_X| < 0.02$, then, by (4), $|\epsilon_X| < 0.02 \cdot |x|$. In words, X approximates x to within 2%. More generally,

$$100\,\rho_X = \frac{100\,\epsilon_X}{x} \text{ is the \textbf{percent error} of approximating } x \text{ by } X \qquad (5)$$

For example, if $x = \frac{1}{30}$ is approximated to $2s$ by $X = 0.033$, then

$$\epsilon_X = \frac{1}{30} - 0.033 = \frac{1}{30} - \frac{33}{1000} = \frac{1}{3000} \qquad \text{and} \qquad \rho_X = \frac{1/3000}{1/30} = \frac{1}{100} = 0.01$$

Thus 0.033 approximates $\frac{1}{30}$ with a 1% error.

---

† Some authors take ϵ_X to be $X - x$ (the negative of our ϵ_X) so that $X = x + \epsilon_X$. The reader is advised to check what is meant by "error" before reading any numerical analysis text.

1.6B RELATING ϵ_X AND ρ_X TO THE ACCURACY OF X

If x and X are part of a hand calculation, a visual inspection can determine whether they agree (after rounding) to d decimal places or s significant digits. For example, 2.3579 and 2.357682 agree to 4s. But how does one tell a computer to check that $x = X$ to a prescribed accuracy? (Think about it!)

In the example in Section 1.1A we saw how the absolute error ϵ_X can be used to impose a desired decimal-place accuracy:

Absolute Error Test *For any positive integer d, the inequality*

$$|\epsilon_X| = |x - X| < \tfrac{1}{2} \cdot 10^{-d} \tag{6}$$

assures that X approximates x to d decimal places.

If $x \neq 0$, then the relative error $\rho_X = \epsilon_X / x$ can be used similarly to impose a desired significant-digit accuracy:

Relative Error Test *For any positive integer s, the inequality*

$$|\rho_X| < \tfrac{1}{2} \cdot 10^{-s} \tag{7a}$$

or, equivalently,

$$|x - X| < \tfrac{1}{2} \cdot 10^{-s}|x| \tag{7b}$$

assures that X approximates x to s significant digits.

To prove this, consider the normalized floating-point *decimal* representation

$$x = \pm M \cdot 10^c, \qquad \text{where } 0.1 \leqslant M = 0.d_{-1}d_{-2} \ldots d_{-s} \ldots < 1 \tag{8}$$

If (7) holds, then by (7b) and (8)

$$|\epsilon_X| = |x - X| < \tfrac{1}{2} \cdot 10^{-s}|x| = (\tfrac{1}{2} \cdot 10^{-s})(M \cdot 10^c) < (\tfrac{1}{2} \cdot 10^{-s})10^c \tag{9}$$

This shows that the magnitude of the error of X is less than $\tfrac{1}{2}$ in the sth decimal place of M in (8) (i.e., X accurate to s significant digits).

The Absolute Error Test (6) and the Relative Error Test (7) will be used frequently in the remainder of the text.

1.6C A QUANTITATIVE DISCUSSION OF ERROR PROPAGATION (OPTIONAL)

Let us suppose that the approximations $X \approx x$ and $Y \approx y$ are "good" in the sense that the errors are small compared to the exact values, that is,

$$|x - X| \ll |x| \qquad \text{and} \qquad |y - Y| \ll |y| \tag{10}$$

ABSOLUTE ERROR PROPAGATION. Since $\epsilon_X = x - X$ and $\epsilon_Y = y - Y$,

$$\epsilon_{X\pm Y} = (x\pm y) - (X\pm Y) = (x-X)\pm(y-Y) = \epsilon_X \pm \epsilon_Y \qquad (11)$$

In words, *the error of a sum or difference is the sum or difference of the errors in the terms.* Since we generally do not know if ϵ_X and ϵ_Y have the same or opposite sign, the best we can be sure of is that

$$|\epsilon_{X\pm Y}| \le |\epsilon_X| + |\epsilon_Y| \qquad (12)$$

It follows that if X and Y are accurate to $4d$ (i.e., both $|\epsilon_X|$ and $|\epsilon_Y|$ are $< \frac{1}{2} \cdot 10^{-4}$), then $X \pm Y$ can differ from $x \pm y$ by almost 10^{-4}. It is therefore possible that $X \pm Y$ has a one-digit error in the fourth decimal place [see (4) of Section 1.4C]. And if X and Y are erroneous in *different* decimal places, then $X \pm Y$ will probably be erroneous in the decimal place corresponding to the *larger* of $|\epsilon_X|$ and $|\epsilon_Y|$ [see (3) and (5) of Section 1.4C.]

Recall from calculus that when (10) holds, differentials can be used to get accurate approximations of the increments $x - X$ and $y - Y$, that is,

$$\epsilon_X = x - X \approx dX \quad \text{and} \quad \epsilon_Y = y - Y \approx dY \qquad (13)$$

It follows from this that

$$\epsilon_{XY} \approx d(XY) = Y\,dX + X\,dY \approx Y\epsilon_X + X\epsilon_Y \qquad (14)$$

$$\epsilon_{X/Y} \approx d\left(\frac{X}{Y}\right) = \frac{Y\,dX - X\,dY}{Y^2} \approx \frac{1}{Y}\epsilon_X - \frac{X}{Y^2}\epsilon_Y \qquad (15)$$

In view of (14), it is easy to see that large values of X or Y will magnify the errors ϵ_X and ϵ_Y to produce larger errors in the product XY. Similarly, (15) shows how a large value of X and/or a small value of Y will magnify ϵ_X and ϵ_Y to produce larger errors in the quotient X/Y. [This is what we saw in (6) and (7) of Section 1.4C.]

RELATIVE ERROR PROPAGATION. Dividing (14) by xy and (15) by x/y gives

$$\rho_{XY} = \frac{\epsilon_{XY}}{xy} \approx \frac{y\,dX + x\,dY}{xy} = \frac{dX}{x} + \frac{dY}{y} \approx \rho_X + \rho_Y \qquad (16)$$

$$\rho_{X/Y} = \frac{\epsilon_{X/Y}}{x/y} \approx \frac{(y\,dX - x\,dY)/y^2}{x/y} = \frac{dX}{x} - \frac{dY}{y} \approx \rho_X - \rho_Y \qquad (17)$$

In words, *the relative error of a product (respectively, quotient) is the sum (respectively, difference) of the relative errors of the factors.* Since we do not know whether ρ_X and ρ_Y have the same or opposite signs, the safest statement we can make is that

$$|\rho_{XY}| \lesssim |\rho_X| + |\rho_Y| \quad \text{and} \quad |\rho_{X/Y}| \lesssim |\rho_X| + |\rho_Y| \qquad (18)$$

where "$\lesssim$" should be read as "is at most a bit larger than." Thus in view of (7), if X and Y have s accurate significant digits then XY and X/Y will have about s significant digits (although the *absolute* errors ϵ_{XY} and $\epsilon_{X/Y}$ may be large). [This is what we saw in (6), (7), and (9) of Section 1.4C.] Finally, if we divide (11) by $x \pm y$, we get

$$\rho_{X\pm Y} = \frac{\epsilon_{X\pm Y}}{x\pm y} = \frac{\epsilon_X}{x\pm y} \pm \frac{\epsilon_Y}{x\pm y} = \left(\frac{x}{x\pm y}\right)\rho_X \pm \left(\frac{y}{x\pm y}\right)\rho_Y \qquad (19)$$

Notice that when $x \pm y$ is much smaller than x or y, then the factors $x/(x \pm y)$ and $y/(x \pm y)$ magnify ρ_X and ρ_Y to produce a much larger value of $\rho_{X\pm Y}$; in view of (7), this is the *loss of significance* we saw in (8) of Section 1.4C.

1.7 Iterative Algorithms

All iterative algorithms for finding a desired value $\bar{x}$ proceed in two steps as follows:

Initialize: Find an **initial guess** x_0 which approximates $\bar{x}$.

Iterate: For $k = 0, 1, 2, \ldots$ until a termination test is satisfied:
      Use x_k to form an improved approximation x_{k+1}.

We shall refer to x_k as the k**th iterate** and let

$$\boxed{\epsilon_k = \bar{x} - x_k = \text{the error of } x_k} \qquad (1)$$

Thus ϵ_k is what must be added to x_k to get exactly $\bar{x}$. The algorithm will be successful if $x_k \to \bar{x}$ (i.e., $\epsilon_k \to 0$) as $k \to \infty$. A desirable algorithm will exhibit the following characteristics in most commonly occurring situations:

1. *Robustness.* x_k will converge to $\bar{x}$ even if x_0 is not a particularly good initial guess.
2. *Rapid convergence.* Once x_k is close to $\bar{x}$, x_{k+1} will be much closer, that is,

$$\boxed{|\epsilon_{k+1}| = |\bar{x} - x_{k+1}| \ll |\bar{x} - x_k| = |\epsilon_k|} \qquad (2)$$

When $|\epsilon_{k+1}| \ll |\epsilon_k|$ then, as can be seen from Figure 1.7-1,

$$\boxed{\Delta x_k = x_{k+1} - x_k \approx \bar{x} - x_k = \epsilon_k} \qquad (3)$$

In words, *the increment from x_k to x_{k+1} (i.e. Δx_k) is a computable approximation of the actual (unknown) error ϵ_k.* Most termination tests for iterative algorithms involve stopping (and taking $x_{k+1} \approx \bar{x}$) when Δx_k is sufficiently small. (See Section 1.7D.)

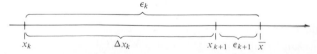

FIGURE 1.7-1 PICTORIAL REPRESENTATION OF Δx_k, ϵ_k, AND ϵ_{k+1}.

1.7A   FLOWCHART FOR A GENERAL ITERATIVE ALGORITHM

Although subscripts are useful for mathematical descriptions of iterative algorithms, they do not reflect the way such algorithms are actually executed (i.e., in a loop). A more realistic description of a general iterative algorithm for finding $\bar{x}$ is given in the flowchart of Figure 1.7-2. Notice that *Xprev* and *X* (without subscripts) play the respective

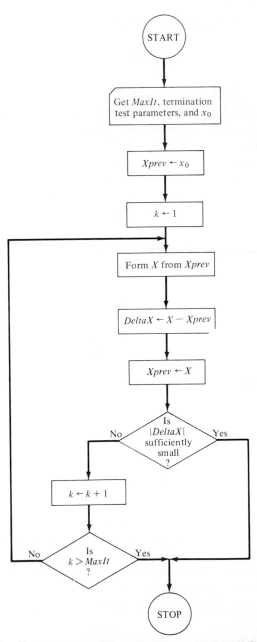

FIGURE 1.7-2   FLOWCHART FOR A GENERAL ITERATIVE ALGORITHM.

roles of x_{k-1} and x_k above. Instead of incrementing the subscript on x by 1, one simply **updates** by making the current X the next *Xprev* before testing for termination and, if necessary, returning to the beginning of the loop. In this way the index k is used only to count iterations (so that the iterations cease after *MaxIt* iterations) and does *not* actually enter into the calculations.

1.7B PSEUDOPROGRAM FOR A GENERAL ITERATIVE ALGORITHM

The information of the flowchart of Figure 1.7-2 can be expressed as shown in Figure 1.7-3.

Figure 1.7-3 describes the flow of control in executing an iterative algorithm much as a computer program does. However, it is written in heuristic **pseudocode** rather than a particular programming language. Consequently, such a description will be referred to as a **pseudoprogram.**

There are two reasons to prefer pseudoprograms to flowcharts. First, although both give the same information, *pseudoprograms can be prepared more compactly and easily.* Second, and more important, *the translation from pseudocode to an actual program including comments (in braces:* {. . .}) *is more natural than the translation from a flowchart*

General Iterative Algorithm

Purpose: To find $\bar{x}$ to a desired accuracy by repeatedly forming an improved approximation X from a current approximation *Xprev* until either X is sufficiently close to *Xprev* (**termination test**) or *MaxIt* iterations occur.

{*initialize*}
GET *MaxIt*, termination parameters, x_0 {initial guess}
Xprev ← x_0

{*iterate*}
DO FOR $k = 1$ TO *MaxIt* UNTIL **termination test** is satisfied
  BEGIN
  {**form** X} X ← (formula involving *Xprev*)
  DeltaX ← $X - Xprev$ {*DeltaX* is $\Delta x_{k-1} = x_k - x_{k-1}$}
  {**update**} *Xprev* ← X {ready for next iteration}
  {**termination test:** $|DeltaX| \approx 0$, as specified by termination parameters}
  END

{If **termination test** succeeded, then $\bar{x} \doteq X$ to the desired accuracy. If not, *MaxIt* iterations failed to yield an X close enough to $\bar{x}$.}

FIGURE 1.7-3 PSEUDOPROGRAM FOR A GENERAL ITERATIVE ALGORITHM.

to a program. In particular, the *label* comments set in boldface (e.g., {*iterate*}, {**form** *X*}, {**update**}) and indentation combine to give a quick "picture" of the algorithm and help the reader visualize its subprogram structure. Consequently, *from this point on, algorithms will be described in the form of pseudoprograms rather than flowcharts.* The conventions to be used in these pseudoprograms are given in Appendix I, which the reader is urged to examine at this time.

We now illustrate the discussion so far with a specific algorithm.

1.7C FINDING FIXED POINTS BY REPEATED SUBSTITUTION

A **fixed point** of a continuous function g is a number $\bar{x}$ that g maps into itself, that is, satisfies $g(\bar{x}) = \bar{x}$. To find the fixed points of g, we must set up and solve the **fixed-point equation**

$$g(x) = x \tag{4}$$

Certain fixed points can be found by **Repeated Substitution:**

$$\boxed{\text{Guess } x_0, \text{ then take } x_{k+1} = g(x_k) \qquad \text{for } k = 0, 1, 2, \ldots} \tag{5a}$$

This simplest of iterative algorithms is illustrated graphically in Figure 1.7-4. The fixed points $\bar{x}$ of g are the x (also y)-coordinates of the points $\bar{P}(\bar{x}, \bar{x})$ where the curve $y = g(x)$ meets the $y = x$ line. The iterates

$$x_1 = g(x_0), \quad x_2 = g(x_1), \quad x_3 = g(x_2), \quad \ldots \tag{5b}$$

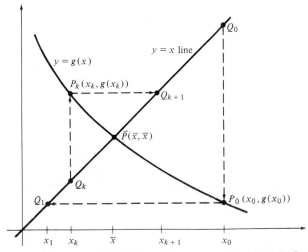

FIGURE 1.7-4   GRAPHICAL REPRESENTATION OF REPEATED SUBSTITUTION.

generated by (5a) are the x-coordinates of the points Q_1, Q_2, Q_3, . . . generated graphically on the $y = x$ line as follows. The initial guess x_0 determines an initial point $Q_0(x_0, x_0)$. Once $Q_k(x_k, x_k)$ has been located, $Q_{k+1}(x_{k+1}, x_{k+1})$ is obtained in two steps:

$$Q_k \xrightarrow[\text{to the graph of } g]{\text{move up or down}} P_k(x_k, g(x_k)) \xrightarrow[\text{to the } y = x \text{ line}]{\text{move right or left}} Q_{k+1} \qquad \textbf{(6)}$$

Figure 1.7-5 gives a graphical demonstration that the x_k's generated by Repeated Substitution can converge to the desired fixed point $\bar{x}$ monotonically (from only the left or only the right) as in (a) or from alternate sides as in (b); or they may diverge from $\bar{x}$ as in (c) or (d).

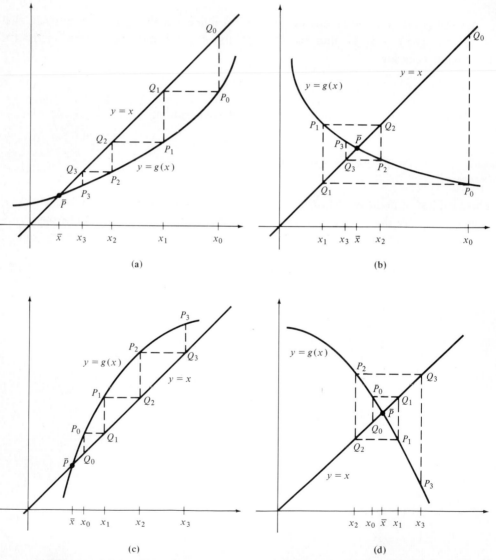

FIGURE 1.7-5 POSSIBLE OUTCOMES OF REPEATED SUBSTITUTION.

In performing Repeated Substitution, we shall use the increment

$$\Delta x_k = x_{k+1} - x_k \tag{7}$$

as a *computable estimate of the error of* x_k [see (3)].

EXAMPLE. Use Repeated Substitution to find to $3s$ the fixed points of

$$g(x) = \tfrac{1}{2}e^{x/2} \tag{8}$$

Solution. A sketch of the graph of g (Figure 1.7-6) shows that g has two fixed points, $\bar{x}_1$ and $\bar{x}_2$, and provides the initial guesses

$$\bar{x}_1 \approx 0.7 \qquad \text{and} \qquad \bar{x}_2 \approx 4.3 \tag{9}$$

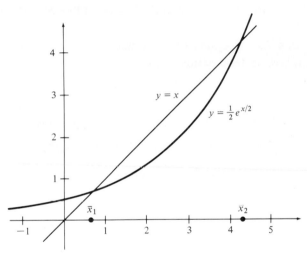

FIGURE 1.7-6   ESTIMATING THE FIXED POINTS OF $g(x) = \tfrac{1}{2}e^{x/2}$ GRAPHICALLY.

TO FIND $\bar{x}_1$: Starting with the graphical estimate $x_0 = 0.7$, we get

$$k = 0: \quad x_1 = g(x_0) = \tfrac{1}{2}e^{(0.7)/2} \doteq 0.7095, \qquad \Delta x_0 = 0.7095 - 0.7 = 0.0095$$
$$k = 1: \quad x_2 = g(x_1) = \tfrac{1}{2}e^{(0.7095)/2} \doteq 0.7129, \qquad \Delta x_1 = 0.7129 - 0.7095 = 0.0033$$
$$k = 2: \quad x_3 = g(x_2) = \tfrac{1}{2}e^{(0.7129)/2} \doteq 0.7141, \qquad \Delta x_2 = 0.7141 - 0.7129 = 0.0012$$
$$k = 3: \quad x_4 = g(x_3) = \tfrac{1}{2}e^{(0.7141)/2} \doteq 0.7146, \qquad \Delta x_3 = 0.7146 - 0.7141 = 0.0005$$

Since $|\Delta x_3| = 0.0005$, x_3 should be accurate to about $3d$ (= $3s$ in this case. Why?) So we stop the iteration and take $x_4 = 0.7146$ as approximating $\bar{x}_1$ to $3s$. In fact, $\bar{x}_1 \doteq 0.714806$. The monotonic convergence corresponds to Figure 1.7-5(a).

TO FIND $\bar{x}_2$: Four iterations of Repeated Substitution, starting with the graphical estimate $x_0 = 4.3$, are displayed on the "Worksheet Table" shown in Table 1.7-1. Since $|\Delta x_k|$ is getting larger as k increases, x_k is not converging to $\bar{x}_2$. This monotonic divergence corresponds to Figure 1.7-5(c). We thus see that

> $\bar{x}_2$ *simply cannot be found directly using Repeated Substitution.*

It will be found by an alternative method in Section 2.2D.

TABLE 1.7-1 FOUR ITERATIONS OF REPEATED
SUBSTITUTION.

k	x_k	$x_{k+1} = g(x_k)$	$\Delta x_k = x_{k+1} - x_k$
0	4.300	4.292	−0.008
1	4.292	4.276	−0.016
2	4.276	4.242	−0.035
3	4.242	4.169	−0.073

1.7D PRACTICAL TERMINATION TESTS FOR ITERATIVE ALGORITHMS

The approximation $\Delta x_k \approx \epsilon_k$ and the Absolute and Relative Error Tests of Section 1.6B suggest the following termination tests:

Absolute Difference Test (for *NumDec* decimal-place accuracy) *If*

$$|DeltaX| \leqslant AbsTol, \qquad where\ AbsTol = Const*10^{-NumDec} \qquad \textbf{(10)}$$

then X should approximate $\bar{x}$ to NumDec decimal places.

Relative Difference Test (for *NumSig* significant-digit accuracy) *If*

$$|DeltaX| \leqslant RelTol*|X|, \qquad where\ RelTol = Const*10^{-NumSig} \qquad \textbf{(11)}$$

then X should approximate $\bar{x}$ to NumSig significant digits.

In both the Absolute and Relative Error Tests,

$$DeltaX = X - Xprev \qquad \textbf{(12)}$$

The parameter *Const* in (10) and (11) will generally be taken as 1. It should be made closer to 0.5 if the convergence is expected to be slow, and larger than 1 (say 2–9) if a lot of roundoff error is expected.

If 5*s* accuracy is desired and we know that $\bar{x} \approx 3000$, we should use *NumDec* = 1 in the Absolute Difference Test; on the other hand, if we know that $\bar{x} \approx -0.003$, we should use *NumDec* = 7. In either case, we would simply use *NumSig* = 5 in the Relative Difference Test. This illustrates why *the Relative Difference Test is the natural one to use in programs that will find $\bar{x}$'s of varying magnitude.*

However, *the Relative Difference Test should never be used to test for closeness to zero.* Indeed, if $\bar{x} = 0$ and the algorithm is rapidly convergent (i.e., $x_n \to 0$ rapidly), then $|X|$ will be much smaller than $|Xprev|$; consequently, in the absence of roundoff error, we have $|DeltaX| \approx |Xprev|$ and (11) will not be satisfied.

In many situations (e.g., finding fixed points or roots) one can "plug in" $x = 0$ by hand to determine if $\bar{x} = 0$ is the desired value. In such situations a numerical method will only be needed to find a *nonzero* $\bar{x}$, so there is no risk in writing code for the Relative Difference Test in a computer program for finding $\bar{x}$. However, in situations where *several* $\bar{x}$'s are obtained simultaneously (see Sections 4.5 and 4.6) the termination test for an iterative algorithm should allow for the possibility that one or more of them is zero.

Some final words about termination tests: Computers have a way of getting into "endless loops" in ways we could never dream of. The only reliable safeguard against this is the following:

> For any iterative algorithm, no matter how sure you are that a termination test will be met, put an upper limit (e.g., *MaxIt*) on the number of iterations (just in case you are wrong).

It is also important not to make unrealistic accuracy demands of a digital device. One must be prepared to accept less than the device accuracy when the amount of "number crunching" per iteration is large.

1.7E A FORTRAN PROGRAM FOR REPEATED SUBSTITUTION

A pseudoprogram for Repeated Substitution can be obtained from the general pseudo-program of Figure 1.7-3 by simply taking

$$X \leftarrow g(Xprev)$$

as the "**form** X" step. The resulting pseudoprogram, with the addition of output statements, is translated into the FORTRAN program FIXPT shown in Figure 1.7-7. The program will perform up to $MaxIt = 10$ iterations to find, to $NumSig = 5$ significant digits, the fixed points of

$$g(x) = \frac{(p-1)x^2 + 78.8}{px} \tag{13}$$

The fixed points of this g are easy to find analytically. Indeed, for any nonzero p, $g(x) = x$ can hold if and only if $x^2 = 78.8$. So

$$\pm\sqrt{78.8} \doteq \pm 8.87693641 \text{ are the fixed points of } g \text{ for } any \text{ nonzero } p$$

A suitable initial guess when seeking $\bar{x} = +\sqrt{78.8}$ is $x_0 = \sqrt{81} = 9$.

The program FIXPT was run five times, for $p = 3$, 2, 1.5, 1, and 0.5, with the results shown in Figure 1.7-8. These runs confirm what we saw graphically in Figure 1.7-5, namely that Repeated Substitution can converge to $\bar{x}$ monotonically ($p = 3$ and 2), from alternate sides ($p = 1.5$), or not at all ($p = 1$ and 0.5).

```
00100   C - - - - - - - - - -        FIXPT      - - - - - - - - - - - - C
00200   C THIS PROGRAM SOLVES  G(X) = X  BY REPEATED SUBSTITUTION.  C
00300   C - - - - - - - - - - - - - - - - -       VERSION 1:   5/1/81  - -  C
00400         DATA IW, IR /5, 5/
00500   C
00600   C INITIALIZE:
00700         DATA MAXIT/10/, CONST/1./, NUMSIG/5/
00800   C
00900             G(X) = ((P-1)*X*X + 78.8)/(P*X)
01000   C
01100         RELTOL = CONST * 10.**(-NUMSIG)
01200         READ(IR,*) XPREV, P
01300         WRITE (IW,1) P
01400       1 FORMAT(' WITH  P =',F5.1,'  REPEATED SUBSTITUTION ',
01500        &'GIVES'//'  K     XPREV     XK=G(XPREV)   DX=XK-XPREV')
01600   C
01700   C ITERATE:
01800         DO 10 K=1,MAXIT
01900   C
02000         X = G(XPREV)
02100         DELTAX = X - XPREV
02200   C
02300         WRITE (IW,2) K, XPREV, X, DELTAX
02400       2 FORMAT(I3, 2X, F10.6, 4X, F10.6, 5X, E10.3)
02500   C
02600   C     UPDATE:
02700         XPREV = X
02800   C
02900   C     TERMINATION TEST (RELATIVE DIFFERENCE TEST):
03000         IF ( ABS(DELTAX) .LE. RELTOL*ABS(X) ) GOTO 20
03100      10 CONTINUE
03200         WRITE (IW,3) NUMSIG
03300       3 FORMAT(I4,' SIGNIFICANT DIGIT ACCURACY NOT APPARENT')
03400         STOP
03500   C
03600      20 WRITE (IW,4) X, NUMSIG
03700       4 FORMAT(3X,F12.6,' SEEMS ACCURATE TO',I3,' DIGITS')
03800         STOP
03900         END
```

FIGURE 1.7-7   FIXPT: A FORTRAN PROGRAM FOR FINDING FIXED POINTS.

1.7F   LINEAR AND QUADRATIC CONVERGENCE

An examination of the DX columns of Figure 1.7-8 reveals that for all $p \neq 2$, the iteration satisfied

$$\boxed{\frac{\text{DX}}{\text{preceding DX}} \approx \text{constant} = C, \qquad \text{that is, } \Delta x_k \approx C\Delta x_{k-1}} \qquad \textbf{(14a)}$$

with the proportionality constants C given in Table 1.7-2. Convergence occurred when $|C| < 1$, with more rapid convergence corresponding to smaller $|C|$. Divergence occurred when $|C| \geqslant 1$ (for x_k near $\bar{x}$). When (14a) holds, that is, when

$$(x_{k+1} - x_k) \text{ is (approximately) proportional to } (x_k - x_{k-1}) \qquad \textbf{(14b)}$$

WITH P = 3.0 REPEATED SUBSTITUTION GIVES

K	XPREV	XK=G(XPREV)	DX=XK-XPREV
1	9.000000	8.918519	-0.815E-01
2	8.918519	8.890862	-0.277E-01
3	8.890862	8.881585	-0.928E-02
4	8.881585	8.878487	-0.310E-02
5	8.878487	8.877453	-0.103E-02
6	8.877453	8.877109	-0.345E-03
7	8.877109	8.876994	-0.115E-03
8	8.876994	8.876956	-0.383E-04

8.876956 SEEMS ACCURATE TO 5 DIGITS

WITH P = 1.0 REPEATED SUBSTITUTION GIVES

K	XPREV	XK=G(XPREV)	DX=XK-XPREV
1	9.000000	8.755556	-0.244E+00
2	8.755556	9.000000	0.244E+00
3	9.000000	8.755556	-0.244E+00
4	8.755556	9.000000	0.244E+00
5	9.000000	8.755556	-0.244E+00
6	8.755556	9.000000	0.244E+00
7	9.000000	8.755556	-0.244E+00
8	8.755556	9.000000	0.244E+00
9	9.000000	8.755556	-0.244E+00
10	8.755556	9.000000	0.244E+00

5 SIGNIFICANT DIGIT ACCURACY NOT APPARENT

WITH P = 2.0 REPEATED SUBSTITUTION GIVES

K	XPREV	XK=G(XPREV)	DX=XK-XPREV
1	9.000000	8.877778	-0.122E+00
2	8.877778	8.876936	-0.841E-03
3	8.876936	8.876936	0.000E+00

8.876936 SEEMS ACCURATE TO 5 DIGITS

WITH P = 0.5 REPEATED SUBSTITUTION GIVES

K	XPREV	XK=G(XPREV)	DX=XK-XPREV
1	9.000000	8.511111	-0.489E+00
2	8.511111	10.005860	0.149E+01
3	10.005860	5.744910	-0.426E+01
4	5.744910	21.688073	0.159E+02
5	21.688073	-14.421406	-0.361E+02
6	-14.421406	3.493206	0.179E+02
7	3.493206	41.622937	0.381E+02
8	41.622937	-37.836563	-0.795E+02
9	-37.836563	33.671279	0.715E+02
10	33.671279	-28.990732	-0.627E+02

5 SIGNIFICANT DIGIT ACCURACY NOT APPARENT

WITH P = 1.5 REPEATED SUBSTITUTION GIVES

K	XPREV	XK=G(XPREV)	DX=XK-XPREV
1	9.000000	8.837037	-0.163E+00
2	8.837037	8.890356	0.533E-01
3	8.890356	8.872477	-0.179E-01
4	8.872477	8.878425	0.595E-02
5	8.878425	8.876441	-0.198E-02
6	8.876441	8.877102	0.661E-03
7	8.877102	8.876881	-0.221E-03
8	8.876881	8.876955	0.736E-04

8.876955 SEEMS ACCURATE TO 5 DIGITS

FIGURE 1.7-8   FIVE RUNS OF FIXPT FOR $g(x) = [(p-1)x^2 + 78.8]/(px)$.

TABLE 1.7-2   CONSTANTS C FOR THE
$p \neq 2$ RUNS OF FIGURE 1.7-8.

p	C
3.0	$\frac{1}{3}$
1.5	$-\frac{1}{3}$
1.0	-1
0.5	-3

the convergence of x_k to $\bar{x}$ is called **linear.** This is to be contrasted with what happened when $p = 2$ where the iteration satisfied

$$\frac{DX}{\text{preceding DX}} \to 0 \text{ as } k \text{ increases} \qquad (15)$$

In fact, if we examine the output of Figure 1.7-9, in which we deliberately used the poor initial guess $x_0 = 14.0$ but left all other parameters of FIXPT as in Figure 1.7-7, we see from the DX column that

```
WITH  P =  2.0  REPEATED SUBSTITUTION GIVES
```

```
K      XPREV        XK=G(XPREV)      DX=XK-XPREV
1    14.000000       9.814286        -0.419E+01
2     9.814286       8.921699        -0.893E+00
3     8.921699       8.877049        -0.447E-01
4     8.877049       8.876936        -0.112E-03
5     8.876936       8.876936         0.000E+00
      8.876936 SEEMS ACCURATE TO  5 DIGITS
```

FIGURE 1.7-9   QUADRATIC CONVERGENCE OF FIXPT WHEN $p = 2$.

$$\frac{\text{DX}}{(\text{preceding DX})^2} \approx \text{constant} = C, \qquad \text{that is, } \Delta x_k \approx C(\Delta x_{k-1})^2 \qquad \textbf{(16a)}$$

with $C \approx 0.055$. When (16a) holds, that is, when

$$(x_{k+1} - x_k) \text{ is (approximately) proportional to } (x_k - x_{k-1})^2 \qquad \textbf{(16b)}$$

the convergence of x_k to $\bar{x}$ is called **quadratic.**

> Throughout this book quadratic convergence will be used as our standard of rapid convergence, and linear convergence will be used as our standard of slow convergence.

In Section 2.4D we prove that the convergence or divergence of the Repeated Substitution algorithm is related to the derivative of g at $\bar{x}$:

> *The Repeated Substitution algorithm will converge linearly to the fixed point $\bar{x}$ if $0 < |g'(\bar{x})| < 1$, and quadratically if $|g'(\bar{x})| = 0$; it will diverge if $|g'(\bar{x})| > 1$,* **(17)** *and may converge or diverge if $g'(\bar{x}) = \pm 1$.*

The Repeated Substitution algorithm can generally be expected to converge only linearly if at all. It is an example of a rather poor algorithm because it is neither robust nor rapidly convergent. A more effective method for finding fixed points is described in Section 2.2D.

Exercises

Section 1.1

1-1. In (a)–(c), find $\text{DQ}[h] = [f(x + h) - f(x)]/h$ and also $\text{E}[h] = f'(x) - \text{DQ}[h]$ for $h = h_0,\ h_0/r,\ \ldots,\ h_0/r^4$ as in Figure 1.1-2. Is $\text{E}[h]$ approaching zero as $h \to 0$?

  (a) $f(x) = e^{-x}$; $x = 0$, $h_0 = 0.1$, $r = 5$; $[f'(x) = -1]$.

  (b) $f(x) = \sin x$ (x in radians); $x = \pi/4$, $h_0 = 0.04$, $r = 4$; $[f'(x) = 1/\sqrt{2}]$.

  (c) $f(x) = x^4$; $x = 0$, $h_0 = \frac{1}{3}$, $r = 3$; $[f'(x) = 0]$.

Section 1.3

1-2. There are seven positive three-bit integers. What are they?

1-3. Show all seven positive three-bit fractions on a number line; circle those that are normalized.

1-4. Which of (a)–(f) are binary numbers? For those that are, give (i) the binary representation [(1b) of Section 1.3A], and (ii) the normalized floating-point binary representation [(5) of Section 1.3B].

(a) $\frac{22}{7}$ (b) -22.75 (c) 0.01 (d) $9\frac{3}{8}$ (e) $-\frac{3}{64}$ (f) $\frac{3}{6}$

1-5. What real numbers have the following binary representations?

(a) $(101.1101)_2$ (b) $-(11100.0011)_2$ (c) $(1.1)_2$ (d) $-(0.01)_2$

1-6. There are 12 positive binary numbers X whose *normalized* floating-point representations that can be stored in a six-bit word as follows:

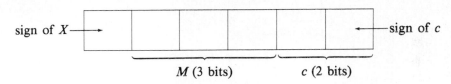

$$M \text{ (3 bits)} \qquad c \text{ (2 bits)}$$

Sketch these 12 X's on a number line, labeling s and L as in Figure 1.3-3.

1-7. (a) Expand $(1 + r + \cdots + r^n)(1 - r)$ to obtain the **geometric series** formula

$$\text{(GS)} \qquad a(1 + r + r^2 + \cdots + r^n) = \frac{a(r^{n+1} - 1)}{r - 1} \qquad (r \neq 1)$$

(b) Use (GS), (i) with $r = 2$ to prove that $2^m - 1$ is the largest m-bit integer, and (ii) with $r = a = \frac{1}{2}$ to prove that $1 - 2^{-k}$ is the largest k-bit fraction.

(c) Show that $M = (0.1100110011001100110010)_2 = \frac{3}{4}(1 + \frac{1}{16} + \cdots + (\frac{1}{16})^5)$. Then use (GS) to deduce that $M = 67108860/83886080$ [see (11) of Section 1.3E].

(d) Use (GS) to show that $\sum_{k=1}^{50} e^{6 - k/5} = e^{5.8}(1 - e^{-10})/(1 - e^{-0.2})$.

1-8. For the 32-bit words in (a) and (b), express as real (base 10) numbers:

(i) The integer stored as in Figure 1.3-1. [HINT: Use (GS) for (b).]

(ii) The binary number stored as in Figure 1.3-2 (*if* it is normalized).

(a) | 0 | 1 | 0 | 0 | 1 | 1 | 0 | 1 | 0 | 0 | 0 | 0 | 0 | 0 | 0 | 0 | 0 | 0 | 0 | 0 | 0 | 0 | 0 | 0 | 0 | 0 | 0 | 0 | 1 | 1 | 0 | 1 |

(b) | 0 | 0 | 1 | 0 | 1 | 0 | 1 | 0 | 1 | 0 | 1 | 0 | 1 | 0 | 1 | 0 | 1 | 0 | 1 | 0 | 1 | 0 | 1 | 0 | 1 | 0 | 1 | 0 | 1 | 0 | 1 | 0 |

1-9. For the computer(s) available to you, find the bit size of the mantissa and characteristic; the numbers s and L (Section 1.3D); the x's that would cause e^x to have overflow and underflow; the number of significant digits that can be stored.

Section 1.4

1-10. Round the following (i) to $2d$ and (ii) to $3s$.

(a) $-\sqrt{204}$ (b) $\pi/4$ (c) $\frac{5}{9}$ (d) -0.003 (e) 4394.94949

1-11. Express as $\pm M \cdot 10^c$ the normalized X that would be stored in a $4s$ base 10 device as in (1) of Section 1.4B to represent

   (a) $-\frac{4}{3}$ **(b)** $-\frac{1}{320}$ **(c)** 0.036546 **(d)** -0.0075351 **(e)** $\frac{9}{11}$

1-12. Let $X = 0.5289$, $Y = 0.8012$, and $Z = 0.6024$. Show that in $4s$ arithmetic (i.e., rounding to $4s$ after *each* operation):

   (a) $X \overset{*}{\ast} (Y \overset{+}{\ast} Z) \neq X \overset{*}{\ast} Y \overset{+}{\ast} X \overset{*}{\ast} Z$ **(b)** $(X \overset{+}{\ast} Y) \overset{+}{\ast} Z \neq X \overset{+}{\ast} (Y \overset{+}{\ast} Z)$

1-13. Make up an example in $2s$ arithmetic for which $(X \overset{*}{\ast} Y) \overset{*}{\ast} Z \neq X \overset{*}{\ast} (Y \overset{*}{\ast} Z)$.

1-14. Let $A = [\ln (x + h) - \ln x]/h$, where x and $x + h$ are positive.

   (a) Explain why A should approach $1/x$ as $h \to 0$.

   (b) Let $x = 20$. Calculate A for $h = 3 \cdot 10^{-2}$, $3 \cdot 10^{-5}$, and $3 \cdot 10^{-8}$.

   (c) Explain the causes of error in A for $|h| << x$.

1-15. Describe the possible causes of serious error in calculating

$$A = \frac{\sin x}{1 + \cos x} \quad \text{for } \cos x \approx -1$$

$$B = \sqrt{x^2 + 1} - x \quad \text{for } x >> 0$$

$$C = \frac{1}{1 + x} - 1 \quad \text{for } x \approx 0$$

Section 1.5

1-16. For A, B, and C of Exercise 1-15:

   (a) Use algebraic and/or trigonometric identities to eliminate (if possible) the possibility of serious roundoff error.

   (b) Write a correct assign statement to implement your answer to part (a) in a programming language of your choice.

1-17. Assuming that $x \approx 0$, $y >> 0$, and $z << 0$, use parentheses and/or algebraic rearrangement to minimize the possibility of overflow or underflow.

   (a) $z(e^y)^x$ **(b)** xe^ye^z **(c)** $e^{(y^2 - z)}/e^{(y^2 - 2z)}$

1-18. Use the nested form of $p(x)$ to find $p(-1.5)$.

   (a) $p(x) = 9x^3 - 3x^2 - 12x + 5$.

   (b) $p(x) = -2x^5 + x^3 - 5x^2 - 10$.

   (c) $p(x) = x^7 - 2x^3 + 1$.

1-19. Describe how the method indicated in parts (a) and (b) can be used to avoid loss of significance in evaluating $A = [\ln (x + h) - \ln x]/h$ when $|h| << x$.

   (a) Use the algebraic properties of the natural logarithm function.

   (b) Use the Maclaurin series $\ln (1 + u) = u - u^2/2 + u^3/3 - u^4/4 + \cdots$ with $u = h/x \approx 0$ (see Section 1.5D).

Section 1.6

1-20. Find the absolute, relative, and percent errors of the approximations

   (a) $\frac{1}{11} \approx 0.1$ **(b)** $\frac{1}{11} \approx 0.09$ **(c)** $\frac{5}{9} \approx 0.56$ **(d)** $\frac{4}{9} \approx 0.44$

1-21. For x in (a)–(d), find all X's for which $|X - x| < \frac{1}{2} \cdot 10^{-3} |x|$.

   (a) $x = 10$ **(b)** $x = -0.46$ **(c)** $x = 510$ **(d)** $x = 0.9$

   Do your answers confirm that $|\rho_x| < \frac{1}{2} \cdot 10^{-3}$ guarantees that $x = X(3s)$? Explain.

Section 1.7

1-22. For the functions shown in (a)–(e), make a large, accurate sketch of $y = g(x)$ on the given interval and use it to estimate all fixed points of g on that interval. On your graph, obtain x_1, x_2, and x_3 graphically (as in Figure 1.7-5) for each x_0 given.

(a) $g(x) = (x - 1)^2/4$ on $[0, 6]$; $x_0 = 1$ and 5.

(b) $g(x) = -x^2 + \frac{9}{2}x - \frac{45}{16}$ on $[0, 3]$; $x_0 = 1.1$, 1.4 and 2.5.

(c) $g(x) = -x^2 + \frac{11}{3}x - \frac{16}{9}$ on $[0, 3]$; $x_0 = 1.0$ and 2.0.

(d) $g(x) = 5 \ln x$ on $[0, 20]$; $x_0 = 2$ and 20.

(e) $g(x) = e^{x/2} - 2$ on $[-4, 4]$; $x_0 = -4$, 0 and 3.

1-23. For $g(x)$ in (a)–(e) of Example 1-22, use a calculator or computer to find to $4s$ all fixed points that can be found by Repeated Substitution. Take your x_0's to be the best initial guesses that you can get from your sketch of $y = g(x)$.

1-24. By examining either $\Delta x_k/\Delta x_{k-1}$ or $\Delta x_k/(\Delta x_{k-1})^2$ for selected successive k's, identify as linear or quadratic the convergence to $\bar{x}$ in your answers to (a)–(e) of Exercise 1-23. Then find $g'(\bar{x})$ and discuss whether your results illustrate the assertions made in (17) of Section 1.7F.

1-25. Suppose that $x_0 = 1$, $x_1 = 1.5$, and $x_2 = 1.7$. Estimate x_3 if the convergence is (a) linear; (b) quadratic.

1-26. Let $g(x) = [(p - 1)x + 78.8/x]/p$ [this is $g(x)$ in (13) of Section 1.7E]. Find $g'(\bar{x})$, where $\bar{x} = \sqrt{78.8}$, for $p = 3$, 2, 1.5, 1, and 0.5. Do the results of Figure 1.7-8 confirm the assertions made in (17) of Section 1.7F?

Computer and Programming Exercises

1-27. Write correct statements in a programming language of your choice for terminating iterations when X and $Xprev$ agree: (a) to five places; (b) to six significant digits.

1-28. Write a pseudoprogram for the computer program shown in:

(a) Figure 1.1-1   (b) Figure 1.2-1   (c) Figure 1.5-2

1-29. (a) Modify your pseudoprogram of Exercise 1-28(a) so as to stop when

$$|DQ[h] - DQ[\text{preceding } h]| < 10^{-NumDec}$$

(where *NumDec*, the desired number of accurate decimal places, is input by the user) if this occurs before performing *MaxIt* iterations.

(b) Write a computer program implementing your pseudocode in part (a). Test it with *NumDec* = 4, and H, R, and NREPS as in Figure 1.1-2.

1-30. Write a computer program that calls a subprogram such as POLVAL of Figure 1.5-1(c) to form a table of values of a polynomial $p(x)$ for $x = a, a + h, \ldots,$ $a + Nh = b$ as follows:

```
GET n, a₁, . . . aₙ₊₁    {p(x) = a₁xⁿ + a₂xⁿ⁻¹ + · · · + aₙx + aₙ₊₁}
GET a, b, N              {table parameters}
h ← (b − a)/N
DO FOR k = 0 TO N   {call POLVAL for the PofX ← p(x) step}
   BEGIN   x ← a + kh;   PofX ← p(x);   OUTPUT (x, PofX)   END
```

1-31. Write a computer program to calculate and print the values of

$$S = \sum_{k=1}^{N} (0.1) \quad \text{and} \quad P = N*(0.1)$$

for $N = 10, 100, 1000$, and 10,000. The exact values of both S and P are of course 1, 10, 100, and 1000 respectively. Which of S or P gets calculated more accurately? Explain.

1-32. In (a)–(c), write a subprogram to evaluate f to the given accuracy.

(a) $f(x) = (1 - \cos x)/x^2$ to 7s if $x \neq 0$; $f(0) = \frac{1}{2}$ (see Section 1.5B).

(b) $f(x) = (e^x - 1)/x$ to 7s if $x \neq 0$; $f(0) = \frac{1}{2}$ (see Section 1.5D).

(c) $f(x, h) = [\ln(x + h) - \ln x]/h$ to 6s if x, $x + h > 0$; $f(x, 0) = 1/x$ (see Exercise 1-19).

1-33. (a) Consider the sum $S_n = \sum_{k=1}^{n} a_k$, where $a_1 > a_2 > \cdots > a_n > 0$ and $a_1 \gg a_n \approx 0$. Explain why summing backward (i.e., $a_n + a_{n-1} + \cdots + a_1$) should give greater accuracy than summing forward (i.e., $a_1 + a_2 + \cdots + a_n$).

(b) Can you use a computer to show that $S_n = \sum_{k=1}^{n} (1/k) \to \infty$ as $n \to \infty$ by summing S_n forward for $n = 100, 100^2, 100^3, 100^4$? Explain.

(c) Write a computer program that sums $S_{50} = \sum_{k=1}^{50} e^{6 - k/5}$ both forward and backward and prints the sums. Does the output verify part (a) [see Exercise 1-7(d)]?

2

Numerical Methods for Finding Roots and Solving Equations

Introduction 2.0

The problem of finding the roots of $f(x)$, that is, solving

$$f(x) = 0$$

arises frequently in engineering and science, either as a problem in itself or as an intermediate step in solving a more complex problem.

For example, important problems such as determining the *natural frequencies* of certain mechanical or electrical systems can be reduced to that of finding the general solution of the linear, homogeneous, nth-order differential equation

$$a_1 \frac{d^n y}{dt^n} + a_2 \frac{d^{n-1} y}{dt^{n-1}} + \cdots + a_n \frac{dy}{dt} + a_{n+1} y = 0 \qquad (a_1 \neq 0) \tag{1}$$

The desired solution $y = y(t)$ can be constructed from functions $e^{r_1 t}, \ldots, e^{r_n t}$, where $r_1, \ldots, r_n$ are the roots of the associated nth-degree polynomial

$$p(x) = a_1 x^n + a_2 x^{n-1} + \cdots + a_n x + a_{n+1} \tag{2}$$

To illustrate, suppose that we find that the cubic polynomial

$$p(x) = x^3 + 7.5x^2 + 18.48x + 15.004 \quad \text{has roots} \quad r_1 = r_2 = -2.2, \; r_3 = -3.1 \tag{3}$$

Then the general solution of the third-order differential equation

$$y''' + 7.5y'' + 18.48y' + 15.004y = 0 \tag{4a}$$

can be written by inspection as

$$y(t) = (At + B)e^{-2.2t} + Ce^{-3.1t} \tag{4b}$$

43

where the constants A, B, and C are determined by three additional conditions given as part of the problem.

Having determined that say $A = 5.9$, $B = 1.3$, and $C = 0$, we may then find it important to know how long it takes for $y(t)$ to assume the value 1.223. To get the desired t, we must solve the equation

$$(5.9t + 1.3)e^{-2.2t} = 1.223 \tag{5}$$

This can be viewed as the problem of finding the smallest positive root of

$$f(t) = (5.9t + 1.3)e^{-2.2t} - 1.223 \tag{6}$$

In analyzing certain types of vibrations, equations such as

$$k \tan x - \tanh x = 0 \quad \text{and} \quad k \cos x + \operatorname{sech} x = 0 \tag{7}$$

arise and must be solved. Other situations that require finding roots of $f(x)$ arise in the natural and social as well as engineering sciences.

Our purpose in this chapter is to introduce practical methods for finding roots of $f(x)$. Most methods will apply whether $f(x)$ is **algebraic** [i.e., involves only the four arithmetic operations and radicals, e.g., (2)] or **transcendental** [i.e., involves trigonometric, exponential, and hyperbolic functions, and possibly their inverses as well, for example, (6) and (7)]. A special method for finding roots of polynomials is given in Section 2.5.

2.1   Solving Equations and Finding Roots

We wish to develop efficient iterative algorithms for finding **roots** $\bar{x}$ of a continuous function f, that is, for solving the equation

$$f(x) = 0 \tag{1}$$

2.1A   CONVERTING $g(x) = h(x)$ TO AN EQUIVALENT EQUATION $f(x) = 0$

To apply a root-finding method to an equation of the form

$$g(x) = h(x) \tag{2}$$

we simply take all terms to one side (and perform other simplifying operations as well) to convert it to an equivalent equation of the form $f(x) = 0$. The graphical interpretation of (1) and (2) is given in Figure 2.1-1.

EXAMPLE 1. FINDING $g^{-1}(c)$. The problem of finding x's such that

$$g(x) = c, \quad \text{where } c \text{ is a given real number} \tag{3a}$$

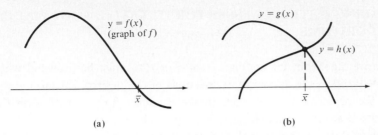

(a)   (b)

FIGURE 2.1-1   (a) ROOT $\bar{x}$ OF $f(x)$; (b) SOLUTION $\bar{x}$ OF $g(x) = h(x)$.

(see Figure 2.1-2) can be formulated as the problem of solving

$$g(x) - c = 0 \tag{3b}$$

that is, finding the roots of $f(x) = g(x) - c$. In particular, since $\bar{x} = \sqrt[n]{c}$ satisfies $\bar{x}^n = c$, the nth roots of a given c can be obtained by solving

$$x^n - c = 0 \tag{4}$$

that is, by finding the roots of the polynomial $f(x) = x^n - c$.

EXAMPLE 2. FINDING FIXED POINTS. Solving the fixed-point equation

$$g(x) = x \tag{5a}$$

is equivalent to solving

$$g(x) - x = 0 \tag{5b}$$

that is, finding the roots of $f(x) = g(x) - x$. We shall soon see that finding roots of $g(x) - x$ generally yields the fixed points of g more effectively than does applying the Repeated Substitution algorithm of Section 1.7C directly.

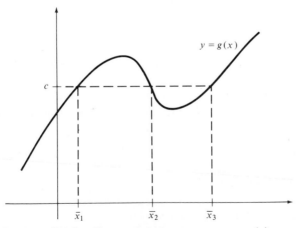

FIGURE 2.1-2   GRAPHICAL SOLUTION OF $g(x) = c$.

2.1B FINDING INITIAL GUESSES FOR ITERATIVE ROOT-FINDING ALGORITHMS

An iterative algorithm for finding a root $\bar{x}$ of $f(x)$ must be provided with an initial guess x_0. Very often the approximate locations of the desired $\bar{x}$'s are known from the nature of the problem that gave rise to the equation $f(x) = 0$. If approximations of the desired $\bar{x}$'s are not available, it may be possible to get estimates of $\bar{x}$ by rewriting $f(x) = 0$ as $g(x) = h(x)$, where the graphs of g and h can be sketched with less work than that of sketching the graph of f.

Example. Estimate all roots of

$$f(x) = e^{-x} \sec x - 1 \tag{6a}$$

Solution. The shape of the graph of f is not immediately evident. However, the equation $f(x) = 0$ has the same solutions as *any* of the equivalent equations

$$e^{-x} \sec x = 1 \quad \text{or} \quad e^{x} \cos x = 1 \quad \text{or} \quad e^{x} = \sec x \quad \text{or} \quad e^{-x} = \cos x \tag{6b}$$

Of these, the functions $g(x) = e^{-x}$ and $h(x) = \cos x$ equated last are probably the most easily sketched from memory (see Figure 2.1-3). From Figure 2.1-3 we can quickly see that $f(x) = e^{-x} \sec x - 1$ has infinitely many roots. The smallest is exactly $\bar{x}_0 = 0$; the next is $\bar{x}_1 \approx 1.3$; and the others are $\bar{x}_k \approx (2k - 1) \pi/2$ for $k = 2, 3, \ldots$ (i.e., positive, odd multiples of $\pi/2$).

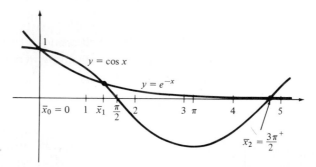

Figure 2.1-3   Estimating the roots of $e^{-x} \sec x - 1$ graphically.

Note: It is usually *not* necessary to get initial guesses with more accuracy than about 2s. Greater accuracy can then be obtained efficiently using one of the methods of Section 2.2.

2.1C TROUBLESOME ROOTS

Simple roots of $f(x)$ are those that correspond to points $\bar{x}$ where the graph of f crosses the x-axis with *nonzero slope*, that is, where $f'(\bar{x}) \neq 0$, as shown in Figure 2.1-1(a). Generally, such roots are easily located by looking for a sign change in $f(x)$.

However, if $f'(\bar{x}) = 0$, or even if $f'(x) \approx 0$ for x near $\bar{x}$, then there may be some trouble locating $\bar{x}$. Some of the possible difficulties are illustrated graphically in Figure 2.1-4.

The trouble in Figure 2.1-4(a)–(c) arises because the graph of f has a turning point (local max or local min) near the x-axis. When this occurs, it may not be clear from a rough sketch whether the x-axis is touched (a) at a single tangency point $\bar{x}$, (b) at two close points $\bar{x}_1$ and $\bar{x}_2$, or (c) not at all. In (d) there is a root, but it is hard to say exactly where. In all of (a)–(d),

$$\text{both} \quad f(x) \approx 0 \quad \text{and} \quad f'(x) \approx 0 \qquad \text{for } x \approx \bar{x} \tag{7}$$

For such x, roundoff error (due to loss of significance) in calculating $f(x)$ can be greater than $|f(x)|$ itself, making $f(x)$ hard to evaluate accurately. As a result, *all root-finding methods will have difficulty finding $\bar{x}$ accurately*. Thus a device that can generally get a simple root to about $7s$ might be capable of attaining only $5s$ accuracy when (7) holds.

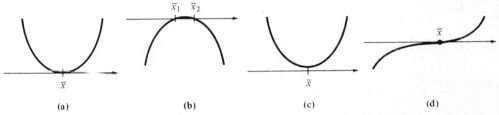

FIGURE 2.1-4   SITUATIONS THAT PRESENT NUMERICAL DIFFICULTIES.

Methods for Finding Roots of $f(x)$ 2.2

Of the many known general-purpose methods for finding real roots $\bar{x}$ of a continuous $f(x)$, we shall consider two in detail: the *Newton–Raphson (NR) method* and the *Secant (SEC) Method*. These will be referred to as **slope methods** because they are based on the following geometric idea.

2.2A   THE SLOPE METHOD STRATEGY

Suppose that x_k is a current approximation of a desired root $\bar{x}$. Define P_k, m_k, and x_{k+1} as follows (see Figure 2.2-1):

P_k is the point (x_k, y_k),   where $y_k = f(x_k)$
m_k is a nonzero number that represents the *slope* of the curve $y = f(x)$ near the point P_k
x_{k+1} is the x-intercept of the straight line through P_k having slope m_k

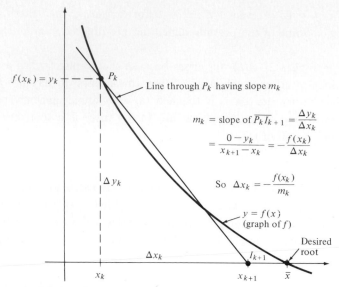

$$f(x_k) = y_k$$

Line through P_k having slope m_k

$$m_k = \text{slope of } \overline{P_k I_{k+1}} = \frac{\Delta y_k}{\Delta x_k}$$

$$= \frac{0 - y_k}{x_{k+1} - x_k} = -\frac{f(x_k)}{\Delta x_k}$$

So $\Delta x_k = -\dfrac{f(x_k)}{m_k}$

$$y = f(x)$$
(graph of f)

Desired root

FIGURE 2.2-1 GRAPHICAL DESCRIPTION OF A SLOPE METHOD.

Then, as the computation in Figure 2.2-1 shows,

$$x_{k+1} = x_k + \Delta x_k, \qquad \text{where } \Delta x_k = \frac{-y_k}{m_k} = \frac{-f(x_k)}{m_k} \tag{1}$$

If the straight line approximates the curve well near both $P_k(x_k, y_k)$ and $I_{k+1}(x_{k+1}, 0)$ then x_{k+1} should approximate $\bar{x}$ better than x_k. And if this procedure is repeated starting with x_{k+1}, then the resulting x_{k+2} should give an even better approximation of $\bar{x}$.

Since (1) defines an iterative algorithm,

$$\Delta x_k = x_{k+1} - x_k \text{ will be used to approximate the error of } x_k \tag{2}$$

[See (7) of Section 1.7C]. Our primary termination test for slope methods will be to take x_{k+1} as approximating $\bar{x}$ to a prescribed accuracy when $|\Delta x_k|$ is sufficiently small to indicate that the desired accuracy was achieved. This test is incorporated in the pseudocode for a slope method shown in Figure 2.2-2.

What distinguishes one slope method from another is the strategy used in the **form** *Slope* step. Two of the most effective strategies are to take *Slope* $= m_{\tan}$ (NR) or *Slope* $= m_{\sec}$ (SEC) as described next.

2.2B THE NEWTON–RAPHSON (NR) METHOD: $m_k = m_{\tan}$

If $f(x)$ is differentiable at x_k, then the natural candidate for m_k is the *tangent slope* at $P_k(x_k, f(x_k))$ which we know from calculus to be

$$m_{\tan} = f'(x_k) = \text{the derivative of } f \text{ at } x_k$$

Algorithm: Slope Method (Special Cases: NR and SEC)

Purpose: To find a root $\bar{x}$ of $f(x)$, that is, to solve $f(x) = 0$ for $\bar{x}$.

{*initialize*}
GET   *MaxIt*,   {maximum number of iterations}
          NumSig, {desired number of accurate significant digits}
          x_0 {an initial guess of $\bar{x}$}
$Xprev \leftarrow x_0$; $Yprev \leftarrow f(x_0)$; $RelTol \leftarrow 10^{-NumSig}$

{*iterate*}
DO FOR $k = 1$ TO *MaxIt* UNTIL **termination test** is satisfied
  BEGIN
  {**form *Slope***} *Slope* $\leftarrow$ (formula involving *Xprev* and *Yprev*)
  $DeltaX \leftarrow -Yprev/Slope$
  $X \leftarrow Xprev + DeltaX$; $Y \leftarrow f(X)$
  OUTPUT (k, X, Y, *DeltaX*)
  {**update**} $Xprev \leftarrow X$; $Yprev \leftarrow Y$
  {**termination test:** $|DeltaX| \leq RelTol*|X|$ or $Yprev = 0$}
  END

IF **termination test** succeeded
  THEN OUTPUT (X approximates $\bar{x}$ to *NumSig* significant digits.)
  ELSE OUTPUT (*MaxIt* iterations failed to yield a suitable X.)

FIGURE 2.2-2   PSEUDOPROGRAM FOR A SLOPE METHOD.

Taking $m_k = m_{\tan}$ in the general slope method formula (1) gives

$$\text{(NR)} \qquad x_{k+1} = x_k + \Delta x_k, \qquad \text{where } \Delta x_k = \frac{-f(x_k)}{m_{\tan}} = \frac{-f(x_k)}{f'(x_k)} \qquad \text{(3)}$$

Formula (3) is the iterative step of the **Newton–Raphson (NR) method** (also called **Newton's method**) for finding a root of $f(x)$. The use of (NR) to find x_1, x_2, and x_3 from an initial guess x_0 is illustrated graphically in Figure 2.2-3. For obvious reasons, the NR method is often called the **method of tangents.**

EXAMPLE
a. Show how to use (NR) to find $\sqrt[n]{c}$ for any $c > 0$ and $n > 0$.
b. Use (NR) to find $\sqrt{78.8}$ to 6s. (NOTE: $\sqrt{78.8} \doteq 8.8769364$.)

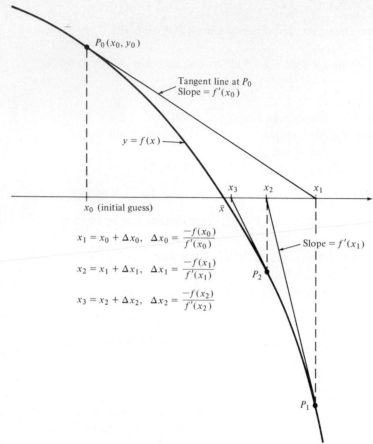

FIGURE 2.2-3   GRAPHICAL REPRESENTATION OF THE NEWTON–RAPHSON METHOD.

Solution

a. For any $c > 0$, $\sqrt[n]{c}$ is the unique positive root of

$$f(x) = x^n - c \tag{4}$$

[see Section 2.1A]. For this $f(x)$, $f'(x) = nx^{n-1}$; so (NR) becomes

$$x_{k+1} = x_k + \Delta x_k, \qquad \text{where } \Delta x_k = -\frac{x_k^n - c}{nx_k^{n-1}} \tag{5}$$

b. Taking $n = 2$ in (5), we get

$$x_{k+1} = x_k + \Delta x_k, \qquad \text{where } \Delta x_k = \frac{c - x_k^2}{2x_k} \tag{6}$$

Using (6) with $c = 78.8$ and the (poor) initial guess $x_0 = 14$, we get

$$k = 0: \quad \Delta x_0 = \frac{78.8 - 14^2}{2(14)} \doteq -4.185714; \qquad \text{so } x_1 = 14 - 4.185714 = 9.814286$$

$$k = 1: \quad \Delta x_1 = \frac{78.8 - x_1^2}{2x_1} \doteq -0.892587; \quad \text{so } x_2 = 9.814286 - 0.892587 = 8.921699$$

$$k = 2: \quad \Delta x_2 = \frac{78.8 - x_2^2}{2x_2} \doteq -0.044650; \quad \text{so } x_3 = 8.921699 - 0.044650 = 8.877049$$

$$k = 3: \quad \Delta x_3 = \frac{78.8 - x_3^2}{2x_3} \doteq -0.000113; \quad \text{so } x_4 = 8.877049 - 0.000113 = 8.876936$$

Since $|\Delta x_3| \doteq 0.0001$, we conclude that x_3 is accurate to about $4d$ (i.e., $5s$). In view of the rapid rate at which $|\Delta x_k|$ is shrinking to zero, x_4 should be accurate to $6s$. In fact, it is accurate to all $7s$ shown!

If we eliminate Δx_k in (6), then we get the iterative formula

$$x_{k+1} = x_k + \frac{78.8 - x_k^2}{2x_k} = \frac{x_k^2 + 78.8}{2x_k} = g(x_k) \tag{7}$$

where $g(x)$ is the $p = 2$ case of the Repeated Substitution example considered in Section 1.7E (cf. Figure 1.7-9). In view of the observations about rate of convergence that we made in Section 1.7F, we see that the NR algorithm converges quadratically to $\bar{x} = \sqrt{78.8}$ when $f(x) = x^2 - 78.8$. It is because of this rapid convergence when $f(x) = x^2 - c$ that most hand calculators and computers calculate $\sqrt{x}$ internally using a formula based on a few iterations of (6). We shall prove in Section 2.4C that more generally, *the iterates generated by the NR method can be expected to exhibit quadratic convergence, that is, satisfy*

$$\boxed{(x_{k+1} - x_k) \approx C(x_k - x_{k-1})^2, \qquad C = \text{constant}} \tag{8}$$

whenever the desired root $\bar{x}$ is a simple root of f.

2.2C REARRANGING EQUATIONS TO MAKE THE NR METHOD EASIER TO USE

Suppose that we wanted the two smallest positive roots of

$$f(x) = e^{-x} \sec x - 1 \tag{9}$$

to $7s$. This $f(x)$ was considered in Section 2.1B, where we noted that

$$e^{-x} \sec x - 1 = 0 \qquad \Longleftrightarrow \qquad e^{-x} = \cos x$$

That is, the roots of the given $f(x)$ are the same as those of

$$f(x) = e^{-x} - \cos x \quad , \quad f(x) = -1e^{-x} + \sin x \tag{10}$$

However, the derivative of $f(x)$ in (10) is easier to obtain and evaluate than that of $f(x)$ in (9). So we shall solve the given problem by using the NR method to find the roots of (10). For this $f(x)$,

$$\Delta x_k = \frac{-f(x_k)}{f'(x_k)}, \qquad \text{where } f'(x_k) = \sin x_k - e^{-x_k}$$

The approximations $\bar{x}_1 \approx 1.3$ and $\bar{x}_2 \approx 3\pi/2$ obtained graphically in the example in Section 2.1B provided good initial guesses of the desired roots. The remaining iterations of the NR method are displayed efficiently on the worksheet table shown in Table 2.2-1. Both $\bar{x}_1$ and $\bar{x}_2$ were obtained to 7s (actually 8s) accuracy in only two iterations! Moreover, the Δx_k column shows that

> the number of accurate decimal places (roughly)
> doubles with each iteration once x_k gets close to $\bar{x}$

This rapid shrinking of Δx_k is characteristic of quadratic convergence when a good initial guess is used.

TABLE 2.2-1 NR METHOD ITERATIONS FOR TWO ROOTS OF $f(x) = e^{-x} - \cos x$.

k	x_k	$y_k = f(x_k)$	$\Delta x_k = \dfrac{-y_k}{f'(x_k)}$	$x_{k+1} = x_k + \Delta x_k$
0	1.3	0.50329644E−2	−0.0072833	1.2927167
1	1.2927167	0.14403021E−4	−0.0000210	1.2926957
0	4.7123890	0.89832910E−2	0.0089033	4.7212923
1	4.7212923	0.46291601E−6	0.0000005	4.7212928

The reader will find it instructive to get $\bar{x}_1$ and $\bar{x}_2$ to 7s on a similar worksheet table, using the same initial guesses, but for the *given $f(x)$* in (9). This should demonstrate how *whatever the method used, rewriting $f(x) = 0$ in a more convenient form at the outset can save considerable energy* (*and reduce the chance of human error*) in the solution of the problem.

2.2D   FINDING FIXED POINTS OF $g(x)$ AS ROOTS OF $g(x) - x$

We saw in the example in Section 1.7C that

$$\bar{x} \approx 4.3 \text{ is a fixed point of } g(x) = \tfrac{1}{2}e^{x/2}$$

that could *not* be found by Repeated Substitution. However, $\bar{x}$ is a root of $g(x) - x$, that is, of

$$f(x) = \tfrac{1}{2}e^{x/2} - x, \qquad \text{for which } f'(x) = \tfrac{1}{4}e^{x/2} - 1$$

For this $f(x)$, one iteration of the NR method with $x_0 = 4.3$ gives

$$x_1 = 4.3 - \frac{\tfrac{1}{2}e^{(4.3)/2} - 4.3}{\tfrac{1}{4}e^{(4.3)/2} - 1} \doteq 4.3066$$

The reader should verify that $g(x_1) \doteq x_1$; so x_1 is accurate to all $5s$ shown! This should convince the reader that *finding roots of $g(x) - x$ will usually yield fixed points of $g(x)$ faster and more reliably than Repeated Substitution.* It is therefore the preferred method for finding fixed points in most situations.

2.2E   THE SECANT (SEC) METHOD: $m_k = m_{sec}$

The NR method was obtained by taking m_k to be the exact tangent slope at $P_k(x_k, y_k)$ in the general slope method formula

$$x_{k+1} = x_k + \Delta x_k, \qquad \text{where } \Delta x_k = \frac{-f(x_k)}{m_k}$$

To use the NR method one must find the derivative $f'(x)$ and then evaluate $m_{tan} = f'(x_k)$ in addition to $f(x_k)$ at *each* iteration. The work required to find and substitute in $f'(x)$ was negligible for $f(x) = x^n - c$ and not too extensive for $f(x) = e^{-x} - \cos x$. But it would have been substantial if, say,

$$f(x) = \sin \sqrt{\sec x + x^3 e^{5x/\tan x}} - e^{-x} \tag{11}$$

For an $f(x)$ as complicated as this, a desirable slope method is one that gets m_k using only the function $f(x)$ itself. Such an m_k is obtained by using the *current point* $P_k(x_k, f(x_k))$ and the *preceding current point* $P_{k-1}(x_{k-1}, f(x_{k-1}))$ to determine the *secant slope*

$$m_{sec} = \frac{f(x_k) - f(x_{k-1})}{x_k - x_{k-1}} = \frac{y_k - y_{k-1}}{\Delta x_{k-1}} \tag{12}$$

Taking $m_k = m_{sec}$ in the general slope method formula gives

$$(SEC) \quad x_{k+1} = x_k + \Delta x_k, \qquad \text{where } \Delta x_k = \frac{-f(x_k)}{m_{sec}} = \frac{-y_k \, \Delta x_{k-1}}{y_k - y_{k-1}} \tag{13}$$

The resulting algorithm, which requires *two* initial guesses, is called the **Secant (SEC) Method.** The use of (SEC) to find x_1, x_2, x_3, and x_4 from two initial guesses x_0 and x_{-1} illustrated graphically in Figure 2.2-4. If x_{k-1} and x_k are both near $\bar{x}$, then

$$m_{sec} \text{ (through } P_{k-1} \text{ and } P_k) \approx m_{tan} \text{ (at } P_k)$$

Hence the Secant Method should converge about as quickly as the Newton–Raphson method. The following example confirms this.

EXAMPLE. Use (SEC) to find $\sqrt{78.8}$ to $6s$. Take $x_{-1} = 14.1$ and $x_0 = 14.0$.

Solution. As in the Example in Section 2.2B, we view $\bar{x} = \sqrt{78.8}$ as the positive root of

$$f(x) = x^2 - 78.8 \tag{14}$$

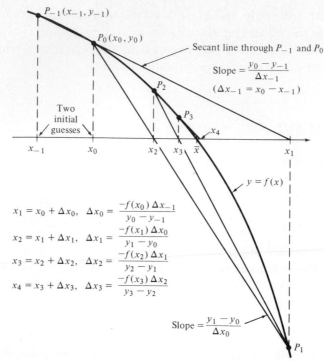

$$x_1 = x_0 + \Delta x_0, \quad \Delta x_0 = \frac{-f(x_0)\,\Delta x_{-1}}{y_0 - y_{-1}}$$
$$x_2 = x_1 + \Delta x_1, \quad \Delta x_1 = \frac{-f(x_1)\,\Delta x_0}{y_1 - y_0}$$
$$x_3 = x_2 + \Delta x_2, \quad \Delta x_2 = \frac{-f(x_2)\,\Delta x_1}{y_2 - y_1}$$
$$x_4 = x_3 + \Delta x_3, \quad \Delta x_3 = \frac{-f(x_3)\,\Delta x_2}{y_3 - y_2}$$

FIGURE 2.2-4 GRAPHICAL REPRESENTATION OF THE SECANT METHOD.

Using (SEC) with $\Delta x_{-1} = x_0 - x_{-1} = 14.0 - 14.1 = -0.1$, we get

$$k = 0: \quad \Delta x_0 = \frac{-y_0\,\Delta x_{-1}}{y_0 - y_{-1}} = \frac{-117.20(-0.1)}{117.20 - 120.01} \doteq -4.170818$$

So $x_1 = x_0 + \Delta x_0 = 14.0 - 4.170818 = 9.829182.$

$$k = 1: \quad \Delta x_1 = \frac{-y_1\,\Delta x_0}{y_1 - y_0} = \frac{-17.81282(-4.170818)}{17.81282 - 117.20} \doteq -0.747521$$

So $x_2 = x_1 + \Delta x_1 = 9.829182 - 0.747521 = 9.081661.$

$$k = 2: \quad \Delta x_2 = \frac{-y_2\,\Delta x_1}{y_2 - y_1} = \frac{-3.676567(-0.747521)}{3.676567 - 17.81282} \doteq -0.194416$$

So $x_3 = x_2 + \Delta x_2 = 9.081661 - 0.194416 = 8.887245.$

These calculations are continued on the worksheet table shown in Table 2.2-2.

Since $|\Delta x_4| = 0.000117 \approx 10^{-4}$, we conclude that $x_4 = 8.877054$ is accurate to about 4d (i.e., 5s); and since $|\Delta x_k|$ is approaching zero rapidly, $x_5 = 8.876937$ should be (and in fact is) accurate to 6s. A comparison of these x_k's with those obtained in the Example in Section 2.2B shows that, starting with the same x_0, (SEC) required about 25% more iterations than (NR) to achieve 6s accuracy. We shall soon see that more generally, *the convergence of the SEC Method is faster than linear but not quite quadratic when $\bar{x}$ is a simple root.*

TABLE 2.2-2   SEC METHOD ITERATIONS FOR A ROOT OF $f(x) = x^2 - 78.8$.

k	x_k	$y_k = f(x_k)$	$\Delta x_k = \dfrac{-y_k\,\Delta x_{k-1}}{y_k - y_{k-1}}$	$x_{k+1} = x_k + \Delta x_k$
−1	14.1	120.01		
0	14.0	117.20	−4.170818	9.829182
1	9.829182	17.81282	−0.747521	9.081661
2	9.081661	3.676567	−0.194416	8.887245
3	8.887245	0.183124	−0.010191	8.877054
4	8.877054	0.002088	−0.000117	8.876937

2.2F   FINDING INITIAL GUESSES FOR THE SEC METHOD

In Section 2.1B we discussed procedures for finding an initial guess. *A second initial guess for the SEC Method is obtained by simply giving this number a small perturbation.* In the preceding example, 14.0 was perturbed by +0.1 to give 14.1. It generally makes little difference which of two such initial guesses is taken as x_0 and which is taken as x_{-1}.

Example. Use the SEC Method to find to 7s the two smallest positive roots of

$$f(x) = e^{-x} - \cos x \qquad\qquad (15)$$

Solution. We saw in Figure 2.1-3 that $\bar{x}_1 \approx 1.3$ and $\bar{x}_2 \approx 3\pi/2$. For $\bar{x}_1$, we take $x_{-1} = 1.2$ and $x_0 = 1.3$ so that $f(x_{-1}) \doteq -0.06116$ and $f(x_0) \doteq 0.00503$. For $\bar{x}_2$, we take $x_{-1} = 3\pi/2 + 0.1$ and $x_0 = 3\pi/2$ so that $f(x_{-1}) \doteq -0.09170$ and $f(x_0) \doteq 0.008983$.

The SEC Method iterations (until 7s accuracy is evident) are shown in Table 2.2-3. Upon comparing the Δx_k column with that of Table 2.2-1, we see again that the convergence of the SEC Method is almost as fast as the quadratic convergence of NR. Indeed,

TABLE 2.2-3   SEC METHOD ITERATIONS FOR TWO ROOTS OF $f(x) = e^{-x} - \cos x$.

k	x_k	$y_k = f(x_k)$	$\Delta x_k = \dfrac{-y_k\,\Delta x_{k-1}}{y_k - y_{k-1}}$	$x_{k+1} = x_k + \Delta x_k$
−1	1.2	−0.6116354E−1		
0	1.3	0.5032964E−2	−0.0076031	1.2923969
1	1.2923969	−0.2052559E−3	0.0002980	1.2926949
2	1.2926949	−0.5943326E−6	0.0000008	1.2926957
−1	4.8123890	−0.9170500E−1		
0	4.7123890	0.8983291E−2	0.0089219	4.7213109
1	4.7213109	−0.1826462E−4	−0.0000181	4.7212928

it can be shown (see [29]) that for most *simple* roots $\bar{x}$, the iterates generated by the SEC Method will satisfy

$$\boxed{|x_{k+1} - x_k| \approx C|x_k - x_{k-1}|^{1.618}, \qquad C = \text{constant}} \qquad \textbf{(16)}$$

once x_k and x_{k-1} are sufficiently close to $\bar{x}$. We shall refer to this as **almost quadratic** convergence.

2.2G WHAT CAN GO WRONG WITH THE NR AND SEC METHODS?

In certain situations, slope methods will either converge to a different root than the one intended or will fail to converge at all. The reasons for this are easily understood graphically.

Figure 2.2-5 shows some possible adverse effects of a *poor initial guess* on the NR method. In (a) x_k will converge to a root that is not the desired root $\bar{x}$; in (b) x_k will diverge to $-\infty$. The trouble in both (a) and (b) occurred because *the tangent line at P_0* $(x_0, f(x_0))$ *was nearly horizontal* [i.e., $m_0 = f'(x_0) \approx 0$] and consequently its x-intercept, x_1, was far from both x_0 and the desired $\bar{x}$. This phenomenon, called **overshoot**, can also occur when the initial m_{sec} is nearly zero. However, the fact that m_{sec} uses P_{k-1} in addition to the current P_k often results in x_2 returning near x_0 even if x_1 overshoots.

Other pathological phenomena that can occur when using slope methods are **cycling** and **wandering**. Figure 2.2-6 shows how these can occur for the NR method if the graph of f has an inflection point near $(\bar{x}, 0)$ or a turning point near but not touching the x-axis. Situations similar to those shown in Figure 2.2-6(b) and (c) can occur for the SEC method as well.

Two conclusions to be reached from Figures 2.2-5 and 2.2-6 are

1. It is important to use accurate initial guesses when using a slope method (e.g., NR or SEC) to find a root near a turning point.
2. It is especially important to include an upper limit of, say, 12–25 iterations in any program for a slope method.

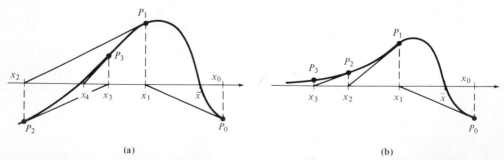

(a)   (b)

FIGURE 2.2-5 POSSIBLE CONSEQUENCES OF A POOR INITIAL GUESS ON NR.

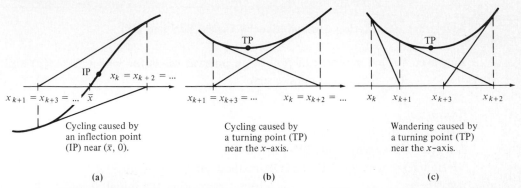

Cycling caused by
an inflection point
(IP) near $(\bar{x}, 0)$.

Cycling caused by
a turning point (TP)
near the x-axis.

Wandering caused by
a turning point (TP)
near the x-axis.

(a)   (b)   (c)

FIGURE 2.2-6   CYCLING AND WANDERING OF NR ITERATES.

All numerical methods converge more slowly and have trouble finding roots accurately in the troublesome situations illustrated in Figure 2.1-4. This problem is examined further in Section 2.3.

2.2H   BRACKETING METHODS

The reader should be aware of a class of methods that we shall call **bracketing methods** because they "bracket" $\bar{x}$ between the endpoints of a closed interval $[a, b]$. All bracketing methods start with an initial interval $[a, b]$ for which

$$L = f(a) \quad \text{and} \quad R = f(b) \quad \text{have opposite sign} \tag{17}$$

If we assume f to be continuous, there must be at least one root $\bar{x}$ bracketed between a and b (Figure 2.2-7). To simplify our discussion, we assume that f has *exactly one* root $\bar{x}$ in $[a, b]$. Our objective is to find algorithms for systematically moving a and b toward each other while keeping $\bar{x}$ bracketed between them.

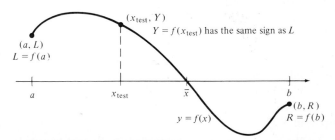

FIGURE 2.2-7   BRACKETING METHOD STRATEGY.

The basic iterative step of a bracketing method is to *find a test value x_{test} in the open interval (a, b)* and then *replace $[a, b]$ by whichever of $[a, x_{\text{test}}]$ or $[x_{\text{test}}, b]$ contains $\bar{x}$*. The correct replacement is easily determined by the *sign* of $Y = f(x_{\text{test}})$:

IF sign(Y) = sign(L) THEN replace (a, L) by (x_{test}, Y)
ELSE {sign(Y) $\neq$ sign(L)}   replace (b, R) by (x_{test}, Y)

Algorithm: Bracketing Method {Special Cases: BIS and FP}

Purpose: To find a root $\bar{x}$ of $f(x)$ in an interval $[a, b]$ for which $L = f(a)$ and $R = f(b)$ have opposite sign.

{*initialize*}
GET *a, b, MaxIt, NumSig*
$L \leftarrow f(a)$; $R \leftarrow f(b)$; $RelTol \leftarrow 10^{-NumSig}$
IF sign(L) = sign(R) THEN STOP {method cannot be used}
$Xprev \leftarrow b$ {this ensures that the initial $DeltaX \neq 0$}

{*iterate:* Repeatedly form X (= x_{test}) in the *open* interval (a, b)}
DO FOR $k = 1$ TO *MaxIt* UNTIL **termination test** is satisfied
   BEGIN
   {**form** X} $X \leftarrow$ (formula for x_{test} involving a, b, L, R)
   $DeltaX \leftarrow X - Xprev$; $Y \leftarrow f(X)$
   OUTPUT ($k, X, Y, DeltaX$) {i.e., $k, x_k, y_k, \Delta x_{k-1}$}
   {**update**}
   IF sign(Y) = sign(L)
      THEN {move a} BEGIN $a \leftarrow X$; $L \leftarrow Y$ END
      ELSE {move b} BEGIN $b \leftarrow X$; $R \leftarrow Y$ END
   $Xprev \leftarrow X$
   {**termination test:** $|DeltaX| \leqslant RelTol*|X|$ or $Y = 0$}
   END

IF **termination test** succeeded
   THEN OUTPUT (X approximates $\bar{x}$ to *NumSig* significant digits.)
   ELSE OUTPUT (*MaxIt* iterations failed to yield a suitable X.)

FIGURE 2.2-8   PSEUDOPROGRAM FOR A BRACKETING METHOD.

In Figure 2.2-7, sign(Y) = sign(L) (both are $\oplus$); we would therefore replace (a, L) by (x_{test}, Y). This iterative step is then repeated for the new (smaller) $[a, b]$ until either $Y = 0$ or two successive x_{test}'s are sufficiently close. Pseudocode for a bracketing method is shown in Figure 2.2-8.

What all bracketing methods have in common is that *they can be used only if $f(x)$ has opposite sign on either side of $\bar{x}$.* What distinguishes one bracketing method from another is the strategy used to get x_{test}. The two most popular choices are†

---

† The BIS Method is also referred to as the **Interval Halving Method** or **Bolzano's method**; the FP Method is also referred to as the **Regula Falsi Method.**

$$x_{\text{test}} = x_{\text{mid}} = \frac{a+b}{2} \qquad \textbf{(Bisection (BIS) Method)} \qquad \textbf{(18)}$$

$$x_{\text{test}} = x_{\text{FP}} = \frac{bL - aR}{L - R} \qquad \textbf{(False Position (FP) Method)} \qquad \textbf{(19)}$$

In the Bisection Method, x_{test} bisects $[a, b]$. In the False Position Method, x_{test} is the x-intercept of the secant line from (a, L) to (b, R) [Figure 2.2-9].

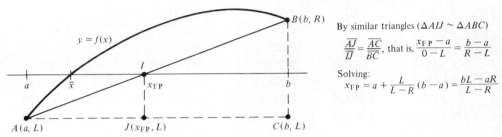

By similar triangles ($\Delta AIJ \sim \Delta ABC$)

$$\frac{\overline{AJ}}{\overline{IJ}} = \frac{\overline{AC}}{\overline{BC}}, \text{ that is, } \frac{x_{\text{FP}} - a}{0 - L} = \frac{b - a}{R - L}$$

Solving:
$$x_{\text{FP}} = a + \frac{L}{L - R}(b - a) = \frac{bL - aR}{L - R}$$

FIGURE 2.2-9   DERIVATION OF THE x_{FP} FORMULA.

EXAMPLE. Perform eight iterations of (a) the BIS Method; (b) the FP Method. Use

$$f(x) = x^2 - 78.8, \qquad a = 6, \quad b = 12 \qquad \textbf{(20)}$$

Solution. See Table 2.2-4 where x_k is the kth x_{test}.
   A look at the Δx columns of Table 2.2-4 reveals that

$$\text{For BIS:} \quad \frac{|\Delta x_k|}{|\Delta x_{k-1}|} = \frac{1}{2} \qquad \left(\text{i.e., } \Delta x_k = \pm \frac{1}{2} \Delta x_{k-1}\right) \qquad \textbf{(21a)}$$

$$\text{For FP:} \quad \frac{\Delta x_k}{\Delta x_{k-1}} \approx \text{constant} \qquad (\text{i.e., } \Delta x_k \approx C \Delta x_{k-1}) \qquad \textbf{(21b)}$$

where $C \approx 0.15$. This *linear* convergence to the *simple* root $\bar{x} = \sqrt{78.8}$ is much slower than either SEC or NR. Also, x_{FP} always replaced a! (Why?) The FP method can be modified to move both a and b so that on the average

$$|\Delta x_k| \approx C|\Delta x_{k-1}|^{1.442} \qquad \textbf{(22)}$$

This **Modified False Position Method** still converges more slowly than the SEC Method [cf. (16)]. Since it is no easier to use or program, it will not be discussed further. The interested reader is referred to [29].
   The Bisection Method generally converges too slowly to be recommended for hand calculation. However, it is easy to program, hence is often used in the "built-in" root-finding routine of a programmable calculator.

TABLE 2.2-4 ITERATIONS OF (a) BIS AND (b) FP FOR $f(x) = x^2 - 78.8$.

$a = 6,$ $L = f(a) = -42.8$ (Sign of L is $\ominus$)
$b = 12,$ $R = f(b) = 65.2$ (Sign of R is $\oplus$)

(a) Bisection Method

k	a	b	$x_k = \dfrac{a+b}{2}$	$Y = f(x_k)$	$\Delta x_{k-1} = x_k - x_{k-1}$
1	6.	12.0	9.0	2.2	—
2	6.	9.0	7.5	-22.55	-1.5
3	7.5	9.0	8.25	-10.7375	0.75
4	8.25	9.0	8.625	-4.409375	0.375
5	8.625	9.0	8.8125	-1.139844	0.1875
6	8.8125	9.0	8.90625	0.5212891	0.09375
7	8.8125	8.90625	8.859375	-0.3114746	-0.046875
8	8.859375	8.90625	8.882813	0.1043579	0.023438

(b) False Position Method

k	a	b	$x_k = \dfrac{bL - aR}{L - R}$	$Y = f(x_k)$	$\Delta x_{k-1} = x_k - x_{k-1}$
1	6.0	12.0	8.377778	-8.612840	—
2	8.377778	12.0	8.800436	-1.352323	0.422658
3	8.800436	12.0	8.865450	-0.2037901	0.065014
4	8.865450	12.0	8.875217	-0.3051934E-1	0.009767
5	8.875217	12.0	8.876679	-0.4566260E-2	0.001462
6	8.876679	12.0	8.876898	-0.6831018E-3	0.000219
7	8.876898	12.0	8.876931	-0.1021884E-3	0.000033
8	8.876931	12.0	8.876936	-0.1528675E-4	0.000005

Used in (18) of Section 2.3B (for rows 5–7)

2.3 Practical Considerations: Convergence Rate and Accuracy

In this section we perform an empirical examination of the convergence rates of the Newton–Raphson and Secant methods and we then show how to accelerate the convergence of any method when it is known to be linear.

2.3A   SOME EXAMPLES ILLUSTRATING CONVERGENCE RATES OF NR AND SEC

We begin by giving several examples which illustrate that in the absence of roundoff error we should expect the convergence of x_k to $\bar{x}$ to satisfy the following:

For Simple Roots $[f'(\bar{x}) \neq 0]$:

Using NR: $\dfrac{\Delta x_k}{(\Delta x_{k-1})^2} \approx C$ (Quadratic Convergence)   **(1a)**

Using SEC: $\dfrac{|\Delta x_k|}{|\Delta x_{k-1}|^{1.618}} \approx C$ (Almost Quadratic Convergence)   **(1b)**

For Multiple Roots $[f'(\bar{x}) = 0]$

Using NR or SEC: $\dfrac{\Delta x_k}{\Delta x_{k-1}} \approx C$ (Linear Convergence)   **(1c)**

More rapid convergence of x_k to $\bar{x}$ corresponds to *larger* powers of Δx_{k-1} (in the denominator) and *smaller* values of C.

Initial guesses will deliberately be made poor to allow enough iterations to determine that (1) holds.

EXAMPLE 1. Consider the fifth-degree polynomial

$$p(x) = x^5 - 4.5x^4 + 4.55x^3 + 2.675x^2 - 3.3x - 1.4375 \tag{2}$$

As shown in Figure 2.3-1, $p(x)$ has a double root -0.5, a simple root 2.5, and a high turning point below the x-axis when $x = 1.5$.

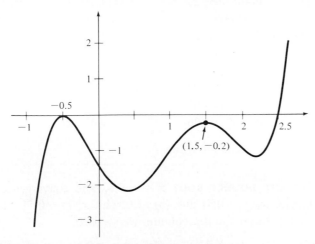

FIGURE 2.3-1   THE GRAPH OF $p(x)$ USED IN EXAMPLE 1.

CONVERGENCE TO THE SIMPLE ROOT $\bar{x} = 2.5$. The convergence of x_k to $\bar{x} = 2.5$ using (a) NR with $x_0 = 3.0$ and (b) SEC with $x_0 = 3.0$ and $x_{-1} = 3.1$ is shown in Table 2.3-1. From the last column, we see that

$$\Delta x_k \approx 2.7 \, \Delta x_{k-1}^2 \text{ for NR} \qquad \text{and} \qquad |\Delta x_k| \approx 2.3 \, |\Delta x_{k-1}|^{1.618} \text{ for SEC} \qquad (3)$$

This is the convergence described in (1a) and (1b), respectively.

TABLE 2.3-1 CONVERGENCE OF (a) NR AND (b) SEC TO A SIMPLE ROOT.

$$p(x) = (((((x - 4.5)x + 4.55)x + 2.675)x - 3.3)x - 1.4375$$
$$p'(x) = (((5x - 18)x + 13.65x + 5.35)x - 3.3$$

(a) Newton–Raphson (NR) method

k	x_k	$y_k = p(x_k)$	$\Delta x_{k-1} = x_k - x_{k-1}$	$\Delta x_{k-1}/(\Delta x_{k-2})^2$
0	3.0000000	0.14088E+02		
1	2.7419872	0.40504E+01	−0.25801E+00	
2	2.5834865	0.97154E+00	−0.15850E+00	−0.24E+01
3	2.5140280	0.13741E+00	−0.69458E−01	−0.28E+01
4	2.5004834	0.45741E−02	−0.13545E−01	−0.28E+01
5	2.5000006	0.59009E−05	−0.48283E−03	−0.26E+01
6	2.5000000	0.17881E−06	−0.62443E−06	−0.27E+01

$x_6 = 2.5000000$ appears accurate to 6s.

(b) Secant (SEC) Method

k	x_k	$y_k = p(x_k)$	$\Delta x_{k-1} = x_k - x_{k-1}$	$|\Delta x_{k-1}|/|\Delta x_{k-2}|^{1.618}$
−1	3.1000000	0.20295E+02		
0	3.0000000	0.14088E+02		
1	2.7730699	0.48875E+01	−0.22693E+00	
2	2.6525142	0.20891E+01	−0.12056E+00	0.13E+01
3	2.5625126	0.69121E+00	−0.90002E−01	0.28E+01
4	2.5180102	0.17821E+00	−0.44502E−01	0.22E+01
5	2.5025509	0.24265E−01	−0.15459E−01	0.24E+01
6	2.5001141	0.10795E−02	−0.24367E−02	0.21E+01
7	2.5000007	0.69141E−05	−0.11345E−03	0.19E+01
8	2.4999999	0.16391E−06	−0.73140E−06	0.18E+01

$x_8 = 2.4999999$ appears accurate to 6s.

CONVERGENCE TO THE DOUBLE ROOT $\bar{x} = -0.5$. The convergence of x_k to $\bar{x} = -0.5$ using (a) NR with $x_0 = -0.51$ and (b) SEC with $x_0 = -0.51$ and $x_{-1} = -0.52$ is shown in Table 2.3-2. From the last column, we see that

$$\Delta x_k \approx 0.50 \, \Delta x_{k-1} \text{ for NR} \qquad \text{and} \qquad \Delta x_k \approx 0.62 \, \Delta x_{k-1} \text{ for SEC} \qquad (4)$$

This is the linear convergence described in (1c).

TABLE **2.3-2**   CONVERGENCE OF (a) NR AND (b) SEC TO A DOUBLE ROOT.

$$p(x) = ((((x-4.5)x + 4.55)x + 2.675)x - 3.3)x - 1.4375$$
$$p'(x) = (((5x - 18)x + 13.65)x + 5.35)x - 3.3$$

(a) Newton-Raphson (NR) method

k	x_k	$y_k = p(x_k)$	$\Delta x_{k-1} = x_k - x_{k-1}$	$\Delta x_{k-1}/\Delta x_{k-2}$	
0	-0.5100000	$-0.12311E-02$			
1	-0.5050327	$-0.30978E-03$	$0.49673E-02$		
2	-0.5025248	$-0.77695E-04$	$0.25080E-02$	$0.50E+00$	
3	-0.5012647	$-0.19446E-04$	$0.12601E-02$	$0.50E+00$	
4	-0.5006335	$-0.48727E-05$	$0.63118E-03$	$0.50E+00$	⎫ Used in (16)
5	-0.5003174	$-0.12219E-05$	$0.31613E-03$	$0.50E+00$	⎬
6	-0.5001590	$-0.29802E-06$	$0.15834E-03$	$0.50E+00$	⎭ of Section 2.3B
7	-0.5000819	$-0.74506E-07$	$0.77099E-04$	$0.49E+00$	
8	-0.5000445	$-0.29802E-07$	$0.37419E-04$	$0.49E+00$	
9	-0.5000170	$0.00000E+00$	$0.27552E-04$	$0.74E+00$	

Computed $p(-0.5000170)$ is zero; iteration discontinued.

(b) Secant (SEC) Method

k	x_k	$y_k = p(x_k)$	$\Delta x_{k-1} = x_k - x_{k-1}$	$\Delta x_{k-1}/\Delta x_{k-2}$	
-1	-0.5200000	$-0.49895E-02$			
0	-0.5100000	$-0.12311E-02$			
1	-0.5067244	$-0.55428E-03$	$0.32756E-02$		
2	-0.5040419	$-0.19954E-03$	$0.26825E-02$	$0.82E+00$	
3	-0.5025330	$-0.78216E-04$	$0.15089E-02$	$0.56E+00$	
4	-0.5015602	$-0.29624E-04$	$0.97278E-03$	$0.64E+00$	
5	-0.5009671	$-0.11370E-04$	$0.59303E-03$	$0.61E+00$	⎫ Used in (14)
6	-0.5005978	$-0.43362E-05$	$0.36938E-03$	$0.62E+00$	⎬
7	-0.5003700	$-0.16689E-05$	$0.22773E-03$	$0.62E+00$	⎭ of Section 2.3B
8	-0.5002276	$-0.62585E-06$	$0.14249E-03$	$0.63E+00$	
9	-0.5001421	$-0.25332E-06$	$0.85491E-04$	$0.60E+00$	
10	-0.5000839	$-0.89407E-07$	$0.58132E-04$	$0.68E+00$	⎫ Used in (13)
11	-0.5000522	$-0.29802E-07$	$0.31707E-04$	$0.55E+00$	⎬
12	-0.5000364	$-0.14901E-07$	$0.15855E-04$	$0.50E+00$	⎭ of Section 2.3B

$x_{12} = -0.5000364$ does not appear to have 6s accuracy.

The calculations were performed on an $8s$ computer. Despite the fact that nesting was used to compute both $p(x)$ and $p'(x)$, roundoff error caused $p(x_9) = p(-0.5000170)$ to be calculated as zero, indicating (erroneously) that $\bar{x} = x_9$ despite the fact that x_9 of Figure 2.3-2(a) has an error in the fifth significant digit! This is the problem mentioned in Section 2.1C.

EXAMPLE 2. If we raise the graph of $p(x)$ in Figure 2.3-1 by 0.1 unit, we get the graph of the polynomial

$$q(x) = p(x) + 0.1 = x^5 - 4.5x^4 + 4.55x^3 + 2.675x^2 - 3.3x - 1.3375 \tag{5}$$

whose graph crosses the x-axis where the graph of $p(x)$ crosses the line $y = -0.1$. Thus $q(x)$ has a high turning point (*but no nearby root*) when $x = 1.5$, and a *simple root* near $x = 2.5$; also, instead of a double root at -0.5, it has *two nearly equal simple roots,* one on either side of -0.5.

CONSEQUENCES OF A POOR INITIAL GUESS. Let us see what happens if we try to get the $\bar{x}$ to the right of -0.5 using the initial guesses (a) $x_0 = -0.4975$ for NR and (b) $x_0 = -0.4975$ and $x_{-1} = -0.5$ for SEC. The results are shown in Table 2.3-3. Note that $q'(x_{-1}) = 0$ and $q'(x_0) \approx 0$. This caused the NR method to overshoot to $x_1 = 1.1555202$, where it "wandered" near the turning point at $x = 1.5$ until it overshot again, finally converging (quadratically) to the simple root $\bar{x} \doteq 2.4891163$! The SEC method also overshot to $x_1 = 2.8026036$, but then returned to converge (almost quadratically) to $\bar{x} \doteq -0.585814$ to the *left* of -0.5. In both cases the method eventually converged but to the wrong root (see Section 2.2G)! Heeding the following advice will avoid this undesirable behavior.

> When using a slope method, try to avoid initial
> guesses that lie between two nearly equal roots.

EXAMPLE 3. It is not immediately apparent that $\bar{x} = 0$ is a multiple root of

$$f(x) = \tan x - xe^{-x^2} \tag{6a}$$

However, it is, because

$$f'(x) = \sec^2 x - e^{-x^2}(1 - 2x^2); \qquad \text{hence } f'(0) = 1 - 1 = 0$$

In fact, replacing $\tan x$ and e^{-x^2} in (6a) by their Maclaurin series gives

$$f(x) = \left(x + \frac{x^3}{3} + \cdots\right) - x\left(1 + \frac{(-x^2)}{1!} + \cdots\right) = \frac{4x^3}{3} + \text{higher (odd) powers of } x \tag{6b}$$

So $f(x)$ behaves like $4x^3/3$ for $x \approx 0$, that is, $\bar{x} = 0$ is a *triple* root of f (see Section 2.4A).

CONVERGENCE TO A TRIPLE ROOT. The convergence of x_k to $\bar{x} = 0$ using (a) NR with $x_0 = 0.05$ and (b) SEC with $x_0 = 0.05$ and $x_{-1} = 0.1$ is shown in Table 2.3-4.

TABLE 2.3-3   CONSEQUENCES OF AN INITIAL GUESS BETWEEN TWO CLOSE ROOTS.

$$q(x) = ((((x - 4.5)x + 4.55)x + 2.675)x - 3.3)x - 1.3375$$
$$q'(x) = (((5x - 18)x + 13.65)x + 5.35)x - 3.3$$

(a) Newton-Raphson (NR) method

k	x_k	$y_k = q(x_k)$	$\Delta x_{k-1} = x_k - x_{k-1}$	$\Delta x_{k-1}/(\Delta x_{k-2})^2$
0	−0.4975000	0.99924E−01		
1	1.1555202	−0.52152E+00	0.16530E+01	
2	1.3872877	−0.14852E+00	0.23177E+00	0.85E−01
3	1.5613136	−0.11442E+00	0.17403E+00	0.32E+01
4	1.3172022	−0.22581E+00	−0.24411E+00	−0.81E+01
5	1.4851089	−0.10085E+00	0.16791E+00	0.28E+01
6	2.3647369	−0.78558E+00	0.87963E+00	0.31E+02
7	2.5606911	0.76808E+00	0.19595E+00	0.25E+00
8	2.4999759	0.99773E−01	−0.60715E−01	−0.16E+01
9	2.4894166	0.26827E−02	−0.10559E−01	−0.29E+01
10	2.4891166	0.23991E−05	−0.29998E−03	−0.27E+01
11	2.4891163	0.17881E−06	−0.26869E−06	−0.30E+01

$x_{11} = 2.4891163$ appears accurate to 6s.

(b) Secant (SEC) Method

k	x_k	$y_k = q(x_k)$	$\Delta x_{k-1} = x_k - x_{k-1}$	$|\Delta x_{k-1}|/|\Delta x_{k-2}|^{1.618}$
−1	−0.5000000	0.10000E+00		
0	−0.4975000	0.99924E−01		
1	2.8026036	0.58653E+01	0.33001E+01	
2	−0.5546964	0.60961E−01	−0.33573E+01	0.49E+00
3	−0.5899570	−0.10469E−01	−0.35261E−01	0.50E−02
4	−0.5847891	0.25015E−02	0.51679E−02	0.12E+01
5	−0.5857858	0.69231E−04	−0.99670E−03	0.50E+01
6	−0.5858142	−0.49174E−06	−0.28369E−04	0.20E+01
7	−0.5858140	0.14901E−07	0.20010E−06	0.46E+01

$x_7 = −0.5858140$ appears accurate to 6s.

We see from the last column that until the effects of roundoff error became evident, both NR and SEC converged linearly, with

$$\Delta x_k \approx 0.67 \Delta x_{k-1} \text{ for NR} \quad \text{and} \quad \Delta x_k \approx 0.75 \Delta x_{k-1} \text{ for SEC} \tag{7}$$

Here again, roundoff error in computing $f(x)$ reduced the attainable accuracy. In view of Tables 2.3-4 and 2.3-2, *it is recommended that extended precision be used when seeking accurate estimates of multiple roots.* Alternatively, we can use the procedure described next to get more accurate estimates from the iterates obtained using single precision.

TABLE 2.3-4 CONVERGENCE OF (a) NR AND (b) SEC TO A TRIPLE ROOT.

$$f(x) = \tan x - xe^{-x^2}$$
$$f'(x) = \sec^2 x - e^{-x^2}(1 - 2x^2)$$

(a) Newton-Raphson (NR) method

k	x_k	$y_k = f(x_k)$	$\Delta x_{k-1} = x_k - x_{k-1}$	$\Delta x_{k-1}/\Delta x_{k-2}$	
0	0.0500000	0.16655E–03			
1	0.0333257	0.49334E–04	–0.16674E–01		
2	0.0222151	0.14616E–04	–0.11111E–01	0.67E+00	
3	0.0148094	0.43305E–05	–0.74057E–02	0.67E+00	
4	0.0098727	0.12830E–05	–0.49367E–02	0.67E+00	
5	0.0065819	0.38015E–06	–0.32908E–02	0.67E+00	
6	0.0043882	0.11263E–06	–0.21937E–02	0.67E+00	⎫ Used in (17a)
7	0.0029262	0.33382E–07	–0.14620E–02	0.67E+00	⎬ of Section 2.3B
8	0.0019524	0.11161E–07	–0.97380E–03	0.67E+00	⎭
9	0.0012199	0.27212E–08	–0.73254E–03	0.75E+00	
10	0.0007616	0.66939E–09	–0.45826E–03	0.63E+00	
11	0.0004755	0.16735E–09	–0.28613E–03	0.62E+00	
12	0.0002943	0.40018E–10	–0.18114E–03	0.63E+00	

$x_{12} = 0.0002943$ does not appear to have $6s$ accuracy.

(b) Secant (SEC) Method

k	x_k	$y_k = f(x_k)$	$\Delta x_{k-1} = x_k - x_{k-1}$	$\Delta x_{k-1}/\Delta x_{k-2}$	
–1	0.1000000	0.13297E–02			
0	0.0500000	0.16655E–03			
1	0.0428404	0.10478E–03	–0.71596E–02		
2	0.0306959	0.38554E–04	–0.12144E–01	0.17E+01	
3	0.0236261	0.17581E–04	–0.70699E–02	0.58E+00	
4	0.0176994	0.73924E 05	–0.59267E–02	0.84E+00	
5	0.0133994	0.32074E–05	–0.43000E–02	0.73E+00	
6	0.0101039	0.13752E–05	–0.32955E–02	0.77E+00	
7	0.0076303	0.59238E–06	–0.24736E–02	0.75E+00	
8	0.0057585	0.25466E–06	–0.18718E–02	0.76E+00	
9	0.0043471	0.10949E–06	–0.14114E–02	0.75E+00	
10	0.0032826	0.47119E–07	–0.10645E–02	0.75E+00	⎫ Used in (17b)
11	0.0024783	0.20256E–07	–0.80422E–03	0.76E+00	⎬ of Section 2.3B
12	0.0018719	0.98516E–08	–0.60644E–03	0.75E+00	⎭

$x_{12} = 0.0018719$ does not appear to have $6s$ accuracy.

2.3B   ACCELERATING LINEAR CONVERGENCE: AITKEN'S FORMULA

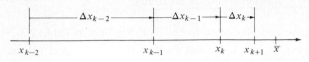

FIGURE 2.3-2   RELATING x_k'S AND Δx_k'S GRAPHICALLY.

Suppose that $x_k \to \bar{x}$. Let Δx_k denote the increment from x_k to x_{k+1}, that is,

$$\Delta x_k = x_{k+1} - x_k \tag{8}$$

Then, as can be seen from Figure 2.3-2, the error of x_{k-2} is

$$\bar{x} - x_{k-2} = \Delta x_{k-2} + \Delta x_{k-1} + \Delta x_k + \Delta x_{k+1} + \cdots \tag{9}$$

Suppose further that linear convergence is indicated by the fact that

$$\Delta x_{k-1} \approx C \Delta x_{k-2} \quad \text{and} \quad \Delta x_k \approx C \Delta x_{k-1} \quad \text{(same } C) \tag{10}$$

If the convergence remains linear as $k \to \infty$, then

$$\Delta x_k \approx C(C \Delta x_{k-2}) \approx C^2 \Delta x_{k-2}, \quad \Delta x_{k+1} \approx C^3 \Delta x_{k-2}, \quad \ldots$$

Hence the geometric series can be used in (9) to get

$$\bar{x} - x_{k-2} \approx \Delta x_{k-2}(1 + C + C^2 + C^3 + \cdots) = \Delta x_{k-2}\left(\frac{1}{1-C}\right) \tag{11}$$

whenever $|C| < 1$. From (10) and Figure 2.3-2,

$$C \approx \frac{\Delta x_{k-1}}{\Delta x_{k-2}} \quad \text{and} \quad x_{k-2} = x_k - (\Delta x_{k-1} + \Delta x_{k-2})$$

Substituting these in (11) gives the following important result:

Aitken's Improvement Formula. *If linear convergence is indicated by the fact that*

$$\frac{\Delta x_{k-1}}{\Delta x_{k-2}} \approx \frac{\Delta x_{k-2}}{\Delta x_{k-3}} \quad (\textit{say to about } 3s) \tag{12a}$$

then the $\bar{x}$ to which x_{k-2}, x_{k-1}, and x_k appear to be converging is

$$\bar{x} \approx (x_k)_{\text{improved}} = x_k - \frac{(\Delta x_{k-1})^2}{\Delta x_{k-1} - \Delta x_{k-2}} = x_k - \frac{(x_k - x_{k-1})^2}{x_k - 2x_{k-1} + x_{k-2}} \tag{12b}$$

Formula (12b) is also called **Aitken's Δ^2 process.** It shows how to get an improved estimate of $\bar{x}$ from three successive iterates. The accuracy of (12b) depends upon how close (12a) is to an equality.

Aitken's formula can be very useful when roundoff error prevents a linearly convergent algorithm from achieving the desired accuracy.

EXAMPLES. The iterates generated by the SEC Method in Table 2.3-2(b) satisfied $\Delta x_{i-1}/\Delta x_{i-2} \approx C$, where $C = 0.6$. If we use the last three tabulated values, namely

$$x_{10} = -0.5000839, \qquad x_{11} = -0.5000522, \qquad x_{12} = -0.5000364$$

in the Aitken formula (12b), then we get the approximation

$$\bar{x} \approx (x_{12})_{\text{improved}} = x_{12} - \frac{(x_{12} - x_{11})^2}{x_{12} - 2x_{11} + x_{10}} \doteq -0.5000207 \qquad \textbf{(13)}$$

Since $\bar{x} = 0.5$, this "improved" x_{12} is only slightly more accurate than the tabulated one. However, if we use *the last three iterates for which* $\Delta x_{i-1}/\Delta x_{i-2}$ *is most nearly constant,* namely

$$x_5 = -0.5009671, \quad x_6 = -0.5005978, \qquad \text{and} \qquad x_7 = -0.5003700$$

(these have 0.61, 0.62, and 0.62, respectively, as $\Delta x_{i-1}/\Delta x_{i-2}$), we get

$$(x_7)_{\text{improved}} = x_7 - \frac{(x_7 - x_6)^2}{x_7 - 2x_6 + x_5} \doteq -0.5000033 \qquad \textbf{(14)}$$

This is accurate to 5s, which is one more place accuracy than x_{12}, the most accurate iterate on Table 2.3-2(b). The calculations (13) and (14) merely reflect the fact that

Aitken's formula works best when the assumption upon which it is based most nearly holds, that is, when $x_{k-2}, x_{k-1},$ *and* x_k *are the last three iterates* x_i *for which* $\Delta x_{i-1}/\Delta x_{i-2}$ *is most nearly constant.*   **(15)**

For the NR iteration shown in Table 2.3-2(a), the last three values satisfying $\Delta x_{i-1}/\Delta x_{i-2} \approx C$ ($C = 0.50$) are $x_4, x_5,$ and x_6 for which (12b) gives

$$\bar{x} \approx -0.5001590 - \frac{(-0.5001590 + 0.5003174)^2}{-0.5001590 + 2(0.5003174) - 0.5006335} \doteq -0.4999999 \qquad \textbf{(16)}$$

This is as accurate as can be expected from 7s tabulated values.

For the triple root $\bar{x} = 0$ in Example 3 of Section 2.3A, strategy (15) yields

For NR [Table 2.3-4(a)]: $\bar{x} \approx (x_8)_{\text{improved}} \doteq 0.0000100$ **(17a)**
For SEC [Table 2.3-4(b)]: $\bar{x} \approx (x_{12})_{\text{improved}} \doteq 0.0000138$ **(17b)**

It can be seen from (13)–(17) that *using the Aitken formula with NR iterates generally gives better accuracy than with those of SEC when* $\bar{x}$ *is a multiple root.* This is because $\Delta x_{i-1}/\Delta x_{i-2}$ is generally more nearly constant for NR.

The Aitken formula should *not* be used to try to improve the accuracy of either NR or SEC when $\bar{x}$ is a *simple* root because the convergence will *not* be linear. However, the Aitken formula can be quite useful when applied to iterates obtained by Repeated Substitution or the False Position Method for which linear convergence is the rule rather than the exception. For example, from the $k = 5, 6, 7$ entries of the Δx_{k-1} column of the FP calculation of Table 2.2-4(b), we see that

$$\frac{\Delta x_5}{\Delta x_4} = \frac{0.000219}{0.001462} \doteq 0.150 \qquad \text{and} \qquad \frac{\Delta x_6}{\Delta x_5} = \frac{0.000033}{0.000219} \doteq 0.151 \qquad \textbf{(18)}$$

So the "Δx form" of Aitken's improvement formula can be used to give

$$\bar{x} \approx x_7 - \frac{(\Delta x_6)^2}{\Delta x_6 - \Delta x_5} = 8.876931 - \frac{(0.000033)^2}{0.000033 - 0.000219} = 8.8769369$$

Since $\bar{x} = \sqrt{78.8} \doteq 8.8769364$, this improved x_7 is accurate to about $7s$.

It is interesting to note that the Aitken formula can be used to get an improved estimate of $\bar{x}$ even if the x_k's are *diverging* from $\bar{x}$, *as long as the divergence is linear.* For example, in the $p = 0.5$ run of Figure 1.7-8, putting the *first* three iterates

$$x_0 = 9.0, \qquad x_1 = 8.511111, \qquad x_2 = 10.005860 \qquad \textbf{(19)}$$

in the Aitken formula gives 8.879508, which approximates $\bar{x} = \sqrt{78.8}$ much more accurately than x_0. A more accurate x_0 (e.g., this improved x_2) would have produced still greater accuracy (Exercise 2-20)!

2.3C SUMMARY: ROOT-FINDING METHODS COMPARED

In most respects, SEC performs at least as effectively as BIS or FP. So we shall only compare NR and SEC.

ACCURACY AND RATE OF CONVERGENCE. For simple roots NR will usually converge quadratically, with the number of accurate decimal places approximately doubling every one or two iterations. SEC converges almost quadratically, with about 25% more iterations needed to obtain the same accuracy as NR with the same (reasonable) x_0.

Both NR and SEC will converge linearly to multiple roots. The formula for m_{sec} is subject to loss of significance which may prevent SEC from getting as much accuracy as NR. Also, the Aitken improvement formula generally works better with NR. So NR is recommended whenever very accurate values of multiple roots are needed.

ROBUSTNESS. Both NR and SEC can fail to converge to the desired root if the slope near x_0 is close to zero. Since m_{sec} depends in part on the behavior near the preceding iterate, the overshoot problem is somewhat less serious for SEC than for NR. For the same reason, SEC is generally less likely to "cycle" or "wander" than NR (see Table 2.3-3).

EASE OF HAND CALCULATION. If $f(x)$ is not too complicated, it is usually worth the trouble to find and simplify $f(x)/f'(x)$ and then use NR as in Table 2.2-1. For a more complicated $f(x)$, use SEC as in Table 2.2-2.

EASE OF PROGRAMMING. Computer code for SEC requires essentially the same amount of programming as NR (Section 2.3D). The NR code requires less updating but must include function definitions for both $f(x)$ and $f'(x)$.

EASE OF USING A PROGRAM. A program for SEC is easier to use, especially if $f(x)$ is complicated, because it does not require the user to find and then (correctly) program $f'(x)$ as well as $f(x)$.

More sophisticated algorithms are discussed in [6].

2.3D FINDING ROOTS ON A COMPUTER

Most computer installations provide software for finding roots. When using these "canned" programs, one must be careful that they come with suitable documentation

```
00100      C * * * * * * * * * CALSEC  * * * * * * * * * * * * *
00200      C INTERACTIVE CALLING PROGRAM FOR SUBROUTINE SECANT
00300            EXTERNAL F3
00400            DATA IW, IR, MAXIT /5, 5, 20/
00500      C
00600            WRITE(IW,1)
00700          1 FORMAT('0ENTER DESIRED # SIGNIFICANT DIGITS, IOUT (0 - 2)')
00800            READ(IR,*) NUMSIG, IOUT
00900            WRITE(IW,2)
01000          2 FORMAT(' ENTER TWO INITIAL GUESSES (SECOND CLOSER IF POSSIBLE)')
01100            READ(IR,*) XPREV, X
01200      C
01300            CALL SECANT(F3, NUMSIG, MAXIT, XPREV, X, Y, IOUT, IEXIT, IW)
01400      C
01500            STOP
01600            END
01700
01800            FUNCTION F3(X)
01900      C     FOR EXAMPLE 3 OF SECTION 2.3A
02000                  F3 = SIN(X)/COS(X) - X*EXP(-X*X)
02100            RETURN
02200            END
```

```
00100            SUBROUTINE SECANT(F,NUMSIG,MAXIT,XPREV,X,Y,IOUT,IEXIT,IW)
00200      C - - - - - - - - - - - - - - - - - - - - - - - - - - - - - - - C
00300      C THIS SUBROUTINE FINDS ROOTS OF F(X) USING THE SECANT METHOD.  C
00400      C                                                               C
00500      C IN THE PARAMETER LIST, THE USER PROVIDES:                     C
00600      C          F = NAME OF SUBPROGRAM FOR FUNCTION F(X)             C
00700      C     NUMSIG = DESIRED NUMBER OF SIGNIFICANT DIGITS             C
00800      C      MAXIT = MAX NUMBER OF ITERATIONS                         C
00900      C   XPREV, X = TWO INITIAL GUESSES                              C
01000      C       IOUT = 0 TO SUPPRESS ALL OUTPUT (TO DEVICE IW)          C
01100      C              1 TO OUTPUT FINAL RESULTS ONLY                   C
01200      C              2 TO OUTPUT DETAILS FOR EACH ITERATION           C
01300      C                                                               C
01400      C THE SUBROUTINE RETURNS:                                       C
01500      C          X = CURRENT X WHEN TERMINATION OCCURRED              C
01600      C          Y = F(X)                                            C
01700      C      IEXIT = 1 IF A ZERO SLOPE WAS ENCOUNTERED                C
01800      C              2 IF A ZERO FUNCTION VALUE WAS ENCOUNTERED       C
01900      C              3 IF CONVERGENCE APPARENTLY OCCURRED             C
02000      C              4 IF CONVERGENCE DIDN'T APPEAR TO OCCUR          C
02100      C                                                               C
02200      C  SUBPROGRAM NAME F MUST BE DECLARED EXTERNAL IN CALLING PROGRAM C
02300      C - - - - - - - - - - - - - - - - - - -  VERSION 1:  5/1/81  - - C
```

FIGURE 2.3-3 USER-PROVIDED CODE AND PROLOGUE FOR SUBROUTINE SECANT.

and were adequately debugged and tested. One of the better known commercially available ones is Brent's ZEROIN program. It is discussed in [15].

For most functions encountered, a general-purpose subprogram for the Secant Method will find all desired roots to any accuracy that is realistic for the device used. The user of such a subprogram must provide a *calling program* and a *function subprogram* such as the FORTRAN code in Figure 2.3-3.

SUBROUTINE SECANT allows the user to control (1) the accuracy it seeks and (2) the amount of output during its execution by selecting values of the parameters NUMSIG and IOUT, respectively. The subroutine can be used with IOUT = 0 to get roots of $f(x)$ as an intermediate step of a more complex problem; when this is done,

```
02400   C INITIALIZE:
02500           RELTOL = 10.**(-NUMSIG)
02600           YPREV = F(XPREV)
02700           Y = F(X)
02800   C
02900           IF (IOUT .GT. 1) WRITE(IW,5) XPREV, YPREV, X, Y
03000       5   FORMAT(' SECANT METHOD    X(0)=SECOND INITIAL GUESS',/,
03100       &          '0 K',6X,'X=XK',10X,'Y=F(X)',8X,'X-XPREV',/,
03200       &          ' -1 ',F12.7,4X,E12.5, / ,' 0 ',F12.7,4X,E12.5)
03300   C
03400   C ITERATE (SECANT METHOD):
03500           IEXIT = 1
03600           DO 100 K=1, MAXIT
03700   C
03800   C      **FORM DELTAX = -Y/SLOPE (PROVIDED SLOPE IS NOT ZERO)
03900           SLOPE = (Y-YPREV)/(X-XPREV)
04000           IF (SLOPE .EQ. 0.) GOTO 200
04100           DELTAX = -Y/SLOPE
04200   C
04300   C      **UPDATE X AND Y
04400           XPREV = X
04500           YPREV = Y
04600           X = XPREV + DELTAX
04700           Y = F(X)
04800   C
04900           IF (IOUT .GT. 1) WRITE(IW,6) K, X, Y, DELTAX
05000       6   FORMAT(I3, 1X, F12.7, 4X, E12.5, 3X, E12.5)
05100   C
05200   C      **CONVERGENCE TESTS
05300           IF (Y .EQ. 0.) IEXIT = 2
05400           IF (ABS(DELTAX) .LE. RELTOL*ABS(X)) IEXIT = 3
05500           IF (IEXIT .GT. 1) GOTO 200
05600     100 CONTINUE
05700           IEXIT = 4
05800   C
05900     200 IF (IOUT .EQ. 0) RETURN
06000           IF (IEXIT .EQ. 1) WRITE(IW,1) X
06100           IF (IEXIT .EQ. 2) WRITE(IW,2) X
06200           IF (IEXIT .EQ. 3) WRITE(IW,3) X, NUMSIG
06300           IF (IEXIT .EQ. 4) WRITE(IW,4) MAXIT
06400       1 FORMAT('0SLOPE=0 WHEN X=',F12.7,'. ITERATION DISCONTINUED')
06500       2 FORMAT('0COMPUTED F(',F12.7,') = ZERO. ITERATION DISCONTINUED')
06600       3 FORMAT('0X=',F12.7,'  APPEARS ACCURATE TO ',I1,'S')
06700       4 FORMAT('0DESIRED ACCURACY IS NOT EVIDENT IN',I3,'ITERATIONS')
06800           RETURN
06900           END
```

FIGURE 2.3-4 BODY OF SUBROUTINE SECANT.

the returned values of X ($\doteq \bar{x}$) and IEXIT provide the information needed by the calling program.

SUBROUTINE SECANT, shown in Figure 2.3-4, is based upon the pseudocode shown in Figure 2.2-2 (with *Slope* calculated as m_{sec} in line 3900.) It was used to obtain the SEC results in Tables 2.3-1–2.3-4.

The reader having no experience using "canned" programs may be wondering why we wrote separate calling and function programs when we could have incorporated the same information in a single program. The reason is that it ensures that the subroutine is not touched, hence cannot accidentally be modified by the user. The resulting guarantee of dependability makes it available for a variety of applications and more than offsets the minor inconvenience of writing separate programs.

2.4 Analytic Discussion of Convergence Rates (Optional)

We wish to confirm analytically what we observed empirically in the preceding sections, namely that (i) NR should converge quadratically to simple roots but only linearly to multiple roots, and (ii) Repeated Substitution should converge either linearly or not at all.

To do this, it will be necessary to assume that $f(x)$ can be represented by its Taylor series about $\bar{x}$, that is, that for all x close to $\bar{x}$

$$f(x) = f(\bar{x}) + f'(\bar{x})(x - \bar{x}) + \frac{f''(\bar{x})}{2!}(x - \bar{x})^2 + \frac{f'''(\bar{x})}{3!}(x - \bar{x})^3 + \cdots \tag{1}$$

This assumption ensures that $f(x)$ has continuous derivatives of all orders at $\bar{x}$ (see Appendix II.2E). Thus for $n = 0, 1, \ldots,$

$$f^{(n)}(x) \to f^{(n)}(\bar{x}) \quad \text{as } x \to \bar{x} \quad \text{so that } f^{(n)}(x) \approx f^{(n)}(\bar{x}) \quad \text{for } x \approx \bar{x} \tag{2}$$

2.4A MULTIPLICITY OF A ROOT

A root $\bar{x}$ of $f(x)$ is of **multiplicity** m if

$$f(\bar{x}) = f'(\bar{x}) = \cdots = f^{(m-1)}(\bar{x}) = 0, \quad \text{but } f^{(m)}(\bar{x}) \neq 0 \tag{3}$$

We shall call $\bar{x}$ a **simple root** if $m = 1$, and a **multiple root** if $m > 1$. When (3) holds, the Taylor expansion (1) becomes

$$f(x) = (x - \bar{x})^m \left\{ \frac{f^{(m)}(\bar{x})}{m!} + \frac{f^{(m+1)}(\bar{x})}{(m+1)!}(x - \bar{x}) + \cdots \right\} = (x - \bar{x})^m h(x) \tag{4}$$

where the function $h(x)$, represented by the power series in braces, is differentiable and satisfies $h(\bar{x}) = f^{(m)}(\bar{x})/m!$. It follows that

$\bar{x}$ *is a root of multiplicity m of f(x) if and only if*

$$f(x) = (x - \bar{x})^m h(x) \tag{5}$$

where h(x) is differentiable and $h(\bar{x}) = f^{(m)}(\bar{x})/m! \neq 0$.

Thus for x near a root $\bar{x}$ of multiplicity m,

$$f(x) \approx K(x - \bar{x})^m, \qquad \text{where } K = \frac{f^{(m)}(\bar{x})}{m!} \neq 0 \tag{6}$$

The behavior of the graph of f near a root of multiplicity m ($m = 1, 2, 3$) is shown in Figure 2.4-1. It can be seen that when $\bar{x}$ is a root of *odd* multiplicity, the graph of f will cross the x-axis at $(\bar{x}, 0)$; and when $\bar{x}$ has *even* multiplicity the graph will be tangent to *but will not cross* the x-axis at $(\bar{x}, 0)$. Moreover, the higher the value of m, the flatter the graph will be near the point $(\bar{x}, 0)$.

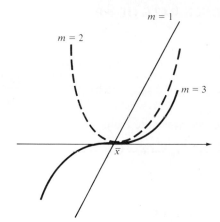

FIGURE 2.4-1 $y = K(x - \bar{x})^m, (K > 0)$.

Using the product rule to differentiate (5), we see that

$$f'(x) = (x - \bar{x})^m h'(x) + m(x - \bar{x})^{m-1} h(x) = (x - \bar{x})^{m-1}[(x - \bar{x})h'(x) + mh(x)] \tag{7}$$

If we let $\phi(x) = h(x)/[(x - \bar{x})h'(x) + mh(x)]$, then, from (5) and (7),

$$\frac{f(x)}{f'(x)} = (x - \bar{x})\phi(x), \qquad \text{where } \phi(x) \to \frac{h(\bar{x})}{0 + mh(\bar{x})} = \frac{1}{m} \neq 0 \quad \text{as } x \to \bar{x} \tag{8}$$

In view of (5), the following useful conclusion can be reached from (8):

> Whatever the multiplicity of $\bar{x}$ as a root of $f(x)$,
> $\bar{x}$ is a *simple* root of the quotient $q(x) = f(x)/f'(x)$. $\tag{9}$

In general, $\bar{x}$ can be found more quickly *but less accurately* as a simple root of $q(x)$ than as a multiple root of $f(x)$ (Exercises 2-24 to 2-26).

2.4B   ORDER OF CONVERGENCE OF AN ITERATIVE METHOD

Let

$$\epsilon_k = \bar{x} - x_k, \quad \text{the error of } x_k, \quad \text{for } k = 0, 1, 2, \ldots \tag{10}$$

The convergence of x_k to $\bar{x}$ is said to be **nth order** if

$$\epsilon_{k+1} \approx C\epsilon_k^n \quad (C = \text{constant} \neq 0) \text{ for } x_k \approx \bar{x} \tag{11}$$

In particular, the convergence of x_k to $\bar{x}$ is called

> **linear** if $n = 1$,   that is, $\epsilon_{k+1} \approx C\epsilon_k$ $(C \neq 0)$ for $x_k \approx \bar{x}$ **(12a)**
>
> **quadratic** if $n = 2$, that is, $\epsilon_{k+1} \approx C\epsilon_k^2$ $(C \neq 0)$ for $x_k \approx \bar{x}$ **(12b)**

2.4C   THE CONVERGENCE RATE OF NR

Recall that for the NR method

$$x_{k+1} = x_k + \Delta x_k, \quad \text{where } \Delta x_k = \frac{-f(x_k)}{f'(x_k)} \tag{13}$$

For the multiple-root case, we first note from (10) that

$$\Delta x_k = x_{k+1} - x_k = (\bar{x} - x_k) - (\bar{x} - x_{k+1}) = \epsilon_k - \epsilon_{k+1} \tag{14}$$

On the other hand, we know from (8) that

$$\Delta x_k = \frac{-f(x_k)}{f'(x_k)} = (\bar{x} - x_k)\phi(x_k) = \epsilon_k\phi(x_k), \quad \text{where } \phi(x) \to \frac{1}{m} \text{ as } x \to \bar{x} \tag{15}$$

Upon eliminating Δx_k from (14) and (15), we get $\epsilon_k\phi(x_k) = \epsilon_k - \epsilon_{k+1}$; hence

$$\frac{\epsilon_{k+1}}{\epsilon_k} = 1 - \phi(x_k) \approx 1 - \frac{1}{m} = \frac{m-1}{m}; \quad \text{that is, } \epsilon_{k+1} \approx \frac{m-1}{m}\epsilon_k \text{ for } x_k \approx \bar{x} \quad \textbf{(16)}$$

So, if $\bar{x}$ is a multiple root $(m > 1)$, then $x_k \to \bar{x}$ linearly by (12a).

To see that NR converges at least quadratically if $\bar{x}$ is a simple root [i.e., if $f'(\bar{x}) \neq 0$], we use the Taylor series about x_k to express $f(\bar{x})$ as

$$0 = f(\bar{x}) = f(x_k) + f'(x_k)(\bar{x} - x_k) + \frac{f''(x_k)}{2}(\bar{x} - x_k)^2 + \frac{f'''(x_k)}{6}(\bar{x} - x_k)^3 + \cdots \tag{17}$$

Since f' is continuous at $\bar{x}$ [see (2)], we can assume that x_k is close enough to $\bar{x}$ so that $f'(x_k) \neq 0$. This allows us to divide by $f'(x_k)$ to solve (17) for x_{k+1}, getting

$$x_{k+1} = x_k - \frac{f(x_k)}{f'(x_k)} = \bar{x} + \frac{(\bar{x} - x_k)^2}{f'(x_k)}\left\{\frac{f''(x_k)}{2} + \frac{f'''(x_k)}{6}(\bar{x} - x_k) + \cdots\right\} \tag{18}$$

Substituting ϵ_{k+1} for $\bar{x} - x_{k+1}$ and ϵ_k for $\bar{x} - x_k$ in (18), we see that

$$\epsilon_{k+1} = \frac{\epsilon_k^2}{f'(x_k)} \left\{ \frac{f''(x_k)}{2} + \frac{f'''(x_k)}{6} \epsilon_k + \cdots \right\} \approx \frac{f''(\bar{x})}{2f'(\bar{x})} \epsilon_k^2 \qquad \text{for } x_k \approx \bar{x} \qquad \textbf{(19)}$$

In view of (12b), this shows that the convergence of x_k to the simple root $\bar{x}$ is quadratic if $f''(\bar{x}) \neq 0$, and even higher order if $f''(\bar{x}) = 0$.

In actually using NR, we know neither ϵ_{k+1} nor ϵ_k; but we do know the increments Δx_k and Δx_{k+1}. If $x_k \to \bar{x}$ quadratically, then by (14) and (12b),

$$\frac{\Delta x_k}{(\Delta x_{k-1})^2} = \frac{\epsilon_k - \epsilon_{k+1}}{(\epsilon_{k-1} - \epsilon_k)^2} \approx \frac{\epsilon_k(1 - C\epsilon_k^2)}{\epsilon_{k-1}^2(1 - C\epsilon_{k-1}^2)^2} \approx \frac{\epsilon_k}{\epsilon_{k-1}^2} \approx C \qquad \text{for } x_k \approx \bar{x} \qquad \textbf{(20)}$$

Similarly, if $\bar{x}$ is a root of multiplicity m, then by (14), (12a), and (16),

$$\frac{\Delta x_k}{\Delta x_{k-1}} = \frac{\epsilon_k - \epsilon_{k+1}}{\epsilon_{k-1} - \epsilon_k} \approx \frac{\epsilon_k}{\epsilon_{k-1}} \cdot \frac{1 - C\epsilon_k}{1 - C\epsilon_{k-1}} \approx \frac{m-1}{m} \qquad \text{for } x_k \approx \bar{x} \qquad \textbf{(21)}$$

So for NR, in the absence of significant roundoff error:

$$\text{A simple root is indicated when } \frac{\Delta x_k}{(\Delta x_{k-1})^2} \approx \text{constant as } x_k \to \bar{x} \qquad \textbf{(22a)}$$

$$\text{A root of multiplicity } m \text{ is indicated when } \frac{\Delta x_k}{\Delta x_{k-1}} \approx \frac{m-1}{m} \text{ as } x_k \to x \qquad \textbf{(22b)}$$

Table 2.4-1 shows the value of $(m - 1)/m$ for several different multiplicities m. In fact, we saw in Table 2.3-2(a) that $\Delta x_k \approx \frac{1}{2}\Delta x_{k-1}$ when $\bar{x}$ is a double root ($m = 2$), and in Table 2.3-4(a) that $\Delta x_k \approx \frac{2}{3}\Delta x_{k-1}$ when $\bar{x}$ is a triple root ($m = 3$).

TABLE 2.4-1   SOME VALUES
OF $(m - 1)/m$.

m	$\dfrac{m-1}{m}$
2	$\frac{1}{2} = 0.50$
3	$\frac{2}{3} \doteq 0.67$
4	$\frac{3}{4} = 0.75$
5	$\frac{4}{5} = 0.80$

2.4D   THE CONVERGENCE RATE OF REPEATED SUBSTITUTION

Recall that this algorithm for finding a fixed point $\bar{x}$ of $g(x)$ starts with an initial guess x_0, then takes

$$x_{k+1} = g(x_k), \qquad k = 0, 1, 2, \ldots \qquad \textbf{(23)}$$

Expanding $g(x)$ about $x = \bar{x}$ and recalling that $\epsilon_k = \bar{x} - x_k$, we get

$$x_{k+1} = g(\bar{x} - \epsilon_k) = g(\bar{x}) + g'(\bar{x})(-\epsilon_k) + \tfrac{1}{2}g''(\bar{x})(-\epsilon_k)^2 + \cdots$$

Since $g(\bar{x}) = \bar{x}$ (this is the definition of a fixed point),

$$\epsilon_{k+1} = \bar{x} - x_{k+1} = g(\bar{x}) - x_{k+1} = g'(\bar{x})\epsilon_k - \tfrac{1}{2}g''(\bar{x})\epsilon_k^2 + \cdots \qquad (24)$$

So when $x_k \approx \bar{x}$ (i.e., $\epsilon_k \approx 0$),

$$\epsilon_{k+1} \approx g'(\bar{x})\epsilon_k \quad \text{if } g'(\bar{x}) \neq 0 \qquad \text{and} \qquad \epsilon_{k+1} \approx -\tfrac{1}{2}g''(\bar{x})\epsilon_k^2 \quad \text{if } g'(\bar{x}) = 0 \qquad (25)$$

In view of the definitions of linear and quadratic convergence [see (12)], we have proved that the Repeated Substitution algorithm will converge to $\bar{x}$ linearly if $0 < |g'(\bar{x})| < 1$, quadratically if $g'(\bar{x}) = 0$, and not at all if $|g'(\bar{x})| > 1$ [see (17) of Section 1.7F].

2.5 Finding Roots of Real Polynomials; Bairstow's Method

The stability of electrical or mechanical systems is related to the real part of the *complex* roots of certain polynomials whose degree can be as high as 30. It has been proved that general formulas such as the quadratic formula *cannot* be found for the roots of polynomials of degree ≥ 5. So we generally have no choice but to use a numerical method to find such roots.

By changing the REAL variables to COMPLEX (and suitably modifying the input/output statements) in a FORTRAN program for the Newton–Raphson method, one can make it find complex roots. However, this approach is quite cumbersome if automated complex arithmetic is not available (e.g., for a hand computation). We now present a more desirable procedure.

2.5A DEFLATING REAL POLYNOMIALS USING QUADRATIC FACTORS

Even if available, complex arithmetic should not be necessary when $p(x)$ is a **real polynomial** [i.e., when all coefficients of $p(x)$ are real]. This is because *the complex roots of real polynomials occur in conjugate pairs*. For any such pair, say $\alpha \pm i\beta$, the real quadratic

$$q(x) = (x - \alpha - i\beta)(x - \alpha + i\beta) = (x - \alpha)^2 + \beta^2$$

is a *real* factor of $p(x)$, that is, there is a *real* polynomial $Q(x)$ such that

$$p(x) = q(x)Q(x), \qquad \text{where degree } Q(x) = \text{degree } p(x) - 2$$

This suggests that when $n \geq 3$, all roots of the *real* polynomial $p(x)$ can be found using the **Quadratic Deflation** algorithm described in Figure 2.5-1.

The **solve** step of the Quadratic Deflation algorithm can be performed by a call to a subroutine such as QROOTS in Figure 1.5-2. The method we will use to find a quadratic factor in the **factor** step is due to Bairstow. It uses real arithmetic and converges quadrati-

---

Algorithm: Quadratic Deflation

Purpose: To find all roots of a real polynomial $p(x) = a_1 x^n + \cdots + a_n x + a_{n+1}$

{*initialize*}
GET n, a_1, . . . , a_{n+1} {$a_1 \neq 0$}

{*iterate*}
DO WHILE $n \geqslant 2$
  BEGIN
  {**factor**} Find a real quadratic $q(x)$ such that $p(x) = q(x)Q(x)$
  {**solve**} Find the two roots r_1, r_2 of $q(x)$ by the quadratic formula
  OUTPUT (Roots: r_1, r_2)
  {**deflate**} BEGIN $p(x) \leftarrow Q(x)$; $n \leftarrow n - 2$ END
  END

IF $n = 1$ THEN BEGIN $LastRoot \leftarrow -a_2 / a_1$; OUTPUT (Root: $LastRoot$) END

FIGURE 2.5-1   PSEUDOPROGRAM FOR QUADRATIC DEFLATION.

cally when the roots of $q(x)$ are *not* also roots of $Q(x) = p(x)/q(x)$. The basis for Bairstow's method is the synthetic division algorithm described next.

2.5B   SYNTHETIC DIVISION BY $q(x)$

If the real nth-degree polynomial

$$p(x) = a_1 x^n + a_2 x^{n-1} + \cdots + a_n x + a_{n+1} \qquad (a_1 \neq 0) \tag{1}$$

is divided by a real quadratic

$$q(x) = x^2 - rx - s \qquad (\textit{notice the minus signs!}) \tag{2}$$

the result will be a *quotient* $Q(x)$ of degree $n - 2$ and a *remainder* $R(x)$ of degree $\leqslant 1$. This division can be displayed as

$$\frac{p(x)}{q(x)} = Q(x) + \frac{R(x)}{q(x)} \qquad \text{or} \qquad p(x) = q(x)Q(x) + R(x) \tag{3}$$

Our notation for this division will be as follows (notice the b_n term):

$$p(x) = \underbrace{(x^2 - rx - s)}_{q(x)} \underbrace{(b_1 x^{n-2} + b_2 x^{n-3} + \cdots + b_{n-2}x + b_{n-1})}_{Q(x)} + \underbrace{b_n(x - r) + b_{n+1}}_{R(x)} \tag{4}$$

Expanding (4) and equating coefficients with (1) gives the following table.

Power of x	Equated Coefficients	Solving for b_i	
x^n	$a_1 = b_1$	$b_1 = a_1$	
x^{n-1}	$a_2 = b_2 - rb_1$	$b_2 = a_2 + rb_1$	
x^{n-2}	$a_3 = b_3 - rb_2 - sb_1$	$b_3 = a_3 + rb_2 + sb_1$	
x^{n-3}	$a_4 = b_4 - rb_3 - sb_2$	$b_4 = a_4 + rb_3 + sb_2$	(5)
$\vdots$	$\vdots$	$\vdots$	
x	$a_n = b_n - rb_{n-1} - sb_{n-2}$	$b_n = a_n + rb_{n-1} + sb_{n-2}$	
constant	$a_{n+1} = b_{n+1} - rb_n - sb_{n-1}$	$b_{n+1} = a_{n+1} + rb_n + sb_{n-1}$	

The right-hand column shows that the b_i's that define $Q(x)$ and $R(x)$ can be obtained **synthetically** [i.e., using only r, s and the coefficients of $p(x)$, as shown in Figure 2.5-2(a)]. This quadratic **synthetic division** algorithm is illustrated in Figure 2.5-2(b) for the division

$$\frac{2x^6 - 4x^5 + x^3 - 40x}{x^2 - x + 4} = (2x^4 - 2x^3 - 10x^2 - x + 39) + \frac{3(x-1) - 153}{x^2 - x + 4} \qquad (6)$$

(a)		a_1	a_2	a_3	a_4	$\cdots$	a_{n-1}	a_n	a_{n+1}
$\times r>$			$+b_1 r$	$+b_2 r$	$+b_3 r$	$\cdots$	$+b_{n-2} r$	$+b_{n-1} r$	$+b_n r$
$\times s>$				$+b_1 s$	$+b_2 s$	$\cdots$	$+b_{n-3} s$	$+b_{n-2} s$	$+b_{n-1} s$
		b_1	b_2	b_3	b_4	$\cdots$	b_{n-1}	b_n	b_{n+1}
(b) a_i's$>$	2	-4	0	1	0	-40		0	
$\times 1>$		2	-2	-10	-1	39		3	
$\times(-4)>$			-8	8	40	4		-156	
b_i's$>$	2	-2	-10	-1	$+39$	$+3$		-153	

FIGURE 2.5-2 QUADRATIC SYNTHETIC DIVISION: (a) $p(x)/(x^2 - rx - s)$; (b) $(2x^6 - 4x^5 + x^3 - 40x)/(x^2 - x + 4)$.

2.5C BAIRSTOW'S METHOD

Our objective is to find quadratics $q(x)$ which are factors of $p(x)$, that is, which make $R(x) = b_x(x - r) + b_{n+1} = 0$. To do this, we must find r and s that make

$$b_n = 0 \qquad \text{and} \qquad b_{n+1} = 0 \qquad (7)$$

This is not a trivial problem because, as can be seen from (5), each of $b_2, \ldots, b_{n+1}$ depends upon the preceding b_i's, which are themselves functions of r and s.

Let $\bar{r}$ and $\bar{s}$ be values that satisfy (7), and suppose that r and s are approximations of $\bar{r}$ and $\bar{s}$. If the increments

$$dr = \bar{r} - r \qquad \text{and} \qquad ds = \bar{s} - s \tag{8}$$

are small and we view b_n and b_{n+1} as functions of (r, s), then we can use the total differentials of b_n and b_{n+1} to get the approximations

$$0 = b_n(\bar{r}, \bar{s}) = b_n(r + dr, s + ds) \approx b_n(r, s) + \frac{\partial b_n}{\partial r}\, dr + \frac{\partial b_n}{\partial s}\, ds \tag{9a}$$

$$0 = b_{n+1}(\bar{r}, \bar{s}) = b_{n+1}(r + dr, s + ds) \approx b_{n+1}(r, s) + \frac{\partial b_{n+1}}{\partial r}\, dr + \frac{\partial b_{n+1}}{\partial s}\, ds \tag{9b}$$

where the partial derivatives are evaluated at (r, s) [see Appendix II-5C]. Hence, if r and s are kth iterates (i.e., $r = r_k$ and $s = s_k$) and we use dr_k and ds_k to denote the solution of (9) with "$\approx$" replaced by "$=$", then in view of (8), r_{k+1} and s_{k+1} defined by

$$r_{k+1} = r_k + dr_k \qquad \text{and} \qquad s_{k+1} = s_k + ds_k \tag{10}$$

should approximate $\bar{r}$ and $\bar{s}$ better than r_k and s_k.

In order to be able to use iteration (10), we must know the values of the four partial derivatives in (9). What Bairstow astutely observed is that if synthetic division by

$$q(x) = x^2 - rx - s$$

is performed *with the b_i's replacing the a_i's* to get $c_1, \ldots, c_n$ as follows:

	b_1	b_2	b_3	$\cdots$	b_n	b_{n+1}	
$\times r>$		$+c_1 r$	$+c_2 r$		$+c_{n-1} r$		**(11)**
$\times s>$			$+c_1 s$		$+c_{n-2} s$		
	c_1	c_2	c_3	$\cdots$	c_n	not needed	

then the required partial derivatives in (9) can be obtained as

$$\frac{\partial b_n}{\partial r} = c_{n-1}, \quad \frac{\partial b_n}{\partial s} = c_{n-2}, \quad \frac{\partial b_{n+1}}{\partial r} = c_n, \quad \text{and} \quad \frac{\partial b_{n+1}}{\partial s} = c_{n-1} \tag{12}$$

A proof of (12) will be given in Section 2.5E. From (12) and (9) we see that dr_k and ds_k in (10) are obtained by solving the *linear* equations

$$\begin{aligned} c_{n-1}\, dr + c_{n-2}\, ds &= -b_n \\ c_n\, dr + c_{n-1}\, ds &= -b_{n+1} \end{aligned} \tag{13}$$

Using Cramer's rule [see (12) of Section 3.5D], we get

$$dr_k = \frac{b_n c_{n-1} - b_{n+1} c_{n-2}}{c_n c_{n-2} - c_{n-1}^2} \qquad \text{and} \qquad ds_k = \frac{b_{n+1} c_{n-1} - b_n c_n}{c_n c_{n-2} - c_{n-1}^2} \tag{14}$$

Algorithm: Bairstow's Method

Purpose: To find a quadratic factor $q(x) = x^2 - rx - s$ of an nth degree polynomial
$p(x) = a_1 x^n + \cdots + a_n x + a_{n+1}$ ($a_1 \neq 0$).

{*initialize*}
GET n, a_1, a_2, . . . , a_{n+1},   {parameters of $p(x)$}
       MaxIt, NumSig,   {termination parameters}
       r_0, s_0 {initial guesses of r, s}
$b_1 \leftarrow a_1$; $c_1 \leftarrow b_1$; $r \leftarrow r_0$; $s \leftarrow s_0$; $Tol \leftarrow 10^{-NumSig}$

{*iterate*}
DO FOR $k = 1$ TO *MaxIt* UNTIL **termination test** is satisfied
   BEGIN {get remaining b's and c's by quadratic synthetic division}
   $b_2 \leftarrow a_2 + b_1 r$; $c_2 \leftarrow b_2 + c_1 r$
   DO FOR $i = 3$ TO $n + 1$
      BEGIN
      $b_i \leftarrow a_i + r b_{i-1} + s b_{i-2}$ {This is (5)}
      $c_i \leftarrow b_i + r c_{i-1} + s c_{i-2}$ {This is (12)}
      END
   {solve}
   $Det \leftarrow c_n c_{n-2} - c_{n-1}^2$
   $dr \leftarrow (b_n c_{n-1} - b_{n+1} c_{n-2})/Det$ }{This is (14)}
   $ds \leftarrow (b_{n+1} c_{n-1} - b_n c_n)/Det$
   $r \leftarrow r + dr$; $s \leftarrow s + ds$ {This is (10)}
   OUTPUT (r, dr, s, ds)
   {termination test: $|dr| \leq Tol * \max(1, |r|)$ and $|ds| \leq Tol * \max(1, |s|)$}
   END

IF **termination test** succeeded {i.e. ($|\rho_r|$ or $|\epsilon_r| \leq Tol$) and ($|\rho_s|$ or $|\epsilon_s| \leq Tol$)}
   THEN OUTPUT ($q(x) = x^2 - rx - s$ is a factor of $p(x)$, and
                $Q(x) = b_1 x^{n-1} + \cdots | b_{n-2} x + b_{n-1}$ is $p(x)/q(x)$.)
       {In this case the $p(x) \leftarrow Q(x)$ step of Quadratic Deflation is simply}
       {   DO FOR $i = 2$ TO $n - 1$ $a_i \leftarrow b_i$ }
   ELSE OUTPUT (Convergence is not apparent in *MaxIt* iterations.)

FIGURE 2.5-3 PSEUDOPROGRAM FOR BAIRSTOW'S METHOD.

The resulting iterative method for finding $q(x)$ is called **Bairstow's method.** Pseudocode for Bairstow's method is shown in Figure 2.5-3.

Initial guesses r_0 and s_0 are usually taken to be 0. Better results are often obtained by doing the following:

For large roots, try $r_0 = -\dfrac{a_2}{a_1}$ and $s_0 = -\dfrac{a_3}{a_1}$ **(15a)**

For small roots (if $a_{n-1} \neq 0$), try $r_0 = -\dfrac{a_n}{a_{n-1}}$ and $s_0 = -\dfrac{a_{n+1}}{a_{n-1}}$ **(15b)**

This is because very large roots $\bar{x}$ will satisfy

$$0 = p(\bar{x}) \approx (a_1\bar{x}^2 + a_2\bar{x} + a_3)\bar{x}^{n-2} \quad \text{so that} \quad \bar{x}^2 + \frac{a_2}{a_1}\bar{x} + \frac{a_3}{a_1} \approx 0$$

and, similarly, very small roots $\bar{x}$ satisfy $a_{n-1}\bar{x}^2 + a_n\bar{x} + a_{n+1} \approx 0$.

EXAMPLE. Find all roots of the fifth-degree polynomial

$$p(x) = x^5 - 4.5x^4 + 4.55x^3 + 2.675x^2 - 3.3x - 1.4375 \tag{16}$$

using Bairstow's method. Try to find $\bar{x}$'s of smallest magnitude first.

Solution. Using (15b), we try as initial guesses for r and s,

$$r_0 = -\frac{-3.3}{2.675} \doteq 1.233645 \quad \text{and} \quad s_0 = -\frac{-1.4375}{2.675} \doteq 0.5373832$$

The c_i values required to get dr_0 and ds_0 are obtained using the "double" synthetic division as follows:

a_i's:	1	-4.5	$+4.55$	$+2.675$	-3.3	-1.4375
$\times 1.233645 >$		$+1.233645$	-4.029522	$+1.305025$	$+2.744540$	$+0.016057$
$\times 0.5373832 >$			$+0.537383$	-1.755284	$+0.568477$	$+1.195538$
b_i's:	1	-3.266355	$+1.057861$	$+2.224740$	$+0.013016$	-0.225904
$\times 1.233645 >$		$+1.233645$	-2.507643	-1.125576	$+0.008414$	
$\times 0.5373832 >$			$+0.537383$	-1.092344	-0.490308	
c_i's:	1	-2.032710	-0.912398	$+0.006820$	-0.468877	

The desired increments are then obtained using (14):

$$dr_0 = \frac{(0.013016)(0.006820) - (-0.225904)(-0.912398)}{(-0.468877)(-0.912398) - (0.006820)^2} = \frac{-0.2060261}{0.4277564} = -0.4816435$$

$$ds_0 = \frac{(0.006820)(-0.225904) - (-0.468877)(0.013016)}{-0.4277564} = +0.01066556$$

Adding these increments to the initial values, we get

$$r_1 = r_0 + dr_0 = 1.233645 - 0.4816435 = 0.752001$$
$$s_1 = s_0 + ds_0 = 0.5373832 + 0.01066556 = 0.5480488$$

If we continue the iteration, we get Table 2.5-1.

TABLE 2.5-1 CONVERGENCE OF BAIRSTOW'S METHOD.

k	Δr	Δs	r	s
0	—	—	1.233645	0.5373832
1	−0.4816435	0.0106656	0.752001	0.5480488
2	0.1478756	0.2232268	0.899877	0.7712756
3	0.5234931	0.1512589	1.423370	0.9225345
4	−0.0828045	−0.7647468	1.340565	0.1577877
5	0.6070840	0.3324581	1.948274	0.4902458
6	−2.8041133	−0.6506271	−0.855840	−0.1603809
7	−0.1514431	−0.0790732	−1.007283	−0.2394512
8	0.766207E−2	−0.990590E−2	0.999620	−0.2493600
9	0.379778E−3	−0.640298E−3	−1.000000	−0.2500003
10	0.262E−6	0.3218E−6	−1.000000	−0.2500000

We see from the Δr and Δs columns of Table 2.5-1 that *the convergence was quadratic once r_k and s_k were near $\bar{r} = -1$ and $\bar{s} = -0.25$* (i.e., for $k \geqslant 7$). However, *both r_k and s_k "wandered" for the first six iterations.* As it turned out, the roots of the quadratic factor obtained, namely

$$q(x) = x^2 - (-1)x - (-0.25) = (x + 0.5)^2 \qquad (-0.5 \text{ is a double root}) \qquad \textbf{(17)}$$

are the two roots of $p(x)$ of smallest magnitude [see (21)].

The initial "wandering" can go on for a long time before converging. In fact, had $r_0 = s_0 = 0$ been used as initial guesses, then over 30 iterations (for which some of the increments are larger than 1000!) would have been needed before finally finding the $q(x)$ in (17). However, it could just as well have found a different quadratic factor or not converged at all. In view of the amount of work needed for a single iteration, *this method is not recommended for hand calculation unless good initial guesses are known.*

Dividing $p(x)$ synthetically by $q(x) = x^2 + x + 0.25$, we get

a_i's >	1	−4.5	+4.55	+2.675	−3.3	−1.4375
×(1) >		−1.0	+5.5	−9.8	+5.75	0
×(−0.25) >			−0.25	+1.375	−2.45	+1.4375
b_i's >	1	−5.5	+9.8	−5.75	0	0

so that

$$p(x) = (x + 0.5)^2 \, Q(x), \qquad \text{where } Q(x) = x^3 - 5.5x^2 + 9.8x - 5.75 \qquad \textbf{(18)}$$

By (15b), initial guesses for getting the smallest roots of $Q(x)$ are

$$r_0 = -\frac{9.8}{-5.5} \doteq 1.7818182 \qquad \text{and} \qquad s_0 = -\frac{-5.75}{-5.5} \doteq -1.0454545 \qquad \textbf{(19)}$$

TABLE 2.5-2   BAIRSTOW'S METHOD FOR THE DEFLATED $p(x)$.

k	Δr	Δs	r	s
0	—	—	1.718182	−1.045455
1	3.500277	8.145488	2.454822	9.927306
2	−0.0652019	−12.29043	2.389620	−2.363122
3	0.3506920	0.2485134	2.740312	−2.114609
4	0.2078440	−0.1189577	2.948156	−2.233567
5	0.508473E−1	−0.633505E−1	2.999003	−2.296917
6	0.999638E−3	−0.308328E−2	3.000003	−2.300001
7	−0.30177E−5	0.5096E−6	3.000000	−2.300000

The iterations of Bairstow's method, with $Q(x)$ in (18) taken as $p(x)$ and r_0 and s_0 given in (19), are shown in Table 2.5-2. After only eight iterations, Bairstow's method found that

$$q(x) = x^2 - (3)x - (-2.3) = (x - 1.5)^2 + 0.05 \qquad (20)$$

This irreducible quadratic has a pair of complex conjugate roots $x = 1.5 \pm \sqrt{0.05}i$. Dividing the deflated $p(x)$ [i.e., $Q(x)$ in (18)] by this $q(x)$ leaves $x - 2.5$; so the five roots of $p(x)$ in (16) are

$$-0.5, \quad -0.5, \quad 1.5 + \sqrt{0.05}i, \quad 1.5 - \sqrt{0.05}i, \quad 2.5 \qquad (21)$$

In fact, the graph of $p(x)$ was given in Figure 2.3-1.

2.5D   HOW INACCURATE COEFFICIENTS CAN AFFECT THE LOCATION OF ROOTS

The reader should be aware of the fact that the problem of finding roots of a polynomial $p(x)$ is **ill conditioned** in the sense that *small changes in the coefficients of $p(x)$ can cause disproportionately large changes in the location of its roots.* The ill conditioning generally becomes more severe as the degree of $p(x)$ and the magnitude of its coefficients increase. For example, the sixth-degree polynomial

$$p(x) = x^6 - 21x^5 + 175x^4 - 735x^3 + 1624x^2 - 1764x + 720 \qquad (22)$$

has six simple roots: $\bar{x} = 1, 2, 3, 4, 5,$ and 6. Table 2.5-3 shows how these roots move as a_5, the coefficient of x^2, is changed from 1624.0 to 1624.25 to 1624.5 without changing the other coefficients. Increasing the coefficient of x^2 by $\frac{1}{4}$ in the fifth significant digit caused changes in the *second* significant digit of $\bar{x}_3, \bar{x}_4, \bar{x}_5,$ and $\bar{x}_6$. And adding another $\frac{1}{4}$ (a net change of about 0.03%) caused $\bar{x}_3$ and $\bar{x}_4$ to become *complex*! If a_5 is further increased to 1625 (a net change of about 0.06%), then $\bar{x}_5$ and $\bar{x}_6$ become complex as well.

TABLE 2.5-3 SENSITIVITY OF SIX ROOTS OF $p(x)$ TO SMALL CHANGES IN a_5.

a_5	$\bar{x}_1$	$\bar{x}_2$	$\bar{x}_3$	$\bar{x}_4$	$\bar{x}_5$	$\bar{x}_6$
1624.00	1.000000	2.000000	3.000000	4.000000	5.000000	6.000000
1624.25	1.002102	1.961491	3.268076	3.621456	5.236785	5.910090
1624.50	1.004243	1.927929	$(3.407987 \pm 0.3728825i)$		5.251515	5.730340

The coefficients in (22) are all integers and hence can be stored without roundoff error. However, when the coefficients *cannot* be stored exactly, inherent roundoff alone may result in a stored polynomial whose roots do not even resemble those of the intended polynomial. Consequently, *extended precision is advised when seeking roots of polynomials of large degree* (say $n \geqslant 5$), especially if some of the coefficients are large. Also, any roots found after deflating should be used as initial guesses for roots of the *original* $p(x)$ to eliminate the effects of propagated roundoff in deflating.

2.5E PROOF OF THE BAIRSTOW'S METHOD FORMULAS

We wish to show by induction that if the b_j's are obtained synthetically from a_1, . . . , a_{n+1}, that is, if

$$b_1 = a_1; \quad b_2 = a_2 + b_1 r; \quad b_j = a_j + b_{j-1}r + b_{j-2}s \quad \text{for } j = 3, \ldots, n+1 \quad \textbf{(23a)}$$

and the c_j's are obtained synthetically from $b_1, \ldots, b_n$, that is, if

$$c_1 = b_1; \quad c_2 = b_2 + c_1 r; \quad c_j = b_j + c_{j-1}r + c_{j-2}s \quad \text{for } j = 3, \ldots, n \quad \textbf{(23b)}$$

then the partial derivatives of b_i satisfy

$$\frac{\partial b_i}{\partial r} = c_{i-1} \quad \text{and} \quad \frac{\partial b_i}{\partial s} = c_{i-2} \quad \text{for } i = 3, 4, \ldots, n \quad \textbf{(24)}$$

When $i = 3$ (to begin the induction) we first note from (23a) that

$$\frac{\partial b_1}{\partial r} = \frac{\partial b_1}{\partial s} = 0, \quad \text{so} \frac{\partial b_2}{\partial r} = 0 + \left[b_1 \cdot 1 + \frac{\partial b_1}{\partial r} r \right] = b_1 \quad \text{and} \quad \frac{\partial b_2}{\partial s} = 0 + \frac{\partial b_1}{\partial s} r = 0 \quad \textbf{(25)}$$

(Recall that $\partial/\partial r$ is with s fixed, and $\partial/\partial s$ is with r fixed.) Hence

$$\frac{\partial b_3}{\partial r} = 0 + \left[b_2 \cdot 1 + \frac{\partial b_2}{\partial r} r \right] + \frac{\partial b_1}{\partial r} s = b_2 + b_1 r = b_2 + c_1 r = c_2$$

$$\frac{\partial b_3}{\partial s} = 0 + \frac{\partial b_2}{\partial s} r + \left[\frac{\partial b_1}{\partial s} s + b_1 \cdot 1 \right] = b_1 = c_1$$

by (25) and (23). Similarly, assuming that (24) holds for $j = 3, \ldots, i - 1$, we get

$$\frac{\partial b_i}{\partial r} = 0 + \left[b_{i-1} \cdot 1 + \frac{\partial b_{i-1}}{\partial r} r \right] + \frac{\partial b_{i-2}}{\partial r} s = b_{i-1} + c_{i-2}r + c_{i-3}s = c_{i-1}$$

$$\frac{\partial b_i}{\partial s} = 0 + \frac{\partial b_{i-1}}{\partial s} r + \left[\frac{\partial b_{i-2}}{\partial s} s + b_{i-2} \cdot 1 \right] = b_{i-2} + c_{i-3}r + c_{i-4}s = c_{i-2}$$

This completes the induction and hence the proof of (24).

Exercises

Section 2.1

2-1. Find a function $f(x)$ that has $\bar{x}$ as a root (see Section 2.1A).

(a) $\bar{x} = \sqrt[5]{c}$ for a given c.

(b) $\bar{x}$ is a fixed point of $\frac{1}{2} \tan x$.

(c) $\bar{x} = \arctan c$ for a given c.

2-2. Get estimates of all positive roots of f by rewriting $f(x) = 0$ as $g(x) = h(x)$ where the graphs of g and h are easily sketched as in Section 2.1B.

(a) $f(x) = e^x + x^2 - 2$ (b) $f(x) = x^5 + x^2 - 9$

(c) $f(x) = x^2 \sin x - \cos x$ (d) $f(x) = (x-1)e^x - 2$

2-3. Give specific examples of functions whose graphs have the shapes shown in Figure 2.1-4.

Section 2.2

2-4. For (a)–(d) of Exercise 2-2: Use the Newton–Raphson (NR) method, with your answers to Exercise 2-2 as initial guesses, to find all roots of $f(x)$ to 5s.

2-5. Same as Exercise 2-4 but use the Secant (SEC) Method with $x_{-1} = x_0 + 0.1$

2-6. Same as Exercise 2-4 but use the Bisection (BIS) Method with $b = a + 0.5$ to get 3s accuracy. (Be sure that $f(a)f(b) < 0$.)

2-7. Same as Exercise 2-4 but use the False Position (FP) Method with $b = a + 0.5$ to get 3s accuracy. [Be sure that $f(a)f(b) < 0$.]

2-8. Let $f(x) = x^3 - 7x$. This f has three simple roots: $\bar{x} = -\sqrt{7}, 0, +\sqrt{7}$.

(a) Use the NR method to find x_1, x_2, and x_3 starting with (i) $x_0 = 1.19$; (ii) $x_0 = 1.5$.

(b) Use a neat sketch of $y = f(x)$ to explain why x_k will converge, but *not* to the root closest to x_0 in both (i) and (ii) of part (a).

2-9. Let $f(x) = 6x^5 + 20x^3 - 9$. This is a continuous function. (Why?)

(a) Show that f has a root $\bar{x}$ between 0 and 1. Deduce from the sign of $f'(x)$ that $\bar{x}$ is the *only* real root of f.

(b) Using a method of your choice, find $\bar{x}$ to 6s.

(c) Find the maximum and minimum value of $F(x) = x^6 + 5x^4 - 9x + 1$ on the interval $[0, 1]$. (See Problem 1 of the introduction to Section 1.1.)

2-10. Use NR or SEC to find to 5s the smallest positive t such that $(5.9t + 1.3)e^{-2.2t} = 1.223$. [See (5) of Section 2.0.] (SUGGESTION: Rearrange first as in Section 2.2C.)

2-11. Use NR or SEC as in Section 2.2E to find to 6s the fixed points of $g(x)$ that were either difficult or impossible to find by Repeated Substitution in (a)–(e) of Exercise 1-23.

2-12. Let $f(x) = x^4 - 3x^3 - 2x^2 + 12x - 8$. Note that $f(1) = f(2) = f(-2) = 0$.
(a) Find x_1, x_2, x_3, and x_4 using the Bisection (BIS) Method with $a = 0.8$ and $b = 1.3$.
(b) Repeat part (a) but using the False Position (FP) Method.
(c) Which of BIS or FP can be used to find $\bar{x} = 2$? Explain. [HINT: Examine $f'(2)$ and $f''(2)$.]

2-13. In (7) of Section 2.0 we mentioned the following functions:
(a) $f(x) = \frac{1}{2}\tan x - \tanh x$ (b) $f(x) = 5\cos x + \operatorname{sech} x$
Use NR or SEC to find the smallest positive root of parts (a) and (b) to 5s.

2-14. Let n be the number of iterations of the Bisection Method needed to ensure that a root $\bar{x}$ is bracketed in an interval of length less than ϵ. Express n in terms of ϵ and the initial a and b.

2-15. The Secant Method formula $x_{k+1} = x_k + \Delta x_{\text{sec}}$ can be written in the alternative form $x_{k+1} = (x_k y_{k-1} - y_k x_{k-1})/(y_{k-1} - y_k)$ [cf. x_{FP}]. Which of these two forms appears more prone to roundoff error? Explain.

Section 2.3

2-16. By examining the ratios $\Delta x_k/(\Delta x_{k-1})^2$ or otherwise in (a)–(d) of Exercise 2-4, show that the convergence to $\bar{x}$ was quadratic.

2-17. By examining the ratios $\Delta x_k/\Delta x_{k-1}$ in (a)–(d) of Exercise 2-7, show that the convergence to $\bar{x}$ was linear.

2-18. Use Aitken's formula, *if it applies,* to get the best $(x_k)_{\text{improved}}$ from your work in (a)–(e) of Exercise 1-23. Discuss the additional accuracy obtained.

2-19. Use Aitken's formula and your answer to Exercise 2-12(b) to get $(x_4)_{\text{improved}}$. How many additional significant digits were obtained?

2-20. Let $g(x) = [-\frac{1}{2}x^2 + 78.8]/(\frac{1}{2}x)$. Find x_1 and x_2 by Repeated Substitution, starting with $x_0 = 8.879508$; then get $(x_2)_{\text{improved}}$ using Aitken's formula. Is it closer to $\bar{x} = \sqrt{78.8}$ than x_0 [see (19) of Section 2.3B]?

2-21. Let $f(x) = x^5 - 6x^4 + 9x^3$, $\bar{x} = 0$, $x_0 = -0.3$, and (for SEC) $x_{-1} = -0.4$.
(a) Find x_1, x_2, x_3, and x_4 by NR. Verify that the convergence to $\bar{x}$ is linear (i.e., $\Delta x_k \approx C\Delta x_{k-1}$) and use Aitken's formula to get $(x_4)_{\text{improved}}$.
(b) Repeat part (a) for x_1, x_2, x_3, and x_4 obtained using SEC. Is $(x_4)_{\text{improved}}$ as accurate as that obtained in part (a)?

2-22. Do (a) and (b) of Exercise 2-21 with $f(x) = x^5 - 6x^4 + 9x^3$ again, but with $\bar{x} = 3$, $x_0 = 3.06$ and (for SEC) $x_{-1} = 3.1$.

2-23. Do (a) and (b) of Exercise 2-21 with $f(x) = e^{2x} - 4e^x + 4$, $\bar{x} = \ln 2$, $x_0 = 0.7$, and (for SEC) $x_{-1} = 0.71$.

Section 2.4

2-24. For $f(x)$, $\bar{x}$, and x_0 of Exercise 2-21, do (a)–(c).

(a) Find the multiplicity m of $\bar{x}$ either using definition (3) of Section 2.4A or using a Maclaurin series as in (6b) of Section 2.3B.

(b) Is $\Delta x_k / \Delta x_{k-1} \approx (m-1)/m$ for $x_1, \ldots, x_4$ obtained by NR? (See Table 2.4-1.)

(c) Use *either* NR *or* SEC, with the indicated x_0, to find x_1, x_2, x_3, and x_4 for $q(x) = f(x)/f'(x)$. Does the convergence rate indicate that $\bar{x}$ is a simple root of q? [See (9) of Section 2.4A.]

2-25. Do (a)–(c) of Exercise 2-24 for $f(x)$, $\bar{x}$, and x_0 of Exercise 2-22.

2-26. Do (a)–(c) of Exercise 2-24 for $f(x)$, $\bar{x}$, and x_0 of Exercise 2-23.

2-27. The function $f(x) = x^{1/3}$ obviously has $\bar{x} = 0$ as a simple root. Show that the NR formula for this $f(x)$ reduces to $x_{k+1} = -2x_k$. So unless x_0 is *exactly* $\bar{x} = 0$, NR will diverge! Why doesn't the quadratic convergence described in Section 2.4C occur?

2-28. Show that finding a simple root $\bar{x}$ by NR can be viewed as finding $\bar{x}$ as a fixed point of a $g(x)$ for which $g'(\bar{x}) = 0$.

Section 2.5

2-29. Perform two iterations of Bairstow's method as indicated.

(a) $p(x) = x^4 - 5x^3 + 8.5x^2 - 6x + 2$, $r_0 = 1$, $s_0 - 0$.

(b) $p(x) = 2x^4 + 5x^3 - 5x^2 - 5x + 3$, $r_0 = -3$, $s_0 = -3$.

(c) $p(x) = x^5 + x^4 - 14.8x^3 + 23.4x^2 - 12.6x + 2$, $r_0 = 2$, $s_0 = -2$.

(d) $p(x) = x^4 - x^3 + x^2 + 2$, $r_0 = 2$, $s_0 = -1$.

2-30. The polynomial $p(x) = x^4 - 10x^3 + 35x^2 - 50x + 24$ has roots $\bar{x} = 1, 2, 3, 4$.

(a) Starting with $r_0 = 3.2$, $s_0 = -2.2$ [to find $q(x) = (x-1)(x-2)$] use Bairstow's method to find r_k and s_k until successive iterates agree to 3s. Deflate $p(x)$ and find the error in the roots of the deflated $p(x)$ (whose roots, if exact, would be 3 and 4).

(b) Starting with $r_0 = 7.3$, $s_0 = -12.3$ [to find $q(x) = (x-3)(x-4)$] use Bairstow's method to find r_k and s_k until successive iterates agree to 3s. Deflate $p(x)$ and find the error in the roots of the deflated $p(x)$ (whose roots, if exact, would be 1 and 2).

(c) Based on your answers to parts (a) and (b), which roots should you seek first when performing deflation, the largest (in magnitude) or the smallest? Explain.

Computer and Programming Exercises

2-31. *An Initial Guess Finder:* Write a computer program FINDX0 that will evaluate $f(x)$ at $x = a, a + h, a + 2h, \ldots$ until $x > b$, where a, h, and b are chosen by the user. It should print a useful message *only* when it detects either a sign change (definite root) or a turning point less than h units from the x-axis (possible root). Test it with both $p(x)$ and $-p(x)$ for $p(x)$ given in (2) of Section 2.3A. (**WARNING:** This is not as easy as it looks.)

2-32. Write a computer program for the Newton–Raphson method. Use the pseudocode of Figure 2.2-2. If FORTRAN is used, just modify the code given in Section 2.3D. Test with $f(x) = x^3 - 2x - 5$ ($\bar{x} = 2.0945515$).

2-33. Write a computer program for the False Position Method. Use the pseudocode of Figure 2.2-8. Test as in Exercise 2-32.

2-34. In (a)–(c), use any computer program available to find to 6s:

    (a) All solutions on (0, 1] of $\sin \sqrt{\sec x + x^3 e^{5x/\tan x}} = e^{-x}$. [See (11) of Section 2.2E.]

    (b) All roots of $p(x) = x^4 - 3.25x^3 - 1.13x^2 + 4.38x - 0.0864$.

    (c) Three values of y defined implicitly by $x \cos y = y^3 e^x - 5y/x$ when $x = 1$.

2-35. Write a computer program to implement the pseudocode in Figure 2.5-1 for finding all roots of an nth-degree polynomial $p(x)$. Include subprograms BAIRST (to implement Figure 2.5-3 in the **factor** step) and DEFLAT (to do the **deflate** step). If in FORTRAN, use QROOTS of Figure 1.5-2 to get the roots of $q(x)$ in the **solve** step.

2-36. Use a computer program for Bairstow's method to find to 6s all real and complex roots of the polynomials in (a)–(d) of Exercise 2-29.

3

Solving Linear Systems
Exactly
Using Direct Methods

Introduction 3.0

A **linear combination** of the variables $x_1, x_2, \ldots, x_n$ is a weighted sum

$$\text{(LC)} \quad a_1 x_1 + a_2 x_2 + \cdots + a_n x_n$$

A **linear equation** in $x_1, \ldots, x_n$ is obtained by requiring (LC) to assume a prescribed value b, that is,

$$a_1 x_1 + a_2 x_2 + \cdots + a_n x_n = b$$

Such equations arise frequently, generally n at a time, that is, as $n \times n$ **linear systems.** For example, the $n \times n$ linear system

$$a_{11}x_1 + a_{12}x_2 + \cdots + a_{1n}x_n = b_1$$
$$\vdots \qquad \qquad \vdots$$
$$a_{n1}x_1 + a_{n2}x_2 + \cdots + a_{nn}x_n = b_n$$

can arise in the contexts shown in Table 3.0-1 as well as many others that occur in the natural, social, and engineering sciences. A very readable reference that presents details of a variety of these occurrences is [31]. Typically, in these contexts, $2 \leq n \leq 20$. However, n as large as 100 to 1000 can occur.

The reader no doubt has had experience solving 2×2 or 3×3 linear systems. Our primary purpose in this chapter is to describe efficient methods that yield the exact solution (if one exists) of an $n \times n$ *linear* system in a finite number of steps if exact arithmetic (i.e., no rounding) is used. Such methods, generally termed **direct methods,** fall into two categories: **elimination methods** and **factorization methods.**

89

TABLE 3.0-1 Situations described by $n \times n$ linear systems.

Discipline	Context	Units of $x_1, \ldots, x_n$
Electrical engineering	Passive networks	Voltage at certain nodes, or current in certain branches
Mechanics	Static equilibrium	Component of force at a point
Transportation, economics, engineering	Efficient allocation among several points	Net flow from one point to another
Biology/sociology	Population growth	Number of individuals in a particular age group at a particular time

To discuss linear systems, it will be necessary to introduce the basic algebraic properties of *matrices*. The time spent doing this will be well rewarded because matrices make it possible to describe linear systems in a concise way that makes solving $n \times n$ linear systems seem like solving the familiar 1×1 linear system as follows:

$$ax = b \quad \Rightarrow \quad x = \frac{b}{a} = a^{-1}b \qquad \text{if } a \neq 0$$

Moreover, matrices can be used to show how to generalize the Newton–Raphson method to solve *nonlinear* $n \times n$ systems.

In this introductory chapter we shall be concerned with the use of direct methods when performed *exactly*, that is, using exact fractions rather than rounded decimals. The errors resulting from *fixed precision* (e.g., 7s) *arithmetic* will be considered in Chapter 4 after the important manipulative techniques of this chapter have been mastered.

3.1 Basic Properties of Matrices

3.1A TERMINOLOGY AND NOTATION

A **matrix** is a rectangular array of numbers, usually enclosed in square brackets. A matrix having m rows and n columns is called an $m \times n$ (read "m by n") **matrix** or an $m \times n$ **array** and will be denoted by any of the notations

$$A = (a_{ij})_{m \times n} = \begin{bmatrix} a_{11} & a_{12} & \cdots & a_{1j} & \cdots & a_{1n} \\ a_{21} & a_{22} & \cdots & a_{2j} & \cdots & a_{2n} \\ \vdots & \vdots & & \vdots & & \vdots \\ a_{i1} & a_{i2} & \cdots & a_{ij} & \cdots & a_{in} \\ \vdots & \vdots & & \vdots & & \vdots \\ a_{m1} & a_{m2} & \cdots & a_{mj} & \cdots & a_{mn} \end{bmatrix} \begin{matrix} \\ \\ \\ \} \text{row}_i \, A \\ (1 \leqslant i \leqslant m = \text{number of rows}) \\ \\ \\ \end{matrix} \tag{1}$$

$$\text{col}_j \, A \quad (1 \leqslant j \leqslant n = \text{number of columns})$$

The number a_{ij} in the ith row and jth column of A (abbreviated row$_i$ A and col$_j$ A as shown) is called the ***ij*th entry** of the matrix A.

Matrices with $m > 1$ and $n > 1$ will be denoted by uppercase letters such as A, B, C, X, Y, . . . as in (1). Matrices with $m = 1$ (respectively, $n = 1$) will be called **row vectors** (respectively, **column vectors**) and denoted by lowercase boldface letters such as $\mathbf{a}$, $\mathbf{b}$, $\mathbf{c}$, $\mathbf{x}$, $\mathbf{y}$, ... This will distinguish matrices from numbers, which will be referred to as **scalars** and denoted by lowercase letters such as a, b, c, x, y, s, t, α, β, γ, ... For example, if

$$A = \begin{bmatrix} 1 & 4 \\ 0 & 5 \\ 0 & 6 \end{bmatrix}, \quad \mathbf{b} = [1 \quad 0 \quad 3], \quad C = \begin{bmatrix} 3 & 0 \\ \sqrt{2} & 0 \\ \pi & -1 \end{bmatrix}, \quad D = \begin{bmatrix} 0 & 0 \\ 0 & 0 \end{bmatrix}, \quad \mathbf{e} = \begin{bmatrix} 3 \\ -7 \\ 0 \end{bmatrix} \quad (2)$$

then A and C are 3×2 matrices with $a_{12} = 4$ and $c_{31} = \pi$; D is a 2×2 matrix; $\mathbf{b}$ is a row vector; and $\mathbf{e}$ is a column vector.

For typographical reasons, it is convenient to use a superscript T, for **transpose**, as an operator that converts a column vector to a row vector, and vice versa. Thus $\mathbf{e}$ above can be written as $[3 \quad -7 \quad 0]^T$ (the transpose of the row vector $[3 \quad -7 \quad 0]$); or we can write $\mathbf{e}^T = [3 \quad -7 \quad 0]$. In this notation, col$_j$ $A = [a_{1j} \quad a_{2j} \quad \cdots \quad a_{nj}]^T$. Unless a row (respectively, column) vector $\mathbf{b}$ is part of a larger matrix, we will usually write its entries as $[b_1 \quad b_2 \quad \cdots \quad b_n]$ (respectively, $[b_1 \quad b_2 \quad \cdots \quad b_n]^T$), that is, using only a *single* subscript. The scalars b_1, . . . , b_n are then called the **components** of $\mathbf{b}$. Thus in (2), $\mathbf{b} = [b_1 \quad b_2 \quad b_3]$ where the second component b_2 is zero, and $\mathbf{e} = [e_1 \quad e_2 \quad e_3]^T$, where $e_1 = 3$.

3.1B   EQUALITY, ADDITION, SUBTRACTION, AND SCALAR MULTIPLICATION OF MATRICES

Two matrices A and B are **equal**, written $A = B$, if they are the same size and have identical entries (i.e., $a_{ij} = b_{ij}$ for all i, j). If A and B are equisized, say $A = (a_{ij})_{m \times n}$ and $B = (b_{ij})_{m \times n}$, then their **sum** $A + B$ and **difference** $A - B$ are the $m \times n$ matrices defined in the natural way by

$$A + B = (a_{ij} + b_{ij})_{m \times n} \quad \text{and} \quad A - B = (a_{ij} - b_{ij})_{m \times n} \quad (3)$$

Similarly for any scalar s, the $m \times n$ matrix $sA^\dagger$ is defined by

$$sA = (sa_{ij})_{m \times n} \quad (4)$$

Of special importance for these algebraic operations is the matrix

$$O_{m \times n} = (0)_{m \times n} \quad \text{(all zeros)} \quad (5)$$

called the **zero matrix,** written as simply O if its size is clear.

$\dagger$ We shall follow customary convention and keep the scalar on the left, that is, use sA rather than As to denote multiplication of A by the scalar s.

For example, for A, $\mathbf{b}$, C, D, and $\mathbf{e}$ in (2),

$$D = O_{2\times2}, \quad (-2)\mathbf{e} = \begin{bmatrix} -6 \\ 14 \\ 0 \end{bmatrix}, \quad 2A - 3C = \begin{bmatrix} -7 & 8 \\ -3\sqrt{2} & 10 \\ -3\pi & 15 \end{bmatrix}, \quad \text{and} \quad \mathbf{b}^T + \mathbf{e} = \begin{bmatrix} 4 \\ -7 \\ 3 \end{bmatrix}$$

whereas $A \pm \mathbf{b}$, $\mathbf{b} \pm C$, $C \pm D$, and $\mathbf{b} \pm \mathbf{e}$ are not defined.

3.1C   PROPERTIES OF MATRIX ADDITION

For any three equisized matrices A, B, and C,

A1: $A + B = B + A$	(Matrix addition is *commutative*)
A2: $A + O = O + A = A$	(O is the *zero* for matrix addition)
A3: $-A$, defined as $(-1)A$, satisfies	
$\quad A + (-A) = (-A) + A = O$	($-A$ is the *negative of* A)
A4: $(A + B) + C = A + (B + C)$	(Matrix addition is *associative*)

These algebraic rules follow directly from definitions (3) and (5).

It follows from the associative law A4 that

$$(A + B) + (C + D) = A + ((B + C) + D) = ((A + B) + C) + D, \quad \text{etc.}$$

and hence that *we can unambiguously write general sums such as $A + B + C + D$ without parentheses.* In particular, for $k = 1, 2, \ldots$,

$$A + A + \cdots + A \ (k \text{ times}) = kA$$

that is, adding A to itself k times has the same effect as multiplying A by the scalar k. Also, if A is $m \times n$, then $0A = O_{m\times n}$. However, *matrix subtraction is not associative,* that is, we *cannot* replace $+$ by $-$ in A4.

Just as the sum of two $m \times n$ matrices A and B was defined "entrywise," we could define their product AB as $(a_{ij}b_{ij})_{m\times n}$. However, there are not enough mathematical applications of this definition to make it worth considering. On the other hand, the less "natural" definition of AB given next is so useful that it is the key to the importance of matrices in studying linear processes.

3.1D   MATRIX MULTIPLICATION

The product AB is only defined if A has as many columns as B has rows, say

$$A = (a_{ij})_{m\times n} \quad \text{and} \quad B = (b_{ij})_{n\times p}$$

In this case, AB is defined as the $m \times p$ matrix

$$AB = (\text{row}_i\, A \, \text{col}_j\, B)_{m\times p} \tag{6a}$$

where $\text{row}_i\, A\, \text{col}_j\, B$ denotes the scalar obtained as the sum

$$\text{row}_i\, A\, \text{col}_j\, B = a_{i1}b_{1j} + a_{i2}b_{2j} + \cdots + a_{in}b_{nj} = \sum_{k=1}^{n} a_{ik}b_{kj} \qquad \textbf{(6b)}$$

The sum (6b) is called the **inner product** of $\text{row}_i\, A$ and $\text{col}_j\, B$. Thus

$$AB = \begin{bmatrix} \text{row}_1\, A\, \text{col}_1\, B & \cdots & \text{row}_1\, A\, \text{col}_j\, B & \cdots & \text{row}_1\, A\, \text{col}_p\, B \\ \text{row}_2\, A\, \text{col}_1\, B & \cdots & \text{row}_2\, A\, \text{col}_j\, B & \cdots & \text{row}_2\, A\, \text{col}_p\, B \\ \vdots & & \vdots & & \vdots \\ \text{row}_i\, A\, \text{col}_1\, B & \cdots & \text{row}_i\, A\, \text{col}_j\, B & \cdots & \text{row}_i\, A\, \text{col}_p\, B \\ \vdots & & \vdots & & \vdots \\ \text{row}_m\, A\, \text{col}_1\, B & \cdots & \text{row}_m\, A\, \text{col}_j\, B & \cdots & \text{row}_m\, A\, \text{col}_p\, B \end{bmatrix} \qquad \textbf{(6c)}$$

$$\underbrace{\phantom{\text{row}_1\, A\, \text{col}_1\, B}}_{\text{col}_1\, AB} \qquad \underbrace{\phantom{\text{row}_1\, A\, \text{col}_j\, B}}_{\text{col}_j\, AB} \qquad \underbrace{\phantom{\text{row}_1\, A\, \text{col}_p\, B}}_{\text{col}_p\, AB}$$

Notice that AB (when defined) has as many *rows* (m) as the *left* factor A and as many *columns* (p) as the *right* factor B. It is immediate from definition (6) that

$$\text{row}_i\, (AB) = (\text{row}_i\, A)B, \qquad i = 1, 2, \ldots, m \qquad \textbf{(7a)}$$
$$\text{col}_j\, (AB) = A(\text{col}_j\, B), \qquad j = 1, 2, \ldots, p \qquad \textbf{(7b)}$$

When using (6b) to form the ijth entry of AB, one scans *across* $\text{row}_i\, A$ and *down* $\text{col}_j\, B$ and accumulates the sum of the n products $a_{i1}b_{1j}, \ldots, a_{in}b_{nj}$. An example of multiplying $A_{3\times2}$ by $B_{2\times2}$ is

$$\begin{bmatrix} 1 & 2 \\ 3 & 4 \\ 5 & 6 \end{bmatrix} \begin{bmatrix} 7 & 9 \\ 8 & 10 \end{bmatrix} = \begin{bmatrix} (1\cdot7+2\cdot8) & (1\cdot9+2\cdot10) \\ (3\cdot7+4\cdot8) & (3\cdot9+4\cdot10) \\ (5\cdot7+6\cdot8) & (5\cdot9+6\cdot10) \end{bmatrix} = \begin{bmatrix} 23 & 29 \\ 53 & 67 \\ 83 & 105 \end{bmatrix}$$

Since the product of $B_{2\times2}$ by $A_{3\times2}$ is not defined, it makes no sense to ask if $AB = BA$. In fact, the only way that AB can possibly equal BA is if A and B are both **square** matrices of the same size (i.e., both $n \times n$). The following example shows that even in this case *we should not expect $AB = BA$*.

EXAMPLE. Consider

$$A = \begin{bmatrix} 1 & -2 \\ -2 & 4 \end{bmatrix} \qquad \text{and} \qquad B = \begin{bmatrix} 2 & 0 \\ 1 & 0 \end{bmatrix}$$

Then

$$AB = \begin{bmatrix} 0 & 0 \\ 0 & 0 \end{bmatrix} = O_{2\times2} \qquad \text{whereas} \qquad BA = \begin{bmatrix} 2 & -4 \\ 1 & -2 \end{bmatrix} \neq O_{2\times2}$$

If it happens that $AB = BA$, then A and B are said to **commute**.

The preceding example shows that unlike the scalar zero, *the zero matrix can have proper divisors*, that is, there can be *nonzero* A and B such that $AB = O$.

3.1E   THE IDENTITY MATRIX

Of special importance for matrix multiplication is

$$I_n = \begin{bmatrix} 1 & 0 & 0 & \cdots & 0 \\ 0 & 1 & 0 & \cdots & 0 \\ 0 & 0 & 1 & \cdots & 0 \\ \vdots & \vdots & \vdots & & \vdots \\ 0 & 0 & 0 & \cdots & 1 \end{bmatrix} \quad \begin{pmatrix} n \times n \text{ matrix with} \\ a_{ii} = 1 \text{ for } 1 \leqslant i \leqslant n \\ \text{and } a_{ij} = 0 \text{ for } i \neq j \end{pmatrix} \tag{8}$$

called the $n \times n$ **identity matrix,** written as simply I when its size is clear.

The following algebraic rules are direct consequences of (6) and (8).

3.1F   PROPERTIES OF MATRIX MULTIPLICATION

Given any scalar s and any matrices A, B, C for which the sums and products described are defined,

M1:	$(sA)B = A(sB) = s(AB)$	(Scalars can be moved through products)
M2:	For $A_{m \times n}$, $I_m A = A I_n = A$	(I is the *identity for matrix multiplication*)
M3a:	$(A + B)C = AC + BC$	(*Right distributive law*)
M3b:	$A(B + C) = AB + AC$	(*Left distributive law*)
M4:	$A(BC) = (AB)C$	(Matrix multiplication is *associative*)

In view of M2, I plays the role for matrices that the number 1 does for scalars. It follows from the associative law M4 that

$$(AB)(CD) = A[B(CD)] = [(AB)C]D = [A(BC)]D \qquad \text{(when defined)}$$

Hence products of four matrices can be written unambiguously as $ABCD$ *without parentheses.* Similarly, for any square matrix A, A^k can be used to denote $A \cdot A \cdots A$ (k times) in which case

$$A^j A^k = A^{j+k} \qquad \text{for any positive integers } j, \, k$$

Although some of the following discussion will apply to nonsquare matrices,

> *the remainder of this chapter will be devoted to square,*
> $n \times n$ *matrices. This will assure that for any two matrices*
> *A and B and all scalars s and t, the linear combination*
> *sA + tB and both products AB and BA are defined, al-*
> *though it may be that AB ≠ BA.*

It then follows from A1–A4 of Section 3.1C and M1–M4 above that the *usual algebraic rules governing addition, subtraction, multiplication and positive exponentiation apply to square matrices as well, as long as we do not try to reverse the order of multiplication.*

For example,

$$(A + 2B)(A - 2B) = AA + 2BA - 2AB - 4B^2 = (A^2 - 4B^2) + 2(BA - AB)$$

This will *not* equal $A^2 - 4B^2$ unless A and B commute (i.e., $BA = AB$).

We shall not define division by a matrix A; however, there may exist a matrix A^{-1} such that multiplication by A^{-1} has the effect of dividing by A.

3.1G   THE INVERSE A^{-1} OF A NONSINGULAR MATRIX A

An $n \times n$ matrix A is called **nonsingular** or **invertible** if an $n \times n$ matrix B can be found such that

$$AB = BA = I_n \tag{9}$$

If no such B exists, then A is called **singular.**

Let us first show that *at most one matrix B can be found to satisfy* (9). Indeed, if also $A\hat{B} = \hat{B}A = I_n$, then, using M2 and M4 of Section 3.1F,

$$B = I_n B = (\hat{B}A)B = \hat{B}(AB) = \hat{B}I_n = \hat{B}, \qquad \text{that is, } B = \hat{B}$$

If A is invertible, then the *unique* matrix B in (9) is called the **inverse** of A and is denoted by A^{-1}. Thus, by definition,

$$\boxed{AA^{-1} = A^{-1}A = I \qquad \text{if } A \text{ is nonsingular}} \tag{10}$$

Since $I_n I_n = I_n$, I_n *is invertible and is in fact its own inverse, that is,* $I_n = I_n^{-1}$ for any n. Also, since $O_{n \times n}B = BO_{n \times n} = O_{n \times n}$, there is no way to satisfy (9) when $A = O_{n \times n}$. So $O_{n \times n}$ *is singular for every n.*

I1: If A and B are invertible, so is AB; in fact, $(AB)^{-1} = B^{-1}A^{-1}$, that is, *the inverse of a product is the product of the inverses in reverse order.*

I2: If A is invertible, so is A^k for any k; in fact, $(A^k)^{-1} = (A^{-1})^k$, that is, *the inverse of A^k is the kth power of the inverse of A.*

I3: If A is invertible, so is sA for any nonzero s; in fact, $(sA)^{-1} = \dfrac{1}{s}A^{-1}$.

I4: If $AB = O$ (but $A \neq O$ and $B \neq O$), then A and B must be singular.

To prove I1, we must show that $B^{-1}A^{-1}$ is the inverse of AB, that is,

$$(AB)(B^{-1}A^{-1}) = (B^{-1}A^{-1})(AB) = I$$

But this is immediate from (10) and the associative law because

$$(AB)(B^{-1}A^{-1}) = A(BB^{-1})A^{-1} = AIA^{-1} = AA^{-1} = I$$

and similarly $(B^{-1}A^{-1})(AB) = I$. The proofs of I2–I4 are left as exercises. It follows from I4 that neither A nor B of the example in Section 3.1D has inverses.

Although, in general, the value of AB tells us nothing about the value of BA, the following remarkable result assures us that if either AB or BA yields the identity matrix, so will the other!

I5: If a matrix B can be found that is *either* a right inverse of A (i.e., $AB = I$) *or* a left inverse of A (i.e., $BA = I$), then A is invertible and $B = A^{-1}$.

Thus verifying *either* that $AB = I$ or that $BA = I$ is sufficient to show that $B = A^{-1}$. The proof of I5 is not trivial. It is given in linear algebra.

3.1H   FORMULA FOR A^{-1} WHEN $n = 2$

We wish to show that

$$A = \begin{bmatrix} a & b \\ c & d \end{bmatrix} \text{ is invertible if and only if } ad - bc \neq 0$$

in which case

$$A^{-1} = \begin{bmatrix} a & b \\ c & d \end{bmatrix}^{-1} = \frac{1}{ad - bc}\begin{bmatrix} d & -b \\ -c & a \end{bmatrix} \qquad \textbf{(11)}$$

To this end, let

$$C = \begin{bmatrix} d & -b \\ -c & a \end{bmatrix} \qquad \text{and} \qquad \delta = ad - bc.$$

Then

$$AC = \begin{bmatrix} a & b \\ c & d \end{bmatrix}\begin{bmatrix} d & -b \\ -c & a \end{bmatrix} = \begin{bmatrix} ad - bc & 0 \\ 0 & -cb + da \end{bmatrix} = \delta\begin{bmatrix} 1 & 0 \\ 0 & 1 \end{bmatrix} = \delta I_2$$

If $\delta = 0$, then $AC = O$; hence A is *not* invertible by I4. If $\delta \neq 0$, then by M1 of Section 3.1F,

$$A\left(\frac{1}{\delta}C\right) = \frac{1}{\delta}(AC) = \frac{1}{\delta}(\delta I_2) = I_2$$

that is, $\dfrac{1}{\delta}C$ is a right inverse of A. By I5, it must be *the inverse* of A.

Formula (11) makes it possible to get the inverse of a nonsingular 2×2 matrix by inspection. For example,

$$\begin{bmatrix} 1 & 2 \\ 3 & 4 \end{bmatrix}^{-1} = \frac{1}{(1)(4) - (2)(3)}\begin{bmatrix} 4 & -2 \\ -3 & 1 \end{bmatrix} = -\frac{1}{2}\begin{bmatrix} 4 & -2 \\ -3 & 1 \end{bmatrix} = \begin{bmatrix} -2 & 1 \\ \frac{3}{2} & -\frac{1}{2} \end{bmatrix}$$

An important special case of (11) occurs when A is the **rotation matrix** $R(\theta)$:

$$\text{If } R(\theta) = \begin{bmatrix} \cos\theta & -\sin\theta \\ \sin\theta & \cos\theta \end{bmatrix}, \quad \text{then } R(\theta)^{-1} = \begin{bmatrix} \cos\theta & \sin\theta \\ -\sin\theta & \cos\theta \end{bmatrix} = R(-\theta) \quad \textbf{(12)}$$

Thus the 2×2 matrix $R(\theta)$ is invertible for any θ and its inverse is obtained by replacing θ by $-\theta$. This matrix will play an important role in Section 9.3.

The general problem of determining whether a given $n \times n$ matrix A is nonsingular, and if so finding A^{-1}, is a difficult one. We shall examine this problem after showing how matrices help us solve systems of linear equations.

Introduction to Linear Systems; Triangular Systems **3.2**

An $n \times n$ **linear system** is a system of n simultaneous linear equations in n unknowns. Our notation for such a system will be

$$\begin{array}{ll} (E_1) & a_{11}x_1 + a_{12}x_2 + \cdots + a_{1n}x_n = b_1 \\ (E_2) & a_{21}x_1 + a_{22}x_2 + \cdots + a_{2n}x_n = b_2 \\ \vdots & \qquad\qquad\qquad\qquad\qquad \vdots \\ (E_n) & a_{n1}x_1 + a_{n2}x_2 + \cdots + a_{nn}x_n = b_n \end{array} \qquad \textbf{(1)}$$

where the a_{ij}'s and the b_i's are scalars, and $x_1, \ldots, x_n$ are the unknowns. The definition of matrix multiplication makes it possible to write this linear system compactly as a single matrix equation

$$A\mathbf{x} = \mathbf{b} \qquad \textbf{(2)}$$

where

$$A = (a_{ij})_{n \times n} = \begin{bmatrix} a_{11} & a_{12} & \cdots & a_{1n} \\ a_{21} & a_{22} & \cdots & a_{2n} \\ \vdots & \vdots & & \vdots \\ a_{n1} & a_{n2} & \cdots & a_{nn} \end{bmatrix}, \quad \mathbf{x} = \begin{bmatrix} x_1 \\ x_2 \\ \vdots \\ x_n \end{bmatrix}, \quad \text{and} \quad \mathbf{b} = \begin{bmatrix} b_1 \\ b_2 \\ \vdots \\ b_n \end{bmatrix} \qquad \textbf{(3)}$$

A is called the **coefficient matrix**, and $\mathbf{x} = [x_1 \ x_2 \ \cdots \ x_n]^T$ the **vector of unknowns,** for the linear system (1). We shall identify the matrix form (2) with the system (1) itself and speak of *the linear system $A\mathbf{x} = \mathbf{b}$.*

3.2A SOLUTIONS OF $n \times n$ LINEAR SYSTEMS

A **solution** of (1) is a set of numerical values $\bar{x}_1, \ldots, \bar{x}_n$ that satisfy $(E_1) \ldots$, (E_n) when substituted for $x_1, \ldots, x_n$. In view of (2), a solution can be viewed as a numerical vector $\bar{\mathbf{x}} = [\bar{x}_1 \ \bar{x}_2 \ \cdots \ \bar{x}_n]^T$, which yields $\mathbf{b}$ when premultiplied by A.

If A is nonsingular, then the numerical vector

$$A^{-1}\mathbf{b}$$

satisfies (2) because $A(A^{-1}\mathbf{b}) = I\mathbf{b} = \mathbf{b}$. Moreover, any numerical vector $\overline{\mathbf{x}}$ such that $A\overline{\mathbf{x}} = \mathbf{b}$ must, upon premultiplication by A^{-1}, satisfy $\overline{\mathbf{x}} = A^{-1}\mathbf{b}$. This proves the following fundamental result.

> If A is nonsingular, then for any $\mathbf{b}$ the system $A\mathbf{x} = \mathbf{b}$
> has a *unique* solution given by the formula $\overline{\mathbf{x}} = A^{-1}\mathbf{b}$. (4)

The formula $\overline{\mathbf{x}} = A^{-1}\mathbf{b}$ makes it easy to solve the system $A\mathbf{x} = \mathbf{b}$ when we know A^{-1}. In fact, *the easiest way to solve a* 2×2 *linear system is to use formula* (11) *of* Section 3.1H. For example, the system

$$\begin{aligned} 3x_1 + 2x_2 &= 3 \\ -5x_1 - 4x_2 &= -4 \end{aligned} \qquad \left(A = \begin{bmatrix} 3 & 2 \\ -5 & -4 \end{bmatrix}, \quad \mathbf{b} = \begin{bmatrix} 3 \\ -4 \end{bmatrix} \right) \tag{5}$$

is easily solved by premultiplying $\mathbf{b}$ by A^{-1} as follows:

$$\begin{bmatrix} \overline{x}_1 \\ \overline{x}_2 \end{bmatrix} = \overline{\mathbf{x}} = A^{-1}\mathbf{b} = \frac{1}{(3)(-4) - (2)(-5)} \begin{bmatrix} -4 & -2 \\ 5 & 3 \end{bmatrix} \begin{bmatrix} 3 \\ -4 \end{bmatrix} = \frac{1}{-2} \begin{bmatrix} -4 \\ 3 \end{bmatrix} \tag{6}$$

The reader can verify that $\overline{\mathbf{x}} = [2 \quad -\frac{3}{2}]^T$ (i.e., $\overline{x}_1 = 2$, $\overline{x}_2 = -\frac{3}{2}$) satisfies (5).

The formula for A^{-1} when $n = 2$ is a special case of a general formula for A^{-1} [see (13) of Section 3.5D]. Unfortunately, this general formula rapidly becomes harder to use as n is increased from 2. There are general *procedures* for getting A^{-1} with less work than the formula; however, as we shall see in Section 3.6, these procedures amount to solving n linear $n \times n$ systems. So if $n > 2$ and all that is required is the solution of a *single* $n \times n$ system $A\mathbf{x} = \mathbf{b}$, then *finding* A^{-1} *and then multiplying by* $\mathbf{b}$ *is generally not the most efficient way to obtain the solution.* However, we shall consistently denote the solution $\overline{\mathbf{x}}$ of $A\mathbf{x} = \mathbf{b}$ as $A^{-1}\mathbf{b}$ even if $\overline{\mathbf{x}}$ is not actually obtained as the product $A^{-1}\mathbf{b}$.

3.2B THE AUGMENTED MATRIX FOR A LINEAR SYSTEM

The unknowns of a linear system are merely placeholders. All the information needed to find a solution of $A\mathbf{x} = \mathbf{b}$ (or $A\mathbf{c} = \mathbf{b}$, or $A\mathbf{u} = \mathbf{b}$, etc.) is contained in the matrix A and the vector $\mathbf{b}$, and is efficiently displayed in the $n \times (n + 1)$ **augmented matrix**

$$[A : \mathbf{b}] = \begin{bmatrix} a_{11} & a_{12} & \cdots & a_{1n} & : & b_1 \\ a_{21} & a_{22} & \cdots & a_{2n} & : & b_2 \\ \vdots & \vdots & & \vdots & & \vdots \\ a_{n1} & a_{n2} & \cdots & a_{nn} & : & b_n \end{bmatrix} \tag{7}$$

3.2C TRIANGULAR MATRICES AND SYSTEMS

Let $A = (a_{ij})_{n \times n}$ be a square matrix. The diagonal that goes from a_{11} to a_{nn} is called the **main diagonal** (or simply the **diagonal**) of A. Matrix A is called **upper triangular** if $a_{ij} = 0$ whenever $i > j$ (i.e., if all entries *below* the main diagonal are zero), **lower**

triangular if $a_{ij} = 0$ whenever $i < j$ (i.e., if all entries *above* the main diagonal are zero), and simply **triangular** if either upper or lower triangular. For example, if

$$A = \begin{bmatrix} 2 & -2 \\ 0 & \pi \end{bmatrix}, \quad B = \begin{bmatrix} -1 & 0 \\ -1 & -1 \end{bmatrix}, \quad C = \begin{bmatrix} 0 & 1 \\ 0 & 0 \end{bmatrix}, \quad D = \begin{bmatrix} 3 & 0 \\ 0 & -5 \end{bmatrix}, \quad E = \begin{bmatrix} 2 & 0 \\ 5 & 0 \end{bmatrix}$$

then A, C, and D are upper triangular, and B, D, and E are lower triangular.

> An $n \times n$ triangular matrix can have at most
> $1 + 2 + \cdots + n = \frac{1}{2}n(n+1)$ nonzero entries.   **(8)**

A linear system will be called **upper triangular** (respectively, **lower triangular, triangular**) if its coefficient matrix is upper triangular (respectively, lower triangular, triangular). Triangular systems are especially easy to solve. Consider for example the 3×3 upper-triangular linear system shown with its augmented matrix in Figure 3.2-1. (*Note:* The entries not shown in the augmented matrix are 0.)

$$
\begin{array}{ll}
\text{(a)} \quad \text{(E}_1\text{)} & x_1 + x_2 + 2x_3 = -1 \\
\quad \text{(E}_2\text{)} & \qquad -2x_2 + 2x_3 = \quad 1 \\
\quad \text{(E}_3\text{)} & \qquad\qquad\quad -4x_3 = \quad 4
\end{array}
\qquad
\text{(b)} \quad
\begin{bmatrix}
1 & 1 & 2 & : & -1 \\
  & -2 & 2 & : & 1 \\
  &   & -4 & : & 4
\end{bmatrix}
$$

FIGURE 3.2-1   (a) AN UPPER TRIANGULAR 3×3 SYSTEM; (b) ITS AUGMENTED MATRIX.

From (E$_3$), $\bar{x}_3 = 4/(-4) = -1$. Substituting $\bar{x}_3 = -1$ for x_3 in (E$_2$) then gives

$$\bar{x}_2 = -\tfrac{1}{2}(1 - 2\bar{x}_3) = -\tfrac{3}{2}$$

Finally, substituting $\bar{x}_2$ and $\bar{x}_3$ for x_2 and x_3 in (E$_1$) gives

$$\bar{x}_1 = -1 - \bar{x}_2 - 2\bar{x}_3 = -1 - (-\tfrac{3}{2}) - 2(-1), \qquad \text{that is, } \bar{x}_1 = \tfrac{5}{2}$$

The systematic procedure illustrated here is called **Backward Substitution.**

Similarly, to solve the 3×3 lower-triangular system $L\mathbf{c} = \mathbf{b}$, that is,

$$
\begin{array}{ll}
\text{(E}_1\text{)} & l_{11}c_1 = b_1 \\
\text{(E}_2\text{)} & l_{21}c_1 + l_{22}c_2 = b_2 \\
\text{(E}_3\text{)} & l_{31}c_1 + l_{32}c_2 + l_{33}c_3 = b_3
\end{array}
\qquad
\left([L : \mathbf{b}] = \begin{bmatrix} l_{11} & & & : & b_1 \\ l_{21} & l_{22} & & : & b_2 \\ l_{31} & l_{32} & l_{33} & : & b_3 \end{bmatrix} \right)
$$

we solve (E$_1$) for $\bar{c}_1 = b_1/l_{11}$ (if $l_{11} \neq 0$) and then substitute for c_1 in (E$_2$) to get

$$\bar{c}_2 = \frac{1}{l_{22}}\{b_2 - l_{21}\bar{c}_1\} \qquad (\text{if } l_{22} \neq 0)$$

Finally, substituting for c_1 and c_2 in (E$_3$) gives (if $l_{33} \neq 0$)

$$\bar{c}_3 = \frac{1}{l_{33}}\{b_3 - l_{31}\bar{c}_1 - l_{32}\bar{c}_2\}$$

The systematic procedure illustrated here is called **Forward Substitution.**

We shall see in Section 3.3A how the solution of a general linear system $A\mathbf{x} = \mathbf{b}$ can be reduced to using Forward Substitution to solve $L\mathbf{c} = \mathbf{b}$ for $\bar{\mathbf{c}}$ then using Backward Substitution to solve $U\mathbf{x} = \bar{\mathbf{c}}$ for the desired $\bar{\mathbf{x}}$. Anticipating this, the reader is urged to master the procedures for Forward and Backward Substitution described next.

3.2D   EFFICIENT FORWARD SUBSTITUTION

Algorithm: Forward Substitution

Purpose: To solve the lower-triangular linear system $L\mathbf{c} = \mathbf{b}$ for $\bar{\mathbf{c}} = L^{-1}\mathbf{b}$. It is assumed that $l_{ii} \neq 0$ for $i = 1, \ldots , n$.

$$\text{GET } n, \ \mathbf{b} = \begin{bmatrix} b_1 \\ b_2 \\ \vdots \\ b_n \end{bmatrix}, \text{ and the lower-triangular entries of } L = \begin{bmatrix} l_{11} & & & \\ l_{21} & l_{22} & & \\ \vdots & \vdots & \ddots & \\ l_{n1} & l_{n2} & \cdots & l_{nn} \end{bmatrix}$$

$$\bar{c}_1 \leftarrow \frac{b_1}{l_{11}} \tag{9a}$$

DO FOR $i = 2$ TO n {Forward: $\bar{c}_k$ is known for $1 \leqslant k \leqslant i - 1$}

$$\bar{c}_i \leftarrow \frac{1}{l_{ii}} \left(b_i - \sum_{k<i} l_{ik} \bar{c}_k \right) \tag{9b}$$

OUTPUT ($\bar{\mathbf{c}} = [\bar{c}_1 \ \bar{c}_2 \ \ldots \ \bar{c}_n]^T$ is the desired solution.)

FIGURE 3.2-2   PSEUDOPROGRAM FOR THE FORWARD SUBSTITUTION ALGORITHM.

An efficient way of using Forward Substitution to solve $L\mathbf{c} = \mathbf{b}$ is to *enter the $\bar{c}_i$'s as they are obtained in a doubly augmented matrix* $[L : \mathbf{b} : \bar{\mathbf{c}}]$. See Figure 3.2-2. Then for any i, (9b) can be expressed as

$$\bar{c}_i = \frac{1}{(l_{ii})}\{b_i - [\leftarrow]_L [\uparrow]_{\bar{c}}\}, \quad \text{where} \quad [\leftarrow]_L = [l_{i1} \cdots l_{i,\ i-1}] \quad \text{and} \quad [\uparrow]_{\bar{c}} = \begin{bmatrix} \bar{c}_1 \\ \vdots \\ \bar{c}_{i-1} \end{bmatrix} \tag{9c}$$

In (9c) the summation in (9b) is viewed as the inner product of

$$[\leftarrow]_L: \quad \textit{look left} \text{ from } \bar{c}_i \text{ to the } \textit{leftmost } i - 1 \text{ entries of } \text{row}_i \ L \tag{9d}$$

$$[\uparrow]_{\bar{c}}: \quad \textit{look up} \text{ from } \bar{c}_i \text{ to the } i - 1 \text{ currently known entries of } \bar{\mathbf{c}} \tag{9e}$$

These two vectors can be obtained *by inspection* of the current $[L : \mathbf{b} : \bar{\mathbf{c}}]$.

EXAMPLE. Solve the 4×4 lower-triangular system

$$
\begin{aligned}
2c_1 & & & & = -2 \\
-2c_1 - & c_2 & & & = 13 \\
-c_1 + & c_2 - 3c_3 & & & = -7 \\
0c_1 + & 2c_2 + 4c_3 + 9c_4 & & & = 10
\end{aligned} \tag{10}
$$

Solution. We form $[L : \mathbf{b} : \bar{\mathbf{c}}]$ using (9) to get $\bar{\mathbf{c}}$ from $[L : \mathbf{b} : \text{current } \bar{\mathbf{c}}]$ as follows:

$$
\begin{array}{c}
\overbrace{\hspace{4cm}}^{L} \quad \overbrace{\hspace{0.5cm}}^{\mathbf{b}} \quad \overbrace{\hspace{0.5cm}}^{\bar{\mathbf{c}}} \quad \text{Calculation of } \bar{c}_1, \bar{c}_2, \bar{c}_3
\end{array}
$$

$$
\begin{bmatrix}
\textcircled{2} & & & & : & -2 & : & -1 \\
-2 & \textcircled{-1} & & & : & 13 & : & -11 \\
-1 & 1 & \textcircled{-3} & & : & -7 & : & -1 \\
0 & 2 & 4 & \textcircled{9} & : & 10 & : & 4
\end{bmatrix}
$$

$$
\bar{c}_1 = \frac{-2}{\textcircled{2}} = -1
$$
$$
\bar{c}_2 = \frac{1}{\textcircled{-1}}\{13 - [-2][-1]\} = -11 \tag{11a}
$$
$$
\bar{c}_3 = \frac{1}{\textcircled{-3}}\left\{-7 - [-1 \ \ 1]\begin{bmatrix}-1 \\ -11\end{bmatrix}\right\} = -1
$$

The calculation of $\bar{c}_4$, using the entries of $\text{row}_4[L : \mathbf{b}]$ and $[\bar{c}_1 \ \ \bar{c}_2 \ \ \bar{c}_3]^T$, is

$$
\bar{c}_4 = \frac{1}{\textcircled{9}}\left\{10 - [0 \ \ 2 \ \ 4]\begin{bmatrix}1 \\ -11 \\ -1\end{bmatrix}\right\} = \frac{1}{9}\{10 - (0 - 22 - 4)\} = 4 \tag{11b}
$$

The diagonal entries l_{ii} were circled as a convenience to help locate $[\leftarrow]_L$ (to the *left* of $\textcircled{l_{ii}}$) and as a reminder that we must divide by $\textcircled{l_{ii}}$ to get $\bar{c}_i$. The reader can verify that $\bar{\mathbf{c}} = [-1 \ \ -11 \ \ -1 \ \ 4]^T$ is indeed the (unique) solution of (10). The reason for using $\mathbf{c}$ rather than $\mathbf{x}$ for the vector of unknowns of lower-triangular systems will become clear in Section 3.3A.

3.2E   EFFICIENT BACKWARD SUBSTITUTION

We can solve $U\mathbf{x} = \bar{\mathbf{c}}$ efficiently by entering the $\bar{x}_i$s in a doubly augmented matrix $[U : \bar{\mathbf{c}} : \bar{\mathbf{x}}]$ as in Figure 3.2-3, that is, by evaluating $\bar{\mathbf{x}}$ and evaluating (12e) as

$$
\bar{x}_i = \frac{1}{\textcircled{u_{ii}}}\{\bar{c}_i - [\leftarrow]_U[\downarrow]_{\bar{\mathbf{x}}}\}, \quad \text{where } [\leftarrow]_U = [u_{i,i+1} \cdots u_{in}] \quad \text{and} \quad [\downarrow]_{\bar{\mathbf{x}}} = \begin{bmatrix}\bar{x}_{i+1} \\ \vdots \\ \bar{x}_n\end{bmatrix} \tag{12a}
$$

In (12a) the summation in (12e) is viewed as the inner product of

$[\leftarrow]_U$:   *look left* from $\bar{x}_i$ to the *rightmost* $i-1$ entries of $\text{row}_i U$ (12b)

$[\downarrow]_{\mathbf{x}}$:   *look down* from $\bar{x}_i$ to the $i-1$ currently known entries of $\bar{\mathbf{x}}$ (12c)

Algorithm: Backward Substitution

Purpose: To solve the upper-triangular linear system $U\mathbf{x} = \bar{\mathbf{c}}$ for $\bar{\mathbf{x}} = U^{-1}\bar{\mathbf{c}}$. It is assumed that $u_{ii} \neq 0$ for $i = 1, \ldots, n$.

GET n, $\bar{\mathbf{c}} = \begin{bmatrix} \bar{c}_1 \\ \bar{c}_2 \\ \vdots \\ \bar{c}_n \end{bmatrix}$ and the upper-triangular entries of $U = \begin{bmatrix} u_{11} & u_{12} & \cdots & u_{1n} \\ & u_{22} & \cdots & u_{2n} \\ & & \ddots & \vdots \\ & & & u_{nn} \end{bmatrix}$.

$$\bar{x}_n \leftarrow \frac{\bar{c}_n}{u_{nn}} \tag{12d}$$

DO FOR $i = n - 1$ TO 1 STEP -1 {Backward: $\bar{x}_k$ is known for $i + 1 \leq k \leq n$}

$$\bar{x}_i \leftarrow \frac{1}{u_{ii}}\left(\bar{c}_i - \sum_{k>i} u_{ik}\bar{x}_k\right) \tag{12e}$$

OUTPUT ($\bar{\mathbf{x}} = [\bar{x}_1\ \bar{x}_2 \ldots \bar{x}_n]^T$ is the desired solution.)

FIGURE 3.2-3 PSEUDOPROGRAM FOR THE BACKWARD SUBSTITUTION ALGORITHM.

These can be obtained by inspection of the current $[U : \bar{\mathbf{c}} : \bar{\mathbf{x}}]$. Notice that when all u_{ii}s are 1, (12) simplifies to

$$\bar{x}_n = \bar{c}_n; \qquad \bar{x}_i = \bar{c}_i - [\leftarrow]_U[\downarrow]_{\bar{\mathbf{x}}}, \qquad i = n - 1, \ldots, 2, 1 \tag{13}$$

EXAMPLE. Solve the 4×4 upper-triangular system

$$\begin{aligned} x_1 + 3x_2 + 0x_3 - x_4 &= -1 \\ x_2 + 3x_3 - 2x_4 &= -11 \\ x_3 + 0x_4 &= -1 \\ x_4 &= 4 \end{aligned} \tag{14}$$

Solution. We form $[U : \bar{\mathbf{c}} : \bar{\mathbf{x}}]$ using (13) to get $\bar{\mathbf{x}}$ from $[U : \bar{\mathbf{c}} : \text{current } \bar{\mathbf{x}}]$ as follows:

$$\overbrace{\begin{bmatrix} 1 & 3 & 0 & -1 \\ & 1 & 3 & -2 \\ & & 1 & 0 \\ & & & 1 \end{bmatrix}}^{U} \begin{array}{c} : \\ : \\ : \\ : \end{array} \overbrace{\begin{matrix} -1 \\ -11 \\ -1 \\ 4 \end{matrix}}^{\bar{\mathbf{c}}} \begin{array}{c} : \\ : \\ : \\ : \end{array} \overbrace{\begin{matrix} 3 \\ 0 \\ -1 \\ 4 \end{matrix}}^{\bar{\mathbf{x}}}$$

Calculation of $\bar{x}_4, \bar{x}_3, \bar{x}_2$

$$\begin{cases} \bar{x}_2 = -11 - [3 \quad -2]\begin{bmatrix} -1 \\ 4 \end{bmatrix} = 0 \\ \bar{x}_3 = -1 - [0][4] = -1 \\ \bar{x}_4 = \bar{c}_4 = 4 \end{cases} \tag{15a}$$

The calculation of $\bar{x}_1$, using $\text{row}_1 [U : \bar{\mathbf{c}}]$ and $[\bar{x}_2 \quad \bar{x}_3 \quad \bar{x}_4]^T$, is

$$\bar{x}_1 = -1 - [3 \quad 0 \quad -1] \begin{bmatrix} 0 \\ -1 \\ 4 \end{bmatrix} = -1 - (0 + 0 - 4) = 3 \qquad \textbf{(15b)}$$

The reader should verify that $\bar{x} = [3 \quad 0 \quad -1 \quad 4]^T$ is indeed the (unique) solution of (14). When all u_{ii}'s are 1, we shall not circle them.

3.2F COUNTING ARITHMETIC OPERATIONS

One of the criteria for comparing numerical methods is the number of arithmetic operations required. This number is an indicator of the amount of time and energy needed and the likelihood of roundoff and human error in using the method by hand, and the run time (hence cost) when executing the method on a computer.

For linear systems, it is especially important to know how the required number of arithmetic operations grows as n (the number of variables) increases. If the system is triangular, then for $i = 1, 2, \ldots , n$ we need

$$i \text{ multiply/divides} \qquad \text{and} \qquad i-1 \text{ add/subtracts}$$

to get $\bar{c}_i$ by (9) or $\bar{x}_{n-i+1}$ by (12). Consequently, the total number of operations needed to solve a general $n \times n$ triangular system by Forward or Backward Substitution is

$$\sum_{i=1}^{n} (2i-1) = 2\sum_{i=1}^{n} i - \sum_{i=1}^{n} 1 = 2 \cdot \frac{n(n+1)}{2} - n = n^2 \qquad \textbf{(16)}$$

If all diagonal entries are 1 [as in (13)], then the n divisions by them are not necessary; hence only $n^2 - n$ operations are required. Since $n^2 - n \approx n^2$ for large n:

> The number of arithmetic operations needed to solve
> a triangular system grows like n^2 for large n.

Factorization Methods for Solving Ax $=$ b   3.3

Our approach to solving the general linear system Ax $=$ b is to "factor" the coefficient matrix A into a product of triangular matrices. This will reduce the problem to that of solving two triangular systems as follows.

3.3A SOLVING Ax $=$ b WHEN $A = LU$

Suppose that we can find a lower-triangular matrix L and an upper-triangular matrix U such that

$$A = LU, \qquad \text{where } l_{ii} \neq 0 \quad \text{and} \quad u_{ii} \neq 0 \quad \text{for } i = 1, \ldots , n \qquad \textbf{(1a)}$$

Then the linear system $Ax = \mathbf{b}$ can be solved in two simple steps:

Forward Substitution Form $[L : \mathbf{b} : \bar{\mathbf{c}}]$ to solve $L\mathbf{c} = \mathbf{b}$ for $\bar{\mathbf{c}} = L^{-1}\mathbf{b}$.

Backward Substitution Form $[U : \bar{\mathbf{c}} : \bar{\mathbf{x}}]$ to solve $U\mathbf{x} = \bar{\mathbf{c}}$ for $\bar{\mathbf{x}} = U^{-1}\bar{\mathbf{c}}$. **(1b)**

In view of the associative law M4 of Section 3.1F and I1 of Section 3.1G,

$$\bar{\mathbf{x}} = U^{-1}\bar{\mathbf{c}} = U^{-1}(L^{-1}\mathbf{b}) = (U^{-1}L^{-1})\mathbf{b} = (LU)^{-1}\mathbf{b} = A^{-1}\mathbf{b} \tag{2}$$

This shows that (1b) will indeed give the unique solution of $Ax = \mathbf{b}$ (i.e., $A^{-1}\mathbf{b}$), provided that we can find triangular factors L and U as in (1a) whose product is A.

EXAMPLE. The following factorization will be obtained in (13) of Section 3.3C.

$$A = \begin{bmatrix} -1 & 1 & -4 \\ 2 & 2 & 0 \\ 3 & 3 & 2 \end{bmatrix} = \begin{bmatrix} \boxed{-1} & & \\ 2 & \boxed{4} & \\ 3 & 6 & \boxed{2} \end{bmatrix} \begin{bmatrix} 1 & -1 & 4 \\ & 1 & -2 \\ & & 1 \end{bmatrix} = LU \tag{3}$$

Use it to solve the 3×3 linear system

$$\begin{array}{lrcl} (E_1) & -x_1 + x_2 - 4x_3 &=& 0 \\ (E_2) & 2x_1 + 2x_2 &=& 1 \\ (E_3) & 3x_1 + 3x_2 + 2x_3 &=& \tfrac{1}{2} \end{array} \qquad \left([A : \mathbf{b}] = \begin{bmatrix} -1 & 1 & -4 & : & 0 \\ 2 & 2 & 0 & : & 1 \\ 3 & 3 & 2 & : & \tfrac{1}{2} \end{bmatrix} \right) \tag{4}$$

Solution. Using (9) then (13) of Section 3.2 to form $[L : \mathbf{b} : \bar{\mathbf{c}}]$, then $[U : \bar{\mathbf{c}} : \bar{\mathbf{x}}]$, we get

$$\begin{bmatrix} \boxed{-1} & & & : & 0 & : & 0 \\ 2 & \boxed{4} & & : & 1 & : & \tfrac{1}{4} \\ 3 & 6 & \boxed{2} & : & \tfrac{1}{2} & : & -\tfrac{1}{2} \end{bmatrix} \quad \text{then} \quad \begin{bmatrix} 1 & -1 & 4 & : & 0 & : & \tfrac{5}{4} \\ & 1 & -2 & : & \tfrac{1}{4} & : & -\tfrac{3}{4} \\ & & 1 & : & -\tfrac{1}{2} & : & -\tfrac{1}{2} \end{bmatrix} \tag{5}$$

$$\underbrace{}_{L} \; \underbrace{}_{\mathbf{b}} \; \underbrace{}_{\bar{\mathbf{c}}} \qquad\qquad \underbrace{}_{U} \; \underbrace{}_{\bar{\mathbf{c}}} \; \underbrace{}_{\bar{\mathbf{x}}}$$

So $\bar{\mathbf{x}} = [\tfrac{5}{4} \quad -\tfrac{3}{4} \quad -\tfrac{1}{2}]^T$. The reader should verify that $A = LU$ and $A\bar{\mathbf{x}} = \mathbf{b}$.

3.3B COMPACT FORWARD AND BACKWARD SUBSTITUTION

The preceding example illustrates how easily (1b) yields $\bar{\mathbf{x}}$ once a factorization (1a) is known. It should be noted that *the representation of A as LU in* (1a) *is not unique.* For example,

$$A = \begin{bmatrix} 4 & 12 \\ 2 & 5 \end{bmatrix} = \begin{bmatrix} 2 & \\ 1 & 1 \end{bmatrix}\begin{bmatrix} 2 & 6 \\ & -1 \end{bmatrix} = \begin{bmatrix} 1 & \\ \tfrac{1}{2} & 1 \end{bmatrix}\begin{bmatrix} 4 & 12 \\ & -1 \end{bmatrix} = \begin{bmatrix} 4 & \\ 2 & -1 \end{bmatrix}\begin{bmatrix} 1 & 3 \\ & 1 \end{bmatrix}$$

In the special case when $A = LU$ and *the diagonal entries of U are all 1's* (such a U is called a **unit upper-triangular matrix**), the forward then backward substitution can be performed and recorded in a single augmented matrix $[L\backslash U : \mathbf{b} : \bar{\mathbf{c}} : \bar{\mathbf{x}}]$, which we shall refer to as a **forback matrix.** For the calculation in (5), this matrix is

$$[L\backslash U : \mathbf{b} : \bar{\mathbf{c}} : \bar{\mathbf{x}}] = \begin{bmatrix} \boxed{-1} & -1 & 4 & : & 0 & : & 0 & : & \frac{5}{4} \\ 2 & ④ & -2 & : & 1 & : & \frac{1}{4} & : & -\frac{3}{4} \\ 3 & 6 & ② & : & \frac{1}{2} & : & -\frac{1}{2} & : & -\frac{1}{2} \end{bmatrix} \tag{6}$$

$$\underbrace{}_{L\backslash U} \quad \underbrace{}_{\mathbf{b}} \quad \underbrace{}_{\bar{\mathbf{c}}} \quad \underbrace{}_{\bar{\mathbf{x}}}$$

Similarly, if A is the product of the L of Section 3.2D and the U of Section 3.2E, that is, if

$$A = \begin{bmatrix} 2 & 6 & 0 & -2 \\ -2 & -7 & -3 & 4 \\ -1 & -2 & 0 & -1 \\ 0 & 2 & 10 & 5 \end{bmatrix} = \begin{bmatrix} ② & & & \\ -2 & ① & & \\ -1 & 1 & ③ & \\ 0 & 2 & 4 & ⑨ \end{bmatrix} \begin{bmatrix} 1 & 3 & 0 & -1 \\ & 1 & 3 & -2 \\ & & 1 & 0 \\ & & & 1 \end{bmatrix} = LU \tag{7a}$$

then the steps of solving $A\mathbf{x} = \mathbf{b} = [-2 \quad 13 \quad -7 \quad 10]^T$ can be displayed compactly in the forback matrix

$$[L\backslash U : \mathbf{b} : \bar{\mathbf{c}} : \bar{\mathbf{x}}] = \begin{bmatrix} ② & 3 & 0 & -1 & : & -2 & : & -1 & : & 3 \\ -2 & ① & 3 & -2 & : & 13 & : & -11 & : & 0 \\ -1 & 1 & ③ & 0 & : & -7 & : & -1 & : & -1 \\ 0 & 2 & 4 & ⑨ & : & 10 & : & 4 & : & 4 \end{bmatrix} \tag{7b}$$

Notice that the circled diagonal entries of $L\backslash U$ are the diagonal entries of L. The 1's on the diagonal of U do not enter into the calculation of $\bar{\mathbf{x}}$ and so need not be displayed.

To form a forback matrix $[L\backslash U : \mathbf{b} : \bar{\mathbf{c}} : \bar{\mathbf{x}}]$ after having obtained the LU-factorization of A, we first use L and $\mathbf{b}$ [shaded in (7b)] to get $\bar{c}_1, \ldots, \bar{c}_n$ *down* the $\bar{\mathbf{c}}$ column [see (11) of Section 3.2D]. Then U and this $\bar{\mathbf{c}}$ are used to get $\bar{x}_n, \ldots, \bar{x}_1$ *up* the $\bar{\mathbf{x}}$ column [see (15) of Section 3.2E]. The problem is to find the entries of $L\backslash U$. We now show that this can be done easily using formulas similar to those used to get $\bar{\mathbf{c}}$ and $\bar{\mathbf{x}}$.

3.3C   THE LU-FACTORIZATION ALGORITHM

Given $A = (a_{ij})_{n \times n}$, we wish to find a lower-triangular matrix L having *nonzero diagonal entries* and a *unit* upper-triangular matrix U such that $LU = A$, that is

$$\begin{bmatrix} ⓛ_{11} & & & & \\ l_{21} & ⓛ_{22} & & & \\ l_{31} & l_{32} & ⓛ_{33} & & \\ \vdots & \vdots & \vdots & \ddots & \\ l_{n1} & l_{n2} & l_{n3} & \cdots & ⓛ_{nn} \end{bmatrix} \begin{bmatrix} 1 & u_{12} & u_{13} & \cdots & u_{1n} \\ & 1 & u_{23} & \cdots & u_{2n} \\ & & 1 & \cdots & u_{3n} \\ & & & \ddots & \vdots \\ & & & & 1 \end{bmatrix} = \begin{bmatrix} a_{11} & a_{12} & a_{13} & \cdots & a_{1n} \\ a_{21} & a_{22} & a_{23} & \cdots & a_{2n} \\ a_{31} & a_{32} & a_{33} & \cdots & a_{3n} \\ \vdots & \vdots & \vdots & & \vdots \\ a_{n1} & a_{n2} & a_{n3} & \cdots & a_{nn} \end{bmatrix} \tag{8}$$

Such a representation will be called the *LU*-**factorization** of A. The circled nonzero entry l_{ii} on the diagonal of L is the *i*th **pivot** of the factorization.

To find the $\frac{1}{2}n(n+1)$ unknown entries of L and the $\frac{1}{2}n(n-1)$ unknown entries of U efficiently, we shall *enter them as they are found* in the $n \times n$ matrix $L\backslash U$, where

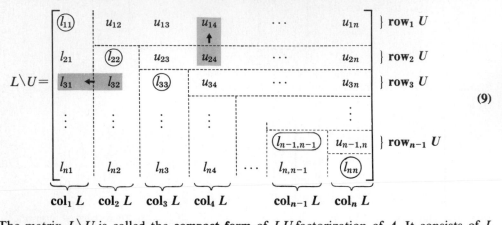

$$(9)$$

The matrix $L\backslash U$ is called the **compact form** of LU-factorization of A. It consists of L superimposed over U, with the (circled) pivots on the diagonal of L covering the (known) 1's on the diagonal of U. Given A, the entries of $L\backslash U$ can be formed quickly using the *LU*-**Factorization Algorithm** shown in Figure 3.3-1.

Algorithm: *LU*-Factorization

Purpose: To get a lower-triangular matrix L and a *unit* upper-triangular matrix U such that the product LU equals a given $n \times n$ matrix A. The unknown entries of L and U are stored in the $n \times n$ matrix $L\backslash U$.

GET n, A
DO FOR $m = 1$ TO n
  BEGIN
  {get col$_m$ L}
  DO FOR $i = m$ TO n {at and below the mmth entry of $L\backslash U$}

$$l_{im} \leftarrow a_{im} - [\leftarrow]_L[\uparrow]_U \tag{10a}$$

IF $l_{mm} = 0$ THEN STOP   {A has no LU-factorization.}
{get row$_m$ U if $m < n$}
DO FOR $j = m + 1$ TO n {to the right of the mmth entry of $L\backslash U$}

$$u_{mj} \leftarrow \frac{1}{l_{mm}} (a_{mj} - [\leftarrow]_L[\uparrow]_U) \tag{10b}$$

END

FIGURE 3.3-1   PSEUDOPROGRAM FOR THE *LU*-FACTORIZATION ALGORITHM.

The "look left in L" vector $[\leftarrow]_L$ and the "look up in U" vector $[\uparrow]_U$ whose inner product is needed to get l_{im} in (10a) and u_{mj} in (10b) are given by

$[\leftarrow]_L$ = the *leftmost $m - 1$ entries (of L)* in the *row* of the entry
    of $L \backslash U$ being calculated

$[\uparrow]_U$ = the *topmost $m - 1$ entries (of U)* in the *column* of the entry
    of $L \backslash U$ being calculated

This algorithm yields the entries of $L \backslash U$ in the order [see (9)]

$$\text{col}_1 L, \quad \text{row}_1 U, \quad \text{col}_2 L, \quad \text{row}_2 U, \quad \cdots \quad , \text{col}_{n-1} L, \quad \text{row}_{n-1} U, \quad \text{col}_n L \qquad \textbf{(11)}$$

using the entries of A and the previously obtained (and recorded) entries of $L \backslash U$. For example, the calculation of u_{34} requires the inner product of

$$[\leftarrow]_L = [l_{31} \quad l_{32}] \qquad \text{and} \qquad [\uparrow]_U = \begin{bmatrix} u_{14} \\ u_{24} \end{bmatrix}$$

These are shaded in (9). Specifically,

$$u_{34} = \frac{1}{l_{33}} \{ a_{34} - [\leftarrow]_L [\uparrow]_U \} = \frac{1}{l_{33}} \{ a_{34} - (l_{31} u_{14} + l_{32} u_{24}) \}$$

Notice that l_{33} is the (circled) pivot to the left of the U-entry being calculated in $L \backslash U$. Notice too that the entry of A required in (10a) or (10b) occupies the same position in A as the entry being calculated in $L \backslash U$.

When $m = 1$, we take $[\leftarrow]_L [\uparrow]_U = 0$. Consequently, $\text{col}_1 L$ and then $\text{row}_1 U$ can be obtained by inspection of A, that is, as

$$\boxed{\text{col}_1 L = \text{col}_1 A \qquad \text{and} \qquad \text{row}_1 U = \frac{1}{l_{11}} \text{row}_1 A = \begin{bmatrix} 1 & \dfrac{a_{12}}{a_{11}} & \cdots & \dfrac{a_{1n}}{a_{11}} \end{bmatrix}} \qquad \textbf{(12)}$$

The formulas (10) will be derived in Section 3.3H. For now we wish to show how the LU-Factorization Algorithm can be used to determine the entries of $L \backslash U$ for a given A. This is done for a 4×4 matrix A in Figure 3.3-2 [see (7a)].

In Figure 3.3-2, the "Resulting current $L \backslash U$" was redrawn for $m = 1, 2, 3$ (with the currently added entries shaded) to indicate the development of $L \backslash U$ in the order (11). *In practice all entries are simply added to the original $L \backslash U$.* For example, to show that

$$A = \begin{bmatrix} -1 & 1 & -4 \\ 2 & 2 & 0 \\ 3 & 3 & 2 \end{bmatrix} \Rightarrow L \backslash U = \begin{bmatrix} \enclose{circle}{-1} & -1 & 4 \\ 2 & \enclose{circle}{4} & -2 \\ 3 & 6 & \enclose{circle}{2} \end{bmatrix} \qquad \textbf{(13)}$$

$$A = \begin{bmatrix} 2 & 6 & 0 & -2 \\ -2 & -7 & -3 & 4 \\ -1 & -2 & 0 & -1 \\ 0 & 2 & 10 & 5 \end{bmatrix}$$

m	Calculations using (12) [for $m = 1$] and (10) [for $m > 1$]	Resulting current $L\backslash U$
1	**col$_1$ L:** col$_1$ $A = [\;②\;\;\;-2\;\;\;-1\;\;\;0\;]^T$ **row$_1$ U:** $\dfrac{1}{②}[2\;\;\;6\;\;\;0\;\;\;-2] = [1\;\;\;3\;\;\;0\;\;\;-1]$	$\begin{bmatrix} ② & 3 & 0 & -1 \\ -2 & & & \\ -1 & & & \\ 0 & & & \end{bmatrix}$
2	**col$_2$ L:** $l_{22} = a_{22} - [\leftarrow]_L[\uparrow]_U = -7 - [-2][3] = ⊝1$ $\qquad l_{32} = a_{32} - [\leftarrow]_L[\uparrow]_U = -2 - [-1][3] = \;\;1$ $\qquad l_{42} = a_{42} - [\leftarrow]_L[\uparrow]_U = \;\;2 - \;\;[0][3] = \;\;2$ **row$_2$ U:** $u_{23} = \dfrac{1}{l_{22}}\{a_{23} - [\leftarrow]_L[\uparrow]_U\} = \dfrac{1}{⊝1}\{-3 - [-2][0]\} = 3$ $\qquad u_{24} = \dfrac{1}{l_{22}}\{a_{24} - [\leftarrow]_L[\uparrow]_U\} = \dfrac{1}{⊝1}\{4 - [-2][-1]\} = -2$	$\begin{bmatrix} ② & 3 & 0 & -1 \\ -2 & ⊝1 & 3 & -2 \\ -1 & 1 & & \\ 0 & 2 & & \end{bmatrix}$
3	**col$_3$ L:** $l_{33} = 0 - [-1\;\;\;1]\begin{bmatrix}0\\3\end{bmatrix} = 0 - (0+3) = ⊝3$ $\qquad l_{43} = 10 - [0\;\;\;2]\begin{bmatrix}0\\3\end{bmatrix} = 10 - (0+6) = 4$ **row$_3$ U:** $u_{34} = \dfrac{1}{⊝3}\left\{-1 - [-1\;\;\;1]\begin{bmatrix}-1\\-2\end{bmatrix}\right\} = \dfrac{-1}{3}\{-1 - (1-2)\} = 0$	$\begin{bmatrix} ② & 3 & 0 & -1 \\ -2 & ⊝1 & 3 & -2 \\ -1 & 1 & ⊝3 & 0 \\ 0 & 2 & 4 & \end{bmatrix}$
4	**col$_4$ L:** $l_{44} = 5 - [0\;\;\;2\;\;\;4]\begin{bmatrix}-1\\-2\\0\end{bmatrix} = 5 - (0 - 4 + 0) = ⑨$	

FIGURE 3.3-2 **FINDING $L\backslash U$ FOR A 4×4 MATRIX (BASIC PIVOTING).**

we perform the following arithmetic calculations:

$$m = 1: \quad \text{col}_1 \, L = \begin{bmatrix} \boxed{-1} \\ 2 \\ 3 \end{bmatrix}, \qquad [u_{12} \quad u_{13}] = \frac{1}{\boxed{-1}} [1 \quad -4] = [-1 \quad 4] \qquad \text{[by (12)]}$$

$$m = 2: \quad l_{22} = 2 - [2][-1] = \boxed{4}, \qquad u_{23} = \frac{1}{\boxed{4}} \{0 - [2][4]\} = -2 \qquad \text{[by (10)]}$$

$$l_{32} = 3 - [3][-1] = 6$$

$$m = 3: \quad l_{33} = 2 - [3 \quad 6] \begin{bmatrix} 4 \\ -2 \end{bmatrix} = 2 - \{3 \cdot 4 + 6(-2)\} = \boxed{2} \qquad \text{[by (10)]}$$

The LU-factorization used in the example in Section 3.3A came from (13).

Note: After obtaining $L \backslash U$ by hand, you can (and should) check the factorization by verifying that the product LU equals A. For example,

$$L \backslash U = \begin{bmatrix} \boxed{4} & \vdots & 3 \\ 2 & \vdots & \boxed{-1} \end{bmatrix} \quad \Rightarrow \quad A = LU = \begin{bmatrix} 4 & 0 \\ 2 & -1 \end{bmatrix} \begin{bmatrix} 1 & 3 \\ 0 & 1 \end{bmatrix} = \begin{bmatrix} 4 & 12 \\ 2 & 5 \end{bmatrix}$$

3.3D AVOIDING $l_{mm} = 0$

Two linear systems $Ax = \mathbf{b}$ and $\hat{A}x = \hat{\mathbf{b}}$ are called **equivalent** if they have the same solution(s). Clearly, rearranging the order in which the equations (E_1), (E_2), . . . (E_n) are written yields an equivalent system. In particular, interchanging two equations (this is called **pivoting**) results in an equivalent system.

The ability to solve $Ax = \mathbf{b}$ rests on the ability to find an LU-factorization of A. This in turn can be done only if *all* pivots l_{mm} produced by the LU-Factorization Algorithm turn out to be *nonzero*. If $l_{mm} = 0$ occurs, it may be possible to interchange equations to form an *equivalent* system $\hat{A}x = \hat{\mathbf{b}}$ for which $\hat{A}$ has an LU-factorization $\hat{L}\hat{U} = \hat{A}$. One strategy for doing this is the following:†

The Basic Pivoting (BP) Strategy for Selecting the *m*th Pivot

If $l_{mm} \neq 0$, simply circle it.
If $l_{mm} = 0$, *circle the first nonzero entry below it,* then interchange the *m*th equation
with the one having the circled entry.
{The circled entry is now the *m*th pivot of the resulting equivalent system.}

---

† Basic Pivoting is also referred to as **trivial pivoting**.

EXAMPLE. Use Basic Pivoting to solve the following system.

$$
\begin{array}{ll}
(E_1) & 2x_1 - 2x_2 \qquad\quad + 4x_4 = 2 \\
(E_2) & 3x_1 - 3x_2 \qquad - x_4 = -18 \\
(E_3) & -x_1 + 6x_2 + 5x_3 - 7x_4 = -26 \\
(E_4) & -5x_1 + x_2 \qquad\quad - 6x_4 = 7
\end{array}
\qquad
\left(
[A : \mathbf{b}] =
\begin{bmatrix}
2 & -2 & 0 & 4 & : & 2 \\
3 & -3 & 0 & -1 & : & -18 \\
-1 & 6 & 5 & -7 & : & -26 \\
-5 & 1 & 0 & -6 & : & 7
\end{bmatrix}
\right)
$$

(14)

Solution. The **get col₁** L, **get row₁** U, and **get col₂** L steps yield

$$
L\backslash U =
\begin{bmatrix}
②\!\!\!\! & -1 & 0 & 2 \\
3 & 0 & & \\
-1 & 5 & & \\
-5 & -4 & &
\end{bmatrix}
\qquad
\begin{aligned}
l_{22} &= -3 - [3][-1] = 0 \\
l_{32} &= 6 - [-1][-1] \doteq 5 \\
l_{42} &= 1 - [-5][-1] = -4
\end{aligned}
$$

(15)

Since $l_{22} = 0$, it is impossible to get row₂ U. So A has no LU-factorization. However, the Basic Pivoting strategy instructs us to circle the 5 below l_{22} and interchange (E_2) and (E_3). The resulting equivalent system, which we will denote by $\tilde{A}\mathbf{x} = \tilde{\mathbf{b}}$, is

$$
\begin{array}{ll}
(\tilde{E}_1) & 2x_1 - 2x_2 \qquad\quad + 4x_4 = 2 \\
(\tilde{E}_2) & -x_1 + 6x_2 + 5x_3 - 7x_4 = -26 \\
(\tilde{E}_3) & 3x_1 - 3x_2 \qquad - x_4 = -18 \\
(\tilde{E}_4) & -5x_1 + x_2 \qquad\quad - 6x_4 = 7
\end{array}
\qquad
\left(
[\tilde{A} : \tilde{\mathbf{b}}] =
\begin{bmatrix}
2 & -2 & 0 & 4 & : & 2 \\
-1 & 6 & 5 & -7 & : & -26 \\
3 & -3 & 0 & -1 & : & -18 \\
-5 & 1 & 0 & -6 & : & 7
\end{bmatrix}
\right)
$$

(16)

The **get col₁** $\tilde{L}$, **get row₁** $\tilde{U}$, **get col₂** $\tilde{L}$, **get row₂** $\tilde{U}$, and **get col₃** $\tilde{L}$ steps yield

$$
\tilde{L}\backslash \tilde{U} =
\begin{bmatrix}
②\!\!\!\! & -1 & 0 & 2 \\
-1 & ⑤ & 1 & -1 \\
3 & 0 & 0 & \\
-5 & -4 & 4 &
\end{bmatrix}
\qquad
\begin{aligned}
\tilde{l}_{33} &= 0 - [3 \quad 0]\begin{bmatrix} 0 \\ 1 \end{bmatrix} = 0 - 0 = 0 \\
\tilde{l}_{43} &= 0 - [-5 \quad -4]\begin{bmatrix} 0 \\ 1 \end{bmatrix} = 0 + 4 = 4
\end{aligned}
$$

(17)

Since $\tilde{l}_{33} = 0$, $\tilde{A}$ also has no LU-factorization. This time the Basic Pivoting strategy instructs us to circle the 4 below $\tilde{l}_{33}$ and to interchange $(\tilde{E}_3)$ and $(\tilde{E}_4)$. The resulting equivalent system, which we denote by $\hat{A}\mathbf{x} = \hat{\mathbf{b}}$, is

$$
\begin{array}{ll}
(\hat{E}_1) & 2x_1 - 2x_2 \qquad\quad + 4x_4 = 2 \\
(\hat{E}_2) & -x_1 + 6x_2 + 5x_3 - 7x_4 = -26 \\
(\hat{E}_3) & -5x_1 + x_2 \qquad\quad - 6x_4 = 7 \\
(\hat{E}_4) & 3x_1 - 3x_2 \qquad - x_4 = -18
\end{array}
\qquad
\left(
[\hat{A} : \hat{\mathbf{b}}] =
\begin{bmatrix}
2 & -2 & 0 & 4 & : & 2 \\
-1 & 6 & 5 & -7 & : & -26 \\
-5 & 1 & 0 & -6 & : & 7 \\
3 & -3 & 0 & -1 & : & -18
\end{bmatrix}
\right)
$$

(18)

At last, $\hat{A}$ does have an LU-factorization. Its compact form is

$$
\hat{L}\backslash\hat{U} =
\begin{bmatrix}
② & -1 & 0 & 2 \\
1 & ⑤ & 1 & -1 \\
-5 & -4 & ④ & 0 \\
3 & 0 & 0 & ⑦
\end{bmatrix}
$$

$$
\hat{u}_{34} = \frac{1}{④}\left\{-6 - \begin{bmatrix}-5 & -4\end{bmatrix}\begin{bmatrix}2 \\ -1\end{bmatrix}\right\} = 0
$$

$$
\hat{l}_{44} = -1 - \begin{bmatrix}3 & 0 & 0\end{bmatrix}\begin{bmatrix}2 \\ -1 \\ 0\end{bmatrix} = ⑦ \tag{19}
$$

So we can solve $\hat{A}\mathbf{x} = \hat{\mathbf{b}}$ in (18) using the following forback matrix:

$$
[\hat{L}\backslash\hat{U} : \hat{\mathbf{b}} : \bar{\mathbf{c}} : \bar{\mathbf{x}}] =
\begin{bmatrix}
② & -1 & 0 & 2 & : & 2 & : & 1 & : & -5 \\
-1 & ⑤ & 1 & -1 & : & -26 & : & -5 & : & 0 \\
-5 & -4 & ④ & 0 & : & 7 & : & -2 & : & -2 \\
3 & 0 & 0 & ⑦ & : & -18 & : & 3 & : & 3
\end{bmatrix} \tag{20}
$$

The reader should verify that $\bar{\mathbf{x}} = \begin{bmatrix}-5 & 0 & -2 & 3\end{bmatrix}^T$, obtained as the solution of $\hat{A}\mathbf{x} = \hat{\mathbf{b}}$, is the solution of the original linear system $A\mathbf{x} = \mathbf{b}$ in (14).

Notice that interchanging rows 2 and 3 of $L\backslash U$ in (15) gave the correct entries of $\hat{L}\backslash\hat{U}$ in (17); and interchanging rows 3 and 4 of $\hat{L}\backslash\hat{U}$ in (17) gave the correct entries of $\hat{L}\backslash\hat{U}$ in (19). So, when pivoting, the previous work is not wasted.

3.3E   THE TRIANGULAR DECOMPOSITION ALGORITHM

If the coefficient matrix A of a given linear system $A\mathbf{x} = \mathbf{b}$ does not have an LU-factorization, then, as we just saw, pivoting can be used to get an equivalent linear system $\hat{A}\mathbf{x} = \hat{\mathbf{b}}$ that can be solved for the desired $\bar{\mathbf{x}}$ using forward and backward substitution. The **Triangular Decomposition Algorithm** described in Figure 3.3-3 summarizes our discussion so far and shows how to get $\hat{L}\backslash\hat{U}$ and $\bar{\mathbf{x}}$ systematically. Not only will this algorithm be our fundamental tool for solving $A\mathbf{x} = \mathbf{b}$, it will provide the primary means of finding A^{-1} and the determinant of A as well.

Figure 3.3-4 shows the detailed progression of the **factorization** step of the Triangular Decomposition Algorithm when applied with Basic Pivoting to the 4×4 linear system in (14) [cf. (14)–(19)]. Each phase after the first begins with a row interchange and ends with the **get col$_m$** $\hat{L}$ step preceding the next row interchange. Note that $\hat{A}$ and $\hat{L}\backslash\hat{U}$ denote the *current* A and $L\backslash U$. These will be just A and $L\backslash U$ until a row interchange is made.

3.3F   THE PARTIAL PIVOTING STRATEGY

A strategy for selecting a nonzero element to circle in the **pivot** step of the Triangular Decomposition Algorithm will be referred to as a **pivoting strategy.** When using exact arithmetic (i.e., fractions rather than rounded decimals), the Triangular Decomposition Algorithm will give the (unique) exact solution $\bar{\mathbf{x}} = A^{-1}\mathbf{b}$ no matter what pivoting strategy is used. In this case we may as well use the pivoting strategy generally requiring the fewest row interchanges, namely Basic Pivoting. With this strategy, $\hat{A}$ and $\hat{L}\backslash\hat{U}$ will be just A and $L\backslash U$ (as in Figure 3.3-2) unless $\hat{l}_{mm} = 0$ occurs.

Algorithm: Triangular Decomposition

Purpose: To solve a given nth order linear system $A\mathbf{x} = \mathbf{b}$ for $\bar{\mathbf{x}} = A^{-1}\mathbf{b}$ by first finding an LU-factorization $\hat{L}\hat{U}$ for the coefficient matrix of an *equivalent* system $\hat{A}\mathbf{x} = \hat{\mathbf{b}}$, and then solving $\hat{A}\mathbf{x} = \hat{\mathbf{b}}$ using forward and backward substitution to get $\bar{\mathbf{x}}$ as $\hat{A}^{-1}\hat{\mathbf{b}}$. The unknown entries of $\hat{L}$ and $\hat{U}$ are stored in an $n \times n$ matrix $\hat{L}\backslash\hat{U}$. It is assumed that the user has selected a pivoting strategy for the **pivot** steps.

GET n, A, $\mathbf{b}$

$\hat{A} \leftarrow A$ {$\hat{A} = (\hat{a}_{ij})$ will be A if no row interchanges are made.}

{*factorization:* Form $\hat{L}\backslash\hat{U}$ for the factorization $\hat{L}\hat{U} = \hat{A}$.}

DO FOR $m = 1$ TO n

  BEGIN

  {**get col$_m$ $\hat{L}$**} DO FOR $i = m$ TO n

$$\hat{l}_{im} \leftarrow \hat{a}_{im} - [\leftarrow]\hat{l}[\uparrow]\hat{u}$$

  IF col$_m$ $\hat{L}$ = **0** THEN STOP {A is singular.}

  {**pivot**} Use a pivoting strategy to select a nonzero $\hat{l}_{im}$ in col$_m$ $\hat{L}$.

  IF $i \neq m$ THEN interchange rows i and m of both $\hat{A}$ and $\hat{L}\backslash\hat{U}$.

  {The selected entry of col$_m$ $\hat{L}$ is now the (circled) mth pivot of $\hat{L}\backslash\hat{U}$.}

  {**get row$_m$ $\hat{U}$**} DO FOR $j = m + 1$ TO n

$$\hat{u}_{mj} \leftarrow \frac{1}{\hat{l}_{mm}}(\hat{a}_{mj} - [\leftarrow]\hat{l}[\uparrow]\hat{u})$$

  END

OUTPUT ($\hat{L}\backslash\hat{U}$, description of row interchanges used)

{*form* $\hat{\mathbf{b}}$} Get $\hat{\mathbf{b}}$ by performing on $\mathbf{b}$ the row interchanges used to get $\hat{A}$ from A.

{*forback*} Use forward then backward substitution to get $\bar{\mathbf{c}}$ then $\bar{\mathbf{x}}$ in the forback matrix $[\hat{L}\backslash\hat{U} : \hat{\mathbf{b}} : \bar{\mathbf{c}} : \bar{\mathbf{x}}]$. {Note: $\hat{\mathbf{b}}$ will *not* be $\mathbf{b}$ *unless* $\hat{A} = A$.}

OUTPUT (Calculated solution is: $\bar{\mathbf{x}} = [\bar{x}_1 \quad \bar{x}_2 \quad \cdots \quad \bar{x}_n]^T$)

FIGURE 3.3-3 PSEUDOCODE FOR THE TRIANGULAR DECOMPOSITION ALGORITHM.

In most realistic situations the calculation of $\bar{\mathbf{x}}$ will be performed using fixed precision (e.g., 7s) arithmetic. We shall see in Section 4.1A that in this case some pivoting strategies yield more accurate calculated $\bar{\mathbf{x}}$'s than others. The pivoting strategy generally recommended for fixed-precision arithmetic is the following:†

† Partial Pivoting is also referred to as the **Maximum Pivotal Element Strategy**. "Full Pivoting" is discussed in Section 4.4C.

	Phase I	Phase II	Phase III

$$A = \begin{bmatrix} 2 & -2 & 0 & 4 \\ 3 & -3 & 0 & -1 \\ -1 & 6 & 5 & -7 \\ -5 & 1 & 0 & -6 \end{bmatrix} \xrightarrow{m=2} \begin{bmatrix} 2 & -2 & 0 & 4 \\ -1 & 6 & 5 & -7 \\ 3 & -3 & 0 & -1 \\ -5 & 1 & 0 & -6 \end{bmatrix} \xrightarrow{m=3} \begin{bmatrix} 2 & -2 & 0 & 4 \\ -1 & 6 & 5 & -7 \\ -5 & 1 & 0 & -6 \\ 3 & -3 & 0 & -1 \end{bmatrix} = \hat{A}$$

$$L\backslash U = \begin{bmatrix} ② & -1 & 0 & 2 \\ 3 & 0 & & \\ -1 & ⑤ & & \\ -5 & -4 & & \end{bmatrix} \xrightarrow{m=2} \begin{bmatrix} ② & -1 & 0 & 2 \\ -1 & ⑤ & 1 & -1 \\ 3 & 0 & 0 & \\ -5 & -4 & ④ & \end{bmatrix} \xrightarrow{m=3} \begin{bmatrix} ② & -1 & 0 & 2 \\ -1 & ⑤ & 1 & -1 \\ -5 & -4 & ④ & 0 \\ 3 & 0 & 0 & ⑦ \end{bmatrix} = \hat{L}\backslash\hat{U}$$

Intermediate calculations [Using (12) for $m = 1$, then (10) for $m > 1$]

m	get $\text{col}_m\ \hat{L}$	pivot	get $\text{row}_m\ \hat{U}$
1	$\text{col}_1\ \hat{L} = \text{col}_1\ A = \begin{bmatrix} ② \\ 3 \\ -1 \\ -5 \end{bmatrix}$	No pivoting (Stay in phase I)	$[\hat{u}_{12}\ \ \hat{u}_{13}\ \ \hat{u}_{14}] = \dfrac{1}{②}[-2 \ \ 0 \ \ 4]$ $= [-1 \ \ 0 \ \ 2]$
2	$\hat{l}_{22} = -3 - [3][-1] = 0$ $\hat{l}_{32} = 6 - [-1][-1] = ⑤$ $\hat{l}_{42} = 1 - [-5][-1] = -4$	Interchange rows 2 and 3 (Enter phase II)	$\hat{u}_{23} = \dfrac{1}{⑤}\{5 - [-1][0]\} = 1$ $\hat{u}_{24} = \dfrac{1}{⑤}\{-7 - [-1][2]\} = -1$
3	$\hat{l}_{33} = 0 - [3\ \ 0]\begin{bmatrix}0\\1\end{bmatrix} = 0$ $\hat{l}_{43} = 0 - [-5\ \ -4]\begin{bmatrix}0\\1\end{bmatrix} = ④$	Interchange rows 3 and 4 (Enter phase III)	$\hat{u}_{34} = \dfrac{1}{④}\left\{-6 - [-5\ \ -4]\begin{bmatrix}2\\-1\end{bmatrix}\right\}$ $= \dfrac{1}{4}\{-6 - (-6)\} = 0$
4	$\hat{l}_{44} = -1 - [3\ \ 0\ \ 0]\begin{bmatrix}2\\-1\\0\end{bmatrix} = -1 - (6 - 0 + 0) = ⑦$		

FIGURE 3.3-4 THE FACTORIZATION STEP (BASIC PIVOTING).

The Partial Pivoting (PP) Strategy for Selecting the mth Pivot

Circle the element of largest magnitude of col_m (current $\hat{L}$). If necessary, make an interchange so that the circled entry becomes the current $\hat{l}_{mm}$.

EXAMPLE. Use the Triangular Decomposition Algorithm with Partial Pivoting to solve:

$$
\begin{array}{ll}
(E_1) & -x_1 + x_2 - 4x_3 = 0 \\
(E_2) & 2x_1 + 2x_2 = 1 \\
(E_3) & 3x_1 + 3x_2 + 2x_3 = \tfrac{1}{2}
\end{array}
\qquad
\left(
[A : \mathbf{b}] =
\begin{bmatrix}
-1 & 1 & -4 & : & 0 \\
2 & 2 & 0 & : & 1 \\
3 & 3 & 2 & : & \tfrac{1}{2}
\end{bmatrix}
\right)
\qquad (21)
$$

Note: We saw in the example in Section 3.3A that $\bar{\mathbf{x}} = [\tfrac{5}{4} \quad -\tfrac{3}{4} \quad -\tfrac{1}{2}]^T$.

Solution. The **factorization** step is carried out in Figure 3.3-5. The circled entries ③, ②, $\left(-\tfrac{4}{3}\right)$ are the entries of largest magnitude of $[-1 \quad 2 \quad 3]^T$, $[0 \quad 2]^T$, and $[-\tfrac{4}{3}]$ obtained in the **get col₁** $\hat{L}$, **get col₂** $\hat{L}$, and **get col₃** $\hat{L}$ steps, respectively. Moreover, upon interchanging first rows 1 and 3, then rows 2 and 3 (see the top line of Figure 3.3-4),

$$
\mathbf{b} =
\begin{bmatrix} 0 \\ 1 \\ \tfrac{1}{2} \end{bmatrix}
\quad \text{becomes} \quad
\begin{bmatrix} \tfrac{1}{2} \\ 1 \\ 0 \end{bmatrix};
\quad \text{then} \quad
\begin{bmatrix} \tfrac{1}{2} \\ 0 \\ 1 \end{bmatrix} = \hat{\mathbf{b}}
\qquad (22)
$$

This is the **get** $\hat{\mathbf{b}}$ step of the Triangular Decomposition Algorithm. All that remains is to solve $\hat{A}\mathbf{x} = \hat{\mathbf{b}}$ in the **forback** step:

$$
[\hat{L}\backslash\hat{U} : \hat{\mathbf{b}} : \bar{\mathbf{c}} : \bar{\mathbf{x}}] =
\begin{bmatrix}
③ & 1 & \tfrac{2}{3} & : & \tfrac{1}{2} & : & \tfrac{1}{6} & : & \tfrac{5}{4} \\
-1 & ② & -\tfrac{5}{3} & : & 0 & : & \tfrac{1}{12} & : & -\tfrac{3}{4} \\
2 & 0 & \left(-\tfrac{4}{3}\right) & : & 1 & : & -\tfrac{1}{2} & : & -\tfrac{1}{2}
\end{bmatrix}
\qquad (23)
$$

As expected, this $\bar{\mathbf{x}}$ obtained as $\hat{A}^{-1}\hat{\mathbf{b}}$ equals $\bar{\mathbf{x}} = A^{-1}\mathbf{b}$ obtained in Section 3.3A.

3.3G   TERMINOLOGY AND NOTATION

The $\hat{L}\backslash\hat{U}$ resulting from the **factorization** step of the Triangular Decomposition Algorithm, *together with the sequence of row interchanges used to get it,* will be referred to as an *LU*-**decomposition** of A. The interchange of rows m and i $(i > m)$ will be denoted by "$\rho_m \rightleftarrows \rho_i$" ($\rho$ is the Greek letter rho) and indicated in parentheses to the right of row$_m$ $\hat{L}\backslash\hat{U}$. For example, the *LU*-decompositions obtained using Basic Pivoting in Figure 3.3-4 and Partial Pivoting in Figure 3.3-5 are, respectively,

$$
\begin{bmatrix}
② & -1 & 0 & 2 \\
1 & ⑤ & 1 & -1 \\
-5 & -4 & ④ & 0 \\
3 & 0 & 0 & ⑦
\end{bmatrix}
\begin{array}{l} \\ (\rho_2 \rightleftarrows \rho_3) \\ (\rho_3 \rightleftarrows \rho_4) \\ {} \end{array}
\quad \text{and} \quad
\begin{bmatrix}
③ & 1 & \tfrac{2}{3} \\
-1 & ② & -\tfrac{5}{3} \\
2 & 0 & \left(-\tfrac{4}{3}\right)
\end{bmatrix}
\begin{array}{l} (\rho_1 \rightleftarrows \rho_3) \\ (\rho_2 \rightleftarrows \rho_3) \\ {} \end{array}
$$

The matrix $\hat{L}\backslash\hat{U}$ by itself is the compact form of the *LU*-factorization of $\hat{A}$ because $\hat{L}\hat{U} = \hat{A}$ and $\hat{U}$ is *unit* upper-triangular. If no row interchanges are used, we shall simply write $\hat{L}\backslash\hat{U} = L\backslash U$ to indicate that $\hat{A} = A$. This would apply, for example, in Figure 3.3-1.

To get A from an *LU*-decomposition, one must first get $\hat{A}$ as the product $\hat{L}\hat{U}$ and

	Phase I	Phase II	Phase III

$$A = \begin{bmatrix} -1 & 1 & -4 \\ 2 & 2 & 0 \\ 3 & 3 & 2 \end{bmatrix} \Biggr) \xrightarrow{m=1} \begin{bmatrix} 3 & 3 & 2 \\ 2 & 2 & 0 \\ -1 & 1 & -4 \end{bmatrix} \Biggl) \xrightarrow{m=2} \begin{bmatrix} 3 & 3 & 2 \\ -1 & 1 & -4 \\ 2 & 2 & 0 \end{bmatrix} = \hat{A}$$

$$L \backslash U = \begin{bmatrix} -1 & & \\ 2 & & \\ ③ & & \end{bmatrix} \Biggr) \xrightarrow{m=1} \begin{bmatrix} ③ & 1 & \frac{2}{3} \\ 2 & 0 & \\ -1 & ② & \end{bmatrix} \Biggl) \xrightarrow{m=2} \begin{bmatrix} ③ & 1 & \frac{2}{3} \\ -1 & ② & -\frac{5}{3} \\ 2 & 0 & ⓸\frac{4}{3} \end{bmatrix} = \hat{L} \backslash \hat{U}$$

Intermediate calculations (Partial Pivoting)

m	get col$_m$ $\hat{L}$	pivot	get row$_m$ $\hat{U}$
1	$\text{col}_1\, \hat{L} = \text{col}_1\, A = \begin{bmatrix} -1 \\ 2 \\ ③ \end{bmatrix}$	$\|3\| = \max\{\|-1\|,\|2\|,\|3\|\}$ Interchange rows 1 and 3 (Enter phase II)	$[\hat{u}_{12} \quad \hat{u}_{13}] = \frac{1}{③}[3 \quad 2]$ $= [1 \quad \frac{2}{3}]$
2	$\hat{l}_{22} = 2 - [2][1] = 0$ $\hat{l}_{32} = 1 - [-1][1] = ②$	$\|2\| = \max\{\|0\|,\|2\|\}$ Interchange rows 2 and 3 (Enter phase III)	$\hat{u}_{23} = \frac{1}{②}\{-4 - [-1][\frac{2}{3}]\}$ $= -\frac{5}{3}$
3	$\hat{l}_{33} = 0 - [2 \quad 0]\begin{bmatrix} \frac{2}{3} \\ -\frac{5}{3} \end{bmatrix} = ⓸\frac{4}{3}$		

FIGURE 3.3-5   THE FACTORIZATION STEP (PARTIAL PIVOTING).

then perform the sequence of row interchanges $\rho_m \rightleftarrows \rho_i$ *in reverse order* ($m = n - 1$, . . . , 2, 1) on $\hat{A}$ to get A (Exercise 3-18).

3.3H   COUNTING ARITHMETIC OPERATIONS

For $m = 2, \ldots , n$, it requires

$(m - 1)$ multiply/divides and $(m - 1)$ add/subtracts to get l_{im}, $i = m, \ldots , n$

as $a_{im} - [\leftarrow]_L[\uparrow]_U$. Similarly, for $m = 1, 2, \ldots , n - 1$, it requires

m multiply/divides and $(m - 1)$ add/subtracts to get u_{mj}, $j = m + 1, \ldots , n$

as $\{a_{mj} - [\leftarrow]_L[\uparrow]_U\}/l_{mm}$. So the total number of arithmetic operations needed to get $L \backslash U$ is

$$\sum_{m=2}^{n} (n - m + 1)(2m - 2) \text{ for } L \quad \text{and} \quad \sum_{m=1}^{n-1} (n - m)(2m - 1) \text{ for } U \quad \textbf{(24)}$$

Simplifying (Exercise 3-21) and referring to Section 3.2F gives Table 3.3-1.

TABLE 3.3-1 COUNT OF ARITHMETIC OPERATIONS NEEDED TO SOLVE $Ax = b$ BY THE TRIANGULAR DECOMPOSITION ALGORITHM.

	Number of Operations	For Large n
factorization step	$\frac{1}{6} n(n-1)(4n+1)$	$\approx \frac{2}{3} n^3$
forback step	$2n^2 - n$	$\approx 2n^2$
Total	$\frac{1}{6} n(4n^2 + 9n - 7)$	$\approx \frac{2}{3} n^3$

Thus, *for large n, the Triangular Decomposition Algorithm requires about $2n^3/3$ arithmetic operations, with most of the "number crunching" performed in the* **factorization** *step.*

3.3I DERIVATION OF THE *LU*-FACTORIZATION FORMULAS

Consider the matrix equation $LU = A$, that is,

$$\begin{bmatrix} l_{11} & & & \\ l_{21} & l_{22} & & \\ \vdots & \vdots & \ddots & \\ l_{n1} & l_{n2} & \cdots & l_{nn} \end{bmatrix} \begin{bmatrix} u_{11} & u_{12} & \cdots & u_{1n} \\ & u_{22} & \cdots & u_{2n} \\ & & \ddots & \vdots \\ & & & u_{nn} \end{bmatrix} = \begin{bmatrix} a_{11} & a_{12} & \cdots & a_{1n} \\ a_{21} & a_{22} & \cdots & a_{2n} \\ \vdots & \vdots & & \vdots \\ a_{n1} & a_{n2} & \cdots & a_{nn} \end{bmatrix} \quad (25)$$

$$\underbrace{l_{ij} = 0 \text{ for } j > i}_{} \qquad \underbrace{u_{ij} = 0 \text{ for } i > j}_{}$$

This represents n^2 scalar equations, which can be grouped as follows:

$m = 1$:　**col₁**:　$l_{i1}u_{11} = a_{i1}$,　　$i = 1, 2, \ldots, n$ 　　　(26a)

　　　　row₁:　$l_{11}u_{1j} = a_{1j}$,　　$j = 1, 2, \ldots, n$ 　　　(26b)

$2 \leqslant m \leqslant n$:　**colₘ**:　$(l_{i1}u_{1m} + \cdots + l_{i,m-1}u_{m-1,m}) + l_{im}u_{mm} = a_{im}$,

$$i = m, \ldots, n \quad (27a)$$

　　　　rowₘ:　$(l_{m1}u_{1j} + \cdots + l_{m,m-1}u_{m-1,j}) + l_{mm}u_{mj} = a_{mj}$,

$$j = m, \ldots, n \quad (27b)$$

The equation for the diagonal entry a_{mm} appears in both the **colₘ** and **rowₘ** equations [when $i = m$ in (26a) and (27a), and $j = m$ in (26b) and (27b)].

If we set $u_{ii} = 1$ for $i = 1, 2, \ldots, n$ and solve the **colₘ** equations for l_{im} ($m = 1, 2, \ldots, n;\ i = m, \ldots, n$) and the **rowₘ** equations for u_{mj} ($m = 1, 2, \ldots, n - 1;\ j = m + 1, \ldots, n$), we get

$$\text{col}_m\ L:\quad l_{im} = a_{im} - \sum_{k<m} l_{ik}u_{km} \tag{28a}$$

$$\text{row}_m\ U:\quad u_{mj} = \frac{1}{l_{mm}}\left\{a_{mj} - \sum_{k<m} l_{mk}u_{kj}\right\} \tag{28b}$$

These are precisely the LU-factorization formulas (10a) and (10b).

3.3J OTHER FACTORIZATIONS

The matrix equation (25) represents n^2 scalar equations in $2[\frac{1}{2}n(n+1)] = n^2 + n$ unknown l's and u's [see (8) of Section 3.2C]. Three ways of imposing n additional conditions are shown in Table 3.3-2. As the table shows, the LU-factorization that we have been using (i.e., with U unit upper triangular) is **Crout's method.** The compact form $L\backslash U$ for **Doolittle's method** (in which L a unit lower-triangular matrix) would have circled u_{ii}'s on the main diagonal. See Exercises 3-13–3-15.

TABLE 3.3-2   THREE FACTORIZATION METHODS.

Method	n Conditions	Formulas Obtained by Solving (26) and (27)
Crout	$u_{ii} = 1,\quad i = 1, \ldots, n$	The LU-factorization formulas (28)
Doolittle	$l_{ii} = 1,\quad i = 1, \ldots, n$	**row**$_m$ U: $u_{mj} = a_{mj} - [\leftarrow]_L[\uparrow]_U$, $\qquad\qquad j \geqslant m = 1, \ldots, n-1$ $\quad$ **col**$_m$ L: $l_{im} = \dfrac{1}{u_{mm}}\{a_{im} - [\leftarrow]_L[\uparrow]_U\}$, $\qquad\qquad i > m = 1, \ldots, n-1$
Choleski	$l_{ii} = u_{ii},\quad i = 1, \ldots, n$	**diag**$_m$: $l_{mm} = u_{mm} = \sqrt{a_{mm} - [\leftarrow]_L[\uparrow]_U}$, $\qquad\qquad m = 1, \ldots, n$ $\quad$ **rowcol**$_m$: $l_{im} = u_{mi} = \dfrac{1}{l_{mm}}\{a_{im} - [\leftarrow]_L[\uparrow]_U\}$, $\qquad\qquad i > m = 1, \ldots, n-1$

Choleski's method is used when A is a **symmetric** matrix, that is, when $a_{ij} = a_{ji}$ for $i \neq j$. In this case the formulas shown make $L\backslash U$ symmetric as well; that is, row$_m$ U is the transpose of col$_m$ L for $m = 1, 2, \ldots, n$. So the work required is about cut in half! The reader is warned, however, that negative numbers under the radical may occur in computing l_{mm} *unless* A happens to be *positive definite*. We shall return to these matters in Chapter 9. (See also Exercises 3-14 and 3-15.)

3.4 Solving Linear Systems Using Gaussian Elimination

In this section we discuss procedures for systematically eliminating variables from the equations of a given linear system $A\mathbf{x} = \mathbf{b}$ so as to produce systems that are equivalent to (i.e., have the same solutions as) $A\mathbf{x} = \mathbf{b}$ but are easier to solve. Direct methods incorporating such procedures are known as **elimination methods.**

3.4A THE ELEMENTARY OPERATIONS

Three **elementary operations** that produce an equivalent system when performed on the ith equation (E_i) of the $n \times n$ linear system

$$
\begin{array}{ll}
(E_1) & a_{11}x_1 + a_{12}x_2 + \cdots + a_{1n}x_n = b_1 \\
(E_2) & a_{21}x_1 + a_{22}x_2 + \cdots + a_{2n}x_n = b_2 \\
\quad \vdots & \qquad\qquad\qquad\qquad\quad \vdots \\
(E_n) & a_{n1}x_1 + a_{n2}x_2 + \cdots + a_{nn}x_n = b_n
\end{array}
\tag{1}
$$

are shown in Table 3.4-1. Also shown are the corresponding operations on ρ_i (read as "rho i"), the ith row of the augmented matrix $[A : \mathbf{b}]$. Notice that a SCALE by p_i *divides* by p_i. We call m_{ij} in "$\rho_i - m_{ij}\rho_j$" the ith **multiplier.**

TABLE 3.4-1 THE THREE ELEMENTARY OPERATIONS: INTERCHANGE, SCALE, AND SUBTRACT.

Elementary Operation on (E_i) *(where $j \neq i$ and $p \neq 0$)*	*Abbreviation*	*Abbreviation for Corresponding Operation on* $\rho_i = \text{row}_i[A : \mathbf{b}]$
INTERCHANGE it with (E_j)	(E_i) $\rightleftarrows$ (E_j)	$\rho_i \rightleftarrows \rho_j$
SCALE (i.e., divide it) by p_i	$\dfrac{1}{p_i}$ (E_i)	$\dfrac{1}{p_i}\rho_i$
SUBTRACT a multiple of (E_j)	(E_i) $- m_{ij}$(E_j)	$\rho_i - m_{ij}\rho_j$

The SUBTRACT operation can be used to eliminate the variable x_j from (E_i) for $i > j$. Doing this for $j = 1, 2, \ldots, n - 1$ (one column at a time) yields an equivalent *upper-triangular* system, which can then be solved easily by Backward Substitution. If necessary or desired, pivoting (i.e., INTERCHANGE operations) can be used to move a nonzero entry below the diagonal into the jth pivot position, and SCALE operations can be used to simplify certain entries.

EXAMPLE. Find several upper-triangular systems that are equivalent to

$$
\begin{array}{ll}
(E_1) & -x_1 + x_2 - 4x_3 = 0 \\
(E_2) & 2x_1 + 2x_2 = 1 \\
(E_3) & 3x_1 + 3x_2 + 2x_3 = \tfrac{1}{2}
\end{array}
\qquad
\left([A : b] = \begin{bmatrix} -1 & 1 & -4 & : & 0 \\ 2 & 2 & 0 & : & 1 \\ 3 & 3 & 2 & : & \tfrac{1}{2} \end{bmatrix}\right)
\tag{2}
$$

Note: We saw in the example in Section 3.3F that $\bar{x} = [\tfrac{5}{4} \quad -\tfrac{3}{4} \quad -\tfrac{1}{2}]^T$.

Solution 1 (Basic Pivoting). To make it easier to eliminate x_1 from (E_2) and (E_3), we first SCALE (E_1) by -1 (the coefficient of x_1).

$$(E_1)_1 \quad x_1 - x_2 + 4x_3 = 0 \qquad [(E_1)_1 \text{ is } \tfrac{1}{-1}(E_1): \text{SCALE}, p_1 = -1]$$

$$(E_2)_1 \qquad\quad 4x_2 - 8x_3 = 1 \qquad [(E_2) - 2(E_1)_1: \text{SUBTRACT}, m_{21} = 2]$$

$$(E_3)_1 \qquad\quad 6x_2 - 10x_3 = \tfrac{1}{2} \qquad [(E_3) - 3(E_1)_1: \text{SUBTRACT}, m_{31} = 3]$$

To eliminate x_2 from $(E_3)_1$, we first SCALE $(E_2)_1$ by 4 (the coefficient of x_2).

$$(E_1)_1 \quad x_1 - x_2 + 4x_3 = 0 \qquad [\text{No change}]$$

$$(E_2)_2 \qquad\quad x_2 - 2x_3 = \tfrac{1}{4} \qquad [(E_2)_2 \text{ is } \tfrac{1}{4}(E_2)_1: \text{SCALE}, p_2 = 4]$$

$$(E_3)_2 \qquad\qquad\quad 2x_3 = -1 \qquad [(E_3)_2 \text{ is } (E_3)_1 - 6(E_2)_2: \text{SUBTRACT}, m_{32} = 6]$$

This upper-triangular system was obtained from (2) using only elementary operations. It is therefore equivalent to (2). An equivalent *unit* upper-triangular system, $Ux = \bar{c}$, is obtained by replacing $(E_3)_2$ by

$$(E_3)_3 \quad x_3 = -\tfrac{1}{2} \qquad [(E_3)_3 \text{ is } \tfrac{1}{2}(E_3)_2: \text{SCALE}, p_3 = 2]$$

The elementary operations just performed can be displayed efficiently using augmented matrices as follows:

$$
[A : b] \begin{array}{c} \tfrac{1}{-1}\rho_1 \\ \xrightarrow{\rho_2 - 2\rho_1} \\ \rho_3 - 3\rho_1 \end{array}
\underbrace{\begin{bmatrix} 1 & -1 & 4 & : & 0 \\ 4 & -8 & : & 1 \\ 6 & -10 & : & \tfrac{1}{2} \end{bmatrix}}_{\text{column 1 reduced}}
\begin{array}{c} \tfrac{1}{4}\rho_2 \\ \xrightarrow{} \\ \rho_3 - 6\rho_2 \end{array}
\underbrace{\begin{bmatrix} 1 & -1 & 4 & : & 0 \\ & 1 & -2 & : & \tfrac{1}{4} \\ & & 2 & : & -1 \end{bmatrix}}_{\text{column 2 reduced}}
$$

$$
\xrightarrow[\tfrac{1}{2}\rho_3]{}
\begin{bmatrix} 1 & -1 & 4 & : & 0 \\ & 1 & -2 & : & \tfrac{1}{4} \\ & & 1 & : & -\tfrac{1}{2} \end{bmatrix} = [U : \bar{c}]
\tag{3a}
$$

Note: In the SUBTRACTs $\rho_i - m_{ij}\rho_j$, ρ_j denotes the SCALEd ρ_j.

Solution 2 (Partial Pivoting). Since $a_{31} = 3$ has the largest magnitude of the x_1 coefficients in (2), we first INTERCHANGE (E_1) and (E_3) to get

$$
\left.\begin{array}{ll}
(\tilde{E}_1) & 3x_1 + 3x_2 + 2x_3 = \tfrac{1}{2} \\
(\tilde{E}_2) & 2x_1 + 2x_2 = 1 \\
(\tilde{E}_3) & -x_1 + x_2 - 4x_3 = 0
\end{array}\right\} \text{After } (E_1) \rightleftarrows (E_3)
$$

Proceeding as in Solution 1 to eliminate x_1 from $(\tilde{E}_2)$ and $(\tilde{E}_3)$, we get

$(\tilde{E}_1)_1$ $\quad x_1 + x_2 + \frac{2}{3}x_3 = \frac{1}{6}$ $\qquad [(\tilde{E}_1)_1$ is $\frac{1}{3}(\tilde{E}_1)$: SCALE, $p_1 = 3]$

$(\tilde{E}_2)_1$ $\qquad\qquad\quad -\frac{4}{3}x_3 = \frac{2}{3}$ $\qquad [(\tilde{E}_2)_1$ is $(\tilde{E}_2) - 2(\tilde{E}_1)_1$: SUBTRACT, $m_{21} = 2]$

$(\tilde{E}_3)_1$ $\qquad\quad 2x_2 - \frac{10}{3}x_3 = \frac{1}{6}$ $\qquad [(\tilde{E}_3)_1$ is $(\tilde{E}_3) - (-1)(\tilde{E}_1)_1$: SUBTRACT, $m_{31} = -1]$

To eliminate x_2 from $(\tilde{E}_3)_1$, we must INTERCHANGE $(\tilde{E}_2)_1$ and $(\tilde{E}_3)_1$. The result is

$(\hat{E}_1)_1$ $\quad x_1 + \quad x_2 + \frac{2}{3}x_3 = \frac{1}{6}$ $\qquad$ [No change: $(\hat{E}_1)_1$ is $(\tilde{E}_1)_1]$

$(\hat{E}_2)_1$ $\qquad\quad 2x_2 - \frac{10}{3}x_3 = \frac{1}{6}$ $\qquad [(\hat{E}_2)_1$ is $(\tilde{E}_3)_1]$

$(\hat{E}_3)_1$ $\qquad\qquad\quad -\frac{4}{3}x_3 = \frac{2}{3}$ $\qquad [(\hat{E}_3)_1$ is $(\tilde{E}_2)_1$: $m_{32} = 0]$

This upper-triangular system is equivalent to (2). An equivalent *unit* upper-triangular system, $\hat{U}\mathbf{x} = \bar{\mathbf{c}}$, is obtained by SCALING $(\hat{E}_2)_1$ and $(\hat{E}_3)_1$:

$(\hat{E}_2)_2$ $\quad x_2 - \frac{5}{3}x_3 = \frac{1}{12}$ $\qquad [(\hat{E}_2)_2$ is $\frac{1}{2}(\hat{E}_2)_1$: SCALE, $p_2 = 2]$

$(\hat{E}_3)_2$ $\qquad\qquad x_3 = -\frac{1}{2}$ $\qquad [(\hat{E}_3)_2$ is $-\frac{3}{4}(\hat{E}_3)_1$: SCALE, $p_3 = -\frac{4}{3}]$

In terms of augmented matrices, the elementary operations used were

$$[A : \mathbf{b}] \xrightarrow{p_1 \rightleftarrows p_3} \begin{bmatrix} 3 & 3 & 2 & : & \frac{1}{2} \\ 2 & 2 & 0 & : & 1 \\ -1 & 1 & -4 & : & 0 \end{bmatrix} \xrightarrow[p_2 - 2p_1]{\frac{1}{3}p_1} \xrightarrow{p_3 - (-1)p_1} \begin{bmatrix} 1 & 1 & \frac{2}{3} & : & \frac{1}{6} \\ 0 & -\frac{4}{3} & : & \frac{2}{3} \\ 2 & \frac{10}{3} & : & \frac{1}{6} \end{bmatrix}$$

$$\underbrace{}_{\text{column 1 reduced}}$$

$$\xrightarrow[-\frac{3}{4}p_3]{\overset{p_2 \rightleftarrows p_3}{\frac{1}{2}p_2}} \begin{bmatrix} 1 & 1 & \frac{2}{3} & : & \frac{1}{6} \\ & 1 & -\frac{5}{3} & : & \frac{1}{12} \\ & & 1 & : & -\frac{1}{2} \end{bmatrix} = [\hat{U} : \bar{\mathbf{c}}] \tag{3b}$$

The SCALE $(1/a_{jj})$ (E_j) causes the coefficient of x_j in (E_j) to become 1; it will therefore be referred to as a **1-SCALE**. Although equivalent upper-triangular systems can be obtained without them, 1-SCALEs make the "zeroing" SUBTRACTs a bit simpler for hand computation [because m_{ij} is simply the coefficient of x_j in (E_i)]. Also, their use results in a *unit* upper-triangular system, as we just saw.

3.4B   GAUSSIAN ELIMINATION

The use of elementary operations to convert $[A : \mathbf{b}]$ to the augmented matrix of an equivalent upper-triangular system $\hat{U}\mathbf{x} = \bar{\mathbf{c}}$ will be written as

$$[A : \mathbf{b}] \rightarrow [\hat{U} : \bar{\mathbf{c}}] \tag{4}$$

and referred to as **reducing** $[A : \mathbf{b}]$ **to upper-triangular form** or simply **upper-triangulating** $[A : \mathbf{b}]$. Since $\hat{U}\mathbf{x} = \bar{\mathbf{c}}$ is equivalent to the given system $A\mathbf{x} = \mathbf{b}$, its solution, obtained easily by backward substitution, is the desired solution $\bar{\mathbf{x}} = A^{-1}\mathbf{b}$. Pseudocode for this strategy, known as **Gaussian Elimination,** is given in Figure 3.4-1. Note that, as we just saw, the **upper triangulation** step yields a *unit* $\hat{U}$ if the **1-SCALE** steps are used.

Algorithm: Gaussian Elimination

Purpose: To solve the nth order linear system $A\mathbf{x} = \mathbf{b}$ for $\bar{\mathbf{x}} = A^{-1}\mathbf{b}$ by first reducing $[A : \mathbf{b}]$ to the upper-triangular form $[\hat{U} : \bar{\mathbf{c}}]$ and then solving $\hat{U}\mathbf{x} = \bar{\mathbf{c}}$ by Backward Substitution; ρ_j refers to the jth row of the current $[A : \mathbf{b}]$. It is assumed that a pivoting strategy has been selected for the **pivot** steps.

GET n, $[A : \mathbf{b}]$

{*upper triangulation:* Reduce $[A : \mathbf{b}] \rightarrow [\hat{U} : \bar{\mathbf{c}}]$, one column at a time.}
DO FOR $j = 1$ TO n {Reduce the jth column.}
  BEGIN
  IF $a_{jj}, a_{j+1,j}, \ldots, a_{nj}$ are all 0 THEN STOP   {A is singular.}
  {**pivot**}
  Select a nonzero a_{ij} where $i \geqslant j$ {a_{ij} is at or below a_{jj}}
  IF $i > j$ THEN interchange rows i and j of the current $[A : \mathbf{b}]$.
  $p_j \leftarrow a_{jj}$ {p_j, the jth pivot, is now a_{jj}}
  {**1-SCALE** (optional)}
  IF desired THEN {scale row_j(current $[A : \mathbf{b}]$) by p_j}
    BEGIN
    DO FOR $k = j$ TO n
      $a_{jk} \leftarrow a_{jk}/p_j$ {This makes $a_{jj} = 1$.}
    $b_j \leftarrow b_j/p_j$
    END
  {**zero column** j: Get zeros below a_{jj} if $j < n$}
  DO FOR $i = j + 1$ TO n {SUBTRACT: $\rho_i - m_{ij}\rho_j$.}
    BEGIN
    $m_{ij} \leftarrow a_{ij}/a_{jj}$; $a_{ij} \leftarrow 0$ {m_{ij} is the ijth multiplier.}
    DO FOR $k = j + 1$ TO n
      $a_{ik} \leftarrow a_{ik} - m_{ij}\,a_{jk}$
    $b_i \leftarrow b_i - m_{ij}\,b_j$
    END
  END
  {The current $[A : \mathbf{b}]$ is now $[\hat{U} : \bar{\mathbf{c}}]$ where $\hat{U}$ is upper-triangular.}

{*backward substitution*} Solve $\hat{U}\mathbf{x} = \bar{\mathbf{c}}$ for $\bar{\mathbf{x}} = \hat{U}^{-1}\bar{\mathbf{c}}$ {form $[\hat{U} : \bar{\mathbf{c}} : \bar{\mathbf{x}}]$}

OUTPUT (Calculated solution is $\bar{\mathbf{x}} = [\bar{x}_1 \;\; \cdots \;\; \bar{x}_n]^T$)

FIGURE **3.4-1** PSEUDOCODE FOR THE GAUSSIAN ELIMINATION ALGORITHM.

3.4C COMPARING GAUSSIAN ELIMINATION TO TRIANGULAR DECOMPOSITION

The square brackets to the right of the equations (E_i), $(\tilde{E}_i)$, and $(\hat{E}_i)$ of the example in Section 3.4A describe the pivots p_j and multipliers m_{ij} used to reduce $[A : \mathbf{b}]$ to the unit upper-triangular forms

$$
[U : \bar{\mathbf{c}}] = \begin{bmatrix} 1 & -1 & 4 & : & 0 \\ & 1 & -2 & : & \frac{1}{4} \\ & & 1 & : & -\frac{1}{2} \end{bmatrix}
\quad \text{and} \quad
[\hat{U} : \bar{\mathbf{c}}] = \begin{bmatrix} 1 & 1 & \frac{2}{3} & : & \frac{1}{6} \\ & 1 & -\frac{5}{3} & : & \frac{1}{12} \\ & & 1 & : & -\frac{1}{2} \end{bmatrix} \quad (5)
$$

in Solutions 1 and 2. Notice that they are precisely the upper-triangular forms obtained in (5) of Section 3.3A and (23) of Section 3.3F, respectively! Further comparison with the examples in Sections 3.3A and 3.3F reveals that

For Solution 1:
$$
\begin{bmatrix} p_1 & & \\ m_{21} & p_2 & \\ m_{31} & m_{32} & p_3 \end{bmatrix} = \begin{bmatrix} \boxed{-1} & & \\ 2 & \boxed{4} & \\ 3 & 6 & \boxed{2} \end{bmatrix} = L \text{ in (5) of Section 3.3A}
$$

For Solution 2:
$$
\begin{bmatrix} p_1 & & \\ m_{21} & p_2 & \\ m_{31} & m_{32} & p_3 \end{bmatrix} = \begin{bmatrix} \boxed{3} & & \\ -1 & \boxed{2} & \\ 2 & 0 & \boxed{-\frac{4}{3}} \end{bmatrix} = \hat{L} \text{ in (23) of Section 3.3F}
$$

This is no accident. Indeed, the following can be proved [38]:

Theorem: *If the* **upper triangulation** *step of the Gaussian Elimination Algorithm is performed with* 1-SCALES *and the same pivoting strategy as the* **factorization** *step of the Triangular Decomposition Algorithm of Figure 3.3-3, then*

1. *The pivots and multipliers of the* **upper triangulation** *satisfy*

$$
\begin{bmatrix} \boxed{p_1} & & & & \\ m_{21} & \boxed{p_2} & & & \\ m_{31} & m_{32} & \boxed{p_3} & & \\ \vdots & \vdots & \vdots & \ddots & \\ m_{n1} & m_{n2} & m_{n3} & \cdots & \boxed{p_n} \end{bmatrix} = \begin{bmatrix} \boxed{\hat{l}_{11}} & & & & \\ \hat{l}_{21} & \boxed{\hat{l}_{22}} & & & \\ \hat{l}_{31} & \hat{l}_{32} & \boxed{\hat{l}_{33}} & & \\ \vdots & \vdots & \vdots & \ddots & \\ \hat{l}_{n1} & \hat{l}_{n2} & \hat{l}_{n3} & \cdots & \boxed{\hat{l}_{nn}} \end{bmatrix} = \hat{L} \quad (6)
$$

where $\hat{L}$ is the lower-triangular factor obtained in the **factorization.**

2. *The $\hat{U}$ and $\bar{\mathbf{c}}$ resulting from the* **upper triangulation** *are identical to those which are used to obtain $\bar{\mathbf{x}}$ in the* **forback** *step of the Triangular Decomposition Algorithm.*

In view of (6), the "pivots" of either algorithm are the numbers $p_m = \hat{l}_{mm},\ m = 1,$ ..., n. Moreover, this theorem tells us how to get the compact form of the LU-factorization of $\hat{A}$ from the steps of the reduction $A \rightarrow \hat{U}$:

$$
\hat{L} \backslash \hat{U} = \begin{bmatrix}
\boxed{p_1} & \hat{u}_{12} & \hat{u}_{13} & \cdots & \hat{u}_{1n} \\
m_{21} & \boxed{p_2} & \hat{u}_{23} & \cdots & \hat{u}_{2n} \\
m_{31} & m_{32} & \boxed{p_3} & \cdots & \hat{u}_{3n} \\
\vdots & \vdots & \vdots & & \vdots \\
m_{n1} & m_{n2} & m_{n3} & \cdots & \boxed{p_n}
\end{bmatrix} \qquad (7)
$$

Similarly, if the optional **1-SCALE** steps of the **upper triangulation** are *never* performed, then the pivots and multipliers in (7) will give the compact form of a factorization with $\hat{l}_{11} = \cdots = \hat{l}_{nn} = 1$ (see Doolittle's method of Section 3.3J).

If exact arithmetic is used then Gaussian elimination will get the exact solution $\overline{\mathbf{x}} = A^{-1}\mathbf{b}$ regardless of the options taken in the **pivot** and **1-SCALE** steps of the **upper triangulation**. However, when using fixed-precision arithmetic, 1-SCALEs may introduce needless roundoff error, hence should not be used. A straightforward count shows that if 1-SCALEs are not used:

> *The number of arithmetic operations needed to solve A**x** =*
> **b** *by Gaussian elimination is identical to that needed to solve*
> *it by the Triangular Decomposition Algorithm; and if the*
> *same pivoting strategy is used, both methods will compute*
> $\overline{\mathbf{x}}$ *with the same accuracy.*

So, there is no reason to expect either method to work any "better" than the other. In terms of ease and efficiency of implementation, however, the methods are not equally desirable.

HAND COMPUTATION. For most readers, Gaussian elimination probably has the advantage of being more familiar. However, once the mechanics of using $[\leftarrow]_L$ and $[\uparrow]_U$ to get $\hat{l}_{im}$ and $\hat{u}_{mj}$ (by inspection of the current $\hat{L} \backslash \hat{U}$ and $\hat{A}$) have been mastered, the **factorization** step of the Triangular Decomposition Algorithm can be performed (and corrected if necessary) more quickly and with less chance of human error than the **upper triangulation** step of the Gaussian Elimination Algorithm.

With either method one can perform the intermediate check that $\hat{A} = \hat{L}\hat{U}$. However, this check is immediate from $\hat{L} \backslash \hat{U}$, whereas (7) must be used to get it from the reduction $[A : \mathbf{b}] \to [\hat{U} : \overline{\mathbf{c}}]$. Also, since the Forward Substitution is "built into" this reduction, mistakes can be detected sooner when using the Triangular Decomposition Algorithm.

In short, factorization methods are generally better suited to hand computation than elimination methods. In fact, factorization methods were developed as "compact schemes" for hand solution of $A\mathbf{x} = \mathbf{b}$ long before computers were even dreamed of!

COMPUTER OR PROGRAMMABLE CALCULATOR CALCULATION. A program for the Triangular Decomposition Algorithm requires a bit more code (the Forward Substitution part of the **forback** step) than one for Gaussian elimination with the same pivoting strategy.

When using either Triangular Decomposition or Gaussian elimination, the entries of $\hat{L}$ (i.e., the pivots and multipliers) and $\hat{U}$ can be written over the original A matrix. This can be important for devices having limited internal storage.

If extended precision is available, a strategy called **partial extended precision** can be used to improve the accuracy of Triangular Decomposition in a very efficient way, which is not possible for Gaussian elimination (see Section 4.1C).

Although generally preferable for *computational* purposes, factorization methods mask many important *theoretical* considerations that are easily illuminated by elimination methods. It is therefore important for the reader to be familiar with both factorization and elimination methods.

3.4D TRIDIAGONAL SYSTEMS

A square matrix $A_{n \times n}$ is called a **band matrix** if there exist positive integers $p < n$ and $q < n$ such that

$$a_{ij} = 0 \quad \text{for } j > i + p \quad \text{or} \quad i > j + q \tag{8}$$

The number $p + q - 1$ is the **bandwidth** of the matrix. For example,

$$\begin{bmatrix} 1 & 1 & & & & \\ 2 & 2 & 0 & & & \\ 3 & 8 & 8 & 3 & & \\ & 0 & 4 & 4 & 0 & \\ & & 5 & 0 & 3 & 2 \\ & & & 1 & 6 & 0 \end{bmatrix} \qquad \text{(Entries not shown are zero.)}$$

is banded with $p = 2$ and $q = 3$; hence bandwidth $= 4$.

Of special importance are band matrices for which $p = q = 2$, that is, all nonzero entries lie either on or directly above or below the main diagonal. Such matrices are called **tridiagonal** and will be denoted by

$$T = \text{trid}(\mathbf{a}, \mathbf{b}, \mathbf{c}) = \begin{bmatrix} b_1 & c_1 & & & & \\ a_2 & b_2 & c_2 & & & \\ & a_3 & b_3 & c_3 \cdots & & \\ & & & a_{n-1} & b_{n-1} & c_{n-1} \\ & & & & a_n & b_n \end{bmatrix} \tag{9a}$$

where a_1 and c_n (not shown) can be left undefined. The vectors

$$\mathbf{a} = [a_1 \quad a_2 \quad \cdots \quad a_n], \qquad \mathbf{b} = [b_1 \quad b_2 \quad \cdots \quad b_n], \text{ and} \qquad \mathbf{c} = [c_1 \quad c_2 \quad \cdots \quad c_n] \tag{9b}$$

contain, respectively, the subdiagonal, diagonal, and superdiagonal entries of T. A **tridiagonal system** is a linear system whose matrix form is

$$T\mathbf{x} = \mathbf{d}, \qquad \text{where } \mathbf{d} = [d_1 \quad d_2 \quad \cdots \quad d_n]^T \text{ and } T \text{ is tridiagonal} \tag{10}$$

For such systems, Gaussian elimination is particularly simple (Figure 3.4-2).

EXAMPLE. Solve the following tridiagonal system without 1-SCALEs.

$$
\begin{aligned}
5x_1 - 3x_2 &= 7 \\
x_1 + 4x_2 - 2x_3 &= 6 \\
-x_2 + 3x_3 + x_4 &= -4 \\
2x_3 + 5x_4 &= -15
\end{aligned}
\qquad
\left(
[T : \mathbf{d}] =
\begin{bmatrix}
5 & -3 & & : & 7 \\
1 & 4 & -2 & : & 6 \\
 & -1 & 3 & 1 & : & -4 \\
 & & 2 & 5 & : & -15
\end{bmatrix}
\right)
\qquad (11)
$$

Solution

Upper triangulation   **Backward substitution**

$$
[T : \mathbf{d}] \xrightarrow[\substack{\rho_3 - (-1/\frac{23}{5})\rho_2 \\ \rho_4 - (2/\frac{59}{23})\rho_3}]{\rho_2 - (1/5)\rho_1}
\begin{bmatrix}
5 & -3 & & : & 7 \\
 & \frac{23}{5} & -2 & : & \frac{23}{5} \\
 & & \frac{59}{23} & 1 & : & -3 \\
 & & & \frac{249}{59} & : & \frac{747}{59}
\end{bmatrix}
$$

$$
\begin{aligned}
\bar{x}_1 &= \tfrac{1}{5}\{7 - (-3)(1)\} = 2 \\
\bar{x}_2 &= \tfrac{5}{23}\{\tfrac{23}{5} - (-2)(0)\} = 1 \\
\bar{x}_3 &= \tfrac{23}{59}\{-3 - (1)(-3)\} = 0 \\
\bar{x}_4 &= -\tfrac{747}{249}
\end{aligned}
$$

The reader should verify that $\bar{\mathbf{x}} = [2 \quad 1 \quad 0 \quad -3]^T$ is the solution. Note that the **upper triangulation** is performed in "one pass," without altering the values of the superdiagonal entries $c_1, \ldots, c_{n-1}$.

Algorithm: Gaussian Elimination for Tridiagonal Systems

Purpose: To solve the $n \times n$ tridiagonal system $T\mathbf{x} = \mathbf{d}$, where $T = \text{trid}(\mathbf{a}, \mathbf{b}, \mathbf{c})$.

GET n, **a, b, c, d** $\{a_1$ and c_n are not used$\}$

$\{upper\ triangulation\}$
DO FOR $i = 2$ TO n $\{$SUBTRACT: $\rho_i - (a_i/b_{i-1})\rho_{i-1}\}$
  BEGIN
  Ratio $\leftarrow a_i/b_{i-1}$
  $b_i \leftarrow b_i - Ratio*c_{i-1}$
  IF $b_i = 0$ THEN STOP $\{T$ is singular.$\}$
  $d_i \leftarrow d_i - Ratio*d_{i-1}$
  END

$\{backward\ substitution\}$
$\bar{x}_n \leftarrow d_n/b_n$
DO FOR $i = n - 1$ TO 1 STEP -1

$$
\bar{x}_i \leftarrow \frac{1}{b_i}(d_i - c_i*\bar{x}_{i+1})
$$

OUTPUT (The calculated solution is $\bar{\mathbf{x}} = [x_1 \quad x_2 \quad \cdots \quad x_n]^T$)

FIGURE 3.4-2   PSEUDOCODE FOR THE GAUSSIAN ELIMINATION ALGORITHM FOR TRI-DIAGONAL SYSTEMS.

A count of arithmetic operations shows that this algorithm requires only

$$5n - 4 \text{ multiply/divides and } 3(n - 1) \text{ add/subtracts} \qquad \textbf{(12)}$$

Thus *for large n the number of arithmetic operations required to solve a tridiagonal system is only about 8n,* considerably less than the $2n^3/3$ operations generally needed to use Gaussian elimination.

The tridiagonal matrix T in the preceding example satisfies

$$|b_1| > |c_1|, \quad |b_n| > |a_n|, \quad \text{and} \quad |b_i| > |a_i| + |c_i| \qquad \text{for } i = 2, 3, \ldots, n-1 \qquad \textbf{(13)}$$

In words, *the magnitude of the diagonal entry of each row is larger than the sum of the magnitudes of all other entries of the row.* It can be shown that this property, called **strict diagonal dominance,** guarantees that *T is nonsingular* and that *Gaussian elimination can be carried out accurately without the need for Partial Pivoting.* Most tridiagonal matrices encountered are diagonally dominant. This is why only Basic Pivoting was incorporated in both the pseudocode of Figure 3.4-2 and the FORTRAN subroutine TRIDAG implementing it in Figure 3.4-3.

3.4E   THE EFFECT OF A SINGULAR COEFFICIENT MATRIX

If exact arithmetic is used in solving $A\mathbf{x} = \mathbf{b}$ by either a factorization or an elimination method, then one of two possibilities can occur:

Possibility 1: *n nonzero pivots can be found.*

Possibility 2: *There will be a column for which only zeros are available to be used as pivots.*

Possibility 1 corresponds to A being nonsingular. In this case, as we have seen, any direct method will find the *unique* solution $\bar{\mathbf{x}} = A^{-1}\mathbf{b}$ no matter what pivoting strategy is used.

Possibility 2 corresponds to A being singular. *If it occurs when one pivoting strategy is used, it will occur for any pivoting strategy.* In this case $A\mathbf{x} = \mathbf{b}$ can *never* have a unique solution. It will have *no solutions* for some $\mathbf{b}$'s and *infinitely many solutions* for others. This is proved in linear algebra and will not be proved here. Let us, however, illustrate Possibility 2 with an example.

EXAMPLE. Use Gaussian elimination to solve

$$\begin{aligned} 2x_1 + x_2 + x_3 &= 2 \\ -2x_1 + x_2 + 3x_3 &= 2 \\ 2x_1 + 0x_2 - x_3 &= b_3 \end{aligned} \qquad \left([A : \mathbf{b}] = \begin{bmatrix} 2 & 1 & 1 & : & 2 \\ -2 & 1 & 3 & : & 2 \\ 2 & 0 & -1 & : & b_3 \end{bmatrix} \right) \qquad \textbf{(14)}$$

```
00100           SUBROUTINE TRIDAG(A, B, C, D, SOLN, N)
00200           DIMENSION A(N), B(N), C(N), D(N), SOLN(N)
00300    C - - - - - - - - - - - - - - - - - - - - - - - - - - - - - C
00400    C THIS SUBROUTINE SOLVES AN N BY N TRIDIAGONAL SYSTEM TX = D.   C
00500    C A, B, AND C ARE THE SUB-, ON-, AND SUPER-DIAGONAL ENTRIES    C
00600    C OF THE TRIDIAGONAL MATRIX T.  A(1) AND C(N) AREN'T USED.     C
00700    C THE ARRAYS  B  AND  D  ARE ALTERED BY THE SUBROUTINE CALL.   C
00800    C - - - - - - - - - - - - - - - - - - - - VERSION 1:  5/1/81 C
00900    C UPPER TRIANGULATION
01000           IF (N .EQ. 1) GOTO 20
01100           DO 10 I=2,N
01200              RATIO = A(I)/B(I-1)
01300              B(I) = B(I) - RATIO * C(I-1)
01400              D(I) = D(I) - RATIO * D(I-1)
01500       10 CONTINUE
01600    C
01700    C BACKWARD SUBSTITUTION
01800       20 SOLN(N) = D(N)/B(N)
01900           IF (N .EQ. 1) RETURN
02000           DO 30 I=2,N
02100              K = N-I+1
02200              SOLN(K) = (D(K) - C(K) * SOLN(K+1)) / B(K)
02300       30 CONTINUE
02400           RETURN
02500           END
```

FIGURE 3.4-3   TRIDAG: A FORTRAN SUBROUTINE FOR SOLVING TRIDIAGONAL SYSTEMS.

Solution. The **upper triangulation,** using Basic Pivoting without 1-SCALEs proceeds as follows:

$$[A : \mathbf{b}] \xrightarrow[\substack{\rho_2 + \rho_1 \\ \rho_3 - \rho_1}]{} \begin{bmatrix} 2 & 1 & 1 & : & 2 \\ 0 & 2 & 4 & : & 4 \\ 0 & -1 & -2 & : & b_3 - 2 \end{bmatrix} \xrightarrow[\rho_3 + \frac{1}{2}\rho_2]{} \begin{bmatrix} 2 & 1 & 1 & : & 2 \\ 0 & 2 & 4 & : & 4 \\ 0 & 0 & 0 & : & b_3 \end{bmatrix} = [\hat{U} : \bar{\mathbf{c}}] \tag{15}$$

The third equation of the equivalent upper-triangular system $[\hat{U} : \bar{\mathbf{c}}]$ is

$$0x_1 + 0x_2 + 0x_3 = b_3 \tag{16}$$

CASE 1 ($b_3 = 0$): In this case (16) puts no constraint on x_1, x_2, x_3; so $[\hat{U} : \bar{\mathbf{c}}]$ represents only *two* nontrivial equations, namely

$$\begin{aligned} 2x_1 + \ x_2 + \ x_3 &= 2 \\ 2x_2 + 4x_3 &= 4 \end{aligned} \tag{17}$$

in *three* unknowns. As a result, one of the unknowns can be chosen arbitrarily, say $x_3 = \bar{x}_3$, and then $\bar{x}_2$ and $\bar{x}_1$ can be obtained by Backward Substitution:

$$\bar{x}_2 = 2 - 2\bar{x}_3; \qquad \bar{x}_1 = \tfrac{1}{2}\{2 - \bar{x}_3 - (2 - 2\bar{x}_3)\} = \tfrac{1}{2}\bar{x}_3$$

Hence the vector

$$\bar{\mathbf{x}} = [\tfrac{1}{2}\bar{x}_3 \quad 2 - 2\bar{x}_3 \quad \bar{x}_3]^T$$

is a solution of (14) for *any* value of $\bar{x}_3$.

Notice that $(E_3) = \frac{1}{2}\{(E_1) - (E_2)\}$ when $b_3 = 0$ in (14). More generally, *the system $Ax = b$ will have infinitely many solutions whenever one or more of the given equations $(E_1), \ldots, (E_n)$ can be expressed as a weighted sum of the others.* Such systems are called **underdetermined.**

CASE 2 ($b_3 \neq 0$): In this case (16) puts a restriction on x_1, x_2, and x_3 that is impossible to satisfy; so (14) cannot have any solutions.

More generally, *$Ax = b$ will have no solutions when one of $(E_1), \ldots, (E_n)$ puts a restriction on $x_1, \ldots, x_n$ that is incompatible with the restrictions posed by the other equations.* Such systems are called **inconsistent.**

In what follows, we shall concentrate on the situation when Possibility 1 occurs (i.e., A^{-1} exists). Nevertheless, *the reader should be prepared to use the occurrence of Possibility 2 to recognize a singular matrix when one is encountered.*

3.5   The Determinant of an $n \times n$ Matrix

If $n > 1$, then $A = (a_{ij})_{n \times n}$ is a square array of scalars; as such, it has no numerical "value." However, there is a number called the *determinant* of A that is formed from the entries of A and assigns a useful scalar value to A. Our purpose here is to survey the basic properties of determinants and to develop efficient methods for calculating them.

3.5A   DEFINITION

If $A = (a_{ij})_{n \times n}$, then the **determinant of** A is the number

$$\det A = \begin{vmatrix} a_{11} \cdots a_{1n} \\ \vdots \quad \vdots \\ a_{n1} \cdots a_{nn} \end{vmatrix} = \Sigma(-1)^\delta \, a_{1\alpha} a_{2\beta} a_{3\gamma} \cdots a_{n\nu} \tag{1}$$

where the sum Σ is taken over all possible permutations (rearrangements) α, β, γ,

TABLE 3.5-1 $(-1)^\delta$ FOR THE SIX TERMS OF $\det(a_{ij})_{3 \times 3}$.

Term	α, β, γ	Inversions	Number of Inversions, δ	$(-1)^\delta$
$a_{11}a_{22}a_{33}$	1, 2, 3	None	0	$+1$
$a_{11}a_{23}a_{32}$	1, 3, 2	$3 > 2$	1	-1
$a_{12}a_{21}a_{33}$	2, 1, 3	$2 > 1$	1	-1
$a_{12}a_{23}a_{31}$	2, 3, 1	$2 > 1, 3 > 1$	2	$+1$
$a_{13}a_{21}a_{32}$	3, 1, 2	$3 > 1, 3 > 2$	2	$+1$
$a_{13}a_{22}a_{31}$	3, 2, 1	$3 > 2, 3 > 1, 2 > 1$	3	-1

. . . , ν of 1, 2, 3, . . . , n (there are $n!$ of them), and δ is the number of inversions (decreases) in the list of column indices $\alpha, \beta, \gamma, \ldots, \nu$ when read left to right.

If $n = 2$, the $2! = 2$ permutations of 1, 2 are $\alpha, \beta = 1, 2$ itself ($\delta = 0$) and $\alpha, \beta = 2, 1$ ($\delta = 1$ because $1 < 2$). So (1) becomes the familiar

$$\det(a_{ij})_{2 \times 2} = \begin{vmatrix} a_{11} & a_{12} \\ a_{21} & a_{22} \end{vmatrix} = (-1)^0 a_{11} a_{22} + (-1)^1 a_{12} a_{21} = a_{11} a_{22} - a_{21} a_{12} \tag{2}$$

If $n = 3$, then the $3! = 6$ terms $a_{1\alpha}, a_{2\beta}, a_{3\gamma}$ and their sign $(-1)^\delta$ are given in Table 3.5-1; so (1) becomes

$$\det(a_{ij})_{3 \times 3} = \begin{vmatrix} a_{11} & a_{12} & a_{13} \\ a_{21} & a_{22} & a_{23} \\ a_{31} & a_{32} & a_{33} \end{vmatrix} = \begin{cases} +a_{11} a_{22} a_{33} + a_{12} a_{23} a_{31} + a_{13} a_{21} a_{32} \\ -a_{11} a_{23} a_{32} - a_{12} a_{21} a_{33} - a_{13} a_{22} a_{31} \end{cases} \tag{3}$$

The determinants (2) and (3) are easily remembered as

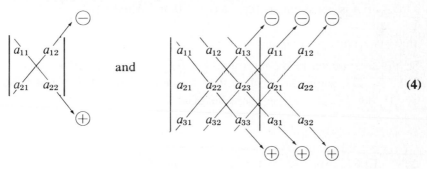

$$\text{(4)}$$

where the $\oplus$ or $\ominus$ gives the sign of $(-1)^\delta$. Unfortunately, these **arrow rules** do *not* extend to $n > 3$. Even for $n = 4$ there is no way of using arrows to describe the sign of $(-1)^\delta$ for the $4! = 24$ terms of the definition. Alternative procedures for evaluating det A for $n \geq 4$ are based on the results described next.

3.5B BASIC PROPERTIES OF DETERMINANTS

Let $A, B, L,$ and U be $n \times n$ matrices.

D1$_U$: If U is upper triangular, then det $U = u_{11} u_{22} \cdots u_{nn}$.

D1$_L$: If L is lower triangular, then det $L = l_{11} l_{22} \cdots l_{nn}$.

D2: If B is obtained from A by interchanging two of its rows, then det $B = -\det A$; thus *every row interchange changes the sign of the determinant.*

D3: If B is obtained from A by multiplying a single row of A by the scalar s, then det $B = s \det A$.

D4: For any scalar s, $\det(sA) = s^n \det A$; in particular,

$$\det(-A) = (-1)^n \det A \tag{5}$$

D5: **Product Theorem:** det $AB = $ det A det B

Properties D1–D3 follow directly from definition (1); and D4 follows from D3 (see Exercise 3–34). The Product Theorem D5 asserts that *the determinant of a product is the product of the determinants,* that is, if we first form the matrix product AB and then find its determinant, we get the same number that we would get by first finding det A and det B and then multiplying these two numbers. This remarkable result is proved in linear algebra. Note that although matrix addition and subtraction are simpler than matrix multiplication, in general

$$\det(A \pm B) \neq \det A \pm \det B$$

Two important immediate consequences of the Product Theorem are

---

D6: det $BA = $ det AB whether or not $BA = AB$.

D7: If A is nonsingular, then det $A \neq 0$ and $\det(A^{-1}) = \dfrac{1}{\det A}$.

So *the determinant of the inverse of A is the reciprocal of* det A.

To get D7, apply the Product Rule to the equality $AA^{-1} = I$ and use the fact that, by D1, det $I = 1$ whatever the value of n.

3.5C   EFFICIENT EVALUATION OF det A

The determinant of $A_{n \times n}$ can be found by inspection of the steps used to form $\hat{L} \backslash \hat{U}$ in the **factorization** step of the Triangular Decomposition Algorithm (Section 3.3E). Indeed, we know that $\hat{L}\hat{U} = \hat{A}$, where $\hat{A}$ is obtained from A by making the same row interchanges that were used to get $\hat{L}\backslash\hat{U}$. So it follows from D5 and D2 that

$$\det \hat{L} \det \hat{U} = \det \hat{A} = (-1)^{\rho} \det A \tag{6}$$

where the sign factor $(-1)^{\rho}$ is $+1$ or -1 depending on whether

$$\rho = \text{number of row interchanges used to get } \hat{L}\backslash\hat{U} \tag{7}$$

is even or odd. But by $D1_L$ and $D1_U$,

$$\det \hat{L} = \hat{l}_{11}\hat{l}_{22} \cdots \hat{l}_{nn} \quad \text{and} \quad \det \hat{U} = 1^n = 1$$

Substituting this in (6) and solving for det A, we get

D8: det $A = (-1)^{\rho} \{\text{product of the pivots of } \hat{L}\backslash\hat{U}\}$

In view of (7) of Section 3.4D, both ρ and the pivots in D8 could be obtained from the reduction $[A : \mathbf{b}] \rightarrow [\hat{U} : \bar{\mathbf{c}}]$ if Gaussian elimination is used.

EXAMPLES. We saw in (13) of Section 3.3C that if Basic Pivoting is used,

$$A = \begin{bmatrix} -1 & 1 & -4 \\ 2 & 2 & 0 \\ 3 & 3 & 2 \end{bmatrix} \;\Rightarrow\; \hat{L}\backslash\hat{U} = \begin{bmatrix} \boxed{-1} & -1 & 4 \\ 2 & \boxed{4} & -2 \\ 3 & 6 & \boxed{2} \end{bmatrix} = L\backslash U \qquad \textbf{(8a)}$$

This decomposition required no row interchanges. So by D8 with $\rho = 0$,

$$\det A = (-1)^0(-1)(4)(2) = -8 \qquad \textbf{(8b)}$$

Alternatively, we saw in Figure 3.3-5 that the use of Partial Pivoting results in the following LU-decomposition:

$$\begin{bmatrix} \boxed{3} & 1 & \frac{2}{3} \\ -1 & \boxed{2} & -\frac{5}{3} \\ 2 & 0 & \boxed{\frac{4}{3}} \end{bmatrix} \begin{matrix} (\rho_1 \rightleftarrows \rho_3) \\ (\rho_2 \rightleftarrows \rho_3) \\ \\ \end{matrix} \qquad \textbf{(9a)}$$

Since two row interchanges were used, D8 with $\rho = 2$ gives

$$\det A = (-1)^2(3)(2)(-\tfrac{4}{3}) = -8 \qquad \textbf{(9b)}$$

The reader can use the arrow rule to verify that $\det A = -8$.

Similarly, we saw in Figure 3.3-4 that (using Basic Pivoting)

$$A = \begin{bmatrix} 2 & -2 & 0 & 4 \\ 3 & -3 & 0 & -1 \\ -1 & 6 & 5 & -7 \\ -5 & 1 & 0 & -6 \end{bmatrix} \text{ has } \begin{bmatrix} \boxed{2} & -1 & 0 & 2 \\ -1 & \boxed{5} & 1 & -1 \\ -5 & -4 & \boxed{4} & 0 \\ 3 & 0 & 0 & \boxed{-7} \end{bmatrix} \begin{matrix} \\ (\rho_2 \rightleftarrows \rho_3) \\ (\rho_3 \rightleftarrows \rho_4) \\ \\ \end{matrix} \qquad \textbf{(10a)}$$

as an LU-decomposition. Since two row interchanges were used,

$$\det A = (+)(2)(5)(4)(-7) = -280 \qquad \textbf{(10b)}$$

To fully appreciate D8, the reader may wish to try to evaluate the determinant of this 4×4 matrix A using the definition of $\det A$.

It follows from D8 that $\det A = 0$ if and only if at least one pivot of $\hat{L}$ is zero; that is, a zero column of $\hat{L}$ is encountered in calculating $\hat{L}\backslash\hat{U}$. We saw in Section 3.4D that this corresponds to A being singular; so

$$A = (a_{ij})_{n \times n} \text{ is singular} \qquad \Longleftrightarrow \qquad \det A = 0 \qquad \textbf{(11)}$$

This result accounts for much of the theoretical importance of determinants.

3.5D CRAMER'S RULE

In linear algebra one obtains the following explicit formula for the components of $\bar{\mathbf{x}} = A^{-1}\mathbf{b}$ when A is nonsingular.

Cramer's Rule *If* det $A \neq 0$, *then the unique solution of* $Ax = b$ *is*

$$\bar{x} = \begin{bmatrix} \bar{x}_1 \\ \bar{x}_2 \\ \vdots \\ \bar{x}_n \end{bmatrix}, \qquad \text{where } \bar{x}_j = \frac{\det A_j}{\det A} \quad (j = 1, \dots, n) \tag{12}$$

and A_j *is the matrix obtained by replacing the jth column of A by* **b**.

Finding $\bar{x}$ by Cramer's rule requires evaluating the determinant of A and of n additional $n \times n$ matrices $A_1, A_2, \dots, A_n$. The arrow rules make Cramer's rule convenient when $n = 2$ and reasonably easy to use when $n = 3$. However, for $n \geq 4$, the efficient evaluation of det A alone (using D8) requires either the **factorization** step of the Triangular Decomposition Algorithm (Section 3.3E) or the **upper triangulation** step of the Gaussian Elimination Algorithm. Therefore, it would be foolish to even consider trying to find det $A_1, \dots,$ det A_n in (12) when with relatively little additional work, one can find $\bar{x}$ by Triangular Factorization or Gaussian elimination. Thus, although Cramer's rule is often useful theoretically, it is emphatically *not* recommended as a computational procedure for $n > 3$.

3.5E   GEOMETRIC INTERPRETATION OF det A

The determinant is related to the concept of volume. To see this, consider the *row* vectors

$$\text{row}_i A = [a_{i1} \quad a_{i2} \quad \cdots \quad a_{in}] \qquad \text{for } i = 1, 2, \dots, n \tag{13}$$

For $n = 2$ we can identify $\text{row}_i A$ with the geometric vector $\overrightarrow{OP_i}$, where P_i is the point in the plane (2-space) having coordinates (a_{i1}, a_{i2}); similarly, for $n = 3$ we can identify $\text{row}_i A$ with $\overrightarrow{OP_i}$, where P_i is the point in 3-space having coordinates (a_{i1}, a_{i2}, a_{i3}) (Figure 3.5-1).

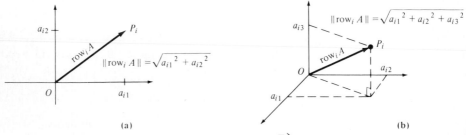

FIGURE 3.5-1   IDENTIFYING row $_i$ A WITH $\overrightarrow{OP_i}$: (a) 2-SPACE; (b) 3-SPACE.

With these identifications, one can show (Figure 3.5-2) that

If $n = 2$, det $A = \pm$(area of parallelogram with sides $\text{row}_1 A$, $\text{row}_2 A$)   **(14a)**

If $n = 3$, det $A = \pm$(volume of parallelepiped with sides $\text{row}_i A$, $i = 1, 2, 3$)   **(14b)**

Although it is impossible to draw n-space for $n > 3$, it is useful to think of the

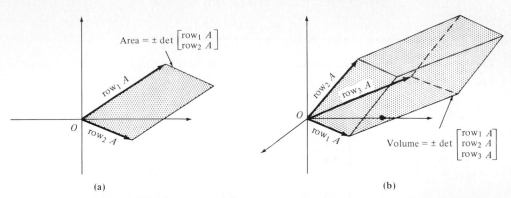

FIGURE 3.5-2   GEOMETRIC INTERPRETATION OF DET A: (a) 2-SPACE; (b) 3-SPACE.

nonnegative number $|\det A|$ as the volume of the "parallelepiped" in n-space having sides $\text{row}_1\, A, \ldots , \text{row}_n\, A$, where $\text{row}_i\, A$ is viewed as the geometric vector from the origin of n-space to the "point" having coordinates $(a_{i1}, a_{i2}, \ldots , a_{in})$. With this interpretation, if we define

$$\|\text{row}_i\, A\| = \textbf{Euclidean length} \text{ of } \text{row}_i\, A = \sqrt{a_{i1}^2 + a_{i2}^2 + \cdots + a_{in}^2} \qquad (15)$$

then the volume $|\det A|$ can be no larger than the product of the lengths of its sides; this occurs when the vectors $\text{row}_1\, A, \ldots , \text{row}_n\, A$ are mutually orthogonal. Stated symbolically (this is **Hadamard's inequality**),

$$|\det A| \leq \|\text{row}_1\, A\|\, \|\text{row}_2\, A\| \cdots \|\text{row}_n\, A\| \qquad (16)$$

Moreover, the volume $|\det A|$ will be "small" if either (i) one or more of the lengths $\|\text{row}_1\, A\|$, $\|\text{row}_2\, A\|$, $\ldots$, $\|\text{row}_n\, A\|$ is "small," or (ii) there is a side $\text{row}_i\, A$ that is almost parallel to the "plane" spanned by some of the other sides. In the limiting cases, we get the following result:

D9: det $A = 0$ *if and only if there is an i such that* (i) $\text{row}_i\, A = \mathbf{0}$ *or* (ii) $\text{row}_i\, A \neq \mathbf{0}$ *but can be expressed as a linear combination of the remaining rows, that is, there exist scalars* m_{ik} *such that*

$$\text{row}_i\, A = \sum_{k \neq i} m_{ik}\, \text{row}_k\, A \qquad (17)$$

The preceding intuitive presentation can be justified rigorously using the results of linear algebra or vector analysis. The characterization of singular matrices given in D9 will be helpful in explaining why some coefficient matrices are more sensitive to roundoff errors than others (see Section 4.2B).

Finding the Inverse of an $n \times n$ Matrix   **3.6**

It is sometimes necessary to find the inverse of a given $n \times n$ matrix. If $n = 2$, this is easily done using the formula given in (11) of Section 3.1H. For example,

$$A = \begin{bmatrix} 2 & -5 \\ 0 & -3 \end{bmatrix} \quad \Rightarrow \quad A^{-1} = -\frac{1}{6} \begin{bmatrix} -3 & 5 \\ 0 & 2 \end{bmatrix}$$

The formula for $(A_{2\times 2})^{-1}$ is a special case of the following general formula for $(A_{n\times n})^{-1}$ whenever A is nonsingular (det $A \neq 0$).

Formula for A^{-1} *If* det $A \neq 0$, *then A is invertible and*

$$A^{-1} = \frac{1}{\det A} \begin{bmatrix} A_{11} & A_{21} & \cdots & A_{n1} \\ A_{12} & A_{22} & \cdots & A_{n2} \\ \vdots & \vdots & & \vdots \\ A_{1n} & A_{2n} & \cdots & A_{nn} \end{bmatrix} \quad \begin{pmatrix} note\ reversal\ of \\ i,\ j\ indices \end{pmatrix} \tag{1a}$$

where

$$A_{ij} = (-1)^{i+j} \det \begin{pmatrix} the\ (n-1) \times (n-1)\ matrix\ obtained\ by \\ deleting\ the\ i\text{th}\ row\ and\ j\text{th}\ column\ of\ A \end{pmatrix} \tag{1b}$$

This formula is obtained in linear algebra. To use it to find A^{-1}, one must evaluate the determinant of the $n \times n$ matrix A and of the n^2 additional $(n-1) \times (n-1)$ matrices $A_{ij}(i, j = 1, \ldots, n)$. Although the work required is not unreasonable when $n = 3$, it is prohibitive for hand calculation when $n \geq 4$! That's the bad news. The good news is that with little more work than is required to find det A, both the factorization methods of Section 3.3 and the elimination methods of Section 3.4 can be generalized to yield algorithms for finding A^{-1}. The basis for these generalizations is given next.

3.6A   VIEWING p LINEAR SYSTEMS AS $AX = B$

Suppose that we had to solve p linear systems having the same invertible coefficient matrix A, say

$$A\mathbf{x} = \mathbf{b}_1, \quad A\mathbf{x} = \mathbf{b}_2, \quad \ldots, \quad A\mathbf{x} = \mathbf{b}_p \tag{2}$$

Let us denote the solution of $A\mathbf{x} = \mathbf{b}_j$ by $\bar{\mathbf{x}}_j$, where

$$\bar{\mathbf{x}}_j = \begin{bmatrix} \bar{x}_{1j} \\ \bar{x}_{2j} \\ \vdots \\ \bar{x}_{nj} \end{bmatrix} \quad \text{and} \quad \mathbf{b}_j = \begin{bmatrix} b_{1j} \\ b_{2j} \\ \vdots \\ b_{nj} \end{bmatrix}, \quad j = 1, 2, \ldots, p \tag{3}$$

To solve the p systems (2) *simultaneously*, consider the $n \times p$ matrices

$$X = [\mathbf{x}_1 \ \vdots \ \mathbf{x}_2 \ \vdots \ \cdots \ \vdots \ \mathbf{x}_p] \quad \text{and} \quad B = [\mathbf{b}_1 \ \vdots \ \mathbf{b}_2 \ \vdots \ \cdots \ \vdots \ \mathbf{b}_p] \tag{4}$$

where $\mathbf{x}_j = \text{col}_j\ X$ and $\mathbf{b}_j = \text{col}_j\ B$, $j = 1, \ldots, p$. We saw in (7b) of Section 3.1D that $\text{col}_j(AX)$ is $A(\text{col}_j\ X)$. It follows that

$$AX = B \quad \Longleftrightarrow \quad A\mathbf{x}_j = \mathbf{b}_j \quad \text{for } j = 1, \ldots, p \tag{5a}$$

upon premultiplying by A^{-1}, we see that

$$\overline{X}= A^{-1}B \iff \overline{\mathbf{x}}_j = \text{col}_j\,\overline{X}= A^{-1}\mathbf{b}_j \qquad \text{for } j=1,\dots,p \qquad (5b)$$

In words, *the solutions of the p systems* $A\mathbf{x}=\mathbf{b}_j$ $(j=1,\dots,p)$ *are the columns of the solution of the single matrix equation* $AX=B$. So any method for solving $AX=B$ can be used to solve all p linear systems in (2) simultaneously.

3.6B EFFICIENT SOLUTION OF $AX=B$

Suppose that we have obtained an LU-decomposition for the matrix A and we wish to solve the matrix equation $AX=B$. If $\hat{A}=\hat{L}\hat{U}$ and we form $\hat{B}$ from B by performing the row interchanges used to get $\hat{A}$ from A, then $\hat{A}X=\hat{B}$ is an equivalent equation that can be solved as follows:

$$\overline{X}= \hat{A}^{-1}\hat{B}=(\hat{L}\hat{U})^{-1}\hat{B}; \qquad \text{that is, } \overline{X}= \hat{U}^{-1}\overline{C} \quad \text{where } \overline{C}=\hat{L}^{-1}\hat{B} \qquad (6)$$

[cf. (2) of Section 3.3A]. This in turn can be carried out compactly by completing the forback matrix

$$[\hat{L}\backslash\hat{U} : \hat{B} : \overline{C} : \overline{X}], \qquad \overline{X}= \text{desired solution of } AX=B \qquad (7)$$

We first use $[\hat{L} : \hat{B}]$ to get $\overline{C}$ one row at a time using *Forward Substitution:*

$$\boxed{\text{row}_i\,\overline{C}=\frac{1}{\hat{l}_{ii}}\{\text{row}_i\,\hat{B}-[\leftarrow]\hat{l}[\uparrow]\overline{c}\}, \qquad i=1,2,\dots,n} \qquad (8a)$$

(with $[\leftarrow]_L[\uparrow]\overline{c}=O_{1\times p}$ when $i=1$ [cf. Section 3.2D]); we then use $[\hat{U} : \overline{C}]$ to get $\overline{X}$ one row at a time using *Backward Substitution:*

$$\boxed{\text{row}_i\,\overline{X}= \text{row}_i\,\overline{C}-[\leftarrow]\hat{u}[\downarrow]\overline{x}, \qquad i=n,n-1,\dots,1} \qquad (8b)$$

(with $[\leftarrow]\hat{u}[\downarrow]\overline{x}=O_{1\times p}$ when $i=n$ [cf. Section 3.2E]) as shown next.

EXAMPLE. Solve $A\mathbf{x}=\mathbf{b}_1$ and $A\mathbf{x}=\mathbf{b}_2$, where

$$A=\begin{bmatrix} 2 & -2 & 0 & 4 \\ 3 & -3 & 0 & -1 \\ -1 & 6 & 5 & -7 \\ -5 & 1 & 0 & -6 \end{bmatrix}, \quad \mathbf{b}_1=\begin{bmatrix} 2 \\ 10 \\ -11 \\ 3 \end{bmatrix}, \quad \text{and} \quad \mathbf{b}_2=\begin{bmatrix} 4 \\ 13 \\ 13 \\ -14 \end{bmatrix} \qquad (9)$$

Solution. Since we are using exact arithmetic, $\hat{L}\backslash\hat{U}$ obtained by *any* pivoting strategy will give the exact solutions $\overline{\mathbf{x}}_1 = A^{-1}\mathbf{b}_1$ and $\overline{\mathbf{x}}_2 = A^{-1}\mathbf{b}_2$. So we will use the $\hat{L}\backslash\hat{U}$ obtained by Basic Pivoting in Figure 3.3-4 and shown in (11) below. Getting this $\hat{L}\backslash\hat{U}$ required the row interchanges $\rho_2 \rightleftarrows \rho_3$ and $\rho_3 \rightleftarrows \rho_4$. So the matrix $\hat{B}$ for the equivalent equation $\hat{A}X=\hat{B}$ is obtained from B as follows:

$$B=\begin{bmatrix} 2 & 4 \\ 10 & 13 \\ -11 & 13 \\ 3 & -14 \end{bmatrix} \overset{\rho_2 \rightleftarrows \rho_3}{\longrightarrow} \begin{bmatrix} 2 & 4 \\ -11 & 13 \\ 10 & 13 \\ 3 & -14 \end{bmatrix} \overset{\rho_3 \rightleftarrows \rho_4}{\longrightarrow} \begin{bmatrix} 2 & 4 \\ -11 & 13 \\ 3 & -14 \\ 10 & 13 \end{bmatrix} = \hat{B} \qquad (10)$$

In this way, the steps used to find $\hat{L}\backslash\hat{U}$ quickly give the $[\hat{L}\backslash\hat{U} : \hat{B}]$ part of the forback matrix.

$$
\begin{bmatrix}
\textcircled{2} & -1 & 0 & 2 & : & 2 & 4 & : & 1 & 2 & : & 0 & 4 \\
-1 & \textcircled{5} & 1 & -1 & : & -11 & 13 & : & -2 & 3 & : & -3 & 0 \\
-5 & -4 & \textcircled{4} & 0 & : & 3 & -14 & : & 0 & 2 & : & 0 & 2 \\
3 & 0 & 0 & \textcircled{-7} & : & 10 & 13 & : & -1 & -1 & : & -1 & -1
\end{bmatrix} \quad \text{(11)}
$$

$$\underbrace{\hphantom{xxxxxxxxxxxxxx}}_{\hat{L}\backslash\hat{U}} \quad \underbrace{\hphantom{xxxxx}}_{\hat{B}} \quad \underbrace{\hphantom{xxxx}}_{\bar{C}} \quad \bar{X}=[\bar{x}_1 : \bar{x}_2]$$

To get $\bar{C}$ from $[\hat{L} : \hat{B}]$, we use (8a):

$$\text{row}_1\ \bar{C} = \frac{1}{\hat{l}_{11}}\text{row}_1\ \hat{B} = \frac{1}{\textcircled{2}}[2 \quad 4] = [1 \quad 2]$$

$$\text{row}_2\ \bar{C} = \frac{1}{\hat{l}_{22}}\{\text{row}_2\ \hat{B} - [\leftarrow]\hat{l}[\uparrow]\bar{c}\} = \frac{1}{\textcircled{5}}\{[-11 \quad 13] - [-1][1 \quad 2]\} = [-2 \quad 3]$$

$$\text{row}_3\ \bar{C} = \frac{1}{\hat{l}_{33}}\{\text{row}_3\ \hat{B} - [\leftarrow]\hat{l}[\uparrow]\bar{c}\} = \frac{1}{\textcircled{4}}\left\{[3 \quad -14] - [-5 \quad -4]\begin{bmatrix} 1 & 2 \\ -2 & 3 \end{bmatrix}\right\} = [0 \quad 2]$$

$$\text{row}_4\ \bar{C} = \frac{1}{\hat{l}_{44}}\{\text{row}_4\ \hat{B} - [\leftarrow]\hat{l}[\uparrow]\bar{c}\} = \frac{1}{\textcircled{-7}}\left\{[10 \quad 13] - [3 \quad 0 \quad 0]\begin{bmatrix} 1 & 2 \\ -2 & 3 \\ 0 & 2 \end{bmatrix}\right\} = [-1 \quad -1]$$

Finally, to get $\bar{X}$ from $[\hat{U} : \bar{C}]$, we use (8b) thus:

$$\text{row}_4\ \bar{X} = \text{row}_4\ \bar{C} = [-1 \quad -1]$$

$$\text{row}_3\ \bar{X} = \text{row}_3\ \bar{C} - [\leftarrow]\hat{v}[\downarrow]\bar{x} = [0 \quad 2] - [0][-1 \quad -1] = [0 \quad 2]$$

$$\text{row}_2\ \bar{X} = \text{row}_2\ \bar{C} - [\leftarrow]\hat{v}[\downarrow]\bar{x} = [-2 \quad 3] - [1 \quad -1]\begin{bmatrix} 0 & 2 \\ -1 & -1 \end{bmatrix} = [-3 \quad 0]$$

$$\text{row}_1\ \bar{X} = \text{row}_1\ \bar{C} - [\leftarrow]\hat{v}[\downarrow]\bar{x} = [1 \quad 2] - [-1 \quad 0 \quad 2]\begin{bmatrix} -3 & 0 \\ 0 & 2 \\ -1 & -1 \end{bmatrix} = [0 \quad 4]$$

The desired solutions $\bar{x}_1 = A^{-1}b_1$ and $\bar{x}_2 = A^{-1}b_2$ are

$$\bar{x}_1 = \text{col}_1\ \bar{X} = [0 \quad -3 \quad 0 \quad -1]^T \quad \text{and} \quad \bar{x}_2 = \text{col}_2\ \bar{X} = [4 \quad 0 \quad 2 \quad -1]^T$$

The reader should verify that $A\bar{x}_1 = b_1$ and $A\bar{x}_2 = b_2$.

The procedure just used will be referred to as the **Triangular Decomposition Algorithm** for solving $AX = B$. It can be described by simply replacing **b**, **c**, and **x** by B, C, and X in Figure 3.3-3.

3.6C FINDING A^{-1}

The problem of finding A^{-1} can be viewed as follows:

$$\text{Solve } AX = I_n \text{ for } \overline{X} = A^{-1}I_n = A^{-1} \tag{12}$$

This is of the form $AX = B$ with $B = I_n$. Once $\hat{L}\backslash\hat{U}$ has been found, A^{-1} can be obtained by first appropriately rearranging the rows of I_n to get $\hat{I}_n$ and then completing the forback matrix

$$[\hat{L}\backslash\hat{U} : \hat{I}_n : \overline{C} : \overline{X} = A^{-1}] \tag{13}$$

EXAMPLE. Use the Triangular Decomposition Algorithm to find the inverse of

$$A = \begin{bmatrix} -1 & 1 & -4 \\ 2 & 2 & 0 \\ 3 & 3 & 2 \end{bmatrix}$$

Solution. Compact forms of LU-decompositions for this A were obtained using Basic Pivoting in (19) of Section 3.3C, and Partial Pivoting in Figure 3.3-4 (Section 3.3F). For variety, let us use the latter, namely

$$\hat{L}\backslash\hat{U} = \begin{bmatrix} ③ & 1 & \frac{2}{3} \\ -1 & ② & -\frac{5}{3} \\ 2 & 0 & \left(-\frac{4}{3}\right) \end{bmatrix} \begin{matrix} (\rho_1 \rightleftarrows \rho_3) \\ (\rho_2 \rightleftarrows \rho_3) \\ {} \end{matrix} \tag{14}$$

Performing the row interchanges $\rho_1 \rightleftarrows \rho_3$, then $\rho_2 \rightleftarrows \rho_3$ on I_3 gives the $\hat{I}_3$ shown in

$$\begin{bmatrix} ③ & 1 & \frac{2}{3} & : & 0 & 0 & 1 & : & 0 & 0 & \frac{1}{3} & : & -\frac{1}{2} & \frac{7}{4} & -1 \\ -1 & ② & -\frac{5}{3} & : & 1 & 0 & 0 & : & \frac{1}{2} & 0 & \frac{1}{6} & : & \frac{1}{2} & -\frac{5}{4} & 1 \\ 2 & 0 & \left(-\frac{4}{3}\right) & : & 0 & 1 & 0 & : & 0 & -\frac{3}{4} & \frac{1}{2} & : & 0 & -\frac{3}{4} & \frac{1}{2} \end{bmatrix} \tag{15}$$

$$\underbrace{\hat{L}\backslash\hat{U}}\qquad\underbrace{\hat{I}_3}\qquad\underbrace{\overline{C}}\qquad\underbrace{\overline{X} = A^{-1}}$$

The detailed calculation of $\overline{C}$ [using (8a)] and $\overline{X}$ [using (8b)] is

$$\text{row}_1\ \overline{C} = \frac{1}{③}[0\quad 0\quad 1] = [0\quad 0\quad \tfrac{1}{3}]$$

$$\text{row}_2\ \overline{C} = \frac{1}{②}\{[1\quad 0\quad 0] - [-1][0\quad 0\quad \tfrac{1}{3}]\} = \tfrac{1}{2}[1\quad 0\quad \tfrac{1}{3}] = [\tfrac{1}{2}\quad 0\quad \tfrac{1}{6}]$$

$$\text{row}_3\ \overline{C} = \frac{1}{\left(-\frac{4}{3}\right)}\left\{[0\quad 1\quad 0] - [2\quad 0]\begin{bmatrix} 0 & 0 & \tfrac{1}{3} \\ \tfrac{1}{2} & 0 & \tfrac{1}{6} \end{bmatrix}\right\} = -\tfrac{3}{4}[0\quad 1\quad -\tfrac{2}{3}] = [0\quad -\tfrac{3}{4}\quad \tfrac{1}{2}]$$

$$\text{row}_3\ \overline{X} = \text{row}_3\ \overline{C} = [0\quad -\tfrac{3}{4}\quad \tfrac{1}{2}]$$

$$\text{row}_2 \; \overline{X} = [\tfrac{1}{2} \quad 0 \quad \tfrac{1}{6}] - [-\tfrac{5}{3}][0 \quad -\tfrac{3}{4} \quad \tfrac{1}{2}] = [\tfrac{1}{2} \quad -\tfrac{5}{4} \quad 1]$$

$$\text{row}_1 \; \overline{X} = [0 \quad 0 \quad \tfrac{1}{3}] - [1 \quad \tfrac{2}{3}]\begin{bmatrix} \tfrac{1}{2} & -\tfrac{5}{4} & 1 \\ 0 & -\tfrac{3}{4} & \tfrac{1}{2} \end{bmatrix} = [-\tfrac{1}{2} \quad \tfrac{7}{4} \quad -1]$$

So the desired inverse, as the reader can verify, is

$$A^{-1} = \overline{X} = \frac{1}{4}\begin{bmatrix} -2 & 7 & -4 \\ 2 & -5 & 4 \\ 0 & -3 & 2 \end{bmatrix} \tag{16}$$

3.6D   COUNTING ARITHMETIC OPERATIONS

The formulas in Table 3.3-1 immediately give those of Table 3.6-1.

TABLE 3.6-1   NUMBER OF ARITHMETIC OPERATIONS NEEDED TO SOLVE $AX = B$ AND TO FIND A^{-1} BY THE TRIANGULAR DECOMPOSITION ALGORITHM.

Problem	Matrix Equivalent	Number of Operations
Solve $A\mathbf{x} = \mathbf{b}_1, \dots, A\mathbf{x} = \mathbf{b}_p$	Solve $AX_{n \times p} = B_{n \times p}$	$\dfrac{n(n-1)(4n+1)}{6} + p(2n^2 - n)$
Find A^{-1}	Solve $AX_{n \times n} = I_n$	$\dfrac{n(16n^2 - 9n - 1)}{6}$

A comparison of Tables 3.6-1 and 3.3-1 provides quantitative justification that finding $\overline{\mathbf{x}}$ as the product $A^{-1}\mathbf{b}$ is *not* the most efficient method of solving a single equation $A\mathbf{x} = \mathbf{b}$ if $n > 2$. Indeed, the larger the value of n, the more desirable it becomes to find $\overline{\mathbf{x}} = A^{-1}\mathbf{b}$ *directly* (using the Triangular Decomposition or Gaussian Elimination Algorithm) *without finding* A^{-1}.

3.6E   GAUSS–JORDAN ELIMINATION

A useful variant of the Gaussian Elimination Algorithm (Figure 3.4-1) consists of performing the **zero column** j step for *all* $i \neq j$ rather than only $i > j$. The result is to *get zeros both above and below the jth pivot* for $j = 1, \dots, n$. This procedure is called **Gauss–Jordan Elimination.** If 1-SCALEs are used, then the solution of $A\mathbf{x} = \mathbf{b}$ can be described as

$$[A : \mathbf{b}] \rightarrow [I_n : \overline{\mathbf{x}}], \qquad \text{where } \overline{\mathbf{x}} = A^{-1}\mathbf{b} \tag{17}$$

Thus A is reduced to I_n one column at a time.

EXAMPLE 1. Use Gauss–Jordan elimination to solve

$$
\begin{array}{ll}
(E_1) & -x_1 + x_2 - 4x_3 = 0 \\
(E_2) & 2x_1 + 2x_2 \qquad = 1 \\
(E_3) & 3x_1 + 3x_2 + 2x_3 = \tfrac{1}{2}
\end{array}
\qquad
\left([A : b] = \begin{bmatrix} -1 & 1 & -4 & : & 0 \\ 2 & 2 & 0 & : & 1 \\ 3 & 3 & 2 & : & \tfrac{1}{2} \end{bmatrix} \right)
\qquad \textbf{(18)}
$$

Solution. If we use Basic Pivoting and 1-SCALEs we get

$$
[A : b] \xrightarrow[\substack{\rho_2 - 2\rho_1 \\ \rho_3 - 3\rho_1}]{(-1)\rho_1}
\begin{bmatrix} 1 & -1 & 4 & : & 0 \\ 0 & 4 & -8 & : & 1 \\ 0 & 6 & -10 & : & \tfrac{1}{2} \end{bmatrix}
\xrightarrow[\substack{\tfrac{1}{4}\rho_2 \\ \rho_3 - 6\rho_2}]{\rho_1 + \rho_2}
\begin{bmatrix} 1 & 0 & 2 & : & \tfrac{1}{4} \\ 0 & 1 & -2 & : & \tfrac{1}{4} \\ 0 & 0 & 2 & : & -1 \end{bmatrix}
$$

$$\underbrace{\hspace{4cm}}_{\text{column 1 reduced}} \qquad\qquad \underbrace{\hspace{4cm}}_{\text{column 2 reduced}}$$

(19)

$$
\xrightarrow[\substack{\rho_2 + 2\rho_3 \\ \tfrac{1}{2}\rho_3}]{\rho_1 - 2\rho_3}
\begin{bmatrix} 1 & 0 & 0 & : & \tfrac{5}{4} \\ 0 & 1 & 0 & : & -\tfrac{3}{4} \\ 0 & 0 & 1 & : & -\tfrac{1}{2} \end{bmatrix} = [I_3 : \bar{\mathbf{x}}]
$$

We saw above that $[\tfrac{5}{4} \quad -\tfrac{3}{4} \quad -\tfrac{1}{2}]^T$ is indeed the solution.

Note: The steps between successive matrices in (19) are performed in the order of the *upper triangulation,* namely INTERCHANGE, SCALE, SUBTRACT (e.g., $\tfrac{1}{4}\rho_2$, then $\rho_1 + \rho_2$ and $\rho_3 - 6\rho_2$ to reduce column 2).

Gauss–Jordan elimination can be used to find A^{-1}; one simply applies it to $[A : I_n]$. If 1-SCALEs are used, it can be described as the single reduction

$$[A : I_n] \to [I_n : A^{-1}] \qquad \textbf{(20)}$$

EXAMPLE 2. Let A be the coefficient matrix in Example 1. Use Gauss–Jordan elimination with Partial Pivoting, but without 1-SCALEs, to find A^{-1}.

Solution. The reduction of $[A : I_3]$ without 1-SCALEs is as follows:

column 1 reduced ($p_1 = 3$)

$$
[A : I_3] = \begin{bmatrix} -1 & 1 & -4 & : & 1 & 0 & 0 \\ 2 & 2 & 0 & : & 0 & 1 & 0 \\ 3 & 3 & 2 & : & 0 & 0 & 1 \end{bmatrix}
\xrightarrow[\substack{\rho_2 - \tfrac{2}{3}\rho_1 \\ \rho_3 + \tfrac{1}{3}\rho_1}]{\rho_1 \rightleftarrows \rho_3}
\begin{bmatrix} ③ & 3 & 2 & : & 0 & 0 & 1 \\ 0 & 0 & -\tfrac{4}{3} & : & 0 & 1 & -\tfrac{2}{3} \\ 0 & 2 & -\tfrac{10}{3} & : & 1 & 0 & \tfrac{1}{3} \end{bmatrix}
$$

$|3|$ is largest of $|-1|, |2|, |3|$ $\qquad\qquad\qquad$ $|2|$ is largest of $|0|, |2|$

(21a)

$$
\xrightarrow[\substack{\rho_2 \rightleftarrows \rho_3}]{\rho_1 - \tfrac{3}{2}\rho_2}
\begin{bmatrix} ③ & 0 & 7 & : & -\tfrac{3}{2} & 0 & \tfrac{1}{2} \\ 0 & ② & -\tfrac{10}{3} & : & 1 & 0 & \tfrac{1}{3} \\ 0 & 0 & -\tfrac{4}{3} & : & 0 & 1 & -\tfrac{2}{3} \end{bmatrix}
\xrightarrow[\substack{\rho_2 - \tfrac{5}{2}\rho_3}]{\rho_1 + \tfrac{21}{4}\rho_3}
\begin{bmatrix} ③ & 0 & 0 & : & -\tfrac{3}{2} & \tfrac{21}{4} & -3 \\ 0 & ② & 0 & : & 1 & -\tfrac{5}{2} & 2 \\ 0 & 0 & ⊖\tfrac{4}{3} & : & 0 & 1 & -\tfrac{2}{3} \end{bmatrix}
$$

column 2 reduced ($p_2 = 2$) $\qquad\qquad\qquad$ column 3 reduced ($p_3 = -\tfrac{4}{3}$)

(21b)

If we *now* SCALE rows 1, 2, and 3 by $p_1 = 3$, $p_2 = 2$, $p_3 = -\frac{4}{3}$, respectively, we get

$$[I_3 : A^{-1}] = \begin{bmatrix} 1 & 0 & 0 & : & -\frac{1}{2} & \frac{7}{4} & -1 \\ 0 & 1 & 0 & : & \frac{1}{2} & -\frac{5}{4} & 1 \\ 0 & 0 & 1 & : & 0 & -\frac{3}{4} & \frac{1}{2} \end{bmatrix} \tag{22}$$

[cf. (15) of Section 3.6C]. Since the calculations were performed in exact arithmetic, the same (unique) inverse would have resulted if we used 1-SCALEs and/or a different pivoting strategy.

To avoid introducing needless roundoff error, Gauss–Jordan elimination should be performed as in the preceding example (i.e., *without* 1-SCALEs) when using fixed-precision arithmetic.

Gauss–Jordan elimination does not require Backward Substitution. So, a computer program that uses it to solve $AX = B_{n \times p}$ is easier to write than one using Gaussian elimination or Triangular Decomposition. However, more arithmetic operations are generally needed to get zeros above the main diagonal than are needed for Backward Substitution. The resulting possibility of extra roundoff error makes Gauss–Jordan elimination less desirable for solving $AX = B$ either by hand or on a computer. However, when A is augmented by n columns (i.e., $p = n$), Gauss–Jordan elimination requires essentially the same number of operations as either Gaussian elimination on Triangular Decomposition (see Table 3.6-1 and Exercise 3-43). Hence it is often incorporated (without 1-SCALEs) in computer programs for finding A^{-1}. Used this way, it is as accurate as the Triangular Decomposition Algorithm with the same pivoting strategy.

Exercises

Section 3.1

3-1. Let

$$A = \begin{bmatrix} 1 & -2 \\ -2 & 3 \end{bmatrix}, \quad B = \begin{bmatrix} -2 & 1 \\ 1 & 1 \end{bmatrix}, \quad \mathbf{c} = [4 \quad 1], \quad \mathbf{d} = \begin{bmatrix} 2 \\ 3 \end{bmatrix}, \quad E = \begin{bmatrix} 1 & 0 & 0 \\ 0 & 1 & 0 \end{bmatrix}$$

Form AB and BA and use your results as needed in (a)–(c).

(a) Form (if defined) (i) $2A - 3B$; (ii) $(AB)A$; (iii) A^2B; (iv) $(AB)E$; (v) $E(AB)$; (vi) $\mathbf{cd}$; (vii) $\mathbf{dc}$; (viii); $\mathbf{c}B$ (ix) $E\mathbf{d}$; (x) $\mathbf{d}^TA$.

(b) Verify that (i) $(\mathbf{c}A)B = \mathbf{c}(AB)$; (ii) $(A + B)\mathbf{d} = A\mathbf{d} + B\mathbf{d}$; (iii) $(AB)A = A(BA)$.

(c) Use formula (11) of Section 3.1H to find (i) A^{-1}; (ii) B^{-1}; (iii) $(AB)^{-1}$. Does $(AB)^{-1} = A^{-1}B^{-1}$? Does $(AB)^{-1} = B^{-1}A^{-1}$?

3-2. Let A and B be $n \times n$ matrices. Find simplified expressions, without parentheses, in terms of A, B, A^{-1}, B^{-1}, and $I = I_n$ for (a)–(f).

(a) $(A - B)(A^{-1} + B^{-1})$ **(b)** $(A - A^{-1})(A + 2A^{-1})$ **(c)** $(A + 3B)^2$

(d) $A^{-1}(A + B)B^{-1}$ **(e)** $B(B + B^{-1})B^{-1}$ **(f)** $(A + 2A^{-1})^2$

3-3. Let $D = \begin{bmatrix} \alpha & 0 \\ 0 & \beta \end{bmatrix}$ (a 2×2 **diagonal matrix**) and $A = \begin{bmatrix} 1 & 2 \\ 3 & 4 \end{bmatrix}$.

    (a) Compute (i) AD; (ii) DA; (iii) D^2; (iv) D^{-1} (assuming that α, $\beta \neq 0$).

    (b) From your answers to part (a), describe in words how the rows of DA and columns of AD are related to the rows and columns of A, and how the entries of D^2 and D^{-1} are related to those of D.

3-4. For $R(\theta)$ as defined in (12) of Section 3.1H, use trigonometric identities to show that $R(\theta_1)R(\theta_2) = R(\theta_1 + \theta_2)$ for any θ_1 and θ_2. Deduce that $R(\theta_1)$ and $R(\theta_2)$ commute.

3-5. Use the definition of matrix multiplication to prove that for any $m \times n$ matrix A and any column vector $\mathbf{x} = [x_1 \quad x_2 \quad \cdots \quad x_n]^T$,

$$A\mathbf{x} = x_1 \, \text{col}_1 \, A + x_2 \, \text{col}_2 \, A + \cdots + x_n \, \text{col}_n \, A$$

3-6. Verify that $(AB)C = A(BC)$ for $A = \begin{bmatrix} a & b \\ c & d \end{bmatrix}$, $B = \begin{bmatrix} e & f \\ g & h \end{bmatrix}$, $C = \begin{bmatrix} w & x \\ y & z \end{bmatrix}$.

3-7. Refer to Section 3.1G. Use I1 and M1–M4 of Section 3.1F to prove

    (a) I2   **(b)** I3   **(c)** I4

You may assume that I5 was proved independently.

Section 3.2

3-8. Consider the 2×2 linear system: $x + 2y = -3$; $4x + 3y = 18$.

    (a) Form A, $\mathbf{x}$, $\mathbf{b}$, and $[A : \mathbf{b}]$ for the matrix form $A\mathbf{x} = \mathbf{b}$.

    (b) Find A^{-1} by (11) of Sections 3.1H and verify that $\bar{\mathbf{x}} = A^{-1}\mathbf{b}$ is a solution.

3-9. Do parts (a) and (b) of Exercise 3-8 for: $-2x + y = -1$; $3x - y = 3$.

3-10. Use Forward Substitution to complete $[L : \mathbf{b} : \bar{\mathbf{c}}]$ as in (11) of Section 3.2D.

    (a)
$$\begin{bmatrix} \textcircled{1} & & & : & 3 & : & \\ 2 & \textcircled{3} & & : & 0 & : & \\ 4 & 5 & \textcircled{6} & : & 4 & : & \end{bmatrix}$$
$$\underbrace{\qquad\qquad}_{L} \quad \underbrace{\ }_{\mathbf{b}} \quad \underbrace{\ }_{\bar{\mathbf{c}}}$$

    (b)
$$\begin{bmatrix} \textcircled{6} & & & : & -6 & : & \\ 5 & \textcircled{4} & & : & 3 & : & \\ 3 & 2 & \textcircled{1} & : & 0 & : & \end{bmatrix}$$
$$\underbrace{\qquad\qquad}_{L} \quad \underbrace{\ }_{\mathbf{b}} \quad \underbrace{\ }_{\bar{\mathbf{c}}}$$

    (c)
$$\begin{bmatrix} \textcircled{2} & & & & : & -2 & : & \\ 0 & \textcircled{1} & & & : & -1 & : & \\ -2 & 0 & \textcircled{3} & & : & 2 & : & \\ 0 & 1 & 1 & \textcircled{2} & : & -1 & : & \end{bmatrix}$$
$$\underbrace{\qquad\qquad}_{L} \quad \underbrace{\ }_{\mathbf{b}} \quad \underbrace{\ }_{\bar{\mathbf{c}}}$$

Verify that the $\bar{\mathbf{c}}$ obtained satisfies $L\bar{\mathbf{c}} = \mathbf{b}$.

3-11. Use Backward Substitution to complete $[U : \bar{\mathbf{c}} : \bar{\mathbf{x}}]$ as in (15) of Section 3.2E.

    (a)
$$\begin{bmatrix} \textcircled{6} & 5 & 4 & : & 4 & : & \\ & \textcircled{3} & 2 & : & 0 & : & \\ & & \textcircled{1} & : & 3 & : & \end{bmatrix}$$
$$\underbrace{\qquad\quad}_{U} \quad \underbrace{\ }_{\bar{\mathbf{c}}} \quad \underbrace{\ }_{\bar{\mathbf{x}}}$$

    (b)
$$\begin{bmatrix} 1 & 5 & -3 & : & -10 & : & \\ & 1 & -2 & : & -5 & : & \\ & & 1 & : & 2 & : & \end{bmatrix}$$
$$\underbrace{\qquad\quad}_{U} \quad \underbrace{\ }_{\bar{\mathbf{c}}} \quad \underbrace{\ }_{\bar{\mathbf{x}}}$$

(c)
$$\begin{bmatrix} 1 & 2 & 3 & 4 & : & 5 & : \\ & 1 & 5 & 6 & : & 4 & : \\ & & 1 & 7 & : & -5 & : \\ & & & 1 & : & -1 & : \end{bmatrix}$$
$$\underbrace{}_{U} \quad \underbrace{}_{\bar{c}}\ \underbrace{}_{x}$$

Verify that the $\bar{x}$ obtained satisfies $U\bar{x} = \bar{c}$.

3-12. How many arithmetic operations are needed when $n = 2, 3, 5, 10$, and 100?

    (a) To complete $[L : b : \bar{c}]$ (Forward Substitution).

    (b) To complete $[U : \bar{c} : \bar{x}]$ (Backward Substitution) when all u_{ii}'s are 1.

Section 3.3

3-13. Let A, L, and U be the following 2×2 matrices:

$$A = \begin{bmatrix} 4 & 3 \\ 2 & 2 \end{bmatrix}, \quad L = \begin{bmatrix} a & 0 \\ b & c \end{bmatrix}, \quad U = \begin{bmatrix} d & e \\ 0 & f \end{bmatrix} \quad (L, U \text{ real})$$

    (a) Form four scalar equations equivalent to the matrix equation $LU = A$.

    (b) Solve $LU = A$ for L and U (if possible) three ways:

        (i) Assuming U is unit upper-triangular (i.e., $d = f = 1$).

        (ii) Assuming L is unit lower-triangular (i.e., $a = c = 1$).

        (iii) Assuming $a = d > 0$ and $c = f > 0$.

3-14. Do parts (a) and (b) of Exercise 3-13 with $A = \begin{bmatrix} 2 & 1 \\ 1 & 0 \end{bmatrix}$.

3-15. Do parts (a) and (b) of Exercise 3-13 with $A = \begin{bmatrix} 4 & -2 \\ -2 & 2 \end{bmatrix}$.

3-16. Let $A = \begin{bmatrix} a_{11} & a_{12} & a_{13} \\ a_{21} & a_{22} & a_{23} \\ a_{31} & a_{32} & a_{33} \end{bmatrix}$, $L = \begin{bmatrix} l_{11} & 0 & 0 \\ l_{21} & l_{22} & 0 \\ l_{31} & l_{32} & l_{33} \end{bmatrix}$, $U = \begin{bmatrix} u_{11} & u_{12} & u_{13} \\ 0 & u_{22} & u_{23} \\ 0 & 0 & u_{33} \end{bmatrix}$.

    (a) Write out nine scalar equations equivalent to $LU = A$.

    (b) Show that the nine equations in part (a) and the conditions

$$u_{11} = u_{22} = u_{33} = 1$$

yield the formulas (10) of Section 3.3, provided that $l_{11}, l_{22}, l_{33} \neq 0$.

3-17. For the A matrices given in (a)–(d), show that the Triangular Decomposition Algorithm with (i) Basic Pivoting and (ii) Partial Pivoting yields the indicated LU-decomposition.

Matrix A	(i) Basic Pivoting	(ii) Partial Pivoting
(a) $\begin{bmatrix} 0 & 2 & 1 \\ -1 & 1 & 0 \\ 2 & -1 & 3 \end{bmatrix}$	$\begin{bmatrix} \textcircled{-1} & -1 & 0 \\ 0 & \textcircled{2} & \frac{1}{2} \\ 2 & 1 & \textcircled{\frac{5}{2}} \end{bmatrix}$ $(\rho_1 \rightleftarrows \rho_2)$	$\begin{bmatrix} \textcircled{2} & -\frac{1}{2} & \frac{3}{2} \\ 0 & \textcircled{2} & \frac{1}{2} \\ -1 & \frac{1}{2} & \textcircled{\frac{5}{4}} \end{bmatrix}$ $(\rho_1 \rightleftarrows \rho_3)$ $(\rho_2 \rightleftarrows \rho_3)$

(b)
$$\begin{bmatrix} 1 & 2 & 1 \\ 2 & -1 & 2 \\ 0 & 1 & 3 \end{bmatrix} \quad \begin{bmatrix} ①& 2 & 1 \\ 2 & -5 & 0 \\ 0 & 1 & ③ \end{bmatrix} = L\backslash U \quad \begin{bmatrix} ② & -\frac{1}{2} & 1 \\ 1 & \frac{5}{2} & 0 \\ 0 & 1 & ③ \end{bmatrix}(\rho_1 \rightleftarrows \rho_2)$$

(c)
$$\begin{bmatrix} 0 & 2 & 1 & 4 \\ 1 & -1 & -2 & 0 \\ 2 & 0 & 0 & 6 \\ -1 & 3 & 2 & 0 \end{bmatrix} \quad \begin{bmatrix} ① & -1 & -2 & 0 \\ 0 & ② & \frac{1}{2} & 2 \\ 2 & 2 & ③ & \frac{2}{3} \\ -1 & 2 & -1 & -\frac{10}{3} \end{bmatrix}(\rho_1 \rightleftarrows \rho_2) \quad \begin{bmatrix} ② & 0 & 0 & 3 \\ -1 & ③ & \frac{2}{3} & 1 \\ 1 & -1 & -\frac{4}{3} & \frac{3}{2} \\ 0 & 2 & -\frac{1}{3} & \frac{5}{2} \end{bmatrix}\begin{matrix}(\rho_1 \rightleftarrows \rho_3)\\(\rho_2 \rightleftarrows \rho_4)\\(\rho_3 \rightleftarrows \rho_4)\end{matrix}$$

(d)
$$\begin{bmatrix} 1 & 0 & -2 & 1 \\ 0 & 2 & 0 & 4 \\ 3 & 0 & -1 & 0 \\ 0 & -1 & -1 & 0 \end{bmatrix} \quad \begin{bmatrix} ① & 0 & -2 & 1 \\ 0 & ② & 0 & 2 \\ 3 & 0 & ⑤ & -\frac{3}{5} \\ 0 & -1 & -1 & \frac{7}{5} \end{bmatrix} = L\backslash U \quad \begin{bmatrix} ③ & 0 & -\frac{1}{3} & 0 \\ 0 & ② & 0 & 2 \\ 1 & 0 & -\frac{5}{3} & -\frac{3}{5} \\ 0 & -1 & -1 & \frac{7}{5} \end{bmatrix}(\rho_1 \rightleftarrows \rho_3)$$

3-18. In (a)–(e), obtain $\hat{A}$ and A from the given LU-decomposition. Show work.

	LU-decomposition	$\hat{A}$	A

(a) $\begin{bmatrix} ② & 4 & 1 \\ 0 & ② & 1 \\ 1 & -1 & ① \end{bmatrix}\begin{matrix}(\rho_1 \rightleftarrows \rho_2)\\(\rho_2 \rightleftarrows \rho_3)\end{matrix}$ $\begin{bmatrix} 2 & 8 & 2 \\ 0 & 2 & 2 \\ 1 & 3 & 1 \end{bmatrix}$ $\begin{bmatrix} 1 & 3 & 1 \\ 2 & 8 & 2 \\ 0 & 2 & 2 \end{bmatrix}$

(b) $\begin{bmatrix} ① & -1 & 0 \\ 0 & ② & 2 \\ 2 & 4 & ① \end{bmatrix}\begin{matrix}(\rho_1 \rightleftarrows \rho_3)\\(\rho_2 \rightleftarrows \rho_3)\end{matrix}$ $\begin{bmatrix} 1 & -1 & 0 \\ 0 & 2 & 4 \\ 2 & 2 & 9 \end{bmatrix}$ $\begin{bmatrix} 0 & 2 & 4 \\ 2 & 2 & 9 \\ 1 & -1 & 0 \end{bmatrix}$

(c) $\begin{bmatrix} ② & 1 & -1 \\ -1 & ② & 1 \\ 2 & 0 & -2 \end{bmatrix}(\rho_2 \rightleftarrows \rho_3)$ $\begin{bmatrix} 2 & 2 & -2 \\ -1 & 1 & 3 \\ 2 & 2 & -4 \end{bmatrix}$ $\begin{bmatrix} 2 & 2 & -2 \\ 2 & 2 & -4 \\ -1 & 1 & 3 \end{bmatrix}$

(d) $\begin{bmatrix} ① & -1 & 0 & 1 \\ 2 & -1 & 1 & -1 \\ 3 & 0 & ② & 1 \\ 4 & 2 & 0 & -2 \end{bmatrix} = L\backslash U$ $\begin{bmatrix} 1 & -1 & 0 & 1 \\ 2 & -3 & -1 & 3 \\ 3 & -3 & 2 & 5 \\ 4 & -2 & 2 & 0 \end{bmatrix}$ $\begin{bmatrix} 1 & -1 & 0 & 1 \\ 2 & -3 & -1 & 3 \\ 3 & -3 & 2 & 5 \\ 4 & -2 & 2 & 0 \end{bmatrix}$

(e) $\begin{bmatrix} ② & -1 & 1 & -1 \\ 4 & ② & 0 & -2 \\ 3 & 0 & ② & 1 \\ 1 & -1 & 0 & ① \end{bmatrix}\begin{matrix}(\rho_1 \rightleftarrows \rho_2)\\(\rho_2 \rightleftarrows \rho_4)\end{matrix}$ $\begin{bmatrix} 2 & -2 & 2 & -2 \\ 4 & -2 & 4 & -8 \\ 3 & -3 & 5 & -1 \\ 1 & -2 & 1 & 2 \end{bmatrix}$ $\begin{bmatrix} 1 & -2 & 1 & 2 \\ 2 & -2 & 2 & -2 \\ 3 & -3 & 5 & -1 \\ 4 & -2 & 4 & -8 \end{bmatrix}$

3-19. By inspection of (a)–(e) of Exercise 3-18, determine whether the given LU-decomposition would have been obtained using Basic Pivoting (BP), Partial Pivoting (PP), both, or neither. Give reasons.

3-20. In (a)–(f), use the indicated LU-decomposition to solve $Ax = b$ by completing a forback matrix $[\hat{L}\backslash\hat{U} : \hat{b} : \bar{c} : \bar{x}]$ as in (22) and (23) of Section 3.3F.

(a) A and $\hat{L}\backslash\hat{U}$ of Exercise 3-18(a); $b = [1 \quad 4 \quad 2]^T$.

(b) A and $\hat{L}\backslash\hat{U}$ of Exercise 3-18(b); $b = [2 \quad -3 \quad -4]^T$.

(c) A and $\hat{L}\backslash\hat{U}$ of Exercise 3-18(d); $b = [2 \quad 3 \quad 8 \quad 10]^T$.

(d) A and $\hat{L}\backslash\hat{U}$ of Exercise 3-18(e); $b = [5 \quad 2 \quad 3 \quad -2]^T$.

(e) A and $\hat{L}\backslash\hat{U}$ of Exercise 3-17(a)(i); $b = [1 \quad -2 \quad 2]^T$.

(f) A and $\hat{L}\backslash\hat{U}$ of Exercise 3-17(d)(ii); $b = [-1 \quad 8 \quad 3 \quad -1]^T$.

3-21. Deduce the **factorization** step formula of Table 3.3-1 from (24) of Section 3.3H. Recall that

$$\sum_{m=1}^{n-1} m = \frac{n(n-1)}{2} \quad \text{and} \quad \sum_{m=1}^{n-1} m^2 = \frac{n(n-1)(2n-1)}{6}$$

3-22. Refer to Table 3.3-1. How many arithmetic operations are needed when $n = 2$, 3, 5, 10, and 100?

(a) To get an LU-decomposition of $A_{n \times n}$ (i.e., to do the **factorization** step).

(b) To complete $[\hat{L}\backslash\hat{U} : \hat{b} : \bar{c} : \bar{x}]$ (i.e. to do the **forback** step [see Exercise 3-12(b)]).

(c) To solve $Ax = b$ by the Triangular Decomposition Algorithm.

Section 3.4

3-23. For $[A : b]$ given in (a)–(d), use Gaussian elimination with *Basic* Pivoting, performing all 1-SCALEs, to solve $Ax = b$.

(a) $\begin{bmatrix} 0 & 2 & 1 & : & 3 \\ -1 & 1 & 0 & : & 2 \\ 2 & -1 & 3 & : & -5 \end{bmatrix}$
(b) $\begin{bmatrix} 1 & 2 & 1 & : & 1 \\ 2 & -1 & 2 & : & -3 \\ 0 & 1 & 3 & : & 1 \end{bmatrix}$

(c) $\begin{bmatrix} 0 & 2 & 1 & 4 & : & -3 \\ 1 & -1 & -2 & 0 & : & 0 \\ 2 & 0 & 0 & 6 & : & -2 \\ -1 & 3 & 2 & 0 & : & 0 \end{bmatrix}$
(d) $\begin{bmatrix} 1 & 0 & -2 & 1 & : & 8 \\ 0 & 2 & 0 & 4 & : & 6 \\ 3 & 0 & -1 & 0 & : & 3 \\ 0 & -1 & -1 & 0 & : & 4 \end{bmatrix}$

3-24. From your solutions of (a)–(d) of Exercise 3-23, form $\hat{L}\backslash\hat{U}$ using (7) of Section 3.4C. Compare to $\hat{L}\backslash\hat{U}$ in (i) of Exercise 3-17.

3-25. For $[A : b]$ given in (a)–(d) of Exercise 3-23, using Gaussian elimination with *Partial* Pivoting, performing all 1-SCALEs, to solve $Ax = b$.

3-26. From your solutions of (a)–(d) of Exercise 3-25, form $\hat{L}\backslash\hat{U}$ using (7) of Section 3.4C. Compare to $\hat{L}\backslash\hat{U}$ in (ii) of Exercise 3-17.

3-27. For $[A : b]$ given in (a)–(d) of Exercise 3-23, use Gaussian elimination with Partial Pivoting but *without using 1-SCALEs*, to solve $Ax = b$.

3-28. Show that the following matrices are singular (see Section 3.4E).

(a) $\begin{bmatrix} 1 & 2 & 3 \\ 4 & 5 & 6 \\ 7 & 8 & 9 \end{bmatrix}$ (b) $\begin{bmatrix} -1 & 2 & 3 \\ 0 & 1 & 4 \\ 2 & -4 & -6 \end{bmatrix}$ (c) $\begin{bmatrix} 1 & -1 & -1 & -2 \\ 2 & -3 & 2 & -1 \\ 3 & -5 & 5 & 0 \\ 1 & -2 & 3 & 1 \end{bmatrix}$

3-29. For $[T : d]$ given in (a)–(c), use Gaussian elimination (Figure 3.4-2) to solve the tridiagonal system $Tx = d$.

(a) $\begin{bmatrix} 3 & 2 & & : & 5 \\ 1 & 2 & 1 & : & 2 \\ & 2 & 6 & : & -4 \end{bmatrix}$ (b) $\begin{bmatrix} 4 & 1 & & & : & 6 \\ 1 & 4 & 1 & & : & -4 \\ & 1 & 4 & 1 & : & 5 \\ & & 1 & 4 & : & -2 \end{bmatrix}$

(c) $\begin{bmatrix} 3 & -1 & & & : & -1 \\ -1 & 3 & -1 & & : & 3 \\ & -1 & 3 & -1 & : & -2 \\ & & -1 & 3 & : & 3 \end{bmatrix}$

3-30. For $n = 2, 3, 5, 10,$ and 100, how many arithmetic operations are needed to solve a tridiagonal system $Tx = d$ using Gaussian elimination? [See (12) of Section 3.4D.]

Section 3.5

3-31. If $\alpha = \det(A_{n \times n})$ and $\beta = \det(B_{n \times n}) \neq 0$, express in terms of α, β, and n:
(a) $\det(-A)$ (b) $\det(AB)$ (c) $\det(3AB^2)$ (d) $\det(AB^{-1})$
(e) $\det(A + A)$ (f) $\det[(B^{-1}A^2)^3]$

3-32. For $A = \begin{bmatrix} a & b \\ c & d \end{bmatrix}$ and $B = \begin{bmatrix} e & f \\ g & h \end{bmatrix}$, verify that

(a) $\det(sA) = s^2 \det A$ for any scalar s.
(b) $\det(AB) = (\det A)(\det B)$. [Product Theorem]
(c) $\det(A^{-1}) = 1/(\det A)$. [Assume $\det A \neq 0$ and use (11) of Section 3.1H.]

(d) $\det(A^T) = \det A$, where $A^T = \begin{bmatrix} a & c \\ b & d \end{bmatrix}$.

3-33. (a) Use the Product Theorem to prove that any $n \times n$ matrix A which is its own inverse must satisfy $|\det A| = 1$ (i.e., $\det A = \pm 1$).
(b) Find an $A_{2 \times 2}$ such that $A^2 = I_2$, $\det A = -1$, and all a_{ij}'s are nonzero.
(c) Show that if $A_{2 \times 2}$ satisfies $A^2 = I_2$ and $\det A = 1$, then $A = \pm I_2$.

3-34. Refer to Section 3.5B. In (a) and (b), A is any $n \times n$ matrix.
(a) Use the definition of $\det A$ to prove (i) D1; (ii) D2; (iii) D3.
(b) Use D3 to prove D4.

3-35. In Table 3.5-1, show that interchanging α and β changes the sign of all $(-1)^\delta$ entries. How is this related to D2 of Section 3.5B?

In Exercises 3-36 through 3-38, use D8 of Section 3.5C to evaluate det A.

3-36. For the matrices A given in (a)–(d) of Exercise 3-17, show that the two given LU-decompositions yield the same value of det A.

3-37. Use D7 of Section 3.5B to find $\det(A^{-1})$ for the matrices A given in (a)–(e) of Exercise 3-18.

3-38. Find the number of arithmetic operations needed to solve $A\mathbf{x} = \mathbf{b}$ by Cramer's rule for $n = 2$, 3, 5, 10, and 100. Assume that determinants are evaluated by finding an LU-decomposition of A, then using D8 of Section 3.5C [see Exercise 3-22(a)]. Compare it to Exercise 3-22(c). What can you conclude from the comparison?

Section 3.6

3-39. Let A and $\hat{L} \backslash \hat{U}$ be given in the indicated exercise. Solve $A\mathbf{x} = \mathbf{b}_j$ for all given $\mathbf{b}_j$'s simultaneously by forming and completing $[\hat{L} \backslash \hat{U} : \hat{B} : \overline{C} : \overline{X}]$ as in Section 3.6A. Verify that $A\overline{X} = B$.
  (a) Exercise 3-18(a); $\mathbf{b}_1 = [1 \quad 4 \quad 2]^T$, $\mathbf{b}_2 = [1 \quad 4 \quad -2]^T$.
  (b) Exercise 3-18(b); $\mathbf{b}_1 = [2 \quad 7 \quad 1]^T$, $\mathbf{b}_2 = [6 \quad 7 \quad -3]^T$, $\mathbf{b}_3 = [0 \quad 2 \quad 1]^T$.
  (c) Exercise 3-18(c); $\mathbf{b}_1 = [1 \quad 0 \quad 0]^T$, $\mathbf{b}_2 = [0 \quad 1 \quad 0]^T$, $\mathbf{b}_3 = [0 \quad 0 \quad 1]^T$.
  (d) Exercise 3-18(d); $\mathbf{b}_1 = [1 \quad 1 \quad 3 \quad 6]^T$, $\mathbf{b}_2 = [3 \quad 9 \quad 9 \quad 4]^T$.
  (e) Exercise 3-18(e); $\mathbf{b}_1 = [4 \quad 2 \quad 5 \quad 0]^T$, $\mathbf{b}_2 = [0 \quad 6 \quad 9 \quad 16]^T$.

3-40. Use the LU-Decomposition given in (a)–(e) of Exercise 3-18 to find A^{-1} by forming and completing $[\hat{L} \backslash \hat{U} : \hat{I}_n : \overline{C} : \overline{X}]$ as in Section 3.6B. Verify that $A\overline{X} = I_n$.

3-41. For $n = 2$, 3, 5, 10, and 100, how many arithmetic operations are needed to find A^{-1} as indicated in parts (a) and (b)?
  (a) Use the Triangular Decomposition Algorithm. (See Table 3.6-1.)
  (b) Use the formula given in (1) of Section 3.6. [See Exercise 3-22(a).]
  What conclusions can you draw from your answers to parts (a) and (b)?

3-42. For A given in (a)–(e) of Exercise 3-18, use Gauss–Jordan elimination with any pivoting strategy, either with or without 1-SCALEs, to find A^{-1}.

3-43. If B is $n \times p$, find a formula for the number of arithmetic operations needed to solve $AX = B$ using Gauss–Jordan elimination without 1-SCALEs. Compare to Table 3.6-1.

Computer and Programming Exercises (See Chapter 4)

4

Solving Linear and Nonlinear Systems Using Fixed Precision Arithmetic

In this chapter we describe how to use the direct methods of Chapter 3 effectively when *fixed precision* rather than exact arithmetic is used. The Gauss–Seidel method, which is an *iterative method* for solving linear systems, is then described. Finally, we show how the Newton–Raphson method can be applied to *nonlinear systems* of equations.

The reader is assumed to be familiar with the use of the Triangular Decomposition Algorithm to solve either a single linear system $A\mathbf{x} = \mathbf{b}$ (Section 3.3E) or several linear systems simultaneously, that is, $AX = B$ (Section 3.6B).

Minimizing the Effects of Roundoff **4.1**

The following example shows that when solving $A\mathbf{x} = \mathbf{b}$ in fixed-precision arithmetic, the accuracy of the solution can depend upon the pivoting strategy used.

4.1A EXAMPLE. Solve the 2×2 linear system

$$
\begin{align}
(E_1) \quad & 0.01x_1 + 100x_2 = 100 \\
(E_2) \quad & x_1 + x_2 = 2
\end{align}
\qquad
\left([A : \mathbf{b}] = \begin{bmatrix} 0.01 & 100 & : & 100 \\ 1 & 1 & : & 2 \end{bmatrix} \right)
\qquad (1)
$$

Use 3s arithmetic; that is, round to 3s after each calculation.

Solution 1. With Basic Pivoting (BP) one quickly gets

$$\hat{L}\backslash\hat{U} = \begin{bmatrix} \boxed{0.01} & 10,000 \\ \hline 1 & \boxed{-10,000} \end{bmatrix} = L\backslash U \tag{2a}$$

Notice that there is roundoff error in the second pivot l_{22} because

$$l_{22} = 1 - (1)(10,000) = -9999 \doteq -1.00 \cdot 10^4 = -10,000 \ (3s) \tag{2b}$$

Forming $[L\backslash U : \mathbf{b} : \bar{\mathbf{c}} : \bar{\mathbf{x}}]$ using $3s$ arithmetic yields

$$\begin{bmatrix} \boxed{0.01} & 10,000 & : & 100 & : & 10,000 & : & 0.00 \\ 1 & \boxed{-10,000} & : & 2 & : & 1.00 & : & 1.00 \end{bmatrix}; \quad \text{so } \bar{\mathbf{x}}_{\text{BP}} = \begin{bmatrix} 0.00 \\ 1.00 \end{bmatrix} \tag{3}$$

The critical intermediate calculations in (3) are

$$\bar{c}_2 = \frac{2 - 1\bar{c}_1}{\boxed{-10,000}} = \frac{2 - 10,000}{-10,000} \doteq \frac{-10,000}{-10,000} = 1.00 \tag{4}$$

$$\bar{x}_1 = 10,000 - 10,000\bar{x}_2 = 10,000 - 10,000\bar{c}_2 = 0.00 \tag{5}$$

Solution 2. Partial Pivoting (PP) results in the LU-decomposition

$$\hat{L}\backslash\hat{U} = \begin{bmatrix} \boxed{1} & 1 \\ \hline 0.01 & \boxed{100} \end{bmatrix} \quad (\rho_1 \rightleftarrows \rho_2) \tag{6a}$$

Here again, roundoff error is introduced in storing the second pivot:

$$\hat{l}_{22} = 100 - (0.01)(1) = 99.99 \doteq 1.00 \cdot 10^2 = 100 \ (3s) \tag{6b}$$

However, this time forming $[\hat{L}\backslash\hat{U} : \hat{\mathbf{b}} : \bar{\mathbf{c}} : \bar{\mathbf{x}}]$ using $3s$ arithmetic yields

$$\begin{bmatrix} \boxed{1} & 1 & : & 2 & : & 2 & : & 1.00 \\ 0.01 & \boxed{100} & : & 100 & : & 1.00 & : & 1.00 \end{bmatrix}; \quad \text{so } \bar{\mathbf{x}}_{\text{PP}} = \begin{bmatrix} 1.00 \\ 1.00 \end{bmatrix} \tag{7}$$

The critical intermediate calculations in (7) are

$$\bar{c}_2 = \frac{100 - 0.01\bar{c}_1}{\boxed{100}} = \frac{100 - 0.02}{\cdot \ 100} \doteq \frac{100}{100} = 1.00 \tag{8}$$

$$\bar{x}_1 = 2 - 1\bar{x}_2 = 2 - 1\bar{c}_2 = 1.00 \tag{9}$$

To get the exact $\bar{\mathbf{x}}$, we use the formula for A^{-1} given in (11) of Section 3.1H:

$$\bar{\mathbf{x}}_{\text{exact}} = A^{-1}\mathbf{b} = \frac{-1}{99.99} \begin{bmatrix} 1 & -100 \\ -1 & 0.01 \end{bmatrix} \begin{bmatrix} 100 \\ 2 \end{bmatrix} = \frac{-1}{99.99} \begin{bmatrix} -100 \\ -99.98 \end{bmatrix} \doteq \begin{bmatrix} 1.0001 \\ 0.9999 \end{bmatrix} \tag{10}$$

Upon comparing (10) with (3) and (7), we see that there is a serious error in the first component of $\bar{\mathbf{x}}_{\text{BP}}$, whereas $\bar{\mathbf{x}}_{\text{PP}}$ is accurate to $3s$.

4.1B   RATIONALE FOR EFFECTIVE PIVOTING STRATEGIES

In both solutions above, the roundoff error in the second pivot [see (2) and (6)] produced a small error in $\bar{c}_2$ [see (4) and (8)]. The troublesome error in Solution 1 occurred in (5) when *the small error in $\bar{c}_2$ got magnified when multiplied by u_{12}* = 10,000 in calculating $\bar{x}_1$. This magnification did not occur in (9) of Solution 2, where $\hat{u}_{12} = 1$. We see from this that when fixed-precision arithmetic is used,

> an effective pivoting strategy is one that produces a $\hat{U}$ whose
> entries are as small as possible, especially in the upper rows

which are used in the last steps of Backward Substitution. (These steps involve the components of $\bar{x}$ that are most likely to have large roundoff error.)

If we select $\hat{l}_{11} = a_{i1}$ (in the ith row of A), then by (12) of Section 3.3C,

$$\text{row}_1 \ \hat{U} = \frac{1}{a_{i1}} \text{row}_i \ A = \begin{bmatrix} 1 & \dfrac{a_{i2}}{a_{i1}} & \dfrac{a_{i3}}{a_{i1}} & \cdots & \dfrac{a_{in}}{a_{i1}} \end{bmatrix} \tag{11}$$

So the entries of row$_1$ $\hat{U}$ will be smallest if $\hat{l}_{11}$ is chosen as the entry of col$_1$ A whose magnitude is largest *compared to the magnitude of the remaining entries of its row*. A pivoting strategy that ensures this, not just for $\hat{l}_{11}$ but for *all* pivots, is the following.

The Scaled Partial Pivoting (SPP) Strategy for Selecting the mth Pivot

After getting col$_m$ $\hat{L}$, form the ratios

$$\frac{|\hat{l}_{im}|}{\hat{s}_i}, \ i = m, \ldots, n, \text{ where } \hat{s}_i = \text{largest absolute value in row}_i \ \hat{A} \tag{12}$$

Circle the $\hat{l}_{im}$ in col$_m$ $\hat{L}$ for which the ratio $|\hat{l}_{im}| / |\hat{s}_i|$ is largest.

Figure 4.1-1 illustrates the use of Scaled Partial Pivoting in getting an LU-decomposition of a 3×3 matrix. Initially, when $\hat{A} = A$, the row scale factors $\hat{s}_i$ (in the augmented part of the $[A \ \vdots \ \mathbf{s}]$ matrix) are

$$\hat{s}_1 = |-4| = 4, \quad \hat{s}_2 = |5| = 5, \quad \text{and} \quad \hat{s}_3 = |\pm 1| = 1 \tag{13}$$

The $\hat{s}_i$'s are then used in the $|\hat{l}_{im}|/\hat{s}_i$ column of Figure 4.1-1 to get the largest $|\hat{l}_{im}|/\hat{s}_i$ ratio in col$_1$ $\hat{L}$ (i.e., 1/1) then in col$_2$ $\hat{L}$ (i.e., 2/4). Once the mth pivot is circled, the factorization proceeds as in Figure 3.3-4. This LU-decomposition can now be used to find the solution $\bar{x}$ of $A\mathbf{x} = [-1 \quad -3 \quad 2]^T$ by forming and completing the forback matrix

$$[\hat{L}\backslash\hat{U} : \hat{\mathbf{b}} : \bar{\mathbf{c}} : \bar{\mathbf{x}}] = \begin{bmatrix} ① & -1 & 0 & \vdots & 2 & \vdots & 2 & \vdots & 3 \\ 2 & ⊝2 & -\frac{3}{2} & \vdots & -1 & \vdots & \frac{5}{2} & \vdots & 1 \\ 0 & 2 & ⑧ & \vdots & -3 & \vdots & -1 & \vdots & -1 \end{bmatrix}; \quad \text{so } \bar{\mathbf{x}} = \begin{bmatrix} 3 \\ 1 \\ -1 \end{bmatrix} \tag{14}$$

$$[A : \mathbf{s}] = \begin{array}{c} \text{Phase I} \\ \begin{bmatrix} 2 & -4 & 3 & : & 4 \\ 0 & 2 & 5 & : & 5 \\ 1 & -1 & 0 & : & 1 \end{bmatrix} \end{array} \!\!\!\succ\!\! \begin{array}{c} \text{Phase II} \\ \begin{bmatrix} 1 & -1 & 0 & : & 1 \\ 0 & 2 & 5 & : & 5 \\ 2 & -4 & 3 & : & 4 \end{bmatrix} \end{array} \!\!\!\succ\!\! \begin{array}{c} \text{Phase III} \\ \begin{bmatrix} 1 & -1 & 0 & : & 1 \\ 2 & -4 & 3 & : & 4 \\ 0 & 2 & 5 & : & 5 \end{bmatrix} \end{array} = [\hat{A} : \hat{\mathbf{s}}]$$

$$L \backslash U = \begin{bmatrix} 2 & & \\ 0 & & \\ \textcircled{1} & & \end{bmatrix} \!\!\!\succ\!\!\! \longrightarrow \begin{bmatrix} \textcircled{1} & -1 & 0 \\ 0 & 2 & \\ 2 & \textcircled{-2} & \end{bmatrix} \!\!\!\succ\!\!\! \longrightarrow \begin{bmatrix} \textcircled{1} & -1 & 0 \\ 2 & \textcircled{-2} & -\frac{3}{2} \\ 0 & 2 & \textcircled{8} \end{bmatrix} = \hat{L} \backslash \hat{U}$$

Intermediate Calculations (Scaled Partial Pivoting)

m	get col$_m$ $\hat{L}$	$|\hat{l}_{im}|/\hat{s}_i$	pivot	get row$_m$ $\hat{U}$
1	$\text{col}_1\ \hat{L} = \text{col}_1\ A = \begin{bmatrix} 2 \\ 0 \\ \textcircled{1} \end{bmatrix}$	$\frac{2}{4}$ $\frac{0}{5}$ $\frac{1}{1}$	$\rho_1 \rightleftarrows \rho_3$ $\left(\begin{array}{c} \text{Enter} \\ \text{phase II} \end{array} \right)$	$[\hat{u}_{12}\quad \hat{u}_{13}] = \dfrac{1}{\textcircled{1}}[-1 \quad 0]$ $= [-1 \quad 0]$
2	$\hat{l}_{22} = 2 - [0][-1] = 2$ $\hat{l}_{32} = -4 - [2][-1] = \textcircled{-2}$	$\frac{2}{5}$ $\frac{2}{4}$	$\rho_2 \rightleftarrows \rho_3$ $\left(\begin{array}{c} \text{Enter} \\ \text{phase III} \end{array} \right)$	$\hat{u}_{23} = \dfrac{1}{\textcircled{-2}}\{3 - [2][0]\}$ $= -\frac{3}{2}$
3	$\hat{l}_{33} = 5 - [0 \quad 2]\begin{bmatrix} 0 \\ -\frac{3}{2} \end{bmatrix} = 5 - (-3) = \textcircled{8}$			

FIGURE 4.1-1   GETTING $\hat{L}\backslash\hat{U}$ USING SCALED PARTIAL PIVOTING.

or (using D8 of Section 3.5C) to determine that

$$\det A = (-1)^2(1)(-2)(8) = -16 \tag{15}$$

Since Scaled Partial Pivoting usually requires more row interchanges than Basic Pivoting, there is generally no reason to use SPP with exact arithmetic. We just did so here for illustrative purposes.

4.1C PIVOTING IN THE PRESENCE OF ROUNDOFF ERRORS

Let s_i be the greatest absolute value in row$_i$ A. If it happens that

$$s_1 = s_2 = \cdots = s_n \tag{16}$$

then the Partial Pivoting (PP) and Scaled Partial Pivoting (SPP) strategies will yield identical LU-decompositions. (Why?)

For coefficient matrices that do not satisfy (16), small $\hat{U}$ entries (and correspondingly accurate solutions) will usually be obtained by simply choosing $\hat{l}_{mm}$ to be the entry of largest magnitude of $\text{col}_m \ \hat{L}$ for $m = 1, \ldots, n - 1$ (i.e., by using Partial Pivoting) provided that the largest s_i is not much larger than the smallest one. However, as the following example shows, Partial Pivoting may not yield the most accurate possible calculated solution when some s_i's are much larger than others.

EXAMPLE. Use 4s arithmetic to find the inverse of

$$A = \begin{bmatrix} 3 & 5 \\ 13 & 22 \end{bmatrix} \quad \left((A^{-1})_{\text{exact}} = \frac{1}{3 \cdot 22 - 5 \cdot 13} \begin{bmatrix} 22 & -5 \\ -13 & 3 \end{bmatrix} = \begin{bmatrix} 22 & -5 \\ -13 & 3 \end{bmatrix} \right) \quad (17)$$

Solution 1 (Using PP). The LU-decomposition, rounding to 4s after each operation, is

$$\hat{L}\backslash\hat{U} = \begin{bmatrix} \boxed{13} & \vdots & 1.692 \\ \hline 3 & \vdots & \boxed{-0.076} \end{bmatrix} \begin{matrix} (\rho_1 \rightleftarrows \rho_2) \end{matrix} \quad (18)$$

Forming $[\hat{L}\backslash\hat{U} : \hat{I}_2 : \overline{C} : \overline{X}]$ using 4s arithmetic gives

$$\begin{bmatrix} \boxed{13} & 1.692 & : & 0 & 1 & : & 0 & 0.0769 & : & 22.27 & -5.060 \\ 3 & \boxed{-0.076} & : & 1 & 0 & : & -13.16 & 3.036 & : & -13.16 & 3.036 \end{bmatrix} \quad (19)$$

$$\underbrace{}_{\hat{L}\backslash\hat{U}} \quad \underbrace{}_{\hat{I}_2} \quad \underbrace{}_{\overline{C}} \quad \underbrace{}_{\overline{X} = (A^{-1})_{\text{PP}}}$$

Solution 2 (Using SPP). This time the LU-decomposition, using 4s arithmetic, is

$$\hat{L}\backslash\hat{U} = \begin{bmatrix} \boxed{3} & \vdots & 1.667 \\ \hline 13 & \vdots & \boxed{0.3300} \end{bmatrix} = L\backslash U \qquad \begin{array}{l} |\hat{l}|/\hat{s} \text{ ratios } (m = 1) \\ \frac{3}{5} = 0.6 \text{ (largest)} \\[4pt] \frac{13}{22} = 0.5909 \end{array} \quad (20)$$

Forming $[\hat{L}\backslash\hat{U} : \hat{I}_2 : \overline{C} : \overline{X}]$ using 4s arithmetic gives

$$\begin{bmatrix} \boxed{3} & 1.667 & : & 1 & 0 & : & 0.3333 & 0 & : & 22.22 & -5.051 \\ 13 & \boxed{0.3300} & : & 0 & 1 & : & -13.13 & 3.030 & : & -13.13 & 3.030 \end{bmatrix} \quad (21)$$

$$\underbrace{}_{\hat{L}\backslash\hat{U}} \quad \underbrace{}_{\hat{I}_2 = I_2} \quad \underbrace{}_{\overline{C}} \quad \underbrace{}_{\overline{X} = (A^{-1})_{\text{SPP}}}$$

Upon comparing the exact inverse in (17) to $(A^{-1})_{\text{PP}}$ in (19) and $(A^{-1})_{\text{SPP}}$ in (21), we see that both solutions have errors in the third significant digit. Also, although the $|\hat{l}|/\hat{s}$ ratios (0.6 and 0.5909) indicated no compelling reason to take 3 (rather than 13) as $\hat{l}_{11}$ in (20), all entries of $(A^{-1})_{\text{SPP}}$ turned out to be more accurate than those of $(A^{-1})_{\text{PP}}$ when rounded to 3s. The conclusion to be reached is:

> When using fixed-precision arithmetic to solve $Ax = b$ or $AX = B$ by a direct method, it is worthwhile to invest the slight extra effort needed to use Scaled Partial Pivoting as the pivoting strategy.

To set a good example, we shall do this routinely from now on.

4.1D PARTIAL EXTENDED PRECISION

We saw in Section 3.3G that the number of algebraic operations needed to solve $A\mathbf{x} = \mathbf{b}$ increases like $2n^3/3$. So for large n, it becomes important to try to minimize propagated roundoff. The most obvious way to do this is simply to use extended precision for say $n \geq 10$. However, this doubles the amount of storage needed for $\hat{A}$, $\hat{L}\backslash\hat{U}$, $\hat{\mathbf{b}}$, $\bar{\mathbf{c}}$, and $\bar{\mathbf{x}}$. Essentially the same accuracy can be obtained if we do the following:

The Partial Extended Precision (PEP) Strategy. *Accumulate the inner products needed to calculate the entries of $\hat{L}\backslash\hat{U}$, $\bar{\mathbf{c}}$, and $\bar{\mathbf{x}}$ in extended precision, but store them rounded to single precision.*

This strategy is performed automatically when using a calculator that stores some "guard digits" in addition to those displayed. When using a computer, however, PEP is not performed automatically. In this situation, one extended precision variable can be used to get all n^2 entries of $\hat{L}\backslash\hat{U}$ and all entries of $\bar{\mathbf{c}}$ and $\bar{\mathbf{x}}$ as well (see Section 4.4B).

The improvement attainable as a result of the PEP strategy is illustrated in the following example.

EXAMPLE. Compare the solutions of $A\mathbf{x} = \mathbf{b}$ with and without PEP if

$$A = \begin{bmatrix} -0.072 & 0.300 & -0.210 \\ 0.874 & -0.267 & 0.133 \\ -0.500 & -0.123 & 0.125 \end{bmatrix} \quad \text{and} \quad \mathbf{b} = \begin{bmatrix} -0.630 \\ 0.399 \\ 0.375 \end{bmatrix} \tag{22}$$

Use $3s$ arithmetic for single precision and $6s$ for double precision.

Solution (Using SPP). For $\text{col}_1 L = \text{col}_1 A$, the $|l|/s$ ratios are

$$\frac{|l_{11}|}{s_1} = \frac{0.072}{0.300} = 0.24, \qquad \frac{|l_{21}|}{s_2} = \frac{0.874}{0.874} = 1, \qquad \text{and} \qquad \frac{|l_{31}|}{s_3} = \frac{0.500}{0.500} = 1 \tag{23}$$

The SPP strategy instructs us to perform *either* $\rho_1 \rightleftarrows \rho_2$ *or* $\rho_1 \rightleftarrows \rho_3$. If we (arbitrarily) choose 0.874 as $\hat{l}_{11}$, we get the LU-decomposition

$$\begin{bmatrix} \boxed{0.874} & -0.305 & 0.152 \\ -0.072 & \boxed{0.278} & -0.716 \\ -0.500 & -0.276 & \widehat{l_{33}} \end{bmatrix} \begin{matrix} (\rho_1 \rightleftarrows \rho_2) \\ \\ \\ \end{matrix} \quad \begin{matrix} |\hat{l}|/\hat{s} \text{ ratios } (m = 2) \\[1ex] \dfrac{0.278}{0.300} \quad \text{(largest)} \\[2ex] \dfrac{0.276}{0.500} \end{matrix} \tag{24}$$

whether extended precision is used in the intermediate calculations or not. (Check this.†) The calculation of $\hat{l}_{33}$ using Partial Extended Precision is

---

† In calculating $\hat{l}_{32} = -0.276$, we arbitrarily rounded $[-0.5][-0.305] = 0.1525$ to 0.153. Had we rounded it to 0.152, we would have obtained a slightly different answer.

$$\hat{l}_{33} = 0.125 - [-0.500 \quad -0.276]\begin{bmatrix} 0.152 \\ -0.716 \end{bmatrix} = 0.125 - 0.121616 \doteq 0.00338 \quad \textbf{(25)}$$

However, if we round to 3s after *each* operation, then

$$\hat{l}_{33} \doteq 0.125 - (-0.076 + 0.198) = 0.125 - 0.122 = 0.003 \quad \textbf{(26)}$$

So for the PEP solution, $[\hat{L}\backslash\hat{U} : \hat{\mathbf{b}} : \bar{\mathbf{c}} : \bar{\mathbf{x}}_{PEP}]$ (rounded to 3s) is

$$\begin{bmatrix} \boxed{0.874} & -0.305 & 0.152 & : & 0.399 & : & 0.457 & : & -0.000274 \\ -0.072 & \boxed{0.278} & -0.716 & : & -0.630 & : & -2.15 & : & -0.00916 \\ -0.500 & -0.276 & \boxed{0.00338} & : & 0.375 & : & 2.99 & : & 2.99 \end{bmatrix} \quad \textbf{(27)}$$

whereas without PEP (in 3s arithmetic), $[\hat{L}\backslash\hat{U} : \hat{\mathbf{b}} : \bar{\mathbf{c}} : \bar{\mathbf{x}}_{noPEP}]$ is

$$\begin{bmatrix} \boxed{0.874} & -0.305 & 0.152 & : & 0.399 & : & 0.457 & : & 0.0212 \\ -0.072 & \boxed{0.278} & -0.716 & : & -0.630 & : & -2.15 & : & 0.23 \\ -0.500 & -0.276 & \boxed{0.003} & : & 0.375 & : & 3.33 & : & 3.33 \end{bmatrix} \quad \textbf{(28)}$$

So

$$\bar{\mathbf{x}}_{PEP} = [-0.000274 \quad -0.00916 \quad 2.99]^T \quad \text{and} \quad \bar{\mathbf{x}}_{noPEP} = [0.0212 \quad 0.23 \quad 3.33]^T$$

The exact solution is $\bar{\mathbf{x}} = [0 \quad 0 \quad 3]^T$. So $\bar{\mathbf{x}}_{PEP}$ is considerably more accurate.

The inaccuracy of the first two components of both $\bar{\mathbf{x}}_{PEP}$ and $\bar{\mathbf{x}}_{noPEP}$ reflects the fact that *in fixed precision, it is difficult for a sum of products to add up to exactly zero.* The problem was not too pronounced because, as a result of the SPP strategy, the entries of row_1 $\hat{U}$ and row_2 $\hat{U}$ were small. Both calculated $\bar{\mathbf{x}}$'s would have been considerably worse if, say, Basic Pivoting were used.

Recognizing an Ill-Conditioned Coefficient Matrix   **4.2**

For most matrix equations $AX = B$, small perturbations in A or B produce correspondingly small changes in the solution $\bar{X} = A^{-1}B$. However, even in the $n = 1$ case of solving $ax = b$ for $\bar{x} = b/a$, it is possible for small variations in a or b to produce large changes in $\bar{x}$. These disproportionate changes occur when a is near zero and the large reciprocal $a^{-1} = 1/a$ causes error magnification. The generalization of $a \approx 0$ is given next.

4.2A   ILL-CONDITIONED MATRICES

An $n \times n$ matrix A is called **ill conditioned** or **nearly singular** if there exist vectors **b** for which small changes in the entries of A and/or **b** can cause disproportionately large changes in those of $\bar{\mathbf{x}} = A^{-1}\mathbf{b}$. Since error magnification in $\bar{\mathbf{x}} = A^{-1}\mathbf{b}$ will be likely when A^{-1} has large entries, *ill conditioning should be suspected whenever A^{-1} has entries that are much larger than 1.*

EXAMPLE. In view of formula (11) of Section 3.1H,

$$A = \begin{bmatrix} -0.1 & 1 \\ 0.12 & -1 \end{bmatrix} \Rightarrow A^{-1} = \frac{1}{0.02}\begin{bmatrix} -1 & -1 \\ -0.12 & -0.1 \end{bmatrix} = \begin{bmatrix} 50 & 50 \\ 6 & 5 \end{bmatrix}$$

Since the entries of A^{-1} are as large as 50, we suspect that A is ill conditioned. To demonstrate that it is, consider the system

$$\begin{array}{ll} (\mathrm{E}_1) & -0.1x_1 + x_2 = -2 \\ (\mathrm{E}_2) & 0.12x_1 - x_2 = 2.2 \end{array} \quad \left(\bar{\mathbf{x}} = A^{-1}\mathbf{b} = \begin{bmatrix} 50 & 50 \\ 6 & 5 \end{bmatrix}\begin{bmatrix} -2 \\ 2.2 \end{bmatrix} = \begin{bmatrix} 10 \\ -1 \end{bmatrix}\right) \qquad (1)$$

The effect of some small perturbations of A and/or $\mathbf{b}$ on $\bar{\mathbf{x}} = A^{-1}\mathbf{b}$ is shown in Table 4.2-1.

TABLE **4.2-1** THREE SYSTEMS OBTAINED AS SMALL PERTURBATIONS OF $A\mathbf{x} = \mathbf{b}$.

New System	Change from (1)	Solution $\bar{\mathbf{x}}$	Change from $[10 \ -1]^T$
(a) $-0.1x_1 + x_2 = -2$ $\quad0.12x_1 - x_2 = 2.0$	$\Delta b_2 = -0.2$	$\bar{\mathbf{x}} = \begin{bmatrix} 0 \\ -2 \end{bmatrix}$	$\Delta\bar{\mathbf{x}} = \begin{bmatrix} 0 \\ -2 \end{bmatrix} - \begin{bmatrix} 10 \\ -1 \end{bmatrix} = \begin{bmatrix} -10 \\ -1 \end{bmatrix}$
(b) $-0.1x_1 + x_2 = -2$ $\quad0.11x_1 - x_2 = 2.2$	$\Delta a_{21} = -0.01$	$\bar{\mathbf{x}} = \begin{bmatrix} 20 \\ 0 \end{bmatrix}$	$\Delta\bar{\mathbf{x}} = \begin{bmatrix} 20 \\ 0 \end{bmatrix} - \begin{bmatrix} 10 \\ -1 \end{bmatrix} = \begin{bmatrix} 10 \\ 1 \end{bmatrix}$
(c) $-0.1x_1 + x_2 = -2$ $\quad0.11x_1 - x_2 = 2.1$	$\Delta b_2 = -0.1$ and $\Delta a_{21} = -0.01$	$\bar{\mathbf{x}} = \begin{bmatrix} 10 \\ -1 \end{bmatrix}$	$\Delta\bar{\mathbf{x}} = \begin{bmatrix} 10 \\ -1 \end{bmatrix} - \begin{bmatrix} 10 \\ -1 \end{bmatrix} = \begin{bmatrix} 0 \\ 0 \end{bmatrix}$

The small changes Δb_2 and Δa_{21} in (a) and (b) of Table 4.2-1 produced large changes in $\bar{\mathbf{x}}$. So A is ill conditioned. However the small changes in (c) produced no change in $\bar{\mathbf{x}}$. In summary:

> When a coefficient matrix A is ill conditioned, small errors in A and/or $\mathbf{b}$ can, *but need not,* produce larger errors in $\bar{\mathbf{x}} = A^{-1}\mathbf{b}$.

If A is severely ill conditioned, inherent error alone may cause $\bar{\mathbf{x}}_{\mathrm{calc}} = (A_{\mathrm{stored}})^{-1}\mathbf{b}_{\mathrm{stored}}$ to differ greatly from $\bar{\mathbf{x}} = A^{-1}\mathbf{b}$; in this case $\bar{\mathbf{x}}_{\mathrm{calc}}$ can be seriously in error even if calculated exactly! So it is important to be able to recognize an ill-conditioned matrix when one is encountered. We now show how this can be done.

4.2B   THE PIVOT CONDITION NUMBER $C_p(A)$

An $n \times n$ matrix is singular if and only if its determinant is zero. The terminology "nearly singular" suggests that ill conditioning is related to det A being "small." But how small is "small"? The answer can be found by examining the equivalent systems

$$A\mathbf{x} = \mathbf{b} \quad \text{and} \quad (sA)\mathbf{x} = s\mathbf{b} \quad (s \text{ is any nonzero scalar}) \qquad (2)$$

The ith equation of $(sA)\mathbf{x} = s\mathbf{b}$ is s times the ith equation of $A\mathbf{x} = \mathbf{b}$. So there is no reason to expect the solutions of either system to be more sensitive to errors in A or $\mathbf{b}$ than the other. However, since $\det(sA) = s^n \det A$ (see D4 of Section 3.5B), the determinant of sA can be made as large or as small as we please by selecting s accordingly. A useful rule of thumb is that

> A is ill conditioned when the number $|\det A|$ is small
> compared to the magnitude of the entries of A. $\qquad$ (3)

This was certainly the case in the example in Section 4.2A. More generally, it follows from the formula for A^{-1} given in (1) of Section 3.6 that if $|\det A|$ is small compared to the entries of A, then A^{-1} is likely to have large entries (indicating that A is ill conditioned).

Much energy has been spent in search of easily computed numbers that indicate how ill conditioned A is. Unfortunately, many of the more reliable formulas found require knowing A^{-1}. Such indicators are of limited practical value when one would not otherwise go to the trouble of finding A^{-1}, for example, when solving a single linear system $A\mathbf{x} = \mathbf{b}$ when $n > 2$.

A reliable indicator that can be obtained by inspection in the course of either the LU-decomposition or Gaussian Elimination Algorithm is the **pivot condition number** $C_p(A)$ defined by

$$C_p(A) = \frac{|\hat{l}_{nn}|}{\hat{s}_n} = \text{the } |\hat{l}|/\hat{s} \text{ ratio for the } n\text{th pivot of } \hat{L}\backslash\hat{U} \qquad (4)$$

The number $|\hat{l}_{nn}|$ is an indicator of the extent to which

$$\text{row}_i \, A \approx \sum_{k \neq i} m_{jk} \, \text{row}_k \, A \qquad \text{for some } i$$

with $\hat{l}_{nn} = 0$ corresponding to equality, in which case A is singular [see (17) of Section 3.5E]. Dividing $|\hat{l}_{nn}|$ by the scale factor for the nth row of $\hat{A}$ compensates for the effects of scaling, so that

$$A \text{ is ill conditioned when } C_p(A) \ll 1, \text{ say } C_p(A) < \frac{1}{20} = 0.05 \qquad (5)$$

Note: The number $C_p(A)$ in (4) depends upon the pivoting strategy used to get $\hat{L}\backslash\hat{U}$. However, criterion (5) will generally reveal an ill-conditioned matrix no matter what pivoting strategy is used, with PP and SPP giving the most reliable results.

EXAMPLE. Discuss the condition of the matrices considered in Section 4.1, namely

$$A_{4.1A} = \begin{bmatrix} 0.01 & 100 \\ 1 & 1 \end{bmatrix}, \quad A_{4.1C} = \begin{bmatrix} 3 & 5 \\ 13 & 22 \end{bmatrix}, \quad A_{4.1D} = \begin{bmatrix} -0.072 & 0.300 & -0.210 \\ 0.874 & -0.267 & 0.133 \\ -0.500 & -0.123 & 0.125 \end{bmatrix} \qquad (6)$$

FOR $A_{4.1\text{A}}$. In (6a) of Section 4.1A we used Partial Pivoting to get

$$\hat{L}\backslash\hat{U}=\begin{bmatrix} ① & \vdots & 1 \\ \cdots\cdots & \cdots & \cdots\cdots \\ 0.01 & \vdots & ⑩⓪ \end{bmatrix}; \qquad \text{hence } C_p(A_{4.1\text{A}})=\frac{|\hat{l}_{22}|}{\hat{s}_2}=\frac{100}{100}=1 \tag{7}$$

view of (5), $A_{4.1\text{A}}$ is *not* ill conditioned. Since $\bar{\mathbf{x}}_{\text{PP}}$ (which would also have been obtained if SPP were used) was much more accurate than $\bar{\mathbf{x}}_{\text{BP}}$, the example in Section 4.1A shows that *PP or SPP can give better accuracy than BP even if A is well conditioned.*

FOR $A_{4.1\text{C}}$. We saw in (18) and (20) of Section 4.1C that PP and SPP give

$$\hat{L}\backslash\hat{U}=\begin{bmatrix} ⑬ & \vdots & 1.692 \\ \cdots\cdots & \cdots & \cdots\cdots \\ 3 & \vdots & \boxed{-0.076} \end{bmatrix}(\rho_1 \rightleftarrows \rho_2) \quad \text{and} \quad \hat{L}\backslash\hat{U}=\begin{bmatrix} ③ & \vdots & 1.667 \\ \cdots\cdots & \cdots & \cdots\cdots \\ 13 & \vdots & \boxed{0.3300} \end{bmatrix}=L\backslash U \tag{8}$$

respectively. These in turn give, respectively,

$$C_p(A_{4.1\text{C}})=\frac{0.076}{5}=0.0152 \qquad \text{and} \qquad C_p(A_{4.1\text{C}})=\frac{0.33}{22}=0.015 \tag{9}$$

Either calculation shows A to be ill conditioned. This explains why both the PP and SPP strategies (without PEP) produced calculated inverses with errors in the second or third significant digit despite the fact that $4s$ arithmetic was used. Since the numbers appearing in $(A_{4.1\text{C}})^{-1}$ are the same as those in $A_{4.1\text{C}}$ itself (with the largest being 22), the example in Section 4.1C shows that *A can be ill conditioned even though the entries of A^{-1} are not much larger than those of A.*

FOR $A_{4.1\text{D}}$. We see from (26) of Section 4.1D that with SPP as the pivoting strategy,

$$C_p(A_{4.1\text{D}})=\frac{|\hat{l}_{33}|}{\hat{s}_3}\doteq\frac{0.003}{0.500}=0.006<<1 \tag{10}$$

So $A_{4.1\text{D}}$ is very ill conditioned. The example in Section 4.1D thus shows that *if both Scaled Partial Pivoting and Partial Extended Precision are used, then reasonably accurate solutions can be obtained even if A is poorly conditioned.*

4.2C   THE CONDITION NUMBER cond A (OPTIONAL)

It is customary to use the word *norm* and the symbol "$\|\cdot\|$" to indicate the "size" or "length" of a member of a vector space. A natural indicator of the size of $\mathbf{x}=[x_1 \cdots x_n]^T$ in n-space is the **Euclidean norm** (or **2-norm**)

$$\|\mathbf{x}\|_2=\sqrt{\mathbf{x}^T\mathbf{x}}=\sqrt{x_1^2+x_2^2+\cdots+x_n^2} \tag{11a}$$

Unfortunately, $\|\mathbf{x}\|_2$ is expensive to compute on a digital device. More frequently used are $\|\mathbf{x}\|_1$ and $\|\mathbf{x}\|_\infty$ defined as follows†:

---

† In this notation, the row scale factor $\hat{s}_n$ used to get $C_p(A)$ is $\|\text{row}_n \hat{A}\|_\infty$.

$$||\mathbf{x}||_1 = \sum_{i=1}^{n} |x_i| \qquad\qquad \text{(the \textbf{1-norm} of x)} \qquad\qquad \textbf{(11b)}$$

and

$$||\mathbf{x}||_\infty = \max\{|x_1|, \ldots, |x_n|\} \qquad \text{(the \textbf{max-norm} of x)} \qquad \textbf{(11c)}$$

Let us select one of $||\cdot||_1$, $||\cdot||_2$, or $||\cdot||_\infty$ as a norm on n-space and denote it by simply $||\cdot||$. Having done this, we wish to introduce a $||\cdot||$ to describe the "size" of an $n \times n$ matrix. In order to be called a **norm,** $||\cdot||$ must satisfy

$$||A|| \geqslant 0 \qquad \text{and} \qquad ||A|| = 0 \Longleftrightarrow A = O_{n \times n} \qquad\qquad \textbf{(12a)}$$

$$||sA|| = |s|\,||A|| \qquad \text{for any scalar } s \qquad\qquad\qquad\qquad \textbf{(12b)}$$

$$||A + B|| \leqslant ||A|| + ||B|| \qquad \text{(Triangle Inequality)} \qquad\qquad \textbf{(12c)}$$

$$||AB|| \leqslant ||A||\,||B|| \qquad\qquad\qquad\qquad\qquad\qquad\qquad\qquad \textbf{(12d)}$$

for any $n \times n$ matrices A and B. There are a variety of definitions of $||A||$ that satisfy these conditions; however, the one that has been found to be especially useful is

$$||A|| = \max_{\mathbf{x} \neq 0} \frac{||A\mathbf{x}||}{||\mathbf{x}||}, \qquad \text{the \textbf{norm} of } A_{n \times n} \qquad\qquad \textbf{(13)}$$

Note that the number $||A||$ depends on the $||\cdot||$ used in n-space.

It is immediate from definition (13) that

$$||A\mathbf{x}|| \leqslant ||A||\,||\mathbf{x}|| \qquad \text{for any } \mathbf{x} \qquad\qquad\qquad \textbf{(14)}$$

Thus **x** *can be "stretched" by at most* $||A||$ *when multiplied by A.*

In certain special cases, $||A||$ is easy to find. For example, $||I_n|| = 1$ for any n and any norm on n-space. However, the norm of $A_{n \times n}$ is usually difficult to determine from (3). More usable formulas for $||A||$ can be given in terms of eigenvalues. This will be done in Section 9.5. For now we just wish to show how $||A||$ can help us better understand ill conditioning.

Consider the linear system $A\mathbf{x} = \mathbf{b}$, where A is nonsingular and $\mathbf{b} \neq \mathbf{0}$. We wish to get a quantitative description of the effect of small changes in A and $\mathbf{b}$ on the solution $\overline{\mathbf{x}} = A^{-1}\mathbf{b}$.

To begin, assume that **b** has an error $\delta\mathbf{b}$ (with A exact). The resulting error in $\overline{\mathbf{x}}$ is $\delta\overline{\mathbf{x}}$, that is, that

$$A(\overline{\mathbf{x}} + \delta\overline{\mathbf{x}}) = \mathbf{b} + \delta\mathbf{b}$$

Since $A(\overline{\mathbf{x}} + \delta\overline{\mathbf{x}}) = A\overline{\mathbf{x}} + A\,\delta\overline{\mathbf{x}} = \mathbf{b} + A\,\delta\overline{\mathbf{x}}$, the errors $\delta\mathbf{b}$ and $\delta\overline{\mathbf{x}}$ satisfy

$$A\,\delta\overline{\mathbf{x}} = \delta\mathbf{b}, \qquad \text{or equivalently,} \qquad \delta\overline{\mathbf{x}} = A^{-1}\,\delta\mathbf{b} \qquad\qquad \textbf{(15)}$$

Applying (14) to the equations $\mathbf{b} = A\overline{\mathbf{x}}$ and $\delta\overline{\mathbf{x}} = A^{-1}\,\delta\mathbf{b}$, we get

$$||\mathbf{b}|| \leqslant ||A||\,||\overline{\mathbf{x}}|| \qquad \text{and} \qquad ||\delta\overline{\mathbf{x}}|| \leqslant ||A^{-1}||\,||\delta\mathbf{b}||$$

Rearranging these inequalities (in which $||\mathbf{b}|| > 0$ and $||\overline{\mathbf{x}}|| > 0$) gives

$$\frac{\|\delta\overline{\mathbf{x}}\|}{\|\overline{\mathbf{x}}\|} \leq \|A\| \, \|A^{-1}\| \, \frac{\|\delta\mathbf{b}\|}{\|\mathbf{b}\|} \tag{16a}$$

Since $\|\delta\mathbf{x}\|/\|\mathbf{x}\|$ and $\|\delta\mathbf{b}\|/\|\mathbf{b}\|$ are the relative errors of $\overline{\mathbf{x}} + \delta\overline{\mathbf{x}}$ and $\mathbf{b} + \delta\mathbf{b}$ (see Section 1.6A), (16a) can be interpreted as follows:

> The relative error of $\overline{\mathbf{x}} + \delta\overline{\mathbf{x}}$ can be at most
> $\|A\| \, \|A^{-1}\|$ times the relative error of $\mathbf{b} + \delta\mathbf{b}$.

Similarly, if A has an error δA with $\mathbf{b}$ exact, the inequality

$$\frac{\|\delta\overline{\mathbf{x}}\|}{\|\overline{\mathbf{x}} + \delta\overline{\mathbf{x}}\|} \leq \|A\| \, \|A^{-1}\| \, \frac{\|\delta A\|}{\|A\|} \tag{16b}$$

can be obtained and given an analogous interpretation.

There is no reason to expect the relative error in $\overline{\mathbf{x}} + \delta\overline{\mathbf{x}}$ to be any smaller than that of $A + \delta A$ or $\mathbf{b} + \delta\mathbf{b}$; that is, the bound $\|A\| \, \|A^{-1}\|$ in (16) should be at least 1. Indeed, this follows from the fact that, by (14),

$$\|\mathbf{x}\| = \|I\mathbf{x}\| = \|A(A^{-1}\mathbf{x})\| \leq \|A\| \, \|A^{-1}\mathbf{x}\| \leq \|A\| \, \|A^{-1}\| \, \|\mathbf{x}\|$$

Thus the **condition number** of A defined by

$$\text{cond } A = \|A\| \, \|A^{-1}\| \quad \text{satisfies} \quad \text{cond } A \geq 1 \text{ for any } A \tag{17a}$$

When $\text{cond } A \approx 1$, (16) assures that small relative errors in A or $\mathbf{b}$ result in comparably small errors in $\overline{\mathbf{x}}$, hence A is well conditioned. However,

$$\text{cond } A \gg 1 \text{ (say cond } A > 100) \quad \Rightarrow \quad A \text{ is ill conditioned} \tag{17b}$$

because small relative errors in A or $\mathbf{b}$ can produce large relative errors in $\overline{\mathbf{x}}$.

Although $\text{cond } A$ is of considerable theoretical importance, it is generally inconvenient to use because of (1) the need to find A^{-1} and (2) the difficulty in finding both $\|A\|$ and $\|A^{-1}\|$ even if A^{-1} is available. The discussion of Section 9.5 shows how knowing the eigenvalues of A can alleviate some of the difficulty. Until then we shall rely on the simpler indicator $C_p(A)$ when assessing the condition of a matrix A.

4.3   Assessing and Improving the Accuracy of a Solution

Up to now our discussion of accuracy of numerical solutions was based on a knowledge of the exact solutions. In this section we discuss the important problem of assessing the accuracy of numerical solution of $AX = B$ in the realistic situation when the exact solution $\overline{X} = A^{-1}B$ is *not* known.

4.3A THE RESIDUAL

Let $\overline{X}_{calc}$ be a numerical solution of the matrix equation $AX = B$. The natural check on the accuracy of $\overline{X}_{calc}$ is to "plug it in," that is, to form the product $A\overline{X}_{calc}$ and see how close it is to B. The extent to which $A\overline{X}_{calc}$ differs from B is shown in the matrix

$$\boxed{R = B - A\overline{X}_{calc} = \text{the } \mathbf{residual\ matrix} \text{ for } \overline{X}_{calc}} \qquad (1)$$

To illustrate, for the inverses obtained in the example in Section 4.1C:

$$A(A^{-1})_{PP} = \begin{bmatrix} 3 & 5 \\ 13 & 22 \end{bmatrix} \begin{bmatrix} 22.27 & -5.060 \\ -13.16 & 3.036 \end{bmatrix} = \begin{bmatrix} 1.01 & 0 \\ -0.01 & 1.012 \end{bmatrix} \qquad (2)$$

$$A(A^{-1})_{SPP} = \begin{bmatrix} 3 & 5 \\ 13 & 22 \end{bmatrix} \begin{bmatrix} 22.22 & -5.051 \\ -13.13 & 3.030 \end{bmatrix} = \begin{bmatrix} 1.01 & -0.003 \\ 0 & 0.997 \end{bmatrix} \qquad (3)$$

Subtracting these from $B = I_2$, we get

$$R_{PP} = \begin{bmatrix} -0.01 & 0 \\ 0.01 & -0.012 \end{bmatrix} \quad \text{and} \quad R_{SPP} = \begin{bmatrix} -0.01 & 0.003 \\ 0 & 0.003 \end{bmatrix} \qquad (4)$$

The rather large residual entries (correctly) suggest that both $(A^{-1})_{PP}$ and $(A^{-1})_{SPP}$ have errors.

Since $A\overline{X}_{calc}$ should be close to B, there is likely to be loss of significance when subtracting it from B in calculating R. Consequently,

$A\overline{X}_{calc}$ should be calculated in extended precision, using enough extra digits (if possible) to allow the entries of R to be rounded accurately to the precision used to obtain $\overline{X}_{calc}$.

Thus for $\overline{\mathbf{x}}_{noPEP}$ obtained using $3s$ arithmetic in (28) of the example in Section 4.1D, the residual $\mathbf{r} = \mathbf{b} - A\mathbf{x}_{noPEP}$ (to $3s$) should be calculated as

$$\mathbf{r} = \begin{bmatrix} -0.630 \\ 0.399 \\ 0.375 \end{bmatrix} - \begin{bmatrix} -0.072 & 0.300 & -0.210 \\ 0.874 & -0.267 & 0.133 \\ -0.500 & -0.123 & 0.125 \end{bmatrix} \begin{bmatrix} 0.0212 \\ 0.230 \\ 3.33 \end{bmatrix}$$

$$\doteq \begin{bmatrix} -0.630 \\ 0.399 \\ 0.375 \end{bmatrix} - \begin{bmatrix} -0.631826 \\ 0.400009 \\ 0.377360 \end{bmatrix} \doteq \begin{bmatrix} 0.00183 \\ -0.00101 \\ -0.00236 \end{bmatrix} \qquad (5)$$

If we did not know that the exact $\overline{\mathbf{x}}$ is $[0 \quad 0 \quad 3]^T$, the small components of $\mathbf{r}$ would *not* have warned us that $\overline{\mathbf{x}}_{noPEP}$ is very inaccurate.

The conclusion to be drawn from (4) to (5) is

Large residual entries indicate that there are errors in the entries of $\overline{X}_{calc}$; however small residual entries do not necessarily guarantee the accuracy of $\overline{X}_{calc}$.

Whether or not small residual entries should be taken as an indication that $\overline{X}_{calc}$ is accurate depends upon the condition of A. Specifically, assuming that PP or SPP is used, we have:

> If $R \approx O$ and $C_p(A)$ indicates that A is well conditioned, then $\overline{X}_{calc}$ should approximate $\overline{X} = A^{-1}B$ to about the accuracy of the device used.

On the other hand, if *either* some residual entries are not small *or* A appears to be ill conditioned, then the residual can be used to improve the accuracy of $\overline{X}_{calc}$ as described next.

4.3B   ITERATIVE IMPROVEMENT

The **error of** $\overline{X}_{calc}$ is the matrix

$$E = \overline{X} - \overline{X}_{calc} \tag{6}$$

where $\overline{X} = A^{-1}B$ is the exact solution of $AX = B$. Consequently,

$$R = B - A\overline{X}_{calc} = A\overline{X} - A\overline{X}_{calc} = A(\overline{X} - \overline{X}_{calc}) = AE \tag{7}$$

that is, *the error matrix E is the solution of the equation $AE = R$.*

Since we know R and we have obtained an LU-decomposition in the solution of $AX = B$, *the determination of $E = A^{-1}R$ requires only forward and backward substitution,* that is, completing a forback matrix to get

$$\boxed{[\hat{L}\backslash\hat{U} : \hat{R} : \overline{C} : \overline{E}_{calc}], \qquad \text{where } \overline{E}_{calc} \approx E = A^{-1}R} \tag{8a}$$

Although $\overline{E}_{calc}$ will itself have some error, we expect from (6) that

$$\boxed{\overline{X}_{improved} = \overline{X}_{calc} + \overline{E}_{calc}} \tag{8b}$$

will approximate $\overline{X}$ better than $\overline{X}_{calc}$. The procedure (8) is called **iterative improvement** because it can be reapplied with $\overline{X}_{improved}$ replacing $\overline{X}_{calc}$.

EXAMPLE 1. Use iterative improvement to improve the accuracy of

$$\overline{\mathbf{x}}_{noPEP} = [0.0212 \quad 0.230 \quad 3.33]^T$$

obtained using $3s$ arithmetic (without PEP) in the example in Section 4.1D.

Solution. We saw in (5) that the residual for $\overline{\mathbf{x}}_{noPEP}$ is

$$\mathbf{r} = [0.00183 \quad -0.00101 \quad -0.00236]^T \qquad (3s)$$

To reuse the LU-decomposition used to get $\bar{\mathbf{x}}_{\text{noPEP}}$ to solve $A\mathbf{e} = \mathbf{r}$ for $\bar{\mathbf{e}}_{\text{calc}}$, we must interchange rows 1 and 2 of $\mathbf{r}$ [see (24) of Section 4.1D]. The resulting calculation, continuing to use $3s$ arithmetic, is

$$
\begin{bmatrix}
\boxed{0.874} & -0.305 & 0.152 & : & -0.00101 & : & -0.00116 & : & -0.0258 \\
-0.072 & \boxed{0.278} & -0.716 & : & 0.00183 & : & 0.00629 & : & -0.280 \\
-0.500 & -0.276 & \boxed{0.003} & : & -0.00236 & : & -0.400 & : & -0.400
\end{bmatrix} \quad \text{(9a)}
$$

$$\underbrace{}_{\hat{L}\backslash\hat{U}} \qquad \underbrace{}_{\hat{\mathbf{r}}} \quad \underbrace{}_{\bar{\mathbf{c}}} \quad \underbrace{}_{\bar{\mathbf{e}}_{\text{calc}}}$$

So, by (8b),

$$
\bar{\mathbf{x}}_{\text{improved}} = \mathbf{x}_{\text{noPEP}} + \bar{\mathbf{e}}_{\text{calc}} = \begin{bmatrix} 0.0212 \\ 0.230 \\ 3.33 \end{bmatrix} + \begin{bmatrix} -0.0258 \\ -0.280 \\ -0.400 \end{bmatrix} = \begin{bmatrix} -0.0046 \\ -0.05 \\ 2.93 \end{bmatrix} \quad \text{(9b)}
$$

All three components of $\bar{\mathbf{x}}_{\text{improved}}$ are about one decimal place closer to $\bar{\mathbf{x}} = \begin{bmatrix} 0 & 0 & 3 \end{bmatrix}^T$ than those of $\bar{\mathbf{x}}_{\text{noPEP}}$. Repeating with $\bar{\mathbf{x}}_{\text{improved}}$ as $\bar{\mathbf{x}}_{\text{calc}}$, we get

$$
\mathbf{r} = \begin{bmatrix} -0.000024 \\ -0.000107 \\ 0.00035 \end{bmatrix}, \qquad \bar{\mathbf{e}}_{\text{calc}} = \begin{bmatrix} 0.000628 \\ 0.0692 \\ 0.0967 \end{bmatrix}, \qquad \bar{\mathbf{x}}_{\text{improved}} = \begin{bmatrix} -0.00387 \\ 0.0192 \\ 3.03 \end{bmatrix} \quad \text{(9c)}
$$

In view of the large error in $\hat{l}_{33}$ [see (27) of Section 4.1D] this $\bar{\mathbf{x}}_{\text{improved}}$ is about as accurate an answer as we can realistically expect. However, had we used the more accurate value $\hat{l}_{33} \doteq 0.00338$ [see (25) of Section 4.1D] and PEP in completing $[\hat{L}\backslash\hat{U} : \hat{\mathbf{r}} : \bar{\mathbf{c}} : \bar{\mathbf{e}}_{\text{calc}}]$ in (9a), we would have obtained

$$
\bar{\mathbf{e}}_{\text{calc}} = \begin{bmatrix} -0.0228 \\ -0.249 \\ -0.357 \end{bmatrix}, \quad \text{hence} \quad \bar{\mathbf{x}}_{\text{improved}} = \begin{bmatrix} 0.0212 \\ 0.230 \\ 3.33 \end{bmatrix} + \begin{bmatrix} -0.0228 \\ -0.249 \\ -0.257 \end{bmatrix} = \begin{bmatrix} -0.0016 \\ -0.019 \\ 2.97 \end{bmatrix} \quad \text{(10)}
$$

Comparing this to (9c), we see that one improvement with PEP gives better accuracy than two improvements without PEP.

EXAMPLE 2. Improve the accuracy of $(A^{-1})_{\text{SPP}}$ of the example in Section 4.1C.

Solution. The residual R_{SPP} was obtained in (4). Since $(A^{-1})_{\text{SPP}}$ is an estimate of A^{-1}, the easiest way to get a calculated value of $E = A^{-1} R_{\text{SPP}}$ is as the product

$$
\bar{E}_{\text{calc}} = (A^{-1})_{\text{SPP}} R_{\text{SPP}} = \begin{bmatrix} 22.22 & -5.051 \\ -13.13 & 3.030 \end{bmatrix} \begin{bmatrix} -0.01 & 0.003 \\ 0 & 0.003 \end{bmatrix} \quad \text{(11a)}
$$

$$
\doteq \begin{bmatrix} -0.2222 & 0.05150 \\ 0.1313 & -0.03030 \end{bmatrix}
$$

Adding $\bar{E}_{\text{calc}}$ to $(A^{-1})_{\text{SPP}}$ gives

$$(A^{-1})_{\text{improved}} = \begin{bmatrix} 22.22 & -5.051 \\ -13.13 & 3.030 \end{bmatrix} + \begin{bmatrix} -0.2222 & 0.05150 \\ 0.1313 & -0.03030 \end{bmatrix} \doteq \begin{bmatrix} 22.00 & -5.001 \\ -13.00 & 3.000 \end{bmatrix}$$

(11b)

Only one iterative improvement yields A^{-1} to just about 4s.

It should be noted that *when A is well conditioned, iterative improvement should not be needed at all, especially if a pivoting strategy such as PP or SPP is used.* We see from the preceding example that if PEP is used as well, then at most one improvement will give the solution to the single precision accuracy of the device used, provided that A is not severely ill conditioned.

4.4 Solving $AX = B$ on a Computer

4.4A SUGGESTIONS FOR USING A CANNED PROGRAM

Before using a program installed on a computer, check to see that it includes some pivoting strategy. If it only contains (unscaled) Partial Pivoting, it may be useful to **equilibrate** the system by multiplying the ith equation by a suitable power of 2 (to avoid introducing roundoff error) so that the largest entry of row$_i$ A has magnitude $\approx$ 1, $i = 1, 2, \ldots , n$. If it contains only Basic Pivoting and you need close to the available accuracy, it may be worthwhile to modify the program to incorporate at least Partial Pivoting.

It is also important to ensure that the program output includes a condition indicator such as $C_p(A)$, or at least $|\det A|$ $(= |\text{product of pivots}|)$, to help assess the accuracy of the solution obtained as described in Section 4.2B.

Finally, the inner products used to get the entries of $\hat{L}\backslash\hat{U}$ (and $\bar{c}$ and $\bar{x}$ as well) should, if possible, be accumulated in extended precision (PEP). (*Note:* This will not be possible for Gauss or Gauss–Jordan elimination.)

Among the more reliable packages that are commercially available in FORTRAN are the LINPAK library developed at the Sandia Laboratory and the NAG Library developed by the Nottingham Algorithm Group.

4.4B PERFORMING THE TRIANGULAR DECOMPOSITION ALGORITHM ON A COMPUTER

In order for a computer to solve $AX = B$ by the Triangular Decomposition Algorithm with Scaled Partial Pivoting, it must allocate space for four REAL arrays, say

$$\mathbf{A}_{n \times n}, \quad \mathbf{S}_{n \times 1}, \quad \mathbf{LUD}_{n \times n}, \quad \text{and} \quad \mathbf{B}_{n \times p} \tag{1}$$

to store the entries of $\hat{A}$, $\hat{s}$ (array of row scale factors), $\hat{L}\backslash\hat{U}$, and $\hat{B}$, respectively. Moreover, every row interchange called for must be performed on all four arrays. Although such interchanges are a convenience for hand calculation, they are awkward for computers and become time consuming (expensive) as n increases.

A simple way to avoid this expense is to *leave* A, S, LUD, *and* B *in the row order of the original system* $[A : B]$ and to indicate the effects of pivoting in a single **pointer array** IROW where for $k = 1, \ldots, n$,

$$\text{IROW}(k) \text{ tells which row of A is row}_k \ \hat{A} \tag{2}$$

and similarly for S, LUD, and B. Initially, when $\hat{A} = A$,

$$\text{IROW} = [1 \quad 2 \quad \cdots \quad n]^T \tag{3}$$

Any desired interchanges are then made in IROW *only*.

For example, we saw in Figure 4.1-1 that if Scaled Partial Pivoting is used as the pivoting strategy, then

$$A = \begin{bmatrix} 2 & -4 & 3 \\ 0 & 2 & 5 \\ 1 & -1 & 0 \end{bmatrix} \quad \text{has} \quad \begin{bmatrix} ① & -1 & 0 \\ 2 & ② & -\frac{3}{2} \\ 0 & 2 & ⑧ \end{bmatrix} \begin{matrix} (\rho_1 \rightleftarrows \rho_3) \\ (\rho_2 \rightleftarrows \rho_3) \\ \ \end{matrix} \tag{4}$$

as an LU-decomposition. By performing the indicated row interchanges on **IROW**,

$$\text{IROW} = \begin{matrix} \overset{\text{Phase I}}{\begin{bmatrix} 1 \\ 2 \\ 3 \end{bmatrix}} \end{matrix} \xrightarrow{m=1} \overset{\text{Phase II}}{\begin{bmatrix} 3 \\ 2 \\ 1 \end{bmatrix}} \xrightarrow{m=2} \overset{\text{Phase III}}{\begin{bmatrix} 3 \\ 1 \\ 2 \end{bmatrix}} \tag{5}$$

The $\hat{L}\backslash\hat{U}$ entries are stored in LUD *in the row ordering corresponding to the original matrix A*. So, at the end of the **factorization** step, we obtain

$$\text{LUD} = \begin{bmatrix} 2 & ② & -\frac{3}{2} \\ 0 & 2 & ⑧ \\ ① & -1 & 0 \end{bmatrix} \begin{matrix} \leftarrow \text{row}_2 \ \hat{L}\backslash\hat{U} \\ \leftarrow \text{row}_3 \ \hat{L}\backslash\hat{U} \\ \leftarrow \text{row}_1 \ \hat{L}\backslash\hat{U} \end{matrix} \tag{6}$$

At any point of the **factorization** step

$$\text{the Kth row of } \hat{L}\backslash\hat{U} \text{ is stored in the IROW(K)th row of LUD} \tag{7}$$

as shown in (6); similarly, IROW shows how to get rows of $\hat{A}$, $\hat{s}$, and $\hat{B}$ from those of the stored arrays A, S, and B.

This strategy is implemented in the FORTRAN subroutine DECOMP shown in Figure 4.4-1. The arrays IROW and S are initialized in lines 1900–2600. Then for M = 1, ..., N − 1, the loop in lines 4200–4800 sets CONDIT to the largest of the ratios

$$\frac{|\hat{l}_{\text{K,M}}|}{\hat{s}_{\text{K}}} = \frac{|\text{LUD(IROW(K), M)}|}{\text{S(IROW(K))}}, \quad \text{K} = \text{M}, \ldots, \text{N} \tag{8}$$

and KPVT to the index in IROW corresponding to this largest ratio. If KPVT $\neq$ M, the interchange $\rho_\text{M} \rightleftarrows \rho_{\text{KPVT}}$ is made *in IROW only* (lines 5100–5300).

The parameter EPS passed to the subroutine controls how small CONDIT must be for the matrix to be considered "nearly singular." If either $|\hat{l}_{mm}|/\hat{s}_m <$ EPS or $|\hat{l}_{mm}|$ < EPS occurs, SNGULR is returned as TRUE (lines 5600–5700). Otherwise, the returned value of CONDIT is $|\hat{l}_{nn}|/\hat{s}_n$, the pivot condition number $C_p(A)$ of Section 4.2B.

Notice how the one DOUBLE PRECISION variable ACCUM is used to accumulate all inner products $[\leftarrow]_L[\uparrow]_U$ in lines 3600–3800 and 6400–6600. This is the Partial Extended Precision strategy of Section 4.1C. It is also used in the FORTRAN subroutine FORBAK shown in Figure 4.4-2. Thus, to solve $AX = B$, we would use the calling statements

CALL DECOMP (N, EPS, A, LUD, IROW, SNGULR, CONDIT, KPVT, S)
CALL FORBAK (N, P, LUD, IROW, B, XBAR)

to form first LUD and IROW, then the solution XBAR $(= \overline{X})$. If there is no further need for A and B (e.g., if iterative improvement will not be used) and storage is limited, then the calls

CALL DECOMP (N, EPS, A, A, IROW, SNGULR, CONDIT, KPVT, S)
CALL FORBAK (N, P, A, IROW, B, B)

could be used to write LUD over A and return $\overline{X}$ in the array B.

4.4C FULL PIVOTING (FP)

The following strategy, called **Full Pivoting (FP),** is guaranteed to yield the smallest possible $\hat{U}$ entries when used to select p_j in the **pivot** step of the **upper triangulation** phase of the Gaussian Elimination Algorithm (Figure 3.4-1).

```
00100          SUBROUTINE DECOMP(N,EPS,A,LUD,IROW,SNGULR,CONDIT,KPVT,S)
00200          REAL  A(N,N), S(N), LUD(N,N), MTHPVT
00300          INTEGER IROW(N)
00400          DOUBLE PRECISION ACCUM
00500          LOGICAL SNGULR
00600   C - - - - - - - - - - - - - - - - - - - - - - - - - - - - - C
00700   C GIVEN AN N BY N MATRIX A, THIS SUBROUTINE RETURNS:         C
00800   C       LUD(N,N) = LU-DECOMPOSITION OF A^ = L^*U^            C
00900   C       IROW(N)  = ROW ORDER VECTOR                          C
01000   C       CONDIT   = CONDITION INDICATOR (0 IF SINGULAR)       C
01100   C                                                            C
01200   C NOTE:  ROW K OF [A^:B^:S^:L^\U^] IS ROW IROW(K) OF [A:B:S:LUD]  C
01300   C                                                            C
01400   C SNGULR IS SET TO TRUE IF FOR SOME M ALL L^/S^ RATIOS ARE < EPS. C
01500   C IF A IS NOT SINGULAR, CONDIT = CP(A) = L^(N,N)/S^(N).      C
01600   C - - - - - - - - - - - - - - - - - - VERSION 1:   5/1/81 - C
01700   C INITIALIZE SNGULR, IROW AND S
01800          SNGULR = .FALSE.
01900          DO 10 I=1,N
02000            IROW(I) = I
02100   C      **SET S(I) = LARGEST ABS VALUE IN ROW I OF A
02200            S(I) = 0.
02300            DO 5 J=1,N
02400              S(I) = AMAX1(S(I),ABS(A(I,J)))
02500      5     CONTINUE
```

FIGURE 4.4-1 SUBROUTINE DECOMP (FORMS LUD AND IROW).

```
02600      10 CONTINUE
02700    C
02800    C ITERATE:  FORM LUD USING SPP AND PEP STRATEGIES
02900           DO 100 M=1,N
03000    C     **GET ENTRIES OF COLUMN M OF L^
03100             KSTOP = M-1
03200             DO 25 I=M,N
03300                II = IROW(I)
03400                ACCUM = DBLE(A(II,M))
03500                IF (M .EQ. 1) GOTO 20
03600                   DO 15 K=1,KSTOP
03700                      ACCUM = ACCUM - DBLE(LUD(II,K))*LUD(IROW(K),M)
03800      15             CONTINUE
03900      20          LUD(II,M) = SNGL(ACCUM)
04000      25       CONTINUE
04100    C     **SET CONDIT = LARGEST L^/S^ RATIO OF COLUMN M OF L^
04200             CONDIT = 0.
04300             DO 30 K=M,N
04400                RATIO= ABS(LUD(IROW(K),M))/S(IROW(K))
04500                IF (RATIO. LE. CONDIT) GOTO 30
04600                   CONDIT = RATIO
04700                   KPVT = K
04800      30       CONTINUE
04900             IM = IROW(KPVT)
05000             IF (KPVT .EQ. M) GOTO 35
05100    C     **INTERCHANGE ROWS M AND KPVT OF IROW
05200             IROW(KPVT) = IROW(M)
05300             IROW(M) = IM
05400    C     **EXIT CHECK:  EXIT IF A IS NEARLY SINGULAR OR M = N
05500      35    MTHPVT = LUD(IM,M)
05600             IF (CONDIT .GT. EPS .AND. ABS(MTHPVT) .GT. EPS) GOTO 40
05700             SNGULR = .TRUE.
05800      40    IF (SNGULR .OR. (M .EQ. N))  RETURN
05900    C     **GET ENTRIES OF ROW M OF U^ (IN ROW IM OF LUD)
06000             JSTART = M+1
06100             DO 55 J=JSTART,N
06200                ACCUM = DBLE(A(IM,J))
06300                IF (M .EQ. 1) GOTO 50
06400                   DO 45 K=1,KSTOP
06500                      ACCUM = ACCUM - DBLE(LUD(IM,K))*LUD(IROW(K),J)
06600      45          CONTINUE
06700      50       LUD(IM,J) = SNGL(ACCUM)/MTHPVT
06800      55    CONTINUE
06900     100 CONTINUE
07000         END
```

FIGURE **4.4–1** (CONTINUED)

The Full Pivoting Strategy for Selecting the jth Pivot. *Choose as the jth pivot the element of largest magnitude in the $(n - j + 1) \times (n - j + 1)$ matrix obtained by deleting the rows and columns containing the preceding $j - 1$ pivot entries from the coefficient part of the current augmented matrix.*

This strategy can be used with Gaussian or Gauss–Jordan elimination but *not* with the Triangular Decomposition Algorithm. (Why?) Note that with the FP strategy the jth pivot need *not* be in the jth column of the augmented matrix.

```
00100          SUBROUTINE FORBAK(N, P, LUD, IROW, B, XBAR)
00200          INTEGER IROW(N), P
00300          REAL B(N,P), XBAR(N,P), LUD(N,N), ITHPVT
00400          DOUBLE PRECISION ACCUM
00500    C - - - - - - - - - - - - - - - - - - - - - - - - - - - - C
00600    C  THIS SUBROUTINE SOLVES  AX = B  BY SOLVING FIRST  L^C = B^   C
00700    C  (FORWARD SUBSTN) THEN U^X = CBAR  (BACKWARD SUBSTN) USING    C
00800    C  LUD AND IROW RETURNED BY SUBROUTINE DECOMP.                  C
00900    C - - - - - - - - - - - - - - - - - - - - - VERSION 1:  5/1/81 C
01000    C FORWARD SUBSTITUTION:  SOLVE  L^C = B^  FOR CBAR (PUT IN XBAR)
01100          DO 40 I=1,N
01200             II = IROW(I)
01300             ITHPVT = LUD(II,I)
01400             KSTOP = I-1
01500             DO 30 J=1,P
01600                ACCUM = DBLE(B(II,J))
01700                IF (I .EQ. 1) GOTO 20
01800                   DO 10 K=1,KSTOP
01900                      ACCUM = ACCUM - DBLE(LUD(II,K))*XBAR(K,J)
02000    10             CONTINUE
02100    20          XBAR(I,J) = SNGL(ACCUM)/ITHPVT
02200    30       CONTINUE
02300    40 CONTINUE
02400          IF (N .EQ. 1) RETURN
02500    C
02600    C BACKWARD SUBSTITUTION:  SOLVE  U^X = CBAR  FOR DESIRED SOLN XBAR
02700          DO 70 INDEX=2,N
02800             I = N-INDEX+1
02900             KSTART = I+1
03000             DO 60 J=1,P
03100                ACCUM = DBLE(XBAR(I,J))
03200                DO 50 K=KSTART,N
03300                   ACCUM = ACCUM - DBLE(LUD(IROW(I),K))*XBAR(K,J)
03400    50          CONTINUE
03500                XBAR(I,J) = SNGL(ACCUM)
03600    60       CONTINUE
03700    70 CONTINUE
03800          RETURN
03900          END
```

FIGURE 4.4-2   SUBROUTINE FORBAK (FORWARD AND
BACKWARD SUBSTITUTION).

EXAMPLE. Use Gaussian elimination with Full Pivoting and without 1-SCALEs to solve
the system

$$-x_1 + x_2 - 4x_3 = 0$$
$$2x_1 + 2x_2 \qquad = 1 \qquad \left(\overline{\mathbf{x}} = \begin{bmatrix} \frac{5}{4} \\ -\frac{3}{4} \\ -\frac{1}{2} \end{bmatrix} \right) \qquad (9)$$
$$3x_1 + 3x_2 + 2x_3 = \frac{1}{2}$$

Solution. The **upper triangulation** proceeds as follows (pivots are circled):

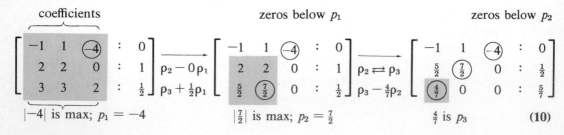

$$(10)$$

Backward Substitution can now be used to solve (E_3) for $\bar{x}_1$, then (E_2) for $\bar{x}_2$, then (E_1) for $\bar{x}_3$ as follows:

$$\bar{x}_1 = \frac{\frac{5}{7}}{\frac{4}{7}} = \frac{5}{4}, \qquad \bar{x}_2 = \frac{2}{7}\left\{\frac{1}{2} - \frac{5}{2}\bar{x}_1\right\} = -\frac{3}{4}, \qquad \bar{x}_3 = -\frac{1}{4}\{0 - \bar{x}_1 + \bar{x}_2\} = -\frac{1}{2}$$

Although the search for the largest possible p_j can be performed by inspection during a hand calculation, it can increase execution time substantially when performed on a computer. Execution time is further increased by the need for a pointer array to keep track of the order in which the *columns* are reduced [cf. (2) of Section 4.4C]. Empirical experience has shown that *in the presence of roundoff errors the improvement in accuracy of FP over the SPP strategy is usually so slight so as not to justify this extra computer expense.* Consequently, Full Pivoting is generally *not* recommended unless for some reason it is necessary to try to get $\bar{x}$ with the maximum possible accuracy.

Iterative Methods for Solving Linear Systems **4.5**

Recall that direct methods require about $2n^3/3$ arithmetic operations to solve the $n \times n$ system $A\mathbf{x} = \mathbf{b}$, that is,

$$
\begin{aligned}
(E_1) \quad & a_{11}x_1 + a_{12}x_2 + \cdots + a_{1n}x_n = b_1 \\
(E_2) \quad & a_{21}x_1 + a_{22}x_2 + \cdots + a_{2n}x_n = b_2 \\
&\vdots \qquad\qquad\qquad\qquad\qquad \vdots \\
(E_3) \quad & a_{n1}x_1 + a_{n2}x_2 + \cdots + a_{nn}x_n = b_n
\end{aligned}
\tag{1}
$$

This limits the range of n's for which they can realistically be applied. Indeed, even assuming that a general $10{,}000 \times 10{,}000$ system can be stored and solved without prohibitive roundoff error, it would take the fastest computers years to use a direct method to get the solution.

Linear systems with n between 1000 and 100,000 do actually arise in the solution of partial differential equations. The coefficient matrices for these systems are generally **sparse** (i.e., most entries are zero). This desirable property, which makes the storage of A possible for such large n, is destroyed by direct methods. Therefore, an alternative approach must be found if these large systems are to be solved. The iterative methods discussed in this section provide the desired alternative. They preserve sparseness and can achieve a high degree of accuracy even for large n.

4.5A THE JACOBI AND GAUSS–SEIDEL METHODS

If the diagonal entries of A are all nonzero, then (E_i) can be solved for x_i, getting

$$x_i = \frac{1}{a_{ii}}\left\{b_i - \sum_{\substack{j=1 \\ j \neq i}}^{n} a_{ij}x_j\right\} \tag{2}$$

for $i = 1, 2, \ldots , n$. It follows that $\bar{\mathbf{x}}$ satisfies $A\mathbf{x} = \mathbf{b}$ if and only if it satisfies the **fixed-point equation**

$$\mathbf{x} = \mathbf{g}(\mathbf{x}) \tag{3a}$$

where $\mathbf{g}(\mathbf{x})$ is the vector function whose ith component is given by

$$g_i(\mathbf{x}) = \frac{1}{a_{ii}} \left\{ b_i - \sum_{j \neq i} a_{ij} x_j \right\}, \qquad i = 1, 2, \ldots , n \tag{3b}$$

The **Jacobi method** for solving $A\mathbf{x} = \mathbf{b}$ consists of solving (3a) by Repeated Substitution, that is, starting with an initial guess $\mathbf{x}$, then replacing $\mathbf{x}$ by

$$\mathbf{x}^{(\text{new})} = \mathbf{g}(\mathbf{x}) \tag{4a}$$

repeatedly until $\mathbf{x}^{(\text{new})}$ is sufficiently close to $\bar{\mathbf{x}}$. As might be expected from our experience in Section 1.7, this method may not converge at all, even with a good initial guess; and when it does converge, it generally does so only linearly.

A slight improvement of the Jacobi method is the **Gauss–Seidel iteration** (also called the **Method of Successive Displacements**) obtained by using the result of the ith equation of (4a), namely

$$x_i^{(\text{new})} = \frac{1}{a_{ii}} \left\{ b_i - \sum_{j \neq i} a_{ij} x_j \right\} \tag{4b}$$

to replace x_i in the array $\mathbf{x}$ *as soon as it is obtained*, for $i = 1, 2, \ldots , n$. This new $\mathbf{x}$ satisfies (E_i) by construction; so it might be expected to be closer to the desired solution $\bar{\mathbf{x}}$ than the $\mathbf{x}$ used to get $x_i^{(\text{new})}$ in (4b). In fact (see [35]), *for those cases when the Jacobi method does converge, Gauss–Seidel iteration can usually be expected to converge even faster.* Consequently, our discussion of iterative methods will be based solely on Gauss–Seidel iteration.

The following example shows that *if Gauss–Seidel iteration converges, it usually does so only linearly.* Moreover, the order in which the equations are written and solved determines whether or not convergence will occur.

EXAMPLE. Use the Gauss–Seidel method to solve $A\mathbf{x} = \mathbf{b}$, where

$$[A : \mathbf{b}] = \begin{bmatrix} 1 & 0 & 3 & : & 2 \\ 5 & 1 & 2 & : & -5 \\ 1 & 6 & 2 & : & -11 \end{bmatrix} \quad \left(\text{Exact solution is } \begin{bmatrix} -1 \\ -2 \\ 1 \end{bmatrix} \right) \tag{5}$$

Solution. Since all diagonal entries are nonzero, we can solve (E_i) for x_i, $i = 1, 2, 3$, getting the following equations:

$$\begin{aligned} x_1^{(\text{new})} &= \tfrac{1}{1}\{2 - 0x_2 - 3x_3\} = 2 - 3x_3 \\ x_2^{(\text{new})} &= \tfrac{1}{1}\{-5 - 5x_1 - 2x_3\} = -[5 + 5x_1 + 2x_3] \\ x_3^{(\text{new})} &= \tfrac{1}{2}\{-11 - 1x_1 - 6x_2\} = -\tfrac{1}{2}[11 + x_1 + 6x_2] \end{aligned} \tag{6}$$

Starting with $\mathbf{x} = \mathbf{x}_0 = [0 \quad 0 \quad 0]^T$, one iteration of (6) gives

$$x_1^{(\text{new})} = 2 - 3 \cdot 0 = 2$$
$$x_2^{(\text{new})} = -\{5 + 5 \cdot 2 + 2 \cdot 0\} = -15 \quad \Bigg\} \text{ Now } \mathbf{x} = \mathbf{x}_1 = \begin{bmatrix} 2 \\ -15 \\ 38.5 \end{bmatrix}$$
$$x_3^{(\text{new})} = -\tfrac{1}{2}\{11 + 2 + 6(-15)\} = 38.5$$

A second iteration of (6) starting with $\mathbf{x} = \mathbf{x}_1$, gives

$$x_1^{(\text{new})} = 2 \quad 3(38.5) = -113.5$$
$$x_2^{(\text{new})} = -\{5 + 5(-113.5) + 2(38.5)\} = 485.5 \quad \Bigg\} \text{ Now } \mathbf{x} = \mathbf{x}_2 = \begin{bmatrix} -113.5 \\ 485.5 \\ 1{,}405.25 \end{bmatrix}$$
$$x_3^{(\text{new})} = -\tfrac{1}{2}\{11 + (-113.5) + 6(485.5)\} = 1405.25$$

Clearly, $\mathbf{x}_k$ is diverging. However, instead of simply solving (E_i) for x_i, suppose we did the following:

$$\text{Solve } (E_1) \text{ for } x_3: \quad x_3^{(\text{new})} = \tfrac{1}{3}\{2 - 1x_1 - 0x_2\} = \tfrac{1}{3}\{2 - x_1\}$$
$$\text{then } (E_3) \text{ for } x_2: \quad x_2^{(\text{new})} = \tfrac{1}{6}\{-11 - 1x_1 - 2x_3\} = -\tfrac{1}{6}\{11 + x_1 + 2x_3\} \quad (7)$$
$$\text{then } (E_2) \text{ for } x_1: \quad x_1^{(\text{new})} = \tfrac{1}{5}\{-5 - 1x_2 - 2x_3\} = -\tfrac{1}{5}\{5 + x_2 + 2x_3\}$$

Starting with $\mathbf{x} = \mathbf{x}_0 = \begin{bmatrix} 0 & 0 & 0 \end{bmatrix}^T$ again, one iteration of (7) gives (to 5s)

$$x_3^{(\text{new})} = \tfrac{1}{3}\{2 - 0\} = 0.66667$$
$$x_2^{(\text{new})} = -\tfrac{1}{6}\{11 + 0 + 2(0.66667)\} = -2.0556 \quad \Bigg\} \text{ Now } \mathbf{x} = \mathbf{x}_1 \doteq \begin{bmatrix} -0.85556 \\ -2.0556 \\ 0.66667 \end{bmatrix}$$
$$x_1^{(\text{new})} = -\tfrac{1}{5}\{5 + (-2.0556) + 2(0.66667)\} = -0.85556$$

(Note the order of the components of $\mathbf{x}_1$!) A second iteration of (7) gives

$$x_3^{(\text{new})} = \tfrac{1}{3}\{2 - (-0.85556)\} \doteq 0.95185, \quad \text{etc.}$$

The results of the first four iterations are shown in Table 4.5-1. This time $\mathbf{x}_k$ is converging to $\overline{\mathbf{x}} = \begin{bmatrix} -1 & -2 & 1 \end{bmatrix}^T$.

TABLE 4.5-1 FOUR ITERATIONS OF GAUSS–SEIDEL ITERATION.

	Coefficients of $\mathbf{x}_k$		
k	x_1	x_2	x_3
1	−0.85556	−2.0556	0.66667
2	−0.97914	−2.0080	0.95185
3	−0.99699	−2.0012	0.99305
4	−0.99956	−2.0002	0.99900

The equations (7) illustrate that *the given equations can be solved in any order, for any variable, as long as each variable is solved for exactly once.* This flexibility is incorporated in the pseudoprogram for Gauss–Seidel iteration given in Figure 4.5-2.

Algorithm: Gauss–Seidel Iteration (Method of Successive Displacements)

Purpose: To solve $A\mathbf{x} = \mathbf{b}$ for $\bar{\mathbf{x}} = A^{-1}\mathbf{b}$ to *NumSig* significant digits. One iteration, starting with $\mathbf{x} = [x_1 \ x_2 \cdots x_n]^T$ goes as follows:

(*) Solve equation $(\hat{E}_i)$ for variable $\hat{x}_i^{(new)}$ for $i = 1, 2, \ldots, n$, replacing $\hat{x}_i$ by $\hat{x}_i^{(new)}$ *before* calculating $\hat{x}_{i+1}^{(new)}$

In (*), $(\hat{E}_1), \ldots, (\hat{E}_n)$ and $\hat{x}_1, \ldots, \hat{x}_n$ are preselected rearrangements of the given equations $(E_1), \ldots, (E_n)$ and the variables $x_1, \ldots, x_n$, respectively. The algorithm terminates after *MaxIt* iterations, or sooner if

$$dx_i = x_i^{(new)} - x_i \text{ is sufficiently small for } i = 1, \ldots, n$$

{*initialize*}
GET n, A, $\mathbf{b}$,   {equation parameters}
         MaxIt, NumSig,   {termination parameters}
         $\mathbf{x}_0$ {an initial guess of $\bar{\mathbf{x}}$}
RelTol $\leftarrow 10^{-NumSig}$
$\mathbf{x} \leftarrow \mathbf{x}_0$ {$\mathbf{x} = [x_1 \quad x_2 \quad \cdots \quad x_n]^T$ is the current approximation of $\bar{\mathbf{x}}$}

{*iterate*}
DO FOR $k = 1$ to *MaxIt* UNTIL **termination test** is satisfied
   BEGIN {form $\mathbf{x}_k$ and $\mathbf{dx} = \mathbf{x}_k - \mathbf{x}_{k-1}$ in rearranged component order}
   DO FOR $i = 1$ TO n
    BEGIN
    {**get** $\hat{x}_i^{(new)}$} Solve $(\hat{E}_i)$ for $\hat{x}_i^{(new)}$ using components of current $\mathbf{x}$
    $d\hat{x}_i \leftarrow \hat{x}_i^{(new)} - \hat{x}_i$
    {**update x**} $\hat{x}_i \leftarrow \hat{x}_i^{(new)}$
    END
   {$\mathbf{x} = [x_1 \ x_2 \cdots x_n]^T$ is now $\mathbf{x}_k$; and $\mathbf{dx} = [dx_1 \ dx_2 \cdots dx_n]^T$}
   OUTPUT (k, x_1, x_2, ..., x_n)
   {**termination test:** $|dx_i| \leqslant RelTol*\max(1, |x_i|)$ for $i = 1, 2, \ldots, n$}
   END

IF **termination test** was satisfied
   THEN OUTPUT ($\mathbf{x}$ approximates $\bar{\mathbf{x}}$ to *NumSig* significant digits)
   ELSE OUTPUT (Convergence not evident in *MaxIt* iterations)

FIGURE 4.5-1 PSEUDOPROGRAM FOR GAUSS–SEIDEL ITERATION.

Note that in (7) each of (E_1), (E_2), (E_3) was solved for the variable having the largest coefficient. The convergence in Table 4.5-1 follows from the results considered next.

4.5B   STRATEGIES FOR IMPROVING THE LIKELIHOOD OF CONVERGENCE

Let us introduce some terminology about the ith equation

$$(E_i)\quad a_{i1} x_1 + a_{i2} x_2 + \cdots + a_{in} x_n = b_i$$

of the linear system $A\mathbf{x} = \mathbf{b}$. We shall call x_k the **strictly dominant variable** of (E_i), and a_{ik} [its coefficient in (E_i)] the **strictly dominant entry** of row$_i$ A if

$$|a_{ik}| > \sum_{j \neq k} |a_{ij}| \tag{8}$$

that is, if the magnitude of a_{ik} is larger than the *sum* of the magnitudes of the remaining coefficients of (E_i). We shall call A a **strictly dominant matrix** if each row of A has a strictly dominant entry in a *different* column than the others. In this case, each variable $x_1, \ldots, x_n$ is the strictly dominant variable of a different (E_i). The A matrix in (5) of the example in Section 4.5A is strictly dominant because in rows 1, 2, and 3:

$$|a_{13}| = 3 > |1| + |0|, \quad |a_{21}| = 5 > |1| + |2|, \quad \text{and} \quad |a_{32}| = 6 > |1| + |2|$$

Dominance Theorem. *Let $A\mathbf{x} = \mathbf{b}$ be a linear system for which A is strictly dominant. If each equation is solved for its strictly dominant variable then the $\mathbf{x}_k$'s generated by Gauss–Seidel iteration will converge to $\overline{\mathbf{x}} = A^{-1}\mathbf{b}$ for any choice of $\mathbf{x}_0$.*

This theorem, to be proved below, could have been used to predict the convergence that resulted from (7).

Most matrices are *not* strictly dominant. However, the Dominance Theorem suggests that we should reason as follows when deciding which variable to solve for in (E_i), $i = 1, \ldots, n$ when using Gauss–Seidel iteration.

Variable Selection Strategy

Try to solve as many equations as possible for the variable having the largest (in magnitude) coefficient.

If A is **strictly diagonally dominant,** that is, if a_{ii} is the strictly dominant entry of row$_i$ A for $i = 1, \ldots, n$, then the convergence of Gauss–Seidel iteration is guaranteed if we

$$\text{solve } (E_i) \text{ for } x_i \text{ for } i = 1, 2, \ldots, n \tag{9}$$

This simplest of selection strategies is also a desirable one to try whenever the coefficient matrix A is **symmetric,** that is, $a_{ij} = a_{ji}$ for all $i \neq j$. The justification for this is a theorem [36], which asserts that if a symmetric matrix A is actually *positive definite* (this means that $\mathbf{x}^T A \mathbf{x} > 0$ for all nonzero $\mathbf{x}$), then (9) will result in convergence to $\bar{\mathbf{x}}$ for any choice of $\mathbf{x}_0$. (See Exercise 4-14 and Section 9.5C.)

Proof of the Dominance Theorem: Since performing row interchanges on a strictly dominant matrix results in another strictly dominant matrix, there is no loss of generality in assuming that A is strictly *diagonally* dominant and (9) is used. Let $\bar{\mathbf{x}} = [\bar{x}_1 \cdots \bar{x}_n]^T$ be the exact solution of the system $A\mathbf{x} = \mathbf{b}$. Then

$$\bar{x}_i = \frac{1}{a_{ii}} \left\{ b_i - \sum_{j \neq i} a_{ij} \bar{x}_j \right\} \qquad \text{for } i = 1, 2, \ldots, n$$

The error of the jth component of the current approximation $\mathbf{x} = [x_1 \cdots x_n]^T$ will be denoted by

$$\epsilon_j = \bar{x}_j - x_j \qquad \text{for } j = 1, 2, \ldots, n$$

Consequently, the error of $x_i^{(\text{new})} = \{ b_i - \sum_{j \neq i} a_{ij} x_j \} / a_{ii}$ satisfies

$$\epsilon_i^{(\text{new})} = \bar{x}_i - x_i^{(\text{new})} = \frac{-1}{a_{ii}} \left\{ \sum_{j \neq i} a_{ij} (\bar{x}_j - x_j) \right\} = \frac{-1}{a_{ii}} \left\{ \sum_{j \neq i} a_{ij} \epsilon_j \right\}$$

So, if we let $|\epsilon_j|_{\max}$ denote the largest $|\epsilon_j|$ for $j \neq i$, then

$$|\epsilon_i^{(\text{new})}| = \frac{1}{|a_{ii}|} \left| \sum_{j \neq i} a_{ij} \epsilon_j \right| \leqslant \frac{\sum_{j \neq i} |a_{ij}|}{|a_{ii}|} |\epsilon_j|_{\max} \leqslant \delta |\epsilon_j|_{\max} \tag{10a}$$

where

$$\delta = \max \left\{ \frac{\sum_{j \neq 1} |a_{1j}|}{|a_{11}|}, \frac{\sum_{j \neq 2} |a_{2j}|}{|a_{22}|}, \ldots, \frac{\sum_{j \neq n} |a_{nj}|}{|a_{nn}|} \right\} \tag{10b}$$

In words, (10) says that the *error of $x_i^{(\text{new})}$ is smaller than the error of the other components of $\mathbf{x}^{(\text{new})}$ by a factor of at least* δ. The convergence of $\mathbf{x}^{(\text{new})}$ to $\bar{\mathbf{x}}$ will therefore be assured if $\delta < 1$, that is, if

$$\boxed{|a_{ii}| > \sum_{j \neq i} |a_{ij}| \qquad \text{for } i = 1, 2, \ldots, n} \tag{10c}$$

This is precisely the condition for strict diagonal dominance.

4.5C   ACCELERATING CONVERGENCE OF GAUSS–SEIDEL ITERATION

If the ith equation of $A\mathbf{x} = \mathbf{b}$ is solved for x_j, the resulting Gauss–Seidel equation is

$$x_j^{(\text{new})} = \frac{1}{a_{ij}}\left\{b_i - \sum_{k \neq j} a_{ik}x_k\right\} = x_j + \frac{1}{a_{ij}}\left\{b_i - \sum_{k=1}^{n} a_{ik}x_k\right\}$$

It will be useful to put this in the "increment form"

$$x_j^{(\text{new})} = x_j + dx_j, \qquad \text{where } dx_j = \frac{1}{a_{ij}}\{b_i - (\text{row}_i\, A)\mathbf{x}\} \tag{11}$$

Note that the increment dx_j can be viewed as

$$dx_j = \frac{1}{a_{ij}}\{i\text{th component of }(\mathbf{b} - A\mathbf{x})\} = \frac{1}{a_{ij}}\{i\text{th residual of }\mathbf{x}\} \tag{12}$$

Clearly, dx_j indicates how well $\mathbf{x}$ satisfies (E_i); moreover, the condition

$$\rho_j = \frac{dx_j}{\text{preceding } dx_j} \approx \text{constant} \tag{13}$$

for successive iterations indicates that the convergence of x_j to $\bar{x}_j$ (or the divergence from $\bar{x}_j$) is *linear* (see Section 1.7F).

EXAMPLE. Examine whether (13) holds for the system $A\mathbf{x} = \mathbf{b}$, where

$$[A : \mathbf{b}] = \begin{bmatrix} -1 & 1 & -4 & : & 0 \\ 2 & 2 & 0 & : & 1 \\ 3 & 3 & 2 & : & \frac{1}{2} \end{bmatrix} \qquad \left(\bar{\mathbf{x}} = \begin{bmatrix} 1.25 \\ -0.75 \\ -0.5 \end{bmatrix}\right) \tag{14}$$

Solution. No rearrangement of equations makes A either symmetric or diagonally dominant. In view of the Variable Selection Strategy, we should solve (E_1) for x_3; (E_2) and (E_3) can be solved for either x_1 or x_2. Three (among many) possibilities are

(a) Solve (E_3) for x_2, then (E_2) for x_1, then (E_1) for x_3.
(b) Solve (E_3) for x_1, then (E_2) for x_2, then (E_1) for x_3.
(c) Solve (E_1) for x_3, then (E_2) for x_1, then (E_3) for x_2.

Figure 4.5-2 shows $\mathbf{x}^{(\text{new})}$ (to 5s) and its ρ_j's (to 3s) for several iterations of (a), (b), and (c), all starting with $\mathbf{x}_0 = [0 \quad 0 \quad 0]^T$.

In Figure 4.5-2, the Aitken improvement formula [(12b) of Section 2.3B] was used when all ρ_j's were constant to about 2s for two successive k's. The shaded entries indicate the result when this was done. In Figure 4.5-2(a) for example, all three ρ_j's satisfied $\rho_j \doteq 0.667$ for $k = 3$ and $k = 4$. Thus the values for $k = 2$, 3, and 4 gives

$$(x_i)_{\text{improved}} = x_{i,4} - \frac{(x_{i,4} - x_{i,3})^2}{x_{i,4} - 2x_{i,3} + x_{i,2}}, \qquad i = 1, 2, 3 \tag{15}$$

Specifically,

$$(x_1)_{\text{improved}} = 0.97840 - \frac{(0.97840 - 0.84259)^2}{0.97840 - 2(0.84259) + 0.63889} \doteq 1.25 = \bar{x}_1$$

$$(x_2)_{\text{improved}} = -0.47840 - \frac{(-0.47840 + 0.34259)^2}{-0.47840 - 2(-0.34259) - 0.13889} \doteq -0.75 = \bar{x}_2$$

$$(x_3)_{\text{improved}} = -0.36420 - \frac{(-0.36420 + 0.29630)^2}{-0.36420 - 2(-0.29630) - 0.19444} \doteq -0.5 = \bar{x}_3$$

The ρ_j values were so nearly constant that a single improvement gave $5s$ accuracy in all three components!

(a) Solve (E_3) for x_2, then (E_2) for x_1, then (E_1) for x_3; $\mathbf{x}_0 = [0 \quad 0 \quad 0]^T$.

k	x_1	ρ_1	x_2	ρ_2	x_3	ρ_3
1	0.33333		0.16667		−4.16667	
2	0.63889	0.917	−0.13889	−1.83	−0.19444	3.67
3	0.84259	0.667	−0.34259	0.667	−0.29630	0.667
4	0.97840	0.667	−0.47840	0.667	−0.36420	0.667
4	1.2500		−0.75000		−0.50000	

(b) Solve (E_3) for x_1, then (E_2) for x_2, then (E_1) for x_3; $\mathbf{x}_0 = [0 \quad 0 \quad 0]^T$.

k	x_1	ρ_1	x_2	ρ_2	x_3	ρ_3
1	0.16667		0.33333		0.041667	
2	−0.19444	−2.17	0.69444	1.08	0.22222	4.33
3	−0.67593	1.33	1.11759	1.33	0.46296	1.33
4	−1.3179	1.33	1.18179	1.33	0.78395	1.33
4	1.2500		−0.75000		−0.50000	

(c) Solve (E_1) for x_3, then (E_2) for x_1, then (E_3) for x_2; $\mathbf{x}_0 = [0 \quad 0 \quad 0]^T$.

k	x_1	ρ_1	x_2	ρ_2	x_3	ρ_3
1	0.50000		−0.33333		0.00000	
2	0.83333	0.667	−0.52778	0.583	−0.20833	
3	1.0278	0.583	−0.63426	0.548	−0.34028	0.633
4	1.1343	0.548	−0.69059	0.529	−0.41551	0.570
5	1.1906	0.529	−0.71798	0.518	−0.45621	0.541
6	1.2198	0.518	−0.73472	0.512	−0.47759	0.525
6	1.2512		−0.75038		−0.50125	

FIGURE 4.5-2 USING GAUSS–SEIDEL ITERATION TO SOLVE A 3×3 SYSTEM.

For $k = 3$ and 4 in Figure 4.5-2(b), all ρ_j values were (to $3s$) $1.33 > 1$, indicating linear *divergence*. Nevertheless, one application of the Aitken formula gave to $5s$ the desired values of $\bar{x}_1$, $\bar{x}_2$, and $\bar{x}_3$ from which the components of $\mathbf{x}_k$ were diverging!

In Figure 4.5-2(c), the ρ_j's did not become constant as well as they did in (a) and (b). As a result, the Aitken formula was not used until $k = 6$, and the improved components of $\mathbf{x}_6$ were only accurate to two or three significant digits.

An examination of the system (14) reveals no reason why the ρ_j's of Figure 4.5-2 should have been more constant in (a) and (b) than in (c). Indeed, a satisfactory, general a priori strategy for determining which (E_i) should be solved for which x_j (and in which order) to ensure rapid, linear convergence has not been found. In the absence of such a strategy, it is desirable to have a computer program for Gauss–Seidel iteration which is interactive so that during execution the user may examine the results of a few iterations and, based on these results, modify the x_j's solved for in the (E_i)'s and/or the order in which the (E_i)'s are to be solved.

4.5D   RELAXATION

A strategy called **relaxation** consists of replacing (11) by

$$x_i^{(\text{new})} = x_i + \lambda\, dx_i, \qquad \text{where } dx_i = \frac{1}{a_{ii}}\{b_i - (\text{row}_i\, A)\mathbf{x}\} \tag{16}$$

Generally, either $0 < \lambda < 1$ (**underrelaxation**) or $1 < \lambda < 2$ (**overrelaxation**) is used, with $\lambda = 1$ corresponding to Gauss–Seidel iteration. It has been found that in certain situations relaxation can improve the likelihood of accelerate the rate of the convergence of Gauss–Seidel iteration, although the convergence will remain linear. Unfortunately, one effect of relaxation is to make the ρ_i's less constant so that the advantage of more rapid linear convergence is offset by the loss of the ability to use the Aitken formula effectively.

The reader wishing to know more about relaxation is referred to [28].

Solving Nonlinear Systems of Equations   **4.6**

An equation that contains expressions such as

$$x^3, \quad y^{-2}, \quad xy, \quad \frac{\sqrt{y}}{x}, \quad (2y - z)^2, \quad \sin x, \quad e^{yz}, \quad z\sqrt{x + y}$$

is called **nonlinear** in $x, y, z, \ldots$ because it *cannot* be written as

$$ax + by + cz + \cdots = \text{constant} \qquad (\text{a } \textit{linear equation in } x, y, z, \ldots)$$

A system of n equations in n unknowns $x_1, x_2, \ldots, x_n$ is called **nonlinear** if one or more of the equations is nonlinear. By bringing all nonzero terms to the left side of all equations, any nonlinear $n \times n$ system can be put in the general form

$$
\left.\begin{array}{ll}
(E_1) & f_1(x_1, x_2, \ldots, x_n) = 0 \\
(E_2) & f_2(x_1, x_2, \ldots, x_n) = 0 \\
& \vdots \\
(E_n) & f_n(x_1, x_2, \ldots, x_n) = 0
\end{array}\right\} \quad \text{or simply} \quad
\begin{cases}
f_1(\mathbf{x}) = 0 \\
f_2(\mathbf{x}) = 0 \\
\quad \vdots \\
f_n(\mathbf{x}) = 0
\end{cases}, \quad \text{where } \mathbf{x} = \begin{bmatrix} x_1 \\ x_2 \\ \vdots \\ x_n \end{bmatrix} \quad (1)
$$

4.6A OBTAINING GRAPHICAL ESTIMATES OF SOLUTIONS OF 2 × 2 SYSTEMS

Consider the 2×2 system

$$
\begin{array}{lll}
(E_1) & ye^x - 2 = 0 & \text{[This is } f_1(\mathbf{x}) = 0, \text{ with } \mathbf{x} = [x \quad y]^T] \\
(E_2) & x^2 + y - 4 = 0 & \text{[This is } f_2(\mathbf{x}) = 0, \text{ with } \mathbf{x} = [x \quad y]^T]
\end{array} \quad (2)
$$

A graphical analysis of this system proceeds as follows:

$$
\begin{array}{lll}
\mathbf{x} \text{ satisfies } (E_1) & \Longleftrightarrow & \mathbf{x} \text{ lies on the exponential curve } y = 2e^{-x} \\
\mathbf{x} \text{ satisfies } (E_2) & \Longleftrightarrow & \mathbf{x} \text{ lies on the parabola } y = 4 - x^2
\end{array}
$$

So, solutions $\bar{\mathbf{x}} = [\bar{x} \quad \bar{y}]^T$ correspond to points where the two curves intersect, as shown in Figure 4.6-1. Evidently, (2) has two solutions, namely

$$
\bar{\mathbf{x}}_1 \approx [-0.6 \quad 3.7]^T \quad \text{and} \quad \bar{\mathbf{x}}_2 \approx [1.9 \quad 0.4]^T
$$

To solve the nonlinear system (2) with greater precision, we could eliminate y, getting

$$
(4 - x^2)e^x - 2 = 0 \quad (3)
$$

This in turn can be solved by the root-finding methods of Chapter 2, with initial guesses (e.g., $x_0 = -0.6$ and $x_0 = 1.9$) obtained from Figure 4.6-1. However, *neither x nor y* can be eliminated from the nonlinear system

$$
\begin{array}{ll}
(E_1) & xe^y - x^5 + y + 3 = 0 \\
(E_2) & x + y + \tan x - \sin y = 0
\end{array} \quad (4)
$$

It is therefore important to have methods for solving nonlinear systems in the general form (1). One of the better known general-purpose ones is given next. A nonlinear system for which Gauss–Seidel iteration can be used is given in Section 8.5C.

4.6B THE NEWTON–RAPHSON METHOD FOR SOLVING NONLINEAR SYSTEMS

Suppose that

$$
\bar{\mathbf{x}} = [\bar{x}_1 \quad \bar{x}_2 \quad \cdots \quad \bar{x}_n]^T \quad (5a)
$$

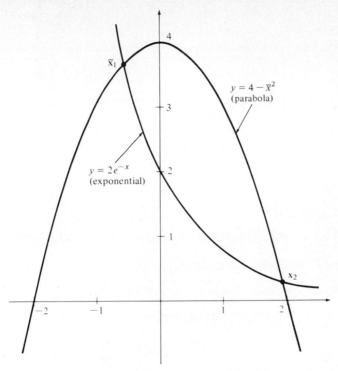

$y = 4 - \bar{x}^2$
(parabola)

$y = 2e^{-x}$
(exponential)

FIGURE 4.6-1   ESTIMATING SOLUTIONS OF $ye^x - 2 = 0$, $x^2 + y - 4 = 0$ GRAPHICALLY.

is a solution of the nonlinear system (1). This means that

$$f_1(\bar{\mathbf{x}}) = f_2(\bar{\mathbf{x}}) = \cdots = f_n(\bar{\mathbf{x}}) = 0 \qquad \textbf{(5b)}$$

If $\mathbf{x}$ approximates $\bar{\mathbf{x}}$, then the increment from $\mathbf{x}$ to $\bar{\mathbf{x}}$ will be denoted by

$$\Delta\mathbf{x} = \bar{\mathbf{x}} - \mathbf{x} = \begin{bmatrix} \bar{x}_1 - x_1 \\ \bar{x}_2 - x_2 \\ \vdots \\ \bar{x}_n - x_n \end{bmatrix} = \begin{bmatrix} \Delta x_1 \\ \Delta x_2 \\ \vdots \\ \Delta x_n \end{bmatrix} \qquad \textbf{(6a)}$$

where Δx_j is the increment from x_j to $\bar{x}_j$ for $j = 1, \ldots, n$. The problem we are faced with is to find the vector $\Delta\mathbf{x}$, that is, to find the *direction* and *distance* to move from $\mathbf{x}$ (in n-space) to get to the desired point

$$\bar{\mathbf{x}} = \mathbf{x} + \Delta\mathbf{x} \qquad \textbf{(6b)}$$

which is mapped into zero by each of $f_1, f_2, \ldots, f_n$ (see Figure 4.6-2).

Rather than seek the exact increment $\Delta\mathbf{x}$ that satisfies

$$f_i(\mathbf{x} + \Delta\mathbf{x}) = 0 \quad \text{for } i = 1, 2, \ldots, n \qquad \textbf{(7a)}$$

our strategy will be to find an approximate increment

$$\mathbf{dx} = [dx_1 \quad dx_2 \quad \cdots \quad dx_n]^T$$

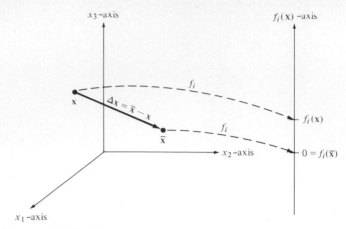

FIGURE 4.6-2 GRAPHICAL VISUALIZATION OF $\mathbf{x}$, $\bar{\mathbf{x}}$, AND $\Delta\mathbf{x}$.

that satisfies the more easily solved system

$$\{\text{linear approximation of } f_i(\mathbf{x} + \mathbf{dx})\} = 0 \quad \text{for } i = 1, 2, \ldots, n \tag{7b}$$

(see Appendix II.5C). Specifically, $\mathbf{dx}$ satisfies the approximating system

$$f_1(\mathbf{x}) + \frac{\partial f_1}{\partial x_1} dx_1 + \frac{\partial f_1}{\partial x_2} dx_2 + \cdots + \frac{\partial f_1}{\partial x_n} dx_n = 0$$

$$f_2(\mathbf{x}) + \frac{\partial f_2}{\partial x_1} dx_1 + \frac{\partial f_2}{\partial x_2} dx_2 + \cdots + \frac{\partial f_2}{\partial x_n} dx_n = 0 \tag{8a}$$

$$\vdots \qquad\qquad \vdots$$

$$f_n(\mathbf{x}) + \frac{\partial f_n}{\partial x_1} dx_1 + \frac{\partial f_n}{\partial x_2} dx_2 + \cdots + \frac{\partial f_n}{\partial x_n} dx_n = 0$$

where the partial derivatives $\partial f_i / \partial x_j$ are evaluated at the currently known $\mathbf{x}$. This *linear* system can be expressed in matrix form as

$$\underbrace{\begin{bmatrix} \dfrac{\partial f_1(\mathbf{x})}{\partial x_1} & \dfrac{\partial f_1(\mathbf{x})}{\partial x_2} & \cdots & \dfrac{\partial f_1(\mathbf{x})}{\partial x_n} \\[2ex] \dfrac{\partial f_2(\mathbf{x})}{\partial x_1} & \dfrac{\partial f_2(\mathbf{x})}{\partial x_2} & \cdots & \dfrac{\partial f_2(\mathbf{x})}{\partial x_n} \\[2ex] \vdots & \vdots & & \vdots \\[2ex] \dfrac{\partial f_n(\mathbf{x})}{\partial x_1} & \dfrac{\partial f_n(\mathbf{x})}{\partial x_2} & \cdots & \dfrac{\partial f_n(\mathbf{x})}{\partial x_n} \end{bmatrix}}_{\mathbf{f}'(\mathbf{x})} \underbrace{\begin{bmatrix} dx_1 \\[2ex] dx_2 \\[2ex] \vdots \\[2ex] dx_n \end{bmatrix}}_{\mathbf{dx}} = - \underbrace{\begin{bmatrix} f_1(\mathbf{x}) \\[2ex] f_2(\mathbf{x}) \\[2ex] \vdots \\[2ex] f_n(\mathbf{x}) \end{bmatrix}}_{\mathbf{f}(\mathbf{x})} \tag{8b}$$

Its solution, when $\mathbf{f}'(\mathbf{x})$ is nonsingular, is $\mathbf{dx} = -\mathbf{f}'(\mathbf{x})^{-1}\mathbf{f}(\mathbf{x})$.

The square matrix $\mathbf{f}'(\mathbf{x})$ in (8b) is called the **Jacobian matrix** of $\mathbf{f}$ at $\mathbf{x}$. Note that row$_i$ $\mathbf{f}'(\mathbf{x})$ contains all partials of f_i whereas col$_j$ $\mathbf{f}'(\mathbf{x})$ contains all partials with respect to x_j. Thus $\mathbf{f}'(\mathbf{x}) = (\partial f_i(\mathbf{x})/\partial x_j)_{n \times n}$.

If $\mathbf{x}$ is close enough to $\bar{\mathbf{x}}$ so that the linear approximation

$$f_i(\mathbf{x} + \Delta\mathbf{x}) \approx f_i(\mathbf{x}) + \frac{\partial f_i(\mathbf{x})}{\partial x_1} dx_1 + \cdots + \frac{\partial f_i(\mathbf{x})}{\partial x_n} dx_n$$

is accurate for $i = 1, \ldots, n$, then $\Delta\mathbf{x}$ [which satisfies (7a)] should be accurately approximated by $\mathbf{dx}$ [which satisfies (8a)]. Hence by (8b),

$$\bar{\mathbf{x}} = \mathbf{x} + \Delta\mathbf{x} \approx \mathbf{x} + \mathbf{dx} = \mathbf{x} - \mathbf{f}'(\mathbf{x})^{-1}\mathbf{f}(\mathbf{x}) \tag{9}$$

The iteration suggested by this is

$$\boxed{\mathbf{x}_{k+1} = \mathbf{x}_k + \mathbf{dx}_k, \qquad \text{where} \quad \mathbf{dx}_k = -\mathbf{f}'(\mathbf{x}_k)^{-1}\mathbf{f}(\mathbf{x}_k)} \tag{10}$$

It should be no surprise that the method based on this formula is called the **Newton–Raphson Method for Nonlinear Systems** (see Section 2.2B). We shall abbreviate it as simply **NRSYS**. The complete algorithm is described in Figure 4.6-3.

Terminology *Since solutions* $\bar{\mathbf{x}}$ *satisfy* $\mathbf{f}(\bar{\mathbf{x}}) = \mathbf{0}$, *we shall refer to them as* **roots** *of the vector function* $\mathbf{f}(\mathbf{x})$.

EXAMPLE. Use NRSYS to find to $5s$ the roots $\mathbf{x}_1$ and $\mathbf{x}_2$ of Figure 4.6-1.

Solution. The vector form of the nonlinear system (2) is $\mathbf{f}(\mathbf{x}) = \mathbf{0}$, where

$$\mathbf{x} = \begin{bmatrix} x \\ y \end{bmatrix} \quad \text{and} \quad \mathbf{f}(\mathbf{x}) = \begin{bmatrix} ye^x - 2 \\ x^2 + y - 4 \end{bmatrix}$$

and the Jacobian matrix is

$$\mathbf{f}'(\mathbf{x}) = \begin{bmatrix} \dfrac{\partial}{\partial x}(ye^x - 2) & \dfrac{\partial}{\partial y}(ye^x - 2) \\ \dfrac{\partial}{\partial x}(x^2 + y - 4) & \dfrac{\partial}{\partial y}(x^2 + y - 4) \end{bmatrix} = \begin{bmatrix} ye^x & e^x \\ 2x & 1 \end{bmatrix}$$

Since $\det[\mathbf{f}'(\mathbf{x})] = (y - 2x)e^x$, we should try to keep $\mathbf{x}_k$ away from the line $y = 2x$.

FOR $\bar{\mathbf{x}}_1$: Starting with the initial guess $\mathbf{x}_0 = [-0.6 \quad 3.7]^T$ obtained from Figure 4.6-1, the NR algorithm proceeds as follows.

$k = 0$:

$$\mathbf{f}(\mathbf{x}_0) = \begin{bmatrix} (3.7)e^{-0.6} - 2 \\ (-0.6)^2 + 3.7 - 4 \end{bmatrix} = \begin{bmatrix} 0.0306031 \\ -0.6 \end{bmatrix}$$

$$\mathbf{f}'(\mathbf{x}_0) = \begin{bmatrix} 3.7e^{-0.6} & e^{-0.6} \\ 2(-0.6) & 1 \end{bmatrix} = \begin{bmatrix} 2.03060 & 0.548812 \\ -1.2 & 1 \end{bmatrix}$$

Algorithm: NRSYS (Newton–Raphson Method for Nonlinear Systems)

Purpose: To solve a nonlinear system of n equations in n unknowns:

$$f_i(x_1, \ldots, x_n) = 0, \qquad i = 1, 2, \ldots, n$$

The method uses the arrays

$$\mathbf{x} = [x_1 \quad x_2 \ldots x_n]^T \qquad \{\text{current approximation of } \mathbf{x}\}$$
$$\mathbf{f} = [f_1(\mathbf{x}) \quad f_2(\mathbf{x}) \ldots f_n(\mathbf{x})]^T \qquad \{\text{array of } f_i(\mathbf{x}) \text{ values, i.e., } \mathbf{f}(\mathbf{x})\}$$
$$\mathbf{dx} = [dx_1 \quad dx_2 \ldots dx_n]^T \qquad \{\mathbf{dx} = \mathbf{x}_k - \mathbf{x}_{k-1}\}$$

and the matrix

$$J = (\partial f_i(\mathbf{x})/\partial x_j)_{n \times n} \qquad \{\text{the Jacobian matrix at } \mathbf{x}, \text{ i.e., } \mathbf{f}'(\mathbf{x})\}$$

to find a solution $\bar{\mathbf{x}}$ to *NumSig* significant digits in *MaxIt* iterations.

{*initialize*}
GET n, *MaxIt*, *NumSig*, $\mathbf{x}_0$ {initial guess}
$RelTol \leftarrow 10^{-NumSig}$; $\quad \mathbf{x} \leftarrow \mathbf{x}_0$

{*iterate*}
DO FOR $k = 1$ TO *MaxIt* UNTIL **termination test** is satisfied
  BEGIN
  $\mathbf{f} \leftarrow \mathbf{f}(\mathbf{x})$; $\quad J \leftarrow \mathbf{f}'(\mathbf{x})$ {Evaluate $\mathbf{f}$ and J at the current $\mathbf{x}$}
  {**get dx**} Solve the linear system $J\,\mathbf{dx} = -\mathbf{f}$ for $\mathbf{dx}$
  {**get x**} $\mathbf{x} \leftarrow \mathbf{x} + \mathbf{dx}$ {$\mathbf{x} = [x_1 \quad \cdots \quad x_n]^T$ is now $\mathbf{x}_k$}
  OUTPUT $(k, x_1, \ldots, x_n)$
  {**termination test:** $|dx_i| \leq RelTol*\max(1, |x_i|)$ for $i = 1, 2, \ldots, n$}
  END

IF **termination test** was satisfied
  THEN OUTPUT ($\mathbf{x}$ approximates $\bar{\mathbf{x}}$ to *NumSig* significant digits)
  ELSE OUTPUT (Convergence not apparent in *MaxIt* iterations)

{*Note:* In the **get dx** step, $\mathbf{dx}$ should be obtained as $-J^{-1}\mathbf{f}$ using the formula for J^{-1} if $n = 2$, and by solving $J\,\mathbf{dx} = -\mathbf{f}$ directly (*without finding* J^{-1}) if $n \geq 3$.}

FIGURE 4.6-3 PSEUDOPROGRAM FOR THE NEWTON–RAPHSON ALGORITHM FOR NON-LINEAR SYSTEMS.

Since $n = 2$, the easiest way to solve $\mathbf{f}'(\mathbf{x}_0)\,\mathbf{dx}_0 = -\mathbf{f}(\mathbf{x}_0)$ is to use the formula for $\mathbf{f}'(\mathbf{x}_0)^{-1}$ to get $\mathbf{dx}_0$ as the product $-\mathbf{f}'(\mathbf{x}_0)^{-1}\mathbf{f}(\mathbf{x}_0)$. Thus

$$\mathbf{dx}_0 = -\frac{1}{2.68917} \begin{bmatrix} 1 & -0.548812 \\ 1.2 & 2.03060 \end{bmatrix} \begin{bmatrix} 0.0306031 \\ 0.06 \end{bmatrix} = \begin{bmatrix} 0.000865 \\ -0.05896 \end{bmatrix}$$

$$\mathbf{x}_1 = \mathbf{x}_0 + \mathbf{dx}_0 = \begin{bmatrix} -0.6 \\ 3.7 \end{bmatrix} + \begin{bmatrix} 0.000865 \\ -0.05896 \end{bmatrix} = \begin{bmatrix} -0.599135 \\ 3.64104 \end{bmatrix}$$

A second iteration gives the following result:

$$k = 1: \qquad \mathbf{f}(\mathbf{x}_1) = \begin{bmatrix} -2.73173\text{E}-5 \\ 5.91353\text{E}-7 \end{bmatrix}, \qquad \mathbf{f}'(\mathbf{x}_1) = \begin{bmatrix} 1.99997 & 0.549286 \\ -1.19827 & 1 \end{bmatrix}$$

$$\mathbf{dx}_1 = -\frac{1}{2.65816} \begin{bmatrix} 1 & -0.549286 \\ 1.19827 & 1.99997 \end{bmatrix} \begin{bmatrix} -2.73173\text{E}-5 \\ 5.91353\text{E}-7 \end{bmatrix} = \begin{bmatrix} 0.000010 \\ 0.000012 \end{bmatrix}$$

$$\mathbf{x}_2 = \mathbf{x}_1 + \mathbf{dx}_1 = \begin{bmatrix} -0.599135 \\ 3.64104 \end{bmatrix} + \begin{bmatrix} 0.000010 \\ 0.000012 \end{bmatrix} = \begin{bmatrix} -0.599125 \\ 3.64105 \end{bmatrix}$$

The small entries of $\mathbf{dx}_1$ indicate that $\mathbf{x}_1$ is accurate to about $5d$. By assuming the convergence to be quadratic, $\mathbf{x}_2$ should certainly be accurate to at least the desired $5s$. Another iteration (which will not be shown) confirms this.

FOR $\bar{\mathbf{x}}_2$: If we start with the initial guess $\mathbf{x}_0 = [1.9 \quad 0.4]^T$ obtained from Figure 4.6–1, a similar computation gives

$$\mathbf{dx}_0 = -\mathbf{f}'(\mathbf{x}_0)^{-1}\mathbf{f}(\mathbf{x}_0) = \begin{bmatrix} 0.02672 \\ -0.111553 \end{bmatrix}, \qquad \mathbf{x}_1 = \mathbf{x}_0 + \mathbf{dx}_0 = \begin{bmatrix} 1.92672 \\ 0.288447 \end{bmatrix}$$

$$\mathbf{dx}_1 = -\mathbf{f}'(\mathbf{x}_1)^{-1}\mathbf{f}(\mathbf{x}_1) = \begin{bmatrix} -0.00098 \\ 0.003086 \end{bmatrix}, \qquad \mathbf{x}_2 = \mathbf{x}_1 + \mathbf{dx}_1 = \begin{bmatrix} 1.92574 \\ 0.291533 \end{bmatrix}$$

$$\mathbf{dx}_2 = -\mathbf{f}'(\mathbf{x}_2)^{-1}\mathbf{f}(\mathbf{x}_2) = \begin{bmatrix} 0.00000 \\ 0.000003 \end{bmatrix}, \qquad \mathbf{x}_3 = \mathbf{x}_2 + \mathbf{dx}_2 = \begin{bmatrix} 1.92574 \\ 0.291536 \end{bmatrix}$$

Here again the $\mathbf{dx}_k$'s demonstrate that if $\bar{\mathbf{x}}$ is a simple root and $\mathbf{x}_0$ is accurate to about $1d$, then the number of accurate decimal places will approximately double with each iteration of NRSYS (quadratic convergence), and two iterations should give about $5s$ accuracy. The convergence will be slower if $\bar{\mathbf{x}}$ is a multiple root (see Exercise 4–18).

4.6C PRACTICAL CONSIDERATIONS WHEN USING NRSYS

From a practical standpoint, NRSYS has three shortcomings.

1. IT IS IMPORTANT TO HAVE A GOOD INITIAL GUESS. Although the $\mathbf{x}_k$'s will converge quadratically once they are sufficiently close to a desired simple root $\bar{\mathbf{x}}$, a poor choice of $\mathbf{x}_0$ can cause the $\mathbf{x}_k$'s either to diverge or to converge to a different root than $\bar{\mathbf{x}}$ (see Section 2.2H). Unfortunately, graphical methods, limited as they are when $n = 2$, are simply not available when $n > 2$. Also, although computer programs can be written to search for roots of systems, they quickly become time-consuming (expensive) as n increases from 1.

This shortcoming is less serious than it appears because the context that gives rise to a nonlinear system usually provides some insight into an approximate value of the desired root(s). However, even with a good initial guess it is important to guard against overshoot. A simple remedy that has been found to be useful is to ensure that $|dx_i|$ never exceeds some preassigned value, for example,

$$\text{IF } |dx_i| > DxMax \text{ THEN } dx_i \leftarrow \text{sign}(dx_i) * DxMax \tag{11}$$

or some similar strategy [8].

2. IT IS A LOT OF WORK TO FIND THE n^2 PARTIAL DERIVATIVE FUNCTIONS $\partial f_i/\partial x_j$ FOR THE JACOBIAN MATRIX $\mathbf{f}'(\mathbf{x})$. Although the extra work (and associated extra possibility of error) in getting derivatives is mostly an inconvenience when $n = 1$, it becomes a serious drawback as n increases, especially if these n^2 partial derivative functions must be included as part of a computer program. This shortcoming is a serious one because it renders computers essentially useless for large n, which is precisely when we need them! (Imagine the likelihood of correctly finding *and* programming the $10^2 = 100$ entries of the Jacobian matrix of a 10×10 nonlinear system.)

The natural remedy is to approximate the partial derivatives numerically. Specifically, it follows directly from the definition of $\partial f_i(\mathbf{x})/\partial x_j$ (the partial derivative of f_i with respect to x_j at the point $\mathbf{x} = [x_1 \cdots x_n]^T$) that

$$\frac{f_i(x_1, \ldots, x_{j-1}, x_j + h_{ij}, x_{j+1}, \ldots, x_n) - f_i(x_1, \ldots, x_n)}{h_{ij}} \tag{12a}$$

can be used to approximate the ijth entry of $\mathbf{f}'(\mathbf{x})$. If the increment h_{ij} is taken to be that suggested by Steffensen, namely

$$h_{ij} = f_i(\mathbf{x}) \qquad \text{for all } j \quad [\text{provided } f_i(\mathbf{x}) \neq 0] \tag{12b}$$

then the convergence of NRSYS will generally be as fast as that obtained using exact partials in $\mathbf{f}'(\mathbf{x})$ (see [9]).

3. IT IS A LOT OF WORK TO SUBSTITUTE THE POINT $\mathbf{x}$ IN $\mathbf{f}'$ AND THEN SOLVE THE LINEAR SYSTEM $\mathbf{f}'(\mathbf{x}) \, \mathbf{dx} = -\mathbf{f}(\mathbf{x})$ EACH ITERATION. Although the formula for A^{-1} can be used to expedite a hand calculation when n is 2, a program is virtually essential for solving for $\mathbf{dx}$ when $n \geq 3$.

A partial remedy for this shortcoming is to assume that all partials $\partial f_i/\partial x_j$ are continuous at $\mathbf{x}_k$ so that

$$\mathbf{f}'(\mathbf{x}_k) \approx \mathbf{f}'(\mathbf{x}_{k+1}) \qquad \text{if } \mathbf{x}_k \approx \mathbf{x}_{k+1} \tag{13}$$

This suggests that we can *save the LU-decomposition of* $\mathbf{f}'(\mathbf{x}_k)$ obtained in getting $\mathbf{dx}_k$ and *reuse it* [rather than that of $\mathbf{f}'(\mathbf{x}_{k+1})$] in solving for (an approximate) $\mathbf{dx}_{k+1}$ and perhaps $\mathbf{dx}_{k+2}, \ldots, \mathbf{dx}_{k+r}$ as well. Experience has shown that reusing $\hat{L}\backslash\hat{U}$ this way generally does not appreciably slow the convergence; however, since each reuse eliminates about $2n^3/3$ arithmetic operations, this strategy can reduce considerably the time and cost of a computer run when n is large.

Exercises

Section 4.1

4-1. Consider the 2×2 linear system $A\mathbf{x} = \mathbf{b}$, where

$$A = \begin{bmatrix} 1.34 & -5.34 \\ -0.252 & 1.00 \end{bmatrix} \text{ and } \mathbf{b} = \begin{bmatrix} -3.98 \\ 0.74 \end{bmatrix} \quad \left(\bar{\mathbf{x}} = A^{-1}\mathbf{b} = \begin{bmatrix} 5 \\ 2 \end{bmatrix} \right)$$

In (a) and (b), use $3s$ arithmetic (i.e., round to $3s$ after *each* operation) for single precision and your calculator accuracy for extended precision. The subscripts BP, PP, and SPP denote the pivoting strategy used to get the calculated $\bar{\mathbf{x}}$.
(a) Solve $A\mathbf{x} = \mathbf{b}$ for $\bar{\mathbf{x}}_{BP}$, $\bar{\mathbf{x}}_{PP}$, and $\bar{\mathbf{x}}_{SPP}$. Do *not* use Partial Extended Precision.
(b) Solve $A\mathbf{x} = \mathbf{b}$ for $\bar{\mathbf{x}}_{BP}$, $\bar{\mathbf{x}}_{PP}$, and $\bar{\mathbf{x}}_{SPP}$. Use Partial Extended Precision.

4-2. Repeat (a) and (b) of Exercise 4-1 for $A\mathbf{x} = \mathbf{b}$, where

$$A = \begin{bmatrix} 0.34 & 2.32 \\ 0.78 & 2.68 \end{bmatrix} \text{ and } \mathbf{b} = \begin{bmatrix} -4.64 \\ -5.36 \end{bmatrix} \quad \left(\bar{\mathbf{x}} = \begin{bmatrix} 0 \\ -2 \end{bmatrix} \right)$$

4-3. Which of the LU-decompositions in (a)–(e) of Exercise 3-18 would have been obtained using Scaled Partial Pivoting? Explain.

4-4. Find the LU-decomposition of the A in (a)–(d) of Exercise 3-17 using Scaled Partial Pivoting and exact arithmetic.

Section 4.2

4-5. By inspection, find the pivot condition number $C_p(A)$ for the matrices A given in (a)–(e) of Exercise 3-18.

4-6. Find $C_p(A)$ from your calculation of $\bar{\mathbf{x}}_{SPP}$ in Exercise 4-1. Is A ill conditioned? What can you deduce from Exercise 4-1?

4-7. Repeat Exercise 4-6 for A of Exercise 4-2.

Section 4.3

4-8. (a) Explain why one iterative improvement, if performed using exact arithmetic, will yield exactly $\bar{\mathbf{x}}$.
(b) Verify part (a) using the (very inaccurate) $\bar{\mathbf{x}}_{calc} = [-1 \quad 5]^T$ for the system

$$\begin{array}{r} -x_1 - x_2 = 1 \\ -2x_1 + 3x_2 = 7 \end{array} \quad \left(\text{The exact } \bar{\mathbf{x}} \text{ is } \begin{bmatrix} -2 \\ 1 \end{bmatrix} \right)$$

4-9. Perform one iterative improvement of $\bar{\mathbf{x}}_{calc}$ using the LU-decomposition obtained in getting $\bar{\mathbf{x}}_{calc}$. Use $3s$ arithmetic throughout except in calculating the residual, which should be done using your calculator accuracy.
(a) $\bar{\mathbf{x}}_{calc} = \bar{\mathbf{x}}_{BP}$ of Exercise 4-1(a)   (b) $\bar{\mathbf{x}}_{calc} = \bar{\mathbf{x}}_{BP}$ of Exercise 4-1(b)
(c) $\bar{\mathbf{x}}_{calc} = \bar{\mathbf{x}}_{BP}$ of Exercise 4-2(a)   (d) $\bar{\mathbf{x}}_{calc} = \bar{\mathbf{x}}_{SPP}$ of Exercise 4-2(a)
Perform a second iterative improvement *only* if you expect to get improved accuracy. Explain your reasoning.

4-10. If $A = \begin{bmatrix} 1 & 2 \\ 3 & 4 \end{bmatrix}$ then $A^{-1} = \begin{bmatrix} -2.0 & 1.0 \\ 1.5 & -0.5 \end{bmatrix}$. Suppose that $(A^{-1})_{calc} = \begin{bmatrix} -1.8 & 1.2 \\ 1.6 & -0.6 \end{bmatrix}$.

Perform iterative improvements using the current $(A^{-1})_{calc}$ to get $\bar{E}_{calc}$ (as in Example 2 of Section 4.3B) until $5s$ accuracy is achieved.

Section 4.4

4-11. Find IROW for the LU-decompositions in (a)–(e) of Exercise 3-18. (See Section 4.4B.)

4-12. Solve (a)–(d) of Exercise 3-23 using Gaussian Elimination with Full Pivoting but without 1-SCALEs. Use exact arithmetic.

Section 4.5

4-13. In (a) and (b), solve the equations so that you are assured that Gauss–Seidel iteration will converge. Then, with $x_0 = 0$, do four iterations.

(a)
$$\begin{aligned}
2x_1 - 6x_2 - x_3 &= -3 \\
-8x_1 + 3x_2 + x_3 &= -4 \\
x_1 + x_2 - 3x_3 &= 5
\end{aligned}$$

(b)
$$\begin{aligned}
x_1 - x_2 \qquad\qquad + 3x_4 \qquad\quad &= 1 \\
5x_1 \qquad + x_3 \qquad - x_5 &= 3 \\
4x_2 + x_3 - x_4 \qquad &= -1 \\
3x_3 + x_4 - x_5 &= -4 \\
x_1 + x_2 \qquad\qquad - 4x_5 &= -3
\end{aligned}$$

4-14. Let

$$A = \begin{bmatrix} 5 & 3 & -2 \\ 3 & 2 & -2 \\ -2 & -2 & 5 \end{bmatrix} \quad \text{and} \quad B = \begin{bmatrix} 2 & 3 & -1 \\ 3 & 4 & -2 \\ -1 & -2 & 1 \end{bmatrix}.$$

We shall see in Exercise 9-46 that A is positive definite, but B is not.
(a) Show that $\bar{x} = [1 \quad -1 \quad 1]^T$ is the solution of both
$$A x = [0 \quad -1 \quad 5]^T \quad \text{and} \quad Bx = [-2 \quad -3 \quad 2]^T$$
(b) For both systems in part (a), solve (E_i) for x_i, $i = 1, 2, 3$ and perform two iterations of Gauss–Seidel iteration starting with $\bar{x}_0 = 0$. Why should you expect the iteration for $Ax = b$ to converge if continued?

Section 4.6

4-15. Use graphical methods to estimate *all* roots of the given nonlinear system.

(a)
$$\begin{aligned}
2 \ln y - x &= 0 \\
xy - y - 1 &= 0
\end{aligned}$$

(b)
$$\begin{aligned}
x + y^2 - 9 &= 0 \\
y - \ln x &= 0
\end{aligned}$$

(c)
$$\begin{aligned}
x^2 - y^2 - 4 &= 0 \\
y + 1 - 2 \sin x &= 0
\end{aligned}$$

4-16. Use NRSYS with your answers to Exercise 4.15 as initial guesses to find to $5s$ all roots of the systems (a)–(c) of Exercise 4.15.

4-17. For the system

$$\begin{aligned}
x^2 - 3 \sin y - z^2 &= 0 \\
z - 2xy + 1 &= 0 \\
e^{x+y} + z^2 &= 0
\end{aligned}$$

(a) Find the Jacobian matrix.
(b) Use NRSYS with $x_0 = 0$ to find x_1. (*Note:* You can solve $\mathbf{f}'(\mathbf{x}_0)\, d\mathbf{x} = -\mathbf{f}(\mathbf{x}_0)$ almost by inspection.)

4-18. Consider the system

$$(E_1) \quad x^2 + y^2 - a^2 = 0$$
$$(E_2) \qquad xy - 1 = 0$$

(a) Use graphical procedures to find the values of a for which the system has (i) 4 solutions; (ii) 2 solutions; (iii) no solutions.

(b) Solve (E_2) for y and use it to eliminate y from (E_1). For which value(s) of $a > 0$ does the resulting equation in x have (i) simple roots; (ii) multiple roots; (iii) no roots?

(c) With $a = 2$ and $x_0 = [2 \quad 0]^T$, find x_1, x_2, x_3 by NRSYS. Carry at least 6s. Does the convergence appear linear or quadratic? ($\bar{x} \doteq [3.73205 \quad 0.267949]^T$)

(d) Repeat part (c) with $a = \sqrt{2}$ and $x_0 = [1 \quad 0]^T$. ($\bar{x} = [1 \quad 1]^T$)

(e) Do your results of parts (c) and (d) agree with those of part (b)? Explain.

4-19. Trial and error shows that the system (4) of Section 4.6A has roots near (a) $[1 \quad -2.5]^T$ and (b) $[-0.5 \quad 2]^T$. Use NRSYS to find them to 5s.

4-20. Use NRSYS with an initial guess $[0.5 \quad 0.5]^T$ to solve to 5s the nonlinear system in Problem 4 of the introduction to Section 1.1A.

4-21. Show that Bairstow's method of Section 2.5C is an application of NRSYS.

Computer and Programming Exercises

4-22. Write a calling program LINSYS that reads n, p, $A_{n \times n}$, and $B_{n \times p}$, calls subprograms DECOMP and FORBAK as in Section 4.4B to solve $AX = B$, then prints $C_p(A)$ and the solution $\bar{X}$. Test LINSYS with $AX = B$ of Section 3.6B and $Ax = b$ of Section 4.1B.

4-23. Modify LINSYS of Exercise 4-23 so that it does the following:

(a) It calls subroutine IMPROV to form the residual R and perform one iterative improvement if *either* $C_p(A)$ is sufficiently small *or* at least one entry of R is unacceptably large. Test with $Ax = b$ in the example in Section 4.1D.

(b) It sets $B = I_n$ and then finds A^{-1} if $p = 0$ is input. Test with A of the example in Section 3.6C.

4-24. Write a program GAUSDL that does up to *MaxIt* Gauss–Seidel iterations. The program should read *MaxIt*, n, $A_{n \times n}$, **b**, and arrays *Iequation* and *Jvariable*, where, for example,

$$Iequation = [3 \quad 1 \quad 2] \qquad \text{and} \qquad Jvariable = [2 \quad 3 \quad 1]$$

means solve (E_3) for x_2 then (E_1) for x_3 then (E_2) for x_1 ($n = 3$). To do the actual iteration, it should call a subprogram SEIDEL. Test GAUSDL with Figure 4.5-2(a)–(c).

4-25. Write a program NRSYS that solves $\mathbf{f}(x) = \mathbf{0}$. It should call a subprogram JACOB to form the Jacobian matrix using the strategy indicated in (12) of Section 4.6C, and subprograms DECOMP and FORBAK to solve for **dx** as in Section 4.4B. It should also ensure that $Hmin < |h_{ij}| < Hmax$ and that $|dx_i|$ does not exceed a specified $DxMax$ [see (11) of Section 4.6C]. Test NRSYS with the example in Section 4.6B.

4-26. Modify NRSYS of the preceding exercise to reuse $\mathbf{f}'(x_k)$ *NumReuse* times as described in (13) of Section 4.6C.

Curve Fitting and Function Approximation

There are many situations where functional relationships are to be deduced from certain relevant experimental readings. For example, a *spring constant* can be determined by examining the forces needed to produce certain deflections from its rest position; or the *specific heat* of a mass can be determined by measuring its temperature at specified times after a heat source is applied. In such situations one must, if possible, take enough experimental readings so that statistical laws in effect cancel the errors introduced by inaccuracies in the measuring instrumentation.

Mathematically, the problem is the following: Given enough data points $P_k(x_k, y_k)$, find a functional equation $y = g(x)$ that relates the measured quantities x and y in the sense that its graph goes *near* (*not through*) the P_k's. This is called *curve fitting*. When the general form of $g(x)$ is known, say

$$g(x) = \alpha + \beta x \quad \text{or} \quad g(x) = \alpha e^{\beta x} \quad \text{or} \quad g(x) = \alpha + \beta x + \gamma x^2$$

the problem becomes that of finding values of the *parameters* (α, β, γ) which make the curve $y = g(x)$ fit the data well. We shall see in Sections 5.2A and 5.3A that for the case of *least square fit*, this can be accomplished by solving a system of *normal equations* for the desired parameters.

If the form of the functional dependence of y on x is *not* known, then one must guess $g(x)$'s until one that gives sufficiently good fit is found. Procedures for doing this are discussed in Sections 5.2B–5.3D.

The second problem considered in this chapter is that of approximating a known function *over a given interval* by a polynomial or a rational function (i.e., a quotient of polynomials). This problem arises in designing the "built-in" functions of a computer or calculator or when using a digital device or programming language that does not have a particular function built in. It is discussed in Section 5.4. In Section 5.4D we show how the methods for least square fit of discrete data can be applied to this continuous approximation problem.

5.1   Fitting Curves to Discrete Data

5.1A   DISCUSSION OF THE PROBLEM

Suppose that we wanted to know how a physical quantity y varies with changes in a second quantity x. A reasonable way to approach the problem is to devise an experimental procedure to get several (x, y) pairs, which can be viewed as m **data points**

$$P_1(x_1, y_1), \quad P_2(x_2, y_2), \quad \ldots, \quad P_m(x_m, y_m) \tag{1}$$

and to plot them on a set of (suitably scaled) xy-axes. Such points, being experimental, will probably *not* lie on the exact (unknown) y versus x curve. However, if the data are accurate enough and enough points are plotted, it may be possible to recognize the shape of a **guess function** $g(x)$ such that

$$g(x) \approx \text{functional dependence of } y \text{ on } x$$

For example, the five points

$$P_1(1, 5.12), \quad P_2(3, 3), \quad P_3(6, 2.48), \quad P_4(9, 2.34), \quad P_5(15, 2.18) \tag{2}$$

shown in Figure 5.1-1 can be fit (poorly) by a *linear* guess function

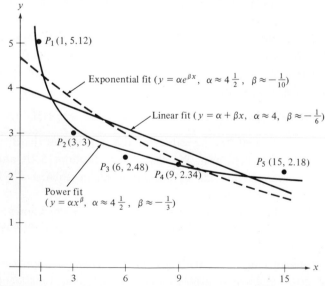

FIGURE 5.1-1   THREE GUESS FUNCTIONS FOR $P_1, \ldots, P_5$.

$$a + bx, \qquad \text{where } a = y\text{-intercept} \approx 4 \quad \text{and} \quad b = \text{slope} \approx -\tfrac{1}{6} \tag{3a}$$

or (slightly better) by an *exponential* guess function

$$\alpha e^{\beta x}, \qquad \text{where } \alpha = y\text{-intercept} \approx 4\tfrac{1}{2} \quad \text{and} \quad \beta = \text{``damping factor''} \approx -\tfrac{1}{10} \tag{3b}$$

or (still better) by a *power* (of x) guess function

$$\alpha x^{\beta}, \qquad \text{where } \alpha = y\text{-scale factor} \approx 4\tfrac{1}{2} \quad \text{and} \quad \beta = \text{power} \approx -\tfrac{1}{3} \tag{3c}$$

as well as others the reader might be able to think of. Having selected a particular $g(x)$, the problem becomes that of finding the values of the **parameters** [a and b in (3a), α and β in (3b) and (3c)] that make $g(x)$ fit the data best. To do this, we must first define what we mean by "good fit."

5.1B   THE LEAST SQUARE ERROR CRITERION

Any quantitative measure of how well a guess function $g(x)$ fits the data $P_1, \ldots, P_m$ should involve the numbers

$$\delta_k = g(x_k) - y_k = \text{the } \textbf{deviation of } g(x) \textbf{ at } x_k \tag{4}$$

for $k = 1, 2, \ldots, m$ (Figure 5.1-2). For example, the nonnegative numbers

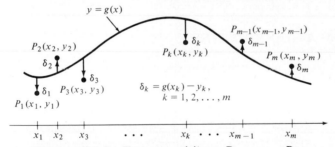

FIGURE 5.1-2   FITTING $g(x)$ TO $P_1, \ldots, P_m$.

$$E_1(g) = |\delta_1| + \cdots + |\delta_m| = \sum_{k=1}^{m} |\delta_k|, \quad \text{the } \textit{absolute sum} \text{ of the } \delta_k\text{'s} \tag{5a}$$

$$E_2(g) = \delta_1^2 + \cdots + \delta_m^2 = \sum_{k=1}^{m} \delta_k^2, \quad \text{the } \textit{square sum} \text{ of the } \delta_k\text{'s} \tag{5b}$$

$$E_\infty(g) = \max\{|\delta_1|, \ldots, |\delta_m|\} = \max_{1 \le k \le m}\{|\delta_k|\}, \quad \text{the } \textit{maximum} \text{ of the } |\delta_k|\text{'s} \tag{5c}$$

will all be zero when $g(x_k) = y_k$ at all x_k, and will all increase as the δ_k's begin to differ from zero whether $g(x_k) > y_k$ or $g(x_k) < y_k$. So *a small value of $E_1(g)$, $E_2(g)$, $E_\infty(g)$, or any other such $E(g)$ indicates that $g(x)$ fits the data well.*

Which of the available $E(g)$'s should we use? In statistics it is shown that if for each k the random variable

$$e_k = \text{the error of } y_k$$

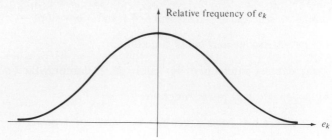

FIGURE 5.1-3 GAUSSIAN DENSITY FUNCTION.

is **normally distributed** (i.e., if its density function is the familiar bell-shaped **Gaussian** curve shown in Figure 5.1-3), then the **square error** $E_2(g)$ is the best possible indicator of how well $g(x)$ approximates the actual dependence of y on x. Moreover, the mathematical problem of minimizing $E(g)$ turns out to be especially easy when $E(g)$ is $E_2(g)$. Consequently, *unless otherwise specified, $E(g)$ will mean $E_2(g)$ and "best fit" will be achieved when we*

$$\text{minimize } E(g), \qquad \text{where } E(g) = \sum_{k=1}^{m} [g(x_k) - y_k]^2 \tag{6}$$

that is, when we obtain the **least square error.**

5.1C FITTING A STRAIGHT LINE

To illustrate least square error approximation, consider the important problem of fitting a straight line. The guess function for this rather special fit will be denoted by

$$L(x) = a + bx \qquad (a = y\text{-intercept, } b = \text{slope}) \tag{7}$$

Given m data points $P_1(x_1, y_1), \ldots, P_m(x_m, y_m)$, we wish to find the values of the parameters a and b that minimize the square error

$$E(L) = \sum_{k=1}^{m} [a + bx_k - y_k]^2 = [a + bx_1 - y_1]^2 + \cdots + [a + bx_m - y_m]^2 \tag{8}$$

We know from calculus that this will occur when

$$\frac{\partial E(L)}{\partial a} = 0 \qquad \text{and} \qquad \frac{\partial E(L)}{\partial b} = 0 \tag{9}$$

Since the x_k's and y_k's are constant,

$$\frac{\partial E(L)}{\partial a} = \sum_{k=1}^{m} 2[a + bx_k - y_k]^1 \frac{\partial}{\partial a} [a + bx_k - y_k]$$

$$= 2 \sum_{k=1}^{m} [a + bx_k - y_k] \cdot 1 = 2\left[ma + b\left(\sum_{k=1}^{m} x_k\right) - \sum_{k=1}^{m} y_k \right] \tag{10a}$$

(recall that $\partial/\partial a$ is with b fixed), and similarly

$$\frac{\partial E(L)}{\partial b} = \sum_{k=1}^{m} 2[a + bx_k - y_k] \cdot x_k = 2\left[a\left(\sum_{k=1}^{m} x_k\right) + b\left(\sum_{k=1}^{m} x_k^2\right) - \sum_{k=1}^{m} x_k y_k \right] \quad \textbf{(10b)}$$

Equating these partial derivatives to zero yields the 2×2 *linear* system†

$$ma + \left(\sum x_k\right) b = \sum y_k \qquad\qquad \textbf{(11a)}$$

$$\left(\sum x_k\right) a + \left(\sum x_k^2\right) b = \sum x_k y_k \qquad\qquad \textbf{(11b)}$$

The matrix form of these so-called **normal equations** is

$$\begin{bmatrix} m & \sum x_k \\ \sum x_k & \sum x_k^2 \end{bmatrix} \begin{bmatrix} a \\ b \end{bmatrix} = \begin{bmatrix} \sum y_k \\ \sum x_k y_k \end{bmatrix} \qquad\qquad \textbf{(11c)}$$

The unique solution of the 2×2 system (11) will be denoted by $[\hat{a} \quad \hat{b}]^T$; it can be obtained quickly as $A^{-1}\mathbf{b}$, that is, as

$$\begin{bmatrix} \hat{a} \\ \hat{b} \end{bmatrix} = \frac{1}{m \sum x_k^2 - \left(\sum x_k\right)^2} \begin{bmatrix} \sum x_k^2 & -\sum x_k \\ -\sum x_k & m \end{bmatrix} \begin{bmatrix} \sum y_k \\ \sum x_k y_k \end{bmatrix} \qquad \textbf{(12)}$$

We shall call $\hat{a}$ and $\hat{b}$ the **least square linear parameters** for the data. The linear guess function with these parameters, that is,

$$\hat{L}(x) = \hat{a} + \hat{b}x \qquad\qquad \textbf{(13)}$$

will be called the **least square line** or **regression line** for the data.

Formula (12) reduces the problem of finding the parameters for least square *linear* fit to a simple matrix multiplication. Hand calculators that do linear regression internally use precisely this formula.

EXAMPLE. Find the least square line for the following data:

$$P_1(1, 5.12), \quad P_2(3, 3), \quad P_3(6, 2.48), \quad P_4(9, 2.34), \quad P_5(15, 2.18) \qquad \textbf{(14)}$$

† In (11) we have used Σ as an abbreviation for $\Sigma_{k=1}^{m}$, the sum over all data points. This (or Σ_k) will be used frequently in what follows.

Solution. For these points, $m = 5$,

$$\sum x_k = 34, \quad \sum x_k^2 = 352, \quad \sum y_k = 15.12, \quad \text{and} \quad \sum x_k y_k = 82.76 \tag{15}$$

So the normal equations (11) are

$$\begin{bmatrix} 5 & 34 \\ 34 & 352 \end{bmatrix} \begin{bmatrix} a \\ b \end{bmatrix} = \begin{bmatrix} 15.12 \\ 82.76 \end{bmatrix} \tag{16a}$$

and the least square parameters, by (12), are

$$\begin{bmatrix} \hat{a} \\ \hat{b} \end{bmatrix} = \frac{1}{604} \begin{bmatrix} 352 & -34 \\ -34 & 5 \end{bmatrix} \begin{bmatrix} 15.12 \\ 82.76 \end{bmatrix} \doteq \begin{bmatrix} 4.15298 \\ -0.166027 \end{bmatrix} \tag{16b}$$

Hence the desired least square line is

$$\hat{L}(x) = \hat{a} + \hat{b}x \doteq 4.153 - 0.1660x \tag{17}$$

It is sketched in Figure 5.1-1. The rather large square error

$$E(\hat{L}) = \sum_{k=1}^{5} [\hat{a} + \hat{b}x_k - y_k]^2 \doteq 2.54 \tag{18}$$

is the smallest square error that a *straight-line fit* can have. To get a better fit, we must try a "curved" guess function.

```
00100          SUBROUTINE LINFIT(M, XDAT, YDAT, SQUERR, YCEPT, SLOPE)
00200          DIMENSION XDAT(M), YDAT(M)
00300          DOUBLE PRECISION SIGMAX, SIGMAY, SIGMXY, SIGMX2, SIGMY2
00400   C - - - - - - - - - - - - - - - - - - - - - - - - - - - - - - - - C
00500   C THIS SUBROUTINE FINDS THE LEAST SQUARE LINE Y = SLOPE*X + YCEPT C
00600   C FOR M DATA PAIRS  (XDAT(I),YDAT(I))  AND SQUERR, THE SQUARE     C
00700   C ERROR FOR THIS FIT.  IT RETURNS SQUERR, YCEPT AND SLOPE.        C
00800   C - - - - - - - - - - - - - - - - - - - - - VERSION 1:  5/1/81 - - C
00900   C FORM THE SUMS NEEDED TO SOLVE THE NORMAL EQUATIONS
01000          SIGMAX = 0.D0
01100          SIGMAY = 0.D0
01200          SIGMXY = 0.D0
01300          SIGMX2 = 0.D0
01400          SIGMY2 = 0.D0
01500          DO 100  K=1,M
01600             SIGMAX = SIGMAX + DBLE(XDAT(K))
01700             SIGMAY = SIGMAY + DBLE(YDAT(K))
01800             SIGMXY = SIGMXY + DBLE(XDAT(K))*DBLE(YDAT(K))
01900             SIGMX2 = SIGMX2 + DBLE(XDAT(K))**2
02000             SIGMY2 = SIGMY2 + DBLE(YDAT(K))**2
02100     100  CONTINUE
02200   C
02300   C SOLVE NORMAL EQUATIONS FOR SLOPE AND YCEPT, AND GET SQUERR
02400          DETER = SNGL(M*SIGMX2 - SIGMAX**2)
02500          YCEPT = SNGL(SIGMX2*SIGMAY - SIGMAX*SIGMXY)/DETER
02600          SLOPE = SNGL(M*SIGMXY - SIGMAX*SIGMAY)/DETER
02700          SQUERR = SNGL(SIGMY2 - YCEPT*SIGMAY - SLOPE*SIGMXY)
02800   C
02900          RETURN
03000          END
```

FIGURE 5.1-4   LINFIT: A FORTRAN SUBROUTINE FOR FITTING STRAIGHT LINES.

5.1D   A FORTRAN SUBROUTINE FOR FITTING STRAIGHT LINES

SUBROUTINE LINFIT shown in Figure 5.1-4 is a FORTRAN subroutine that returns the slope (SLOPE), y-intercept (YCEPT), and square error (SQUERR), of the least square line for (X(K), Y(K)), K = 1, . . . , M. SLOPE and YCEPT are computed by (12) of Section 5.1C. SQUERR is determined by the formula

$$E(\hat{L}) = \sum_k y_k^2 - \left[\text{YCEPT} \cdot \sum_k y_k + \text{SLOPE} \cdot \sum_k x_k y_k \right] \tag{19}$$

which the reader is asked to derive in Exercise 5-10. The sums Σ_k are computed in extended precision to avoid loss of significance when performing the subtraction in (19) when $E(\hat{L})$ is small.

Fitting Two-Parameter Curves to Monotone,   5.2
Convex Data

Let us restrict our attention to data for which good fit can be achieved by a guess function $g(x)$ whose graph is

1. **Monotone,** that is, either strictly increasing or strictly decreasing.
2. **Convex,** that is, either concave up or concave down.

on the entire **fitting interval** $[x_1, x_m]$. Thus we are for now considering only data that have *no apparent turning points* and *no apparent inflection points* on $[x_1, x_m]$. The data in Figure 5.1-1 are monotone and convex because they are strictly decreasing and concave up on $[1, 15]$.

Monotone, convex data arise frequently in practice and lend themselves to being fit by guess functions such as

$$g(x) = \alpha e^{\beta x}, \qquad g(x) = \alpha x^\beta, \qquad g(x) = \alpha + \frac{\beta}{x}$$

which have *two parameters* α and β.

5.2A   THE NORMAL EQUATIONS FOR A TWO-PARAMETER
GUESS FUNCTION

Given points $P_k(x_k, y_k)$, $k = 1, \ldots, m$, and a two-parameter guess function $g(x)$, we wish to

$$\text{minimize } E(g), \qquad \text{where } E(g) = \sum_{k=1}^{m} [g(x_k) - y_k]^2 \tag{1}$$

This requires solving the **normal equations**

$$\frac{\partial E(g)}{\partial \alpha} = 0 \quad \text{and} \quad \frac{\partial E(g)}{\partial \beta} = 0 \tag{2}$$

for the **least square parameters** $\hat{\alpha}$ and $\hat{\beta}$; the $g(x)$ with these parameters will be called the **least square** $g(x)$ for these data and denoted by $\hat{g}(x)$.

The normal equations (2) are generally *nonlinear* in α and β, and hence do *not* give rise to a simple matrix formula like (12) of Section 5.1C.

EXAMPLE. Find the normal equations for the **exponential guess function**

$$g(x) = \alpha e^{\beta x} \tag{3}$$

Solution. We want to minimize the square error

$$E(g) = \sum_{k=1}^{m} [\alpha e^{\beta x_k} - y_k]^2 = [\alpha e^{\beta x_1} - y_1]^2 + \cdots + [\alpha e^{\beta x_m} - y_m]^2$$

To do this, we must solve the normal equations

$$0 = \frac{\partial E(g)}{\partial \alpha} = \sum_{k=1}^{m} 2[\alpha e^{\beta x_k} - y_k]^1 \frac{\partial}{\partial \alpha}[\alpha e^{\beta x_k} - y_k] = 2\sum_{k=1}^{m}[\alpha e^{\beta x_k} - y_k]e^{\beta x_k}$$

$$0 = \frac{\partial E(g)}{\partial \beta} = \sum_{k=1}^{m} 2[\alpha e^{\beta x_k} - y_k]^1 \frac{\partial}{\partial \beta}[\alpha e^{\beta x_k} - y_k] = 2\alpha\sum_{k=1}^{m}[\alpha e^{\beta x_k} - y_k]x_k e^{\beta x_k}$$

or, upon canceling 2 and 2α in the first and second equations, respectively,

$$\alpha(e^{2\beta x_1} + e^{2\beta x_2} + \cdots + e^{2\beta x_m}) - (y_1 e^{\beta x_1} + y_2 e^{\beta x_2} + \cdots + y_m e^{\beta x_m}) = 0 \tag{4a}$$

$$\alpha(x_1 e^{2\beta x_1} + \cdots + x_m e^{2\beta x_m}) - (x_1 y_1 e^{\beta x_1} + \cdots + x_m y_m e^{\beta x_m}) = 0 \tag{4b}$$

These equations are *nonlinear* in α and β. To solve them, one could either (1) eliminate α and then use the Secant Method to get β, or (2) use NRSYS (Section 4.6) directly. In either case, *initial guesses $\alpha \approx 4\frac{1}{2}$ and $\beta \approx -\frac{1}{10}$ can be obtained from a rough sketch of a suitable exponential $g(x)$* (see Figure 5.1-1) and a computer or programmable calculator would be a virtual necessity in carrying out the iteration. For the data discussed in Section 5.1, namely

$$P_1(1, 5.12), \quad P_2(3, 3), \quad P_3(6, 2.48), \quad P_4(9, 2.34), \quad P_5(15, 2.18) \tag{5}$$

the least square parameters turn out to be (to 4s) $\hat{\alpha} \doteq 4.677$ and $\hat{\beta} \doteq -0.07472$. So the **least square exponential** for these data is

$$\hat{g}(x) \doteq 4.677 e^{-0.07472x} \quad \text{for which } E(\hat{g}) = \sum_{k=1}^{5} [\hat{g}(x_k) - y_k]^2 \doteq 1.84 \tag{6}$$

Notice that $E(\hat{g})$ is not much smaller than $E(\hat{L}) = 2.54$ [see (18) of Section 5.1C], indicating that the least square exponential does not fit the data much better than the least square line. This is confirmed graphically in Figure 5.1-1, where both $\hat{g}(x)$ and $\hat{L}(x)$ are accurately sketched.

The preceding discussion shows how messy the normal equations can be when they turn out to be nonlinear. Fortunately, good fit to most mononotone, convex data $P_k(x_k, y_k)$ can be obtained quickly by fitting a straight line to a related set of data points $Q_k(X_k, Y_k)$ as described next.

5.2B LINEARIZING MONOTONE, CONVEX DATA

The graphs of six guess functions that can be used to fit monotone, convex data are shown in Figure 5.2-1. A plot of the given data will quickly reveal the approximate

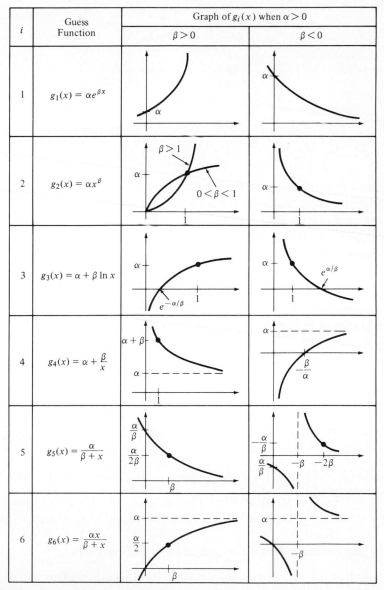

FIGURE 5.2-1 SKETCHES OF SIX GUESS FUNCTIONS FOR MONOTONE, CONVEX DATA.

locations of any *horizontal or vertical asymptotes* or *x- or y-intercepts,* and these in turn can help determine which of g_1–g_6 might fit the data well.

For example, for $P_1, \ldots, P_5$ shown in Figure 5.2-2(a),

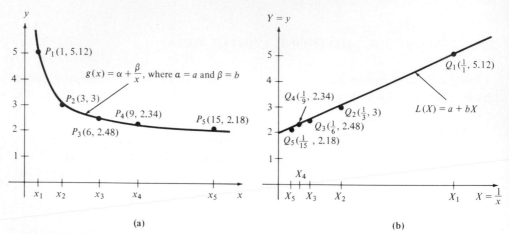

(a) (b)

FIGURE 5.2-2 LINEARIZING $P_1, \ldots, P_5$ USING THE TRANSFORMATION $Y = y$, $X = 1/x$.

1. The y-axis ($x = 0$) appears to be a vertical asymptote.
2. The line $y = 2$ appears to be a horizontal asymptote.
3. There appear to be no x- or y-intercepts.

The only curve of Figure 5.2-1 that can satisfy these three conditions is

$$y = g_4(x) = \alpha + \frac{\beta}{x} \qquad (\alpha > 0, \beta > 0) \tag{7a}$$

We should therefore expect the *hyperbolic* guess function $\alpha + \beta/x$ to fit $P_1, \ldots, P_5$ better than $a + bx$, $\alpha e^{\beta x}$, or any other curve on Figure 5.2-1. For further confirmation, notice that (7a) can be written as the *linear* equation

$$Y = L(X) = a + bX, \qquad \text{where } a = \alpha \text{ and } b = \beta, Y = y, \text{ and } X = \frac{1}{x} \tag{7b}$$

So if we transform the points $P_k(x_k, y_k)$ in Figure 5.2-2(a) to the points $Q_k(X_k, Y_k)$ where $X_k = 1/x_k$ and $Y_k = y_k$, that is, to

$$Q_1(\tfrac{1}{1}, 5.12), \quad Q_2(\tfrac{1}{3}, 3), \quad Q_3(\tfrac{1}{6}, 2.48), \quad Q_4(\tfrac{1}{9}, 2.34), \quad Q_5(\tfrac{1}{15}, 2.18) \tag{8}$$

then $Q_1, \ldots, Q_5$ appear linear when plotted on a set of XY-axes [see Figure 5.2-2(b)]. In view of (7), the fact that $Y_k \approx L(X_k)$ indicates that $y_k \approx g_4(x_k) = \alpha + \beta/x_k$, for $k = 1, \ldots, 5$.

By taking the natural logarithm of both sides of the equations

$$y = g_1(x) = \alpha e^{\beta x} \qquad \text{and} \qquad y = g_2(x) = \alpha x^{\beta}$$

and by straightforward rearrangement of $y = g_3(x)$, . . . , $y = g_6(x)$,

> $y = g_i(x)$ can be transformed to the *linear* form $Y = L(X) = a + bX$ (9)

For example, the transformation of $y = g_5(x)$ is

$$y = \frac{\alpha}{\beta + x} \quad \Leftrightarrow \quad \beta y + xy = \alpha \quad \Leftrightarrow \quad y = \frac{\alpha}{\beta} - \frac{1}{\beta} xy$$

The last expression is of the form $Y = a + bX$, where $a = \alpha/\beta$, $b = -1/\beta$, $X = xy$, and $Y = y$. The conversion of $y = g(x)$ to $Y = L(X)$ is called **linearizing** $y = g(x)$. It is summarized in Table 5.2-1 for $g_1(x)$, . . . , $g_6(x)$ of Figure 5.2-1.

TABLE 5.2-1 TRANSFORMATIONS FOR LINEARIZING THE SIX CURVES IN FIGURE 5.2-1.

					Transformation Relations			
		Linearized Form						
i	$y = g_i(x)$	$Y = L(X) = a + bX$	$X =$	$Y =$	$a =$	$b =$	$\alpha =$	$\beta =$
1	$y = \alpha e^{\beta x}$	$\ln y = \ln \alpha + \beta x$	x	$\ln y$	$\ln \alpha$	β	e^a	b
2	$y = \alpha x^\beta$	$\ln y = \ln \alpha + \beta(\ln x)$	$\ln x$	$\ln y$	$\ln \alpha$	β	e^a	b
3	$y = \alpha + \beta \ln x$	$y = \alpha + \beta(\ln x)$	$\ln x$	y	α	β	a	b
4	$y = \alpha + \dfrac{\beta}{x}$	$y = \alpha + \beta\left(\dfrac{1}{x}\right)$	$\dfrac{1}{x}$	y	α	β	a	b
5	$y = \dfrac{\alpha}{\beta + x}$	$y = \dfrac{\alpha}{\beta} + \dfrac{-1}{\beta}(xy)$	xy	y	$\dfrac{\alpha}{\beta}$	$\dfrac{1}{\beta}$	$\dfrac{-a}{b}$	$\dfrac{-1}{b}$
6	$y = \dfrac{\alpha x}{\beta + x}$	$y = \alpha + (-\beta)\left(\dfrac{y}{x}\right)$	$\dfrac{y}{x}$	y	α	$-\beta$	a	$-b$

The preceding discussion suggests that we can avoid the need to solve nonlinear normal equations by using the **Linearization Algorithm** described in Figure 5.2-3.

EXAMPLE. Use the Linearization Algorithm to fit

$$\text{(a) } g_4(x) = \alpha + \frac{\beta}{x} \quad \text{(b) } g_1(x) = \alpha e^{\beta x}$$

to the data

$$P_1(1, 5.12), \quad P_2(3, 3), \quad P_3(6, 2.48), \quad P_4(9, 2.34), \quad P_5(15, 2.18) \quad (10)$$

Solution

a. Linearize: For $g_4(x)$, $X_k = 1/x_k$ and $Y_k = y_k$. So the transformed points are

$$Q_1(\tfrac{1}{1}, 5.12), \quad Q_2(\tfrac{1}{3}, 3), \quad Q_3(\tfrac{1}{6}, 2.48), \quad Q_4(\tfrac{1}{9}, 2.34), \quad Q_5(\tfrac{1}{15}, 2.18) \quad (11)$$

Linearization Algorithm

Purpose: To fit a two-parameter $g(x)$ to the monotone, convex data $P_1(x_1, y_1)$, . . . , $P_m(x_m, y_m)$ when $g(x)$ is one of $g_1(x)$, . . . , $g_6(x)$ in Table 5.2-1.

GET m, **x**, **y** {arrays of x_k, y_k values}

{*linearize*} Form the "linearized points" $Q_k(X_k, Y_k)$ from the given points $P_k(x_k, y_k)$ as indicated in the "$X =$" and "$Y =$" columns of Table 5.2-1.

{*get â, b̂*} Get $\hat{a}$ and $\hat{b}$ for the least square line $\hat{L}(X) = \hat{a} + \hat{b}X$ for the *linearized* points $Q_k(X_k, Y_k)$ using the formula

$$\begin{bmatrix} \hat{a} \\ \hat{b} \end{bmatrix} = \frac{1}{m(\Sigma\, X_k^2) - (\Sigma\, X_k)^2} \begin{bmatrix} \Sigma\, X_k^2 & -\Sigma\, X_k \\ -\Sigma\, X_k & m \end{bmatrix} \begin{bmatrix} \Sigma\, Y_k \\ \Sigma\, X_k Y_k \end{bmatrix} \qquad (12)$$

{*get α, β*} Get α and β from $\hat{a}$ and $\hat{b}$ using the last two columns of Table 5.2-1.

OUTPUT (α and β are the desired parameters of $g(x)$.)

{*Note:* The $g(x)$ obtained by using α and β of the *get α, β* step will generally *not* be the least square $g(x)$, that is, $g(x) \neq \hat{g}(x)$. However, this $g(x)$ will give good fit to the *given* data P_1, . . . , P_m whenever $\hat{L}(X)$ obtained in the *get â, b̂* step gives good fit to the *linearized* data Q_1, . . . , Q_m.}

FIGURE 5.2-3   PSEUDOPROGRAM FOR THE LINEARIZATION ALGORITHM.

Get â, b̂: To get $\hat{L}(X) = \hat{a} + \hat{b}X$ for Q_1, . . . , Q_5 we use (12):

$$\begin{bmatrix} \hat{a} \\ \hat{b} \end{bmatrix} = \frac{1}{5(\frac{9361}{8100}) - (\frac{151}{90})^2} \begin{bmatrix} \frac{9361}{8100} & -\frac{151}{90} \\ -\frac{151}{90} & 5 \end{bmatrix} \begin{bmatrix} 15.12 \\ 6.9387 \end{bmatrix} \doteq \begin{bmatrix} 1.9681 \\ 3.1468 \end{bmatrix}$$

Get α, β: For this particular guess function, $\alpha = \hat{a}$ and $\beta = \hat{b}$; so to 4s:

$$g_4(x) \doteq 1.968 + \frac{3.147}{x} \qquad (13)$$

b. Linearize: For $g_1(x)$, $X_k = x_k$ and $Y_k = \ln y_k$. So the transformed points are

$$Q_1(1, 1.6332), \quad Q_2(3, 1.0986), \quad Q_3(6, 0.90826), \quad Q_4(9, 0.85015), \quad Q_5(15, 0.77832)$$
$$(14)$$

Get â, b̂: Since $X_k = x_k$, the coefficient matrix is the same as in (16) of the example in Section 5.1C; but $[\Sigma\, Y_k \quad \Sigma\, X_k Y_k]^T = [5.2695 \quad 29.720]^T$. Hence

$$\begin{bmatrix} \hat{a} \\ \hat{b} \end{bmatrix} = \frac{1}{604} \begin{bmatrix} 352 & -34 \\ -34 & 5 \end{bmatrix} \begin{bmatrix} 5.2695 \\ 29.720 \end{bmatrix} \doteq \begin{bmatrix} 1.3980 \\ -0.050601 \end{bmatrix} \qquad (15)$$

Get α, β: From Table 5.2-1, $\alpha = e^{\hat{a}} \doteq e^{1.398} \doteq 4.047$ and $\beta = \hat{b} \doteq -0.0506$. So

$$g_1(x) \doteq 4.047 e^{-0.0506\,x} \tag{16}$$

The parameters of $g_1(x)$ are fairly close to those of the least square exponential guess function $\hat{g}_1(x) = 4.677 e^{-0.07472\,x}$ obtained in the example in Section 5.2A. A look at Figure 5.2-4 reveals that $g_1(x)$ and $\hat{g}_1(x)$ appear to fit the data about as well to the eye, although [see (6)]

$$E(\hat{g}_1) = 1.84 < 2.24 = \sum_{k=1}^{5} [4.047 e^{-0.0506\,x_k} - y_k]^2 = E(g_1) \tag{17}$$

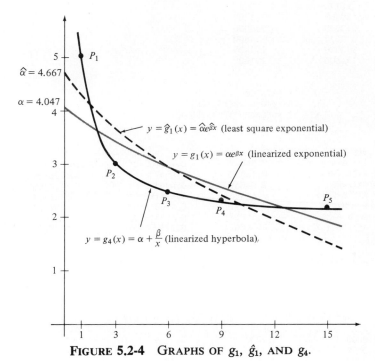

FIGURE 5.2-4   **GRAPHS OF g_1, $\hat{g}_1$, AND g_4.**

On the other hand, the linearized hyperbola $g_4(x)$ in (13) satisfies

$$E(g_4) = \sum_{k=1}^{5} \left[\left(1.968 + \frac{3.147}{x_k} \right) - y_k \right]^2 \doteq 0.00097 \tag{18}$$

which indicates a considerably better fit than either $g_1(x)$ or $\hat{g}_1(x)$ (see Figure 5.2-4.). In fact, $y_1, \ldots, y_5$ of the data were obtained by perturbing $2 + 3/x_k$ for $k = 1, \ldots, 5$.

5.2C   COMPUTER PROGRAMS FOR FITTING MONOTONE, CONVEX DATA

Most computer installations have a "canned" program, usually bearing a name such as CURFIT, which fits a straight line and uses the Linearization Algorithm to fit the six monotone, convex curves of Figure 5.2-1 to any provided data. A run of such a

```
RUN CURFIT


INPUT NUMBER OF DATA PAIRS
5

INPUT X[I] , Y[I] (I=1,N)
1, 5.12
3, 3
6, 2.48
9, 2.34
15, 2.18


CURRENT LISTING OF DATA PAIRS:
I          X[I]              Y[I]
1         1.0000            5.1200
2         3.0000            3.0000
3         6.0000            2.4800
4         9.0000            2.3400
5        15.000             2.1800


INPUT:         0    IF DATA OK
              -K    TO REMOVE (X[K],Y[K])
               K    TO REPLACE (X[K],Y[K])

0

    CURVE TYPE            SQUARE ERROR          A                  B
    1. Y = A + B*X          2.54009        0.41530E+01       -0.16603E+00
    2. Y = A*EXP(B*X)       0.16632        0.40471E+01       -0.50603E-01
    3. Y = A*(X**B)         0.03069        0.47037E+01       -0.31713E+00
    4. Y = A + B*LN(X)      0.68486        0.47119E+01       -0.10826E+01
    5. Y = A + B/X          0.00097        0.19681E+01        0.31468E+01
    6. Y = A/(B + X)        2.54757        0.52580E+02        0.11914E+02
    7. Y = A*X/(B + X)      0.06007        0.22322E+01       -0.57059E+00


       EQUATION #5. Y = A + B/X      HAS THE BEST LINEARIZED FIT

INPUT EQUATION # (1-7) FOR DETAILS OF FIT   (TYPE "0" FOR NO DETAILS).
5

DETAILS:  YCALC IS OBTAINED USING CURVE #5. Y = A + B/X
    XDATA           YDATA           YCALC          % DIFF.
    1.0000          5.1200          5.1149          0.1
    3.0000          3.0000          3.0170         -0.6
    6.0000          2.4800          2.4925         -0.5
    9.0000          2.3400          2.3177          1.0
   15.0000          2.1800          2.1779          0.1
```

FIGURE 5.2-5 A RUN FOR A "CURFIT" PROGRAM.

program for $P_1, \ldots, P_5$ considered in the preceding sections is shown in Figure 5.2-5. $E(\hat{L})$ [rather than $E(g_i)$] was used in the SQUARE ERROR column as an indicator of how well the $g_i(x)$ fit the given data (see Exercises 5-5 to 5-8).

5.3 Fitting Curves That Are Linear in n Parameters; Polynomial Fitting

If the given data appear to have either turning points or inflection points, then guess functions with more than two parameters are generally needed for adequate fit. As a rule, the greater the number of apparent inflection points, the greater the number of parameters $g(x)$ must have. However, the number of parameters needed is often not known in advance. In particular, data that appear to be convex and monotone may, in fact, require a $g(x)$ with more than two parameters for satisfactory fit.

Our discussion of n-parameter guess functions will be confined to $g(x)$'s that are linear combinations of n specified functions $\phi_j(x)$, that is,

$$g(x) = \gamma_1\phi_1(x) + \gamma_2\phi_2(x) + \cdots + \gamma_n\phi_n(x) = \sum_{j=1}^{n} \gamma_j\phi_j(x) \tag{1}$$

Guess functions of this form are especially convenient because, as we shall see, their normal equations are linear in the parameters $\gamma_1, \ldots, \gamma_n$, and hence are easily solved by the methods of Chapter 3. Fortunately, most data encountered can be fit by such a $g(x)$ using a suitable n and appropriate choices of $\phi_j(x)$. An important special case, obtained by taking $\phi_j(x) = x^{j-1}$, is the $(n-1)$st-degree polynomial

$$g_n(x) = \gamma_1 + \gamma_2 x + \gamma_3 x^2 + \cdots + \gamma_n x^{n-1} = \sum_{j=1}^{n} \gamma_j x^{j-1} \tag{2}$$

5.3A   THE NORMAL EQUATIONS FOR $g(x) = \sum_{j=1}^{n} \gamma_j\phi_j(x)$

Given m data points

$$P_1(x_1, y_1), \quad P_2(x_2, y_2), \quad \ldots, \quad P_m(x_m, y_m) \tag{3}$$

and a prescribed n (number of parameters), we wish to find the **least square parameters** $\hat{\gamma}_1, \ldots, \hat{\gamma}_n$ that minimize the square error

$$E(g) = \sum_{k=1}^{m} [g(x_k) - y_k]^2 = \sum_{k=1}^{m} [\gamma_1\phi_1(x_k) + \cdots + \gamma_n\phi_n(x_k) - y_k]^2 \tag{4}$$

The particular $g(x)$ with these n parameters will be denoted by

$$\hat{g}(x) = \hat{\gamma}_1\phi_1 + \hat{\gamma}_2\phi_2 + \cdots + \hat{\gamma}_n\phi_n(x) = \sum_{j=1}^{n} \hat{\gamma}_j\phi_j(x) \tag{5a}$$

and called the **least square $g(x)$** for the data. Thus, by definition,

$$E(\hat{g}) \leq E(g) \qquad \text{for any } g(x) = \gamma_1\phi_1(x) + \cdots + \gamma_n\phi_n(x) \tag{5b}$$

If we view $E(g)$ in (4) as a function of $\gamma_1, \ldots, \gamma_n$, then the values $\hat{\gamma}_1, \ldots, \hat{\gamma}_n$ that minimize $E(g)$ are obtained by solving the n equations

$$0 = \frac{\partial E(g)}{\partial \gamma_i} = \sum_{k=1}^{m} 2[g(x_k) - y_k]\frac{\partial}{\partial \gamma_i}[g(x_k) - y_k], \qquad i = 1, \ldots, n \tag{6}$$

Since $\phi_1(x_k), \ldots, \phi_n(x_k)$ and y_k are constant and $\partial\gamma_j/\partial\gamma_i = 0$ for $j \neq i$, we see from (4) that $\partial[g(x_k) - y_k]/\partial\gamma_i = \phi_i(x_k)$. So (6) gives

$$\sum_{k=1}^{m} \left[\sum_{j=1}^{n} \gamma_j\phi_j(x_k) - y_k \right] \phi_i(x_k) = 0, \qquad i = 1, \ldots, n \tag{7a}$$

or

$$\sum_{k=1}^{m} \sum_{j=1}^{n} \gamma_j \phi_j(x_k)\phi_i(x_k) = \sum_{k=1}^{m} y_k \phi_i(x_k), \qquad i = 1, \ldots, n \tag{7b}$$

Upon interchanging the order of the j and k summations, we see that the **normal equations** of $g(x)$ are

$$\sum_{j=1}^{n} \gamma_j \left(\sum_{k=1}^{m} \phi_i(x_k)\phi_j(x_k) \right) = \sum_{k=1}^{m} \phi_i(x_k)y_k, \qquad i = 1, 2, \ldots, n \tag{8a}$$

These constitute a *linear* system whose matrix form is

$$\underbrace{\begin{bmatrix} \sum \phi_1(x_k)\phi_1(x_k) & \cdots & \sum \phi_1(x_k)\phi_n(x_k) \\ \sum \phi_2(x_k)\phi_1(x_k) & \cdots & \sum \phi_2(x_k)\phi_n(x_k) \\ \vdots & & \vdots \\ \sum \phi_n(x_k)\phi_1(x_k) & \cdots & \sum \phi_n(x_k)\phi_n(x_k) \end{bmatrix}}_{A_{n \times n}} \underbrace{\begin{bmatrix} \gamma_1 \\ \gamma_2 \\ \vdots \\ \gamma_n \end{bmatrix}}_{\boldsymbol{\gamma}} = \underbrace{\begin{bmatrix} \sum \phi_1(x_k)y_k \\ \sum \phi_2(x_k)y_k \\ \vdots \\ \sum \phi_n(x_k)y_k \end{bmatrix}}_{\mathbf{b}} \tag{8b}$$

As before, Σ denotes $\sum_{k=1}^{m}$ (the sum over all data points). The solution of (8b) is the **least square parameter vector**

$$\hat{\boldsymbol{\gamma}} = A^{-1}\mathbf{b} = [\hat{\gamma}_1 \quad \hat{\gamma}_2 \quad \cdots \quad \hat{\gamma}_n]^T \tag{9}$$

whose components are the desired coefficients of $\hat{g}(x) = \sum_{j=1}^{n} \hat{\gamma}_j \phi_j(x)$.

EXAMPLE. Fitting an $(n-1)$st-degree polynomial $g_n(x)$

a. Find the normal equations for the polynomial guess function

$$g_n(x) = \gamma_1 + \gamma_2 x + \gamma_3 x^2 + \cdots + \gamma_n x^{n-1} = \sum_{j=1}^{n} \gamma_j x^{j-1} \tag{10}$$

b. Find the least square polynomials $\hat{g}_2(x), \ldots, \hat{g}_6(x)$ for

$$P_1(1, 6), \quad P_2(2, 1), \quad P_3(4, 2), \quad P_4(5, 3), \quad P_5(10, 4), \quad P_6(16, 5) \tag{11}$$

assuming the data to be reasonably accurate.

Solution
a. Here $\phi_i(x_k)\phi_j(x_k) = x_k^{i-1}x_k^{j-1} = x_k^{i+j-2}$. So the matrix form (8b) of the normal equations for the $(n-1)$st-degree polynomial $g_n(x)$ is

$$\underbrace{\begin{bmatrix} m & \sum x_k & \sum x_k^2 & \cdots & \sum x_k^{n-1} \\ \sum x_k & \sum x_k^2 & \sum x_k^3 & \cdots & \sum x_k^n \\ \sum x_k^2 & \sum x_k^3 & \sum x_k^4 & \cdots & \sum x_k^{n+1} \\ \vdots & \vdots & \vdots & & \vdots \\ \sum x_k^{n-1} & \sum x_k^n & \sum x_k^{n+1} & \cdots & \sum x_k^{2n-2} \end{bmatrix}}_{A_{n \times n}} \underbrace{\begin{bmatrix} \gamma_1 \\ \gamma_2 \\ \gamma_3 \\ \vdots \\ \gamma_n \end{bmatrix}}_{\gamma} = \underbrace{\begin{bmatrix} \sum y_k \\ \sum x_k y_k \\ \sum x_k^2 y_k \\ \vdots \\ \sum x_k^{n-1} y_k \end{bmatrix}}_{b} \qquad (12)$$

b. For $g_2(x) = \gamma_1 + \gamma_2 x$ $(n = 2)$ and the data (11), (12) become

$$\begin{bmatrix} m & \sum x_k \\ \sum x_k & \sum x_k^2 \end{bmatrix}\begin{bmatrix} \gamma_1 \\ \gamma_2 \end{bmatrix} = \begin{bmatrix} \sum y_k \\ \sum x_k y_k \end{bmatrix}; \quad \text{that is,} \quad \begin{bmatrix} 6 & 38 \\ 38 & 402 \end{bmatrix}\begin{bmatrix} \gamma_1 \\ \gamma_2 \end{bmatrix} = \begin{bmatrix} 21 \\ 151 \end{bmatrix} \qquad (13)$$

The reader may recognize this as (11c) of Section 5.1C. The normal equations for $g_3(x)$, . . . , $g_6(x)$ are obtained similarly. For example, for the cubic

$$g_4(x) = \gamma_1 + \gamma_2 x + \gamma_3 x^2 + \gamma_4 x^3 \qquad (n = 4) \qquad (14)$$

and the data (11), the matrix form (12) of the normal equations is

$$\begin{bmatrix} 6 & 38 & 402 & 5,294 \\ 38 & 402 & 5,294 & 76,434 \\ 402 & 5,294 & 76,434 & 1,152,758 \\ 5,294 & 76,434 & 1,152,758 & 17,797,002 \end{bmatrix}\begin{bmatrix} \gamma_1 \\ \gamma_2 \\ \gamma_3 \\ \gamma_4 \end{bmatrix} = \begin{bmatrix} 21 \\ 151 \\ 1,797 \\ 24,997 \end{bmatrix} \qquad (15)$$

Solving (12) for the least square parameters for $n = 2, \ldots, 6$ yields the coefficients of $\hat{g}_2(x), \ldots, \hat{g}_6(x)$ shown in Figure 5.3-1. Unfortunately, *none of $\hat{g}_2, \ldots, \hat{g}_6$ really fits the data well!*

5.3B   THE POLYNOMIAL WIGGLE PROBLEM

The preceding attempt to fit polynomials to nonpolynomial data illustrates the following phenomenon, which we shall refer to as the **Polynomial Wiggle Problem:**

If $P_1, \ldots, P_m$ do not actually lie on a polynomial curve, then an attempt to make a polynomial $p(x)$ go near (or through) them will cause $p(x)$ to have oscillations between successive P_k's. These oscillations get larger as the degree of $p(x)$ is allowed to increase.

So the remedy for poor polynomial fit is *not* to try higher-degree polynomials. Instead, one should *seek a more suitable guess function* (see Section 5.3D).

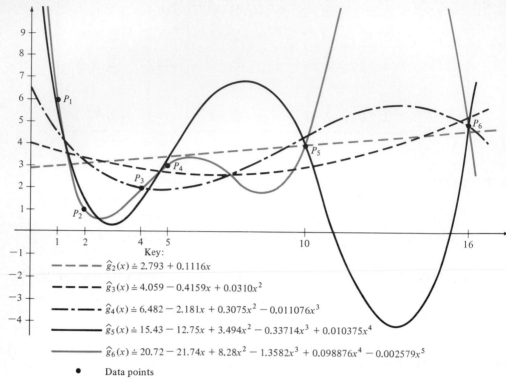

Key:

$\hat{g}_2(x) \doteq 2.793 + 0.1116x$

$\hat{g}_3(x) \doteq 4.059 - 0.4159x + 0.0310x^2$

$\hat{g}_4(x) \doteq 6.482 - 2.181x + 0.3075x^2 - 0.011076x^3$

$\hat{g}_5(x) \doteq 15.43 - 12.75x + 3.494x^2 - 0.33714x^3 + 0.010375x^4$

$\hat{g}_6(x) \doteq 20.72 - 21.74x + 8.28x^2 - 1.3582x^3 + 0.098876x^4 - 0.002579x^5$

●   Data points

FIGURE 5.3-1   LEAST SQUARE POLYNOMIALS OF DEGREE 1, 2, 3, 4, 5.

5.3C   DEFICIENCIES OF $E(\hat{g})$ AS AN INDICATOR OF GOOD FIT

The square errors of $\hat{g}_i(x)$, that is, the numbers

$$E(\hat{g}_i) = \sum_{k=1}^{m} [\hat{g}_i(x_k) - y_k]^2 \tag{16}$$

for $\hat{g}_2, \ldots, \hat{g}_6$ of Figure 5.3-1, are given in the following table:

$\hat{g}(x)$	$\hat{g}_2(x)$	$\hat{g}_3(x)$	$\hat{g}_4(x)$	$\hat{g}_5(x)$	$\hat{g}_6(x)$
$E(\hat{g})$	15.492	12.909	8.460	0.648	0.000

(17)

It can be seen from these values and Figure 5.3-1 that *a small value of $E(\hat{g})$ does not necessarily indicate that $\hat{g}(x)$ fits the data well on* $[x_1, x_m]$. In fact, $E(\hat{g}_6) = 0$ [indicating that the graph of $\hat{g}_6(x)$ goes *through* $P_1, \ldots, P_6$] despite the fact that for $x > 5$ the graph of $\hat{g}_6(x)$ bears no resemblance to the curve that gave rise to the data! (See Figure 5.3-2.)

The explanation for this is quite simple. *Each additional parameter allows $\hat{g}_n(x)$ to have one more inflection point and so increases the ability of $\hat{g}_n(x)$ to "wiggle" in order*

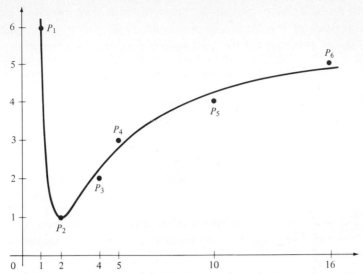

FIGURE 5.3-2   THE CURVE THAT GAVE RISE TO $P_1, \ldots, P_6$.

to come closer to the data points $P_1, \ldots, P_m$ (Section 5.3B). In fact, $\hat{g}_n(x)$ will generally satisfy

$$\hat{g}_n(x_k) \to y_k \text{ for all } k \qquad \text{as } n \text{ gets closer to } m \tag{18}$$

that is, as the number of parameters approaches the number of data points. In the limiting case when $n = m$, the normal equations in effect impose the m constraints $\hat{g}_m(x_k) = y_k$, $k = 1, 2, \ldots, m$, so that $E(\hat{g}_m)$ *will be zero whether or not $\hat{g}_m(x)$ looks like the actual y versus x curve.* Thus, although minimizing $E(g)$ ensures good fit *near* the P_k's, the size of the least square error $E(\hat{g})$ does not necessarily tell us whether the fit is good *between* the P_k's.

There are two other serious deficiencies of $E(\hat{g})$ as an indicator of good fit. First, since $E(\hat{g})$ is defined as $\Sigma_{k=1}^{m} [\hat{g}(x_k) - y_k]^2$, it can be large simply because m (the number of data points) is large, even if the fit is fairly good. More important, it is an *absolute* indicator that depends upon the scale used for the y values. For example, if y had units of length, then $E(\hat{g})$ can be reduced by a factor of 10,000 by simply measuring y in meters rather than centimeters!

5.3D   USING THE DETERMINATION INDEX TO ASSESS THE FIT OF $\hat{g}(x)$

In statistics, the **index of determination,** defined as the ratio

$$R(g) = \frac{\Sigma_k[g(x_k) - \hat{y}]^2}{\Sigma_k[y_k - \hat{y}]^2}, \qquad \text{where } \hat{y} = \frac{1}{m} \Sigma_k y_k \tag{19}$$

is used to indicate how well $g(x)$ fits $P_k(x_k, y_k)$, $k = 1, \ldots, m$. The denominator of

$R(g)$ is a measure of the dispersion of the y_k's about their **mean** $\hat{y}$. The numerator indicates how much of this dispersion is accounted for when y_k is replaced by $g(x_k)$. It can be shown [11] that for the least square $g(x)$, that is, when $g(x) = \hat{g}(x)$,

$$0 \leqslant R(\hat{g}) \leqslant 1, \text{ with better fit corresponding to } R(\hat{g}) \approx 1 \qquad (20)$$

Moreover, if $g(x)$ is a linear combination $\gamma_1\phi_1(x) + \cdots + \gamma_n\phi_n(x)$, the index of determination for $\hat{g}(x)$ can be obtained easily as

$$R(\hat{g}) = \frac{\sum_{i=1}^{n} \hat{\gamma}_i b_i - (1/m)(\sum_k y_k)^2}{\sum_k y_k^2 - (1/m)(\sum_k y_k)^2} = \frac{\hat{\boldsymbol{\gamma}}^T \mathbf{b} - m\hat{y}^2}{\mathbf{y}\mathbf{y}^T - m\hat{y}^2} \qquad (21)$$

where $\mathbf{y} = [y_1 \cdots y_m]$ is the row vector of y-values, $\hat{\boldsymbol{\gamma}}$ is the least square parameter vector, and $\mathbf{b}$ is the vector on the right-hand side of the linear system $A\boldsymbol{\gamma} = \mathbf{b}$ solved to obtain $\hat{\boldsymbol{\gamma}}$ (see [11]).

Note: When the fit is good, the numbers $\hat{\boldsymbol{\gamma}}^T\mathbf{b}$, $\mathbf{y}\mathbf{y}^T$, and $m\hat{y}^2$ will be large whereas the differences $\boldsymbol{\gamma}^T\mathbf{b} - m\hat{y}^2$ and $\mathbf{y}^T - m\hat{y}^2$ are small. So to avoid loss of significance when using (21), *it is recommended that the summations in $\hat{\boldsymbol{\gamma}}^T\mathbf{b}$, $\mathbf{y}\mathbf{y}^T$, and $\hat{y}$ be accumulated in extended precision if possible.*

In view of (18) and (19), $R(\hat{g})$ will approach 1 as n approaches m. To avoid a false indication of good fit, there must be enough *excess* data points. It is recommended that m be large enough so that $n < 2\sqrt{m} - 1$, that is,

$$\text{number of parameters} < 2\sqrt{\text{number of data points}} - 1 \qquad (22)$$

EXAMPLE. Find $R(\hat{g}_2), \ldots, R(\hat{g}_6)$ for the polynomials shown in Figure 5.3-1, and discuss the appropriateness of using polynomials to fit the given data.

Solution. Since $\mathbf{y} = [6 \quad 1 \quad 2 \quad 3 \quad 4 \quad 5]$ for the given data,

$$\mathbf{y}\mathbf{y}^T = \sum_k y_k^2 = 91 \qquad \text{and} \qquad \hat{y} = \frac{1}{m}\sum_k y_k = \frac{1}{6}(21) = 3.5 \qquad (23)$$

For the four-parameter fit in Figure 5.3-1,

$$\hat{g}_4(x) \doteq \underbrace{6.482161}_{\hat{\gamma}_1} + \underbrace{(-2.181341)x}_{\hat{\gamma}_2} + \underbrace{0.3075475x^2}_{\hat{\gamma}_3} + \underbrace{(-0.01107595)x^3}_{\hat{\gamma}_4} \qquad (24)$$

Also, from (15), $\mathbf{b} = [21 \quad 151 \quad 1797 \quad 24{,}997]^T$. So formula (21) gives

$$R(\hat{g}_4) = \frac{(21\hat{\gamma}_1 + 151\hat{\gamma}_2 + 1797\hat{\gamma}_3 + 24997\hat{\gamma}_4) - 6(3.5)^2}{91 - 6(3.5)^2} \doteq 0.516584 \qquad (25)$$

The remaining entries of the following table are obtained similarly.

$\hat{g}(x)$	$\hat{g}_2(x)$	$\hat{g}_3(x)$	$\hat{g}_4(x)$	$\hat{g}_5(x)$	$\hat{g}_6(x)$
$R(\hat{g})$	0.1148	0.2624	0.5166	0.9630	1.0000

$$(26)$$

In view of (22), reliable conclusions can be drawn from $R(\hat{g}_n)$ when

$$n < 2\sqrt{m} - 1 = 2\sqrt{6} - 1 \approx 4 \tag{27}$$

Since $R(\hat{g}_n)$ is not near 1 until $n = 5$, we can conclude that $\hat{g}_2$, $\hat{g}_3$, and $\hat{g}_4(x)$ do not fit the data well; but we *cannot* conclude from six data points that $\hat{g}_5(x)$ or $\hat{g}_6(x)$ give good fit. (In fact, we know from Figure 5.3-1 that they do not!)

5.3E   THE IMPORTANCE OF SKETCHING THE DATA

The data points

$$P_1(1, 6), \quad P_2(2, 1), \quad P_3(4, 2), \quad P_4(5, 3), \quad P_5(10, 4), \quad P_6(16, 5)$$

of the preceding discussion were sketched in Figure 5.3-2. There is something disturbing about $P_1(1, 6)$ because it forces a rather abrupt change in the derivative behavior of a fitting curve $y = g(x)$. Indeed, if this point were removed, the data would appear to be much more "well behaved." But should the point be removed?

If we know the functional form of $g(x)$, then it is generally easy to tell if an anomalous-looking data point is seriously in error. Such points are referred to as **outliers;** they should be removed from the data. If the form of $g(x)$ is *not* known, a repeated reading should be obtained (if possible) and/or the instrumentation examined to try to determine whether the point should be included as part of the data.

The phrase "assuming the data to be reasonably accurate" was inserted after (11) to indicate that $P_1(1, 6)$ is *not* an outlier. An examination of a plot of $P_1, \ldots, P_6$ reveals that to fit the data well, $g(x)$ should satisfy the following:

PROPERTY 1.   It should have a vertical asymptote near $x = 0$.
PROPERTY 2.   Its slope should approach zero as $x \to \infty$.

Nonconstant polynomial curves have *neither* of these properties. So *it is simply unrealistic to expect a polynomial to give good fit to data that exhibits either Property 1 or Property 2*. Indeed, had we sketched the data beforehand, we would not have wasted our time even trying to fit the polynomials $g_2(x), \ldots, g_6(x)$ to $P_1, \ldots, P_6$.† The general point to be made here is this:

> When the functional form of the y versus x curve is not known,
> it is important to sketch the data to help determine what $g(x)$'s
> might be suitable for good fit.

† A nongraphical method that can help determine when a polynomial of a certain degree is suitable for fitting the given data is given in Section 6.2D.

A useful approach when the data exhibit Property 1 or Property 2 is to *try a guess function that is a polynomial in* $1/x$, that is,

$$g_n(x) = \gamma_1 + \frac{\gamma_2}{x} + \frac{\gamma_3}{x^2} + \cdots + \frac{\gamma_n}{x^{n-1}} = \sum_{j=1}^{n} \gamma_j x^{1-j} \tag{28}$$

Indeed, a guess function of this form satisfies

$$g_n(x) \approx \frac{\gamma_n}{x^{n-1}} \quad \text{for } x \approx 0 \qquad \text{and} \qquad g_n(x) \approx \gamma_1 + \frac{\gamma_2}{x} \quad \text{for } x \gg 0 \tag{29}$$

and hence is well suited to fitting such data.

The $g_n(x)$ in (28) is of the form $\Sigma_j \gamma_j \phi_j(x)$ with $\phi_j(x) = x^{1-j}$. Hence $\phi_i(x_k)\phi_j(x_k) = x_k^{2-i-j}$, and the normal equations (8) for this $g_n(x)$ are

$$
\begin{bmatrix}
m & \sum \frac{1}{x_k} & \cdots & \sum \frac{1}{x_k^{n-1}} \\[2mm]
\sum \frac{1}{x_k} & \sum \frac{1}{x_k^2} & \cdots & \sum \frac{1}{x_k^n} \\[1mm]
\vdots & \vdots & & \vdots \\[1mm]
\sum \frac{1}{x_k^{n-1}} & \sum \frac{1}{x_k^n} & \cdots & \sum \frac{1}{x_k^{2n-2}}
\end{bmatrix}
\begin{bmatrix}
\gamma_1 \\[2mm] \gamma_2 \\[1mm] \vdots \\[1mm] \gamma_n
\end{bmatrix}
=
\begin{bmatrix}
\sum y_k \\[2mm] \sum \frac{y_k}{x_k} \\[1mm] \vdots \\[1mm] \sum \frac{y_k}{x_k^{n-1}}
\end{bmatrix}
\tag{30}
$$

EXAMPLE. Show that $g_3(x) = \gamma_1 + \gamma_2/x + \gamma_3/x^2$ fits the data

$$P_1(1, 6), \quad P_2(2, 1), \quad P_3(4, 2), \quad P_4(5, 3), \quad P_5(10, 4), \quad P_6(16, 5) \tag{31}$$

Solution. For these data the linear system (30) with $n = 3$ is

$$
\begin{bmatrix}
6 & 2.1125 & 1.3664062 \\
2.1125 & 1.3664062 & 1.1149869 \\
1.3664062 & 1.1149869 & 1.0681215
\end{bmatrix}
\begin{bmatrix}
\gamma_1 \\ \gamma_2 \\ \gamma_3
\end{bmatrix}
=
\begin{bmatrix}
21 \\ 8.3125 \\ 6.5545313
\end{bmatrix}
\tag{32}
$$

Solving gives $\hat{\boldsymbol{\gamma}} \doteq [6.041638 \quad -20.379906 \quad 20.347333]^T$, from which

$$\hat{g}_3(x) = 6.041638 + \frac{-20.379906}{x} + \frac{20.347333}{x^2} \tag{33a}$$

Using (23) with $\mathbf{b} = [21 \quad 8.3125 \quad 6.5545313]^T$, we get [see (25)]

$$R(\hat{g}_3) = \frac{\hat{\boldsymbol{\gamma}}^T \mathbf{b} - 6(3.5)^2}{91 - 6(3.5)^2} \doteq 0.9905 \approx 1 \tag{33b}$$

Since $n = 3$, this suggests good fit [see (27)].

As a general rule when fitting polynomials, one should use the smallest possible degree that provides good fit. Specifically, assuming that $n < 2\sqrt{m} - 1$, we obtain

Criterion for Selecting the Best n for Polynomial Fit

$$\textit{Use } \hat{g}_n(x) \textit{ if it happens that } R(\hat{g}_n) \approx 1 \textit{ but } R(\hat{g}_{n-1}) \not\approx 1. \tag{34}$$

To apply this criterion to the problem at hand, we try $n = 2$; that is, we examine the fit of $g_2(k) = \gamma_1 + \gamma_2/x$. The result is

$$\hat{g}_2(x) \doteq 2.980468 + \frac{1.475595}{x} \quad \text{for which } R(\hat{g}_2) = 0.07747 \neq 1 \tag{35}$$

Since $R(\hat{g}_2) \ll R(\hat{g}_3) \approx 1$ and $n = 3 < 2\sqrt{6} - 1$, we conclude from (34) that the most suitable polynomial in $1/x$ for the data is $\hat{g}_3(x)$ in (33a). In fact, the curve that gave rise to $P_1, \ldots, P_6$ (see Figure 5.3-2) is

$$y = 6 - \frac{20}{x} + \frac{20}{x^2} \tag{36}$$

5.3F   ILL CONDITIONING IN POLYNOMIAL CURVE FITTING

The ijth term of the A matrix for fitting a polynomial is Σx_k^{i+j-2} [see (12)]. The limit of x_k^{i+j-2} as i and j increase is as follows:

Interval containing x_k	$(-\infty, -1)$	$(-1, 0)$	$(0, 1)$	$(1, \infty)$
Limit of x_k^{i+j-2} as $i, j \to \infty$	$\pm\infty$	± 0	0^+	$+\infty$

$$(37)$$

If all x_k's are either in $(0, 1)$ or in $(1, \infty)$, then

$$a_{ij} = \sum_k x_k^{i+j-2} \approx x_m^{i+j-2} \text{ for large values of } i+j$$

As a result, the lower rows of A become nearly proportional, hence A *becomes nearly singular,* as n grows. This effect is particularly severe if

$$x_1 > 0 \quad \text{and} \quad (x_m - x_1) \text{ is small compared to } x_1 \tag{38}$$

This will happen, for example, for historical data, say for the years

$$x_1 = 1600, \quad x_2 = 1700, \quad x_3 = 1800, \quad x_4 = 1900 \tag{39a}$$

The A matrix for quadratic fit of such data is

$$A \doteq \begin{bmatrix} 4 & 7000 & 1.23 \cdot 10^7 \\ 7000 & 1.23 \cdot 10^7 & 2.17 \cdot 10^{10} \\ 1.23 \cdot 10^7 & 2.17 \cdot 10^{10} & 3.84354 \cdot 10^{13} \end{bmatrix} \tag{39b}$$

That A is ill conditioned is suggested by the fact that

$$\text{row}_2 \, A \approx 1750 \, \text{row}_1 \, A \quad \text{and} \quad \text{row}_3 \, A \approx 1757 \, \text{row}_2 \, A$$

and further indicated by the widely different orders of magnitude of the entries of A. In fact, the pivot condition number $C_p(A)$ is about $3 \cdot 10^{-7}$.

This A matrix thus presents double jeopardy: On the one hand, being severely ill conditioned, it is sensitive to roundoff errors in its entries; on the other hand, its large entries make such errors inevitable! Indeed, given data values $y_1, \ldots, y_4$, an attempt to find $\hat{\gamma} = A^{-1}\mathbf{b}$ accurately may fail even if done in extended precision.

The nonuniform behavior of x_k^{i+j-2} on $[-2, 2]$ indicated in (37) suggests that we can lessen the possibility of proportional rows of A by scaling the given x_k's (in $[x_1, x_m]$) into X_k's in $[-2, 2]$, say by a straight line as in Figure 5.3-3, *before* fitting a

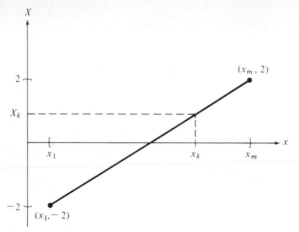

FIGURE 5.3-3 SCALING x_k SO AS TO BECOME X_k IN $[-2, 2]$.

polynomial. This strategy provides the basis for the SCALEDFIT Algorithm described in Figure 5.3-4.

If Algorithm SCALEDFIT is performed in exact arithmetic, then $\hat{g}(x)$ in (46) will be exactly the desired $\hat{g}(x)$. However, if fixed precision is used and the A matrix for the given data is ill conditioned [e.g., if (38) holds], then $\hat{g}(x)$ calculated as in (46) will be much more accurate than that obtained without scaling.

EXAMPLE. Use Algorithm SCALEDFIT to find the least square quadratic for the historical data

$$(1600, 0), \quad (1700, 1), \quad (1800, 4), \quad (1900, 9) \tag{40}$$

Note: These points lie on the parabola

$$y = \left(\frac{x}{100} - 16\right)^2 = 256 - 0.32x + \frac{x^2}{10,000} \tag{41}$$

Solution:

SCALE x: We first use the transformation

$$X = -2 + \frac{4}{1900 - 1600}(x - 1600) = -\frac{70}{3} + \frac{x}{75} \tag{42}$$

to scale $x_1, \ldots, x_4$ to the following values in $[-2, 2]$:

$$X_1 = -2, \qquad X_2 = -\tfrac{2}{3}, \qquad X_3 = \tfrac{2}{3}, \qquad X_4 = 2 \tag{43}$$

Algorithm: SCALEDFIT (Scaled Polynomial Fit)

Purpose: To improve the accuracy of the calculated parameters of the least square $(n-1)$st degree polynomial $\hat{g}(x)$ for m given data points

$$P_1(x_1, y_1), \quad \ldots, \quad P_m(x_m, y_m)$$

GET n, m, $\mathbf{x}$, $\mathbf{y}$ {arrays of x_k, y_k values}

{*scale x*} DO FOR $k = 1$ TO m {Form $X_1 = -2 < X_2 < \cdots < X_m = +2$.}

$$X_k \leftarrow -2 + \frac{4}{x_m - x_1}(x_k - x_1) \tag{44}$$

{*fit (X, y)*} Find the parameters for least square nth degree polynomial $\hat{G}(X)$ for the transformed data

$$(X_1, y_1), \quad (X_2, y_2), \quad \ldots, \quad (X_m, y_m) \tag{45}$$

{Note that the y_k values are *not* changed.}

{*un-scale X*} Replace X in $\hat{G}(X)$ by $-2 + \dfrac{4}{x_m - x_1}(x - x_1)$, getting

$$\hat{g}(x) = \hat{G}\left(-2 + \frac{4}{x_m - x_1}(x - x_1)\right) = \hat{\gamma}_1 + \hat{\gamma}_2 x + \cdots + \hat{\gamma}_n x^{n-1} \tag{46}$$

OUTPUT (The coefficients of $\hat{g}(x)$, constant term first, are $\hat{\gamma}_1, \ldots, \hat{\gamma}_n$)

FIGURE **5.3-4**   PSEUDOPROGRAM FOR THE SCALEDFIT ALGORITHM.

FIT (X, y): To fit the quadratic $G(X) = a + bX + cX^2$ to the scaled data

$$(-2, 0), \quad (-\tfrac{2}{3}, 1), \quad (\tfrac{2}{3}, 4), \quad (2, 9) \tag{47}$$

we form the normal equations whose matrix form (in exact arithmetic) is

$$
\begin{bmatrix} 4 & 0 & \frac{80}{9} \\ 0 & \frac{80}{9} & 0 \\ \frac{80}{9} & 0 & \frac{2624}{81} \end{bmatrix}
\begin{bmatrix} a \\ b \\ c \end{bmatrix}
=
\begin{bmatrix} 14 \\ 20 \\ \frac{344}{9} \end{bmatrix};
\quad \text{so} \quad
\begin{bmatrix} \hat{a} \\ \hat{b} \\ \hat{c} \end{bmatrix}
=
\begin{bmatrix} \frac{9}{4} \\ \frac{9}{4} \\ \frac{9}{16} \end{bmatrix}
\tag{48}
$$

Thus the least square quadratic for the scaled data (47) is

$$\hat{G}(X) = \tfrac{9}{4} + \tfrac{9}{4}X + \tfrac{9}{16}X^2 = \tfrac{9}{16}(2 + X)^2 \tag{49}$$

UN-SCALE X: Replacing X by $-\tfrac{70}{3} + \tfrac{1}{75}x$ gives

$$\hat{g}(x) = \hat{G}\left(-\frac{70}{3} + \frac{x}{75}\right) = \frac{9}{16}\left(-\frac{64}{3} + \frac{x}{75}\right)^2 = 256 - 0.32x + \frac{x^2}{10{,}000} \tag{50}$$

in agreement with (41).

For the coefficient matrix A in (48), the pivot condition number $C_p(A)$ is about 1. This A is quite well conditioned, so there would have been no problem solving (48) in fixed-precision arithmetic. Contrast this with the coefficient matrix A obtained directly from the unscaled x_k's in (39b); this A matrix was so ill conditioned that we could not hope to use it to fit data such as (40) directly!

Even with the use of scaling, *extended precision is generally recommended for fitting polynomials of degree* > 3, and alternative methods based on orthogonal polynomials are recommended if for some reason a polynomial of degree $\geqslant 6$ is needed. In such a situation, it might also be possible to "piece together" several lower-degree polynomials, each over a suitable subinterval of $[x_1, x_m]$.

5.4 Polynomial and Rational Function Approximation of $f(x)$

Modern hand calculators give values of elementary functions such as e^x, $\ln x$, and the trigonometric and hyperbolic functions (and their inverses) at the touch of a button. To do so, the calculations performed internally must be reduced to the four arithmetic operations $+$, $-$, $*$, and $/$. The natural expressions that result are quotients of polynomials (i.e., *rational functions*). On devices that perform division much more slowly than multiplication, division is used sparingly and *polynomial approximation* becomes the objective. We now show how this is done.

In what follows, a will denote a fixed **base point** about which a given function f has a power series expansion with a positive (possibly infinite) radius of convergence R. This means that for any point x within R units of a, the function value at x is given *exactly* by the **Taylor series** expansion

$$f(x) = f(a) + \frac{f'(a)}{1!}(x-a) + \frac{f''(a)}{2!}(x-a)^2 + \cdots = \sum_{k=0}^{\infty} \frac{f^{(k)}(a)}{k!}(x-a)^k \qquad \textbf{(1)}$$

This series is usually referred to as a **Maclaurin series** when $a = 0$. A brief review of Taylor series is given in Appendix II.2B.

5.4A TAYLOR POLYNOMIAL APPROXIMATION

Truncating the series (1) after the $(x-a)^n$ term gives the *n*th **Taylor approximation**

$$f(x) \approx P_n(x) = f(a) + \frac{f'(a)}{1!}(x-a) + \frac{f''(a)}{2!}(x-a)^2 + \cdots + \frac{f^{(n)}(a)}{n!}(x-a)^n \qquad \textbf{(2)}$$

We shall refer to $P_n(x)$ as the *n*th **Taylor polynomial** based at a if $a \neq 0$, and the *n*th

Maclaurin polynomial if $a = 0$. The error of the nth Taylor approximation is referred to as the *nth remainder* at x and denoted by $R_n(x)$. Thus

$$f(x) = P_n(x) + R_n(x), \qquad \text{so that } R_n(x) = f(x) - P_n(x) \tag{3a}$$

The **Lagrange form** of the nth remainder is

$$R_n(x) = \frac{f^{(n+1)}(c)}{(n+1)!}(x-a)^{n+1}, \qquad \text{where } c \text{ lies between } a \text{ and } x \tag{3b}$$

$P_n(x)$ and $R_n(x)$ are illustrated graphically in Figure 5.4-1.

Some of the more frequently occurring Taylor polynomials are summarized in Table 5.4-1. For $f(x) = \sin x$, all even derivatives at $a = 0$ are zero; so the Maclaurin polynomial shown can be interpreted as either $P_{2n+1}(x)$ or $P_{2n+2}(x)$. The remainder shown is $R_{2n+2}(x)$ because it is more accurate than $R_{2n+1}(x)$. Similarly, the remainder for the $\cos x$ approximation is $R_{2n+1}(x)$ rather than $R_{2n}(x)$.

5.4B   RATIONAL FUNCTION APPROXIMATION FOR $x \approx 0$

Rational functions that approximate $f(x)$ for $x \approx 0$† are obtained in two steps as follows:

Step 1: Find an N big enough so that the Nth Maclaurin approximation

$$f(x) \approx P_N(x) = c_0 + c_1 x + c_2 x^2 + \cdots c_N x^N \tag{4a}$$

is a bit more accurate than the desired accuracy over a prescribed interval I such as $[-R, R]$, $[0, R]$ or $[-R, 0]$.

Step 2: Find a rational function $r(x)$ such that the approximation

$$P_N(x) \approx r(x) = \frac{a_0 + a_1 x + \cdots + a_n x^n}{1 + b_1 x + \cdots + b_m x^m} \tag{4b}$$

is accurate enough on I to ensure that

$$f(x) - r(x) = \text{error of approximating } f(x) \text{ by } r(x) \tag{4c}$$

is sufficiently small for all x in I.

The denominator of $r(x)$ should have a nonzero constant term to avoid roundoff problems for $x \approx 0$. Since we can divide the numerator and denominator of $r(x)$ by this nonzero b_0, there is no loss of generality in assuming b_0 to be 1 as we did in

---

† If an approximation of $f(x)$ for $x \approx a \neq 0$ is desired, the change of variable $u = x - a$ converts the problem to that of approximating $f(a + u)$ for $u \approx 0$.

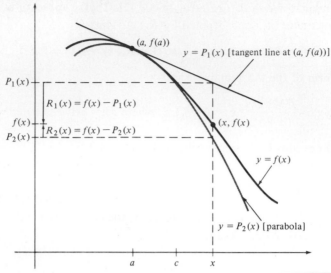

FIGURE 5.4-1 $f(x) = P_n(x) + R_n(x)$ FOR $n = 1$ AND 2.

TABLE 5.4-1 SOME FAMILIAR TAYLOR POLYNOMIAL APPROXIMATIONS.

Base Point	Taylor Approximation	Remainder (c is between a and x)
$a = 0$	$e^x \approx 1 + \dfrac{x}{1!} + \dfrac{x^2}{2!} + \cdots + \dfrac{x^n}{n!}$	$\dfrac{e^c}{(n+1)!} x^{n-1}$
$a = 1$	$\ln x \approx \dfrac{x-1}{1} - \dfrac{(x-1)^2}{2} + \cdots + (-1)^{n-1} \dfrac{(x-1)^n}{n}$	$\dfrac{(-1)^n (x-1)^{n+1}}{(n+1) c^{n+1}}$
$a = 0$	$\sin x \approx x - \dfrac{x^3}{3!} + \dfrac{x^5}{5!} - \cdots + (-1)^n \dfrac{x^{2n+1}}{(2n+1)!}$	$\dfrac{(-1)^{n+1} \cos c}{(2n+3)!} x^{2n+3}$
$a = 0$	$\cos x \approx 1 - \dfrac{x^2}{2!} + \dfrac{x^4}{4!} - \cdots + (-1)^n \dfrac{x^{2n}}{(2n)!}$	$\dfrac{(-1)^{n+1} \cos c}{(2n+2)!} x^{2n+2}$
$a = 1$	$x^p \approx 1 + p(x-1) + \dfrac{p(p-1)}{2!} (x-1)^2$ $+ \cdots + \dfrac{p(p-1)\cdots(p-n+1)}{n!} (x-1)^n$	$\dfrac{p(p-1)\cdots(p-n)(1-x)^{n+1}}{(n+1)! \, c^{n+1-p}}$

(4b). The degrees m and n in $r(x)$ of Step 2 are generally chosen so as to achieve the desired accuracy in a way that either requires the *fewest operations* or can be evaluated in the *least amount of time*. Whatever the criterion, the following strategy, known as **Padé Approximation**, usually proves to be efficient because it ensures that

$$P_N(x) - r(x) \text{ behaves like } Cx^{N+1}, \quad \text{hence is small for } x \approx 0 \tag{5}$$

Padé Approximation. *Choose m and n such that*

$$m + n = N \quad \text{and} \quad \text{either} \quad m = n \quad \text{or} \quad n = m + 1 \qquad \textbf{(6a)}$$

Then choose the $N + 1$ unknowns $a_0, \ldots, a_n, b_1, \ldots, b_m$ so that the constant term and the coefficients of $x, x^2, \ldots, x^N$ in the numerator of the error

$$P_N(x) - r(x) = \frac{(c_0 + \cdots + c_N x^N)(1 + b_1 x + \cdots + b_m x^m) - (a_0 + \cdots + a_n x^n)}{1 + b_1 x + \cdots + b_m x^m} \qquad \textbf{(6b)}$$

are all zero.

EXAMPLE. Use Padé approximation to approximate e^x to $4d$ on $I = [-\frac{1}{2}, \frac{1}{2}]$.

Solution

STEP 1: We must find an N such that the approximation

$$e^x \approx P_N(x) = 1 + x + \frac{x^2}{2!} + \frac{x^3}{3!} + \cdots + \frac{x^N}{N!} \qquad \textbf{(7)}$$

is accurate to a bit more than $4d$ on I. We know from the Lagrange form of the Nth remainder that for any fixed x in I, the error of the approximation (7) is

$$e^x - P_N(x) = \frac{e^c}{(N+1)!} x^{N+1}, \qquad \text{where } c \text{ lies between 0 and } x \qquad \textbf{(8a)}$$

Since e^x is increasing on I, e^c can be no larger than $e^{1/2}$. So

$$|e^x - P_N(x)| = \frac{e^c}{(N+1)!} |x|^{N+1} \leq \frac{e^{1/2}}{(N+1)!} \left(\frac{1}{2}\right)^{N+1} \qquad \text{for any } x \text{ in } I \qquad \textbf{(8b)}$$

We can thus ensure $4d$ accuracy on I by taking N large enough so that

$$\frac{e^{1/2}}{2^{N+1}(N+1)!} < 0.5 \cdot 10^{-4}$$

Trial and error shows that $N = 5$ is suitable. In fact,

$$|e^x - P_5(x)| \leq \frac{e^{1/2}}{6!2^6} \doteq 0.36 \cdot 10^{-4} \qquad \text{for all } x \text{ in } I = \left[-\frac{1}{2}, \frac{1}{2}\right] \qquad \textbf{(9)}$$

STEP 2: For $N = 5$, (6a) instructs us to take $n = 3$ and $m = 2$. So (6b) becomes

$$P_5(x) - r(x) = \frac{\left(1 + \frac{x}{1} + \frac{x^2}{2} + \frac{x^3}{6} + \frac{x^4}{24} + \frac{x^5}{120}\right)(1 + b_1 x + b_2 x^2) - (a_0 + a_1 x + a_2 x^2 + a_3 x^3)}{1 + b_1 x + b_2 x^2}$$

The coefficients we must equate to zero in the numerator to get the $N + 1 \, (= 6)$ unknowns $b_1, b_2, a_0, a_1, a_2, a_3$ are

constant:	$1 + 0b_1 + 0b_2 - a_0 = 0$	(hence $a_0 = 1$)
coeff. of x^1:	$\frac{1}{1} + 1b_1 + 0b_2 - a_1 = 0$	(hence $a_1 = 1 + b_1$)
coeff. of x^2:	$\frac{1}{2} + \frac{1}{1}b_1 + 1b_2 - a_2 = 0$	(hence $a_2 = \frac{1}{2} + b_1 + b_2$)
coeff. of x^3:	$\frac{1}{6} + \frac{1}{2}b_1 + \frac{1}{1}b_2 - a_3 = 0$	(hence $a_3 = \frac{1}{6} + \frac{1}{2}b_1 + b_2$)
coeff. of x^4:	$\frac{1}{24} + \frac{1}{6}b_1 + \frac{1}{2}b_2 = 0$	
coeff. of x^5:	$\frac{1}{120} + \frac{1}{24}b_1 + \frac{1}{6}b_2 = 0$	

(10a)

The last two equations are linear in b_1 and b_2. (In general, the last m will be linear in $b_1, \ldots, b_m$.) Solving them for b_1 and b_2, we get

$$\begin{bmatrix} b_1 \\ b_2 \end{bmatrix} = \begin{bmatrix} \frac{1}{6} & \frac{1}{2} \\ \frac{1}{24} & \frac{1}{6} \end{bmatrix}^{-1} \begin{bmatrix} -\frac{1}{24} \\ -\frac{1}{120} \end{bmatrix} = \frac{1}{\frac{1}{36} - \frac{1}{48}} \begin{bmatrix} \frac{1}{6} & -\frac{1}{2} \\ -\frac{1}{24} & \frac{1}{6} \end{bmatrix} \begin{bmatrix} -\frac{1}{24} \\ -\frac{1}{120} \end{bmatrix} = \begin{bmatrix} -\frac{2}{5} \\ \frac{1}{20} \end{bmatrix} \tag{10b}$$

From (10a), $a_1 = \frac{3}{5}$, $a_2 = \frac{3}{20}$, and $a_3 = \frac{1}{60}$. So

$$r(x) = \frac{1 + \frac{3}{5}x + \frac{3}{20}x^2 + \frac{1}{60}x^3}{1 - \frac{2}{5}x + \frac{1}{20}x^2} = \frac{[(\frac{1}{60}x + \frac{3}{20})x + \frac{3}{5}]x + 1}{(\frac{1}{20}x - \frac{2}{5})x + 1} \tag{11a}$$

The nested form on the right requires five multiply/divides† and five add/subtracts. If we divide numerator and denominator by $b_2 = \frac{1}{20}$ in (11a), we get

$$r(x) = \frac{\frac{1}{3}x^3 + 3x^2 + 12x + 20}{x^2 - 8x + 20} = \frac{[(\frac{1}{3}x + 3)x + 12]x + 20}{(x - 8)x + 20} \tag{11b}$$

which also requires five add/subtracts, but only four multiply/divides. This is one less than the nested form of $P_5(x)$, that is,

$$P_5(x) = \left(\left(\left(\left(\frac{x}{120} + \frac{1}{24}\right)x + \frac{1}{6}\right)x + \frac{1}{2}\right)x + 1\right)x + 1 \tag{12}$$

We can further improve the ease of calculating $r(x)$ by putting (11b) in **continued fraction** form as follows:

$$r(x) = \frac{1}{3}\left\{\frac{x^3 + 9x^2 + 36x + 60}{x^2 - 8x + 20}\right\} = \frac{1}{3}\left\{(x + 17) + \frac{152x - 280}{x^2 - 8x + 20}\right\}$$

$$= \frac{1}{3}\left\{(x + 17) + \frac{152}{\dfrac{x^2 - 8x + 20}{x - \frac{280}{152}}}\right\} = \frac{1}{3}\left\{(x + 17) + \frac{152}{(x - \frac{117}{19}) + \dfrac{\frac{3125}{361}}{x - \frac{280}{152}}}\right\} \tag{13}$$

$$\doteq 0.33333\left\{(x + 17) + \frac{152}{(x - 6.1579) + \dfrac{8.6565}{x - 1.8421}}\right\}$$

This requires only three multiply/divides! On a device that divides about as quickly as it multiplies, (13) will evaluate $r(x)$ more quickly than (11) or (12).

---

† The divisions in the rational coefficients (e.g., $\frac{3}{5}$, $\frac{3}{20}$, $\frac{1}{60}$, etc.) are not counted because they are stored as 0.6, 0.15, 0.01666 . . . , and so on.

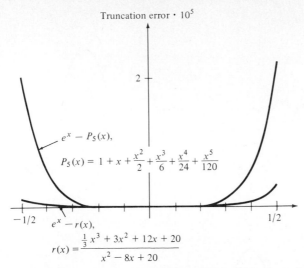

Truncation error · 10^5

$e^x - P_5(x)$,

$P_5(x) = 1 + x + \dfrac{x^2}{2} + \dfrac{x^3}{6} + \dfrac{x^4}{24} + \dfrac{x^5}{120}$

$e^x - r(x)$,

$r(x) = \dfrac{\frac{1}{3}x^3 + 3x^2 + 12x + 20}{x^2 - 8x + 20}$

FIGURE 5.4-2   THE ERRORS OF $P_5(x)$ AND $r(x)$ ON $I = [-\frac{1}{2}, \frac{1}{2}]$.

The accuracy of $r(x)$ and $P_5(x)$ is compared in Figure 5.4-2. In this example, the error of the approximation $P_5(x) \approx r(x)$ cancels much of the error of the Maclaurin approximation $e^x \approx P_5(x)$. As a result, $r(x)$ approximates e^x to $5d$ on $[-\frac{1}{2}, \frac{1}{2}]$! In general, *one can expect Padé approximation to yield a rational function $r(x)$ that approximates f(x) with about the same accuracy as $P_N(x)$ but with fewer multiply/divides.*

Figure 5.4-2 illustrates a shortcoming of Taylor polynomial approximation. Although the Nth Taylor polynomial provides a good approximation of $f(x)$ near the base point (here it is 0), it is *not* well suited to approximating $f(x)$ *uniformly* on a whole interval I. A procedure for obtaining a more uniform *polynomial* approximation from $P_N(x)$ is given next.

5.4C   CHEBYSHEV ECONOMIZATION

We wish to get polynomials that approximate $f(x)$ with about the same maximum error all along a given interval I. The problem of **uniform approximation** on $[-1, 1]$ was studied in detail by P. L. Chebyshev, who introduced the nth **Chebyshev polynomial**†

$$T_n(\xi) = \cos n\theta, \qquad \text{where } \theta = \cos^{-1}\xi \text{ for } -1 \leqslant \xi \leqslant 1 \qquad \textbf{(14a)}$$

for $n = 0, 1, 2, \ldots$. Since $|\cos u| \leqslant 1$ for all u, it is clear that for any n,

$$|T_n(\xi)| \leqslant 1 \qquad \text{for all } \xi \text{ in } [-1, 1] \qquad \textbf{(14b)}$$

In fact, $T_n(\xi)$ oscillates between $+1$ and -1 exactly n times as ξ goes from -1 to 1. This **"equiripple property"** is illustrated in Figure 5.4-3. What is *not* clear is that $T_n(\xi)$ is a polynomial in ξ on $[-1, 1]$. If we write ξ as $\cos \theta$ in definition (14a), we get

† The letter T comes from "Tsebychev," which is the French transliteration of the man's (Russian) name.

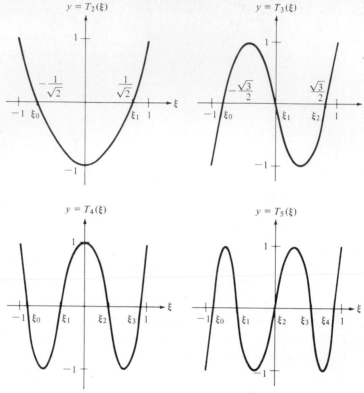

FIGURE 5.4-3 GRAPHS OF T_2, T_3, T_4, T_5.

$$T_0(\xi) = \cos 0 \equiv 1, \qquad T_1(\xi) = \cos(\cos^{-1}\xi) = \xi \tag{15a}$$

$$\xi T_n(\xi) = \cos\theta \cdot \cos n\theta = \tfrac{1}{2}[\cos(n-1)\theta + \cos(n+1)\theta] = \tfrac{1}{2}[T_{n-1}(\xi) + T_{n+1}(\xi)] \tag{15b}$$

The **three-term recurrence relation** (15) is best expressed as

$$\boxed{T_0(\xi) \equiv 1, \qquad T_1(\xi) = \xi, \qquad T_{n+1}(\xi) = 2\xi T_n(\xi) - T_{n-1}(\xi)} \tag{16}$$

TABLE 5.4-2 THE POLYNOMIAL FORM OF $T_0(\xi)$, . . . , $T_7(\xi)$.

$T_0(\xi) = 1$
$T_1(\xi) = \xi$
$T_2(\xi) = 2\xi^2 - 1$
$T_3(\xi) = 4\xi^3 - 3\xi$
$T_4(\xi) = 8\xi^4 - 8\xi^2 + 1$
$T_5(\xi) = 16\xi^5 - 20\xi^3 + 5\xi$
$T_6(\xi) = 32\xi^6 - 48\xi^4 + 18\xi^2 - 1$
$T_7(\xi) = 64\xi^7 - 112\xi^5 + 56\xi^3 - 7\xi$

TABLE 5.4-3 THE CHEBYSHEV EXPANSION OF 1, ξ, . . . , ξ^7.

$1 = T_0$
$\xi = T_1$
$\xi^2 = \tfrac{1}{2}(T_0 + T_2)$
$\xi^3 = \tfrac{1}{4}(3T_1 + T_3)$
$\xi^4 = \tfrac{1}{8}(3T_0 + 4T_2 + T_4)$
$\xi^5 = \tfrac{1}{16}(10T_1 + 5T_3 + T_5)$
$\xi^6 = \tfrac{1}{32}(10T_0 + 15T_2 + 6T_4 + T_6)$
$\xi^7 = \tfrac{1}{64}(35T_1 + 21T_3 + 7T_5 + T_7)$

This generates $T_0(\xi)$–$T_7(\xi)$ shown in Table 5.4-2. Notice that for $n \geq 1$, the leading coefficient of $T_n(\xi)$ is 2^{n-1}. Solving $T_0(\xi)$, $T_1(\xi)$, $T_2(\xi)$, . . . for 1, ξ, ξ^2, . . . gives the expansions shown in Table 5.4-3.

Given any Nth-degree polynomial $p_N(x)$ and a prescribed interval $[a, b]$, Chebyshev polynomials can be used to obtain a lower-degree polynomial $p_{econ}(x)$, which approximates $p(x)$ uniformly on $[a, b]$. The idea is to change variables from x in $[a, b]$ to the "normalized" variable ξ in $[-1, 1]$ where the $T_n(\xi)$'s have the equiripple property. This procedure, called **Chebyshev economization,** is described in Figure 5.4-4 and illustrated in Figure 5.4-5.

Algorithm: Chebyshev Economization

Purpose: To approximate a given Nth degree polynomial

$$p_N(x) = c_0 + c_1 x + c_2 x^2 + \cdots + c_N x^N, \qquad c_N \neq 0$$

uniformly on $I = [a, b]$ by a polynomial $p_{econ}(x)$ of lower degree.

GET $a, b, N, c_0, \ldots, c_N$

{*scale x*} Change from the x-interval $I = [a, b]$ to the normalized ξ-interval $[-1, 1]$ {where $|T_n(\xi)| \leq 1$} by forming

$$q_N(\xi) = p_N\left(a + \frac{b-a}{2}(\xi + 1)\right) \qquad \text{for } -1 \leq \xi \leq 1 \qquad \text{(17)}$$

{*expand*} Use Table 5.4-3 to get the **Chebyshev expansion**

$$q_N(\xi) = d_0 + d_1 T_1(\xi) + \cdots + d_{N-1} T_{N-1}(\xi) + d_N T_N(\xi) \qquad \text{(18)}$$

{*economize*} Truncate this summation after the $d_k T_k(\xi)$ term, getting

$$q_{econ}(\xi) = d_0 + d_1 T_1(\xi) + \cdots + d_k T_k(\xi), \qquad \text{where } k < N \qquad \text{(19)}$$

{*un-expand*} Use Table 5.4-2 to express this as a polynomial in ξ:

$$q_{econ}(\xi) = e_0 + e_1 \xi + e_2 \xi^2 + \cdots + e_k \xi^k \qquad \text{for } -1 \leq \xi \leq 1 \qquad \text{(20)}$$

{This lower-degree polynomial approximates $q_N(\xi)$ uniformly on $[-1, 1]$.}

{*un-scale ξ*} Convert back to $I = [a, b]$ by forming

$$p_{econ}(x) = q_{econ}\left(-1 + 2\frac{x-a}{b-a}\right) = \gamma_0 + \gamma_1 x + \cdots + \gamma_k x^k \qquad \text{for } a \leq x \leq b \qquad \text{(21)}$$

OUTPUT (The coefficients of $p_{econ}(x)$, constant term first, are: $\gamma_0, \ldots, \gamma_k$.)

FIGURE 5.4-4   PSEUDOPROGRAM FOR THE CHEBYSHEV ECONOMIZATION ALGORITHM.

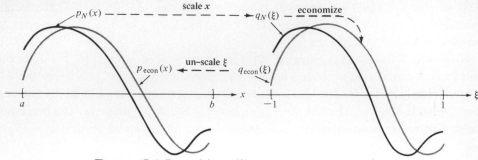

FIGURE 5.4-5 $p_N(x)$, $q_N(\xi)$, $q_{econ}(\xi)$, AND $p_{econ}(x)$.

Since $|T_j(\xi)| \leqslant 1$ for $j = k+1, \ldots, N$, (18)–(21) give the following uniform bound for the error of approximating $p_N(x)$ by $p_{econ}(x)$ on $[a, b]$:

$$|p_N(x) - p_{econ}(x)| \leqslant |d_{k+1}| + \cdots + |d_N| \qquad \text{for all } x \text{ in } [a, b] \tag{22}$$

If $p_N(x)$ is an Nth Taylor polynomial approximation of $f(x)$, then $p_{econ}(x)$ provides a more uniform approximation of $f(x)$ than $p_N(x)$ on $[a, b]$ while requiring fewer arithmetic operations.

EXAMPLE. The fifth Maclaurin polynomial approximation of e^x is

$$e^x \approx p_5(x) = 1 + x + \frac{x^2}{2} + \frac{x^3}{6} + \frac{x^4}{24} + \frac{x^5}{120}$$

a. Find the fourth-degree $p_{econ}(x)$ for $p_5(x)$ on $I = [-\frac{1}{2}, \frac{1}{2}]$.
b. Compare the accuracy of $p_{econ}(x)$ to that of $p_5(x)$ on $[-\frac{1}{2}, \frac{1}{2}]$.

Solution
a. We follow steps of the Chebyshev Economization Algorithm.

   SCALE x: Since $[a, b] = [-\frac{1}{2}, \frac{1}{2}]$, $x = a + \frac{1}{2}(\xi + 1)/(b - a) = \frac{1}{2}\xi$. By (17),

$$q_5(\xi) = p_5\left(\frac{\xi}{2}\right) = 1 + \frac{\xi}{2} + \frac{\xi^2}{8} + \frac{\xi^3}{48} + \frac{\xi^4}{384} + \frac{\xi^5}{3840} \qquad \text{for } -1 \leqslant \xi \leqslant 1 \tag{23}$$

   EXPAND: Using Table 5.4-3, we get the Chebyshev expansion

$$q_5(\xi) = T_0 + \frac{T_1}{2} + \frac{T_0 + T_2}{8 \cdot 2} + \frac{3T_1 + T_3}{48 \cdot 4} + \frac{3T_0 + 4T_2 + T_4}{384 \cdot 8} + \frac{10T_1 + 5T_3 + T_5}{3840 \cdot 16}$$

$$\doteq 1.063477T_0 + 0.515788T_1 + 0.063802T_2 + 0.005290T_3 + 0.000326T_4$$
$$+ 0.000052T_5 \tag{24}$$

ECONOMIZE AND UN-EXPAND: Dropping only the $T_5(\xi)$ term and using Table 5.4-2, we get

$$q_{econ}(\xi) = 1.063477 + 0.515788\xi + 0.063802\,(2\xi^2 - 1) + 0.005290\,(4\xi^3 - 3\xi)$$
$$+ 0.000326(8\xi^4 - 8\xi^2 + 1)$$
$$= 1 + 0.4999186\xi + 0.125\xi^2 + 0.0211589\xi^3 + 0.00260417\xi^4 \qquad (25)$$

UN-SCALE ξ: Finally replacing ξ by $-1 + 2(x - a)/(b - a) = 2x$, we obtain

$$p_{econ}(x) = q_{econ}(2x) = 1 + 0.999837x + 0.5x^2 + 0.169271x^3 + 0.041667x^4 \qquad (26)$$

b. We know from (9) that $|e^x - p_5(x)| < 0.36\text{E-}4$ and from (22) and (24) that

$$|p_5(x) - p_{econ}(x)| \leqslant |d_5| \doteq 0.000052$$

We are thus assured that for $-\frac{1}{2} \leqslant x \leqslant \frac{1}{2}$,

$$|e^x - p_{econ}(x)| \leqslant |e^x - p_5(x)| + |p_5(x) - p_{econ}(x)| \leqslant 0.36\text{E-}4 + 0.52\text{E-}4$$

In fact, the two errors partly cancel (rather than add to) each other so that $p_{econ}(x)$ actually approximates e^x to within 0.5E-4 (i.e., to $4d$) on $[-\frac{1}{2}, \frac{1}{2}]$ (see Figure 5.4-6). This fourth-degree economized approximation is as efficient to evaluate as the Padé approximation (13) and is preferable for devices that perform division more slowly than multiplication. However, in this case its maximum error (near $\frac{1}{2}$) on $[-\frac{1}{2}, \frac{1}{2}]$ is larger.

Note: If $[a, b]$ happens to be $[-1, 1]$, then

$$x = \xi, \qquad \text{hence } q_N(\xi) = p_N(\xi) \quad \text{and} \quad p_{econ}(x) = q_{econ}(x)$$

So the **scale** x and **un-scale** ξ steps are not necessary (Exercise 5-21).

Our illustrative function $f(x) = e^x$ has a Taylor series that converges rapidly as $n \to \infty$. As a result, the improved efficiency resulting from Chebyshev economization was not too dramatic. Substantial decreases in the degree needed for a prescribed accuracy have been obtained (and used internally in calculators and computers) for functions such as $\ln x$ and $\tan^{-1} x$, whose Taylor series converge slowly as $n \to \infty$. And approximations involving *both* rational functions *and* Chebyshev economization have been used successfully. The reader interested in further details is referred to [29].

5.4D   LEAST SQUARE APPROXIMATION OF $f(x)$ ON $I = [a, b]$

An alternative approach to approximating $f(x)$ uniformly on $I = [a, b]$ by an Nth-degree polynomial

$$p_N(x) = c_0 + c_1 x + c_2 x^2 + \cdots + c_N x^N \qquad (27)$$

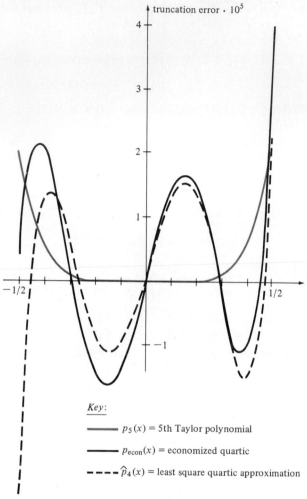

Key:

———— $p_5(x)$ = 5th Taylor polynomial

———— $p_{econ}(x)$ = economized quartic

— — — $\hat{p}_4(x)$ = least square quartic approximation

FIGURE 5.4-6 TRUNCATION ERROR OF SEVERAL APPROXIMATIONS OF e^x ON $[-\frac{1}{2}, \frac{1}{2}]$.

is to choose $N + 1$ coefficients $c_0, \ldots, c_N$ so as to minimize the **square error**

$$E(p_N) = \int_a^b [p_N(x) - f(x)]^2 \, dx \tag{28}$$

An argument almost identical to that given in Section 5.3A shows that the **least square** coefficients $\hat{c}_0, \hat{c}_1, \ldots, \hat{c}_N$ which do this satisfy the $(N + 1) \times (N + 1)$ linear system of **normal equations** $A\mathbf{c} = \mathbf{b}$, where

$$a_{ij} = a_{ji} = \int_a^b x^{i+j-2} \, dx \qquad \text{and} \qquad b_i = \int_a^b x^{i-1} f(x) \, dx \tag{29}$$

for $i, j = 1, 2, \ldots, N + 1$ [cf. (12) of Section 5.3A]. The Nth degree polynomial having these coefficients will be denoted by $\hat{p}_N(x)$.

EXAMPLE. Find the least square quartic $\hat{p}_4(x)$ that approximates e^x on $[-\frac{1}{2}, \frac{1}{2}]$.

Solution. For $p_4(x) = c_0 + c_1 x + c_2 x^2 + c_3 x^3 + c_4 x^4$, we must solve

$$
\begin{bmatrix}
\int x^0\,dx & \int x^1\,dx & \int x^2\,dx & \int x^3\,dx & \int x^4\,dx \\[2mm]
\int x^1\,dx & \int x^2\,dx & \int x^3\,dx & \int x^4\,dx & \int x^5\,dx \\[2mm]
\int x^2\,dx & \int x^3\,dx & \int x^4\,dx & \int x^5\,dx & \int x^6\,dx \\[2mm]
\int x^3\,dx & \int x^4\,dx & \int x^5\,dx & \int x^6\,dx & \int x^7\,dx \\[2mm]
\int x^4\,dx & \int x^5\,dx & \int x^6\,dx & \int x^7\,dx & \int x^8\,dx
\end{bmatrix}
\begin{bmatrix} c_0 \\[2mm] c_1 \\[2mm] c_2 \\[2mm] c_3 \\[2mm] c_4 \end{bmatrix}
=
\begin{bmatrix}
\int 1 e^x\,dx \\[2mm]
\int x e^x\,dx \\[2mm]
\int x^2 e^x\,dx \\[2mm]
\int x^3 e^x\,dx \\[2mm]
\int x^4 e^x\,dx
\end{bmatrix}
\tag{30}
$$

$$\underbrace{}_{A}\quad \underbrace{}_{\mathbf{c}}\quad \underbrace{}_{\mathbf{b}}$$

where $\int$ means $\int_{-1/2}^{1/2}$. When evaluated, (30) becomes

$$
\begin{bmatrix}
1 & 0 & \frac{1}{12} & 0 & \frac{1}{80} \\[1mm]
0 & \frac{1}{12} & 0 & \frac{1}{80} & 0 \\[1mm]
\frac{1}{12} & 0 & \frac{1}{80} & 0 & \frac{1}{448} \\[1mm]
0 & \frac{1}{80} & 0 & \frac{1}{448} & 0 \\[1mm]
\frac{1}{80} & 0 & \frac{1}{448} & 0 & \frac{1}{2304}
\end{bmatrix}
\begin{bmatrix} c_0 \\[1mm] c_1 \\[1mm] c_2 \\[1mm] c_3 \\[1mm] c_4 \end{bmatrix}
=
\begin{bmatrix}
1.042190611 \\
0.0854353542 \\
0.0896769443 \\
0.0128756584 \\
0.0136342797
\end{bmatrix}
\tag{31}
$$

The entries of the **b** vector were obtained recursively as follows:

$$b_1 = \int_{-1/2}^{1/2} e^x\,dx = e^{0.5} - e^{-0.5} = 1.042190611 \tag{32a}$$

$$b_{i+1} = \int_{-1/2}^{1/2} x^i e^x\,dx = x^i e^x \Big]_{-1/2}^{1/2} - i \int_{-1/2}^{1/2} x^{i-1} e^x\,dx$$

$$= (\tfrac{1}{2})^i [e^{1/2} - (-1)^i e^{-1/2}] - i b_1 \tag{32b}$$

for $i = 1, 2, 3, 4$. Solving (31) for $\hat{\mathbf{c}} = [\hat{c}_0 \cdots \hat{c}_4]^T$, we get (to 5s)

$$\hat{p}_4(x) \doteq 1.0 + 0.99986x + 0.49994x^2 + 0.16909x^3 + 0.042358x^4 \tag{33}$$

The error of the approximation $e^x \approx \hat{p}_4(x)$ is shown in Figure 5.4-6. The accuracy achieved is comparable to the economized quartic in (26).

Chebyshev economization generally requires less work than setting up and solving $A\mathbf{c} = \mathbf{b}$. However, the ideas introduced here provide the basis for the use of *orthogonal polynomials,* which make uniform approximation by polynomials quite simple. The details can be found in [25 and 29].

Exercises

Section 5.1

5-1. Find $\hat{a}$, $\hat{b}$, and $E(\hat{L})$ for $\hat{L}(x) = \hat{a} + \hat{b}x$, the least square straight line for the data shown in (a) and (b).

(a)

x	0	1	2	3
y	3.0	1.2	-0.3	-1.5

(b)

x	1.0	1.2	1.4	1.6	1.8
y	-5	-3	-2	0	3

Section 5.2

5-2. Why was the Secant Method and not the Newton–Raphson method suggested as a means of solving (4) of Section 5.2 for β?

5-3. Find the normal equations for the following guess functions. Are they linear?
  (a) $g(x) = \alpha x^\beta$. [NOTE: $d(x^\beta)/d\beta = x^\beta \ln x$.]

  (b) $g(x) = \dfrac{\alpha x}{\beta + x}$.

  (c) $g(x) = \alpha e^{-x} + \beta e^{-4x}$.

  (d) $g(x) = \alpha + \beta \sin \gamma x$. (NOTE: The answer is a 3×3 system.)

5-4. *Supplement to Figure 5.2-1:* Figure 5.2-1 does not show some useful possibilities for hyperbolic fit. With α *negative,* sketch the graph of:

  (a) $g_4(x)$ for $\beta > 0$ **(b)** $g_5(x)$ for $\beta < 0$ **(c)** $g_6(x)$ for $\beta < 0$

As in Figure 5.2-1, show all horizontal and vertical asymptotes (dashed) and all x- and y-intercepts, and describe how they are related to α and β.

5-5. (a) Determine graphically from Figure 5.2-1 which of $g(x) = \alpha e^{\beta x}$ or $h(x) = \alpha x^\beta$ seems best suited to fit the following data:

$$P_1(1, 2.3), \quad P_2(2, 6.1), \quad P_3(3, 10.7), \quad P_4(4, 16.0), \quad P_5(5, 21.9), \quad P_6(6, 28.3)$$

  (b) Use the Linearization Algorithm to fit $g(x)$ and $h(x)$ to the data, and find $E(g)$ and $E(h)$. Do your results confirm your answer to part (a)?

(c) Find $E(\hat{L})$ for the *linearized* data [i.e., $Q_k(X_k, Y_k)$] for $g(x)$ and for $h(x)$. Do your results confirm your answer to part (a)?

5-6. Do (a)–(c) of Exercise 5-5 for $g(x) = \alpha/(\beta + x)$, $h(x) = \alpha x/(\beta + x)$, and

$$P_1(0.1, 0.04), \quad P_2(1, 0.51), \quad P_3(2, 1.2), \quad P_4(3, 2.2), \quad P_5(4, 3.8), \quad P_6(6, 13.2)$$

NOTE: See Exercise 5-4 before doing part (a).

5-7. Do (a)–(c) of Exercise 5-5 for $g(x) = \alpha + \beta \ln x$, $h(x) = \alpha + \beta/x$, and

$$P_1(1, 0.2), \quad P_2(2, 1.8), \quad P_3(3, 2.6), \quad P_4(5, 3.8), \quad P_5(7, 4.5), \quad P_6(10, 5.3)$$

5-8. Do (a)–(c) of Exercise 5-5 for $g(x) = \alpha/(\beta + x)$, $h(x) = \alpha e^{\beta x}$, and

$$P_1(1, 0.9), \quad P_2(2, 2.2), \quad P_3(3, 5.4), \quad P_4(4, 13.2), \quad P_5(5, 32.6), \quad P_6(6, 77.4)$$

5-9. For which i's of Figure 5.2-1 does the curve $y = g_i(x)$ become a straight line when plotted on semilog paper? On log-log paper? Explain.

Section 5.3

5-10. Prove that if $g(x) = \Sigma_i \hat{\gamma}_i \phi_i(x)$, then $E(\hat{g})$ can be calculated as

$$E(\hat{g}) = \sum_k y_k^2 - \sum_i \hat{\gamma}_i b_i = \mathbf{y}\mathbf{y}^T - \hat{\boldsymbol{\gamma}}^T \mathbf{b}$$

where $\mathbf{y}$, $\hat{\boldsymbol{\gamma}}$, and $\mathbf{b}$ have the same meaning as in formula (21) for $R(\hat{g})$.

OUTLINE: Apply (7a) and (8b) of Section 5.3A after showing that

$$E(\hat{g}) = \sum_k [\hat{g}(x_k) - y_k]\left[\sum_i \hat{\gamma}_i \phi_i(x_k) - y_k \right]$$

$$= \sum_i \hat{\gamma}_i \left\{ \sum_k [\hat{g}(x_k) - y_k]\phi_i(x_k) \right\} - \sum_i \hat{\gamma}_i \left\{ \sum_k \phi_i(x_k)y_k \right\} + \sum_k y_k^2$$

5-11. Refer to the formula for $E(\hat{g})$ given in Exercise 5-10.

(a) Use the formula to obtain $E(\hat{g}_2)$ and $E(\hat{g}_4)$ in (17) of Section 5.3B. [**NOTE:** Much of the necessary information may be found in (15), (23), (24), and (25) of Section 5.3.]

(b) Why can the formula be used for $E(\hat{L})$? Verify it by using it to obtain $E(\hat{L})$ in (18) of Section 5.1C.

(c) Can the formula be used to obtain $E(g)$ where $g(x) = \alpha e^{\beta x}$ is obtained by the Linearization Algorithm? Explain.

5-12. For the data in (a) and (b) of Exercise 5-1, find $E(\hat{g})$ and $R(\hat{g})$ for the least square quadratic $g(x)$. [You must first find $\hat{g}(x)$.]

5-13. Show that the following data appear to be quadratic by doing (a) and (b).

x	1	2	3	4	5	6	7	8
y	−5	−12.4	−15.7	−15.1	−10.5	−1.9	10.7	27.4

(a) Fit a straight line $g_2(x) = \gamma_1 + \gamma_2 x$ and find $R(\hat{g}_2)$.

(b) Fit a quadratic $g_3(x) = \gamma_1 + \gamma_2 x + \gamma_3 x^2$, find $R(\hat{g}_3)$, and compare $R(\hat{g}_3)$ to $R(\hat{g}_2)$ obtained in part (a). [See (27a) of Section 5.3c.]

5-14. (a) Fit a quadratic $g_3(x)$ and a cubic $g_4(x)$ to the following data:

x	0	1.5	2.5	4.0	6.5	8.1	9.3	11.3	13.0	15.5	17.5	19.0
y	1.2	3.5	4.5	5.3	4.5	2.3	0.7	-2.0	-3.9	-4.2	-2.6	-0.5

(b) Find $R(\hat{g}_3)$ and $R(\hat{g}_4)$ for your answers to part (a). What can you conclude about the data? Explain.

5-15. The data of Exercise 5-14 looks somewhat like a sinusoid with period about 20. This suggests that the data can be fit by

$$g(x) = \gamma_1 + \gamma_2 \sin\left(\frac{\pi x}{10}\right) \quad \left[\phi_1(x) \equiv 1, \quad \phi_2(x) = \sin\left(\frac{\pi x}{10}\right)\right]$$

(a) Find the normal equations for this $g(x)$. Use (8b) of Section 5.3A.

(b) Use your answer to part (a) to find $\hat{g}(x)$ and $R(\hat{g})$.

(c) Plot $\hat{g}(x)$ and the data on the same axes.

(d) Does $\hat{g}(x)$ fit the data better than $\hat{g}_4(x)$ obtained in Exercise 5-14?

5-16. Do (a)–(d) of Exercise 5-15 for $g(x) = \gamma_1 + \gamma_2 \sin(\pi x/10) + \gamma_3 \cos(\pi x/10)$.

5-17. Do (a)–(d) of Exercise 5-15 for $g(x) = \gamma_1 + \gamma_2 \sin(\pi x/10) + \gamma_3 \sin(2\pi x/10)$.

5-18. Suppose that the population in a certain city was 12,500 in 1600; 14,000 in 1700; 16,000 in 1800; and 19,000 in 1900. Use the matrix A in (48) of Section 5.3F to find the least square quadratic $\hat{g}(x)$ that describes population as a function of $x = $ year.

5-19. Suppose that you wanted to fit a cubic to $P_1, \ldots, P_5$, where

$$x_1 = 20, \quad x_2 = 22, \quad x_3 = 25, \quad x_4 = 28, \quad x_5 = 30$$

Find the scaled variables $X_1, \ldots, X_5$ resulting from the transformation (44) of Section 5.3F, then form the matrix $A = (\Sigma X^{i+j-2})_{4 \times 4}$ needed to fit a cubic. Is A ill conditioned?

Section 5.4

5-20. Use Padé approximation to find a rational function $r(x)$ that approximates $p(x)$ for $x \approx 0$.

(a) $p(x) = p_4(x) = 1 - x + \dfrac{x^2}{2} - \dfrac{x^3}{6} + \dfrac{x^4}{24}$ $(\approx e^{-x})$.

(b) $p(x) = p_6(x) = x - \dfrac{x^3}{6} + \dfrac{x^5}{120}$ $(\approx \sin x)$.

(c) $p(x) = p_4(x) = 1 + \dfrac{x}{4} - \dfrac{x^2}{32} + \dfrac{x^3}{128} - \dfrac{5x^4}{2048}$ $\left(\approx \sqrt{1 + \dfrac{x}{2}}\right)$.

(d) $p(x) = p_5(x) = 1 - \dfrac{x^2}{2} + \dfrac{x^4}{24}$ $(\approx \cos x)$.

5-21. For (a)–(d) of Exercise 5-20, use Chebyshev economization to approximate $p(x) = p_N(x)$ on $[-1, 1]$ by a polynomial $p_{econ}(x)$ (i) of degree $\leq N - 1$ (remove only the x^N term); (ii) of degree $\leq N - 2$ (remove the x^N and x^{N-1} terms).

5-22. Same as Exercise 5-21 but on $[-2, 2]$.

5-23. For (a)–(d) of Exercise 5-20, use the Lagrange form of the remainder $R_n(x)$ to estimate the accuracy of the indicated approximation on $[-\frac{1}{2}, \frac{1}{2}]$ and on $[-1, 1]$.

5-24. The second-degree Maclaurin approximation of e^x is

$$p(x) = p_2(x) = 1 + x + \frac{x^2}{2}$$

(a) Apply Chebyshev economization to get a linear (first degree) $p_{econ}(x)$ on $[-1, 1]$.

(b) Sketch your answer to part (a) and the first-degree Maclaurin approximation $p_1(x) = 1 + x$ for $-1 \leq x \leq 1$ on the same axes. Which straight-line approximates e^x more uniformly on $[-1, 1]$?

Computer and Programming Exercises

5-25. Write a program CURFIT that produces the run shown in Figure 5.2-3. It should call the following subprograms:

LINRIZ (I, M, X, Y, XLIN, YLIN, OK) This subprogram forms the linearized data (XLIN(k), YLIN(k)) from the given data (X(k), Y(k)) for $k = 1, \ldots ,$ M to fit the I th curve of Table 5.2-1. If this can be done for each k, OK is returned as TRUE. If not (e.g., the transformation requires division by zero or taking the logarithm of a negative number), OK is returned as FALSE.

LINFIT See the FORTRAN subprogram of Figure 5.1-4.

ALPBET (I, SLOPE, YCEPT, ALPHA, BETA) This subprogram uses YCEPT ($= \hat{a}$) and SLOPE ($= \hat{b}$) returned from LINFIT to calculate ALPHA ($= \alpha$) and BETA ($= \beta$) for the I th curve of Table 5.2-1.

To fit up to 100 data points, the program should use arrays dimensioned as:

X(100), Y(100), XLIN(100), YLIN(100), OK(7), ALPHA(7), BETA(7), SQERR(7)

where OK assumes LOGICAL (i.e., Boolean) values.

5-26. Modify LINFIT of Figure 5.1-4 so that instead of returning $E(\hat{L})$, it returns $R(\hat{L})$ as computed by (21) of Section 5.3D. Note that $\hat{\gamma} = [\text{YCEPT SLOPE}]^T$.

5-27. Write a program POLFIT to do polynomial curve fitting. It should read m data points (x_k, y_k) and then fit polynomials $g(x)$ of degree *Nstart* to *Nstop*, printing the coefficients of $\hat{g}(x)$ and $R(\hat{g})$ for each degree. A and $\mathbf{b}$ for the normal equations should be formed only once (for $n = Nstop$), using extended precision to accumulate the sums, in a subprogram GETAB. The solution for each degree can then make use of any available linear system solvers (e.g., DECOMP and FORBAK of Section 4.4B).

5-28. Write a general scaling subprogram SCALE that takes x_k values in $[a, b]$ and forms an array of X_k values in $[c, d]$. It should also return SLOPE and CEPT, where

$$X_k = \text{SLOPE} * x_k + \text{CEPT}$$

using the line from (a, c) to (b, d) in the xX-plane as in Figure 5.3-3.

5-29. (a) Write a pseudoprogram for getting the coefficients of $1, x, x^2, \ldots, x^n$ in the expansion of

$$p(x) = a_1 + a_2(b + mx) + a_3(b + mx)^2 + \cdots + a_{n+1}(b + mx)^n$$

(b) Write a subprogram that forms these coefficients from n, $\mathbf{a} = [a_1, \ldots, a_{n+1}]$, b, and m and puts them in an array $\mathbf{c} = [c_1, \ldots, c_{n+1}]$.

5-30. Write a program that uses the $N + 1$ coefficients of a given Nth degree polynomial $p_N(x)$ to form and return the coefficients of the numerator and denominator of a rational function $r(x)$ that approximates $p_N(x)$ for $x \approx 0$ as in Section 5.4B. Test it with the example of Section 5.4B.

6

Interpolation

Introduction 6.0

The curve-fitting methods of Chapter 5 were developed to describe functions that gave rise to data pairs $P_k(x_k, y_k)$ for which the y_k values are likely to be in error. The mathematical problem when the y_k's are assumed to be *accurate* is the analytic counterpart of the children's game of "follow the dots," namely to find a smooth function whose graph goes *through* (not just near) the P_k's. This is called *interpolation*.

Not too long ago, when the available digital devices performed only the four arithmetic operations, interpolation was an important tool for getting accurate estimates from tabulated values, say of trigonometric, exponential, or logarithmic functions. Needless to say, modern hand-held calculators, which give values of these elementary functions to eight or more significant digits at the touch of a button, have eliminated much of the need for interpolation. Nevertheless, there are still situations that currently arise in statistical and scientific analysis for which only certain tabulated values are available and accurate values at nontabulated abscissas are needed. Another reason to understand interpolation is that most numerical methods for finding integrals and solving differential equations are based upon interpolation formulas.

The most natural curve to try to pass through $m + 1$ points is a polynomial having $m + 1$ coefficients (i.e., of degree $\leq m$). This is called *polynomial interpolation*. Two methods for doing this are considered in detail. The first, *Lagrange's method* (Section 6.1), will be an important theoretical tool for obtaining formulas for integrating functions and differential equations. The second, *Newton's method* (Section 6.2), is based on difference tables and provides a mechanism for determining the polynomial degree that appears best suited for interpolating a particular value. The error of polynomial interpolation is analyzed in Section 6.3D and is used to motivate *Chebyshev interpolation* in Section 6.3E.

The Polynomial Wiggle Problem of Section 5.3B makes polynomial interpolation unsuitable when m, the number of P_k's, is large. In this situation *piecewise cubic splines* can be used. These are described in Section 6.4.

6.1 The Unique Interpolating Polynomial for P_k, P_{k+1}, . . . , P_{k+m}

Suppose that we are given a set of $n + 1$ points

$$P_0(x_0, y_0), \quad P_1(x_1, y_1), \quad \ldots, \quad P_n(x_n, y_n) \tag{1a}$$

which we shall refer to as **knots,** on the xy-plane. No restriction is made on the y_k's, but we do assume that the x_k's, which we shall refer to as **nodes,** are distinct and in their natural order, that is, that

$$x_0 < x_1 < \cdots < x_k < x_{k+1} < \cdots < x_n \tag{1b}$$

Our objective is to find polynomials that **interpolate** one or more of these knots, that is, whose graph goes through some or all of P_0, . . . , P_n, as illustrated in Figure 6.1-1.

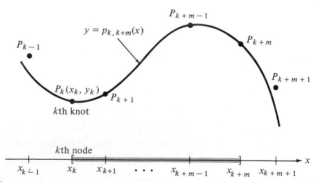

FIGURE 6.1-1 INTERPOLATING POLYNOMIAL FOR $m + 1$ KNOTS P_k, P_{k+1}, . . . , P_{k+m}.

Notation To avoid confusion, we shall use lowercase p's for polynomials and capital P's for the knots they interpolate. In particular, $p_{k,k+m}(x)$ will denote a polynomial that interpolates the $m + 1$ *consecutive* knots P_k, P_{k+1}, . . . , P_{k+m}. The closed interval $[x_k, x_{k+m}]$ (shaded in Figure 6.1-1) will be referred to as the **interpolation interval** for $p_{k,k+m}(x)$.

6.1A EXAMPLE (QUADRATIC INTERPOLATION)

Find $p_{2,4}(x)$ for the five knots

$$P_0(-2, -8), \quad P_1(0, 0), \quad P_2(1, 1), \quad P_3(4, 64), \quad P_4(5, 125)$$

Solution. Since $p_{2,4}(x)$ must interpolate the three consecutive knots P_2, P_3, and P_4, we try a polynomial having three coefficients, say

$$p_{2,4}(x) = A + Bx + Cx^2 \qquad \text{(degree} \leqslant 2)$$

To determine A, B, and C, we impose the three interpolating constraints

$$
\begin{aligned}
p_{2,4}(x_2) &= y_2, & \text{that is,} & & p_{2,4}(1) &= A + B + C = 1 \\
p_{2,4}(x_3) &= y_3, & \text{that is,} & & p_{2,4}(4) &= A + 4B + 16C = 64 \\
p_{2,4}(x_4) &= y_4, & \text{that is,} & & p_{2,4}(5) &= A + 5B + 25C = 125
\end{aligned}
$$

This *linear* system can be solved for $[\bar{A} \quad \bar{B} \quad \bar{C}]^T = [20 \quad -29 \quad 10]^T$ using any of the direct methods of Chapter 3. The reader should verify that the quadratic $p_{2,4}(x) = 20 - 29x + 10x^2$ does indeed interpolate P_2, P_3, and P_4.

6.1B THE POLYNOMIAL INTERPOLATION PROBLEM

The procedure just used is called the **method of undetermined coefficients**. Requiring the graph of $p_{k,k+m}(x)$ to pass through $m + 1$ knots P_k, P_{k+1}, . . . , P_{k+m} imposes $m + 1$ constraints

$$p_{k,k+m}(x_i) = y_i \qquad \text{for } i = k, k+1, \ldots, k+m \tag{2a}$$

This suggests that $p_{k,k+m}(x)$ has at most $m + 1$ coefficients, that is, that

$$p_{k,k+m}(x) \text{ is of degree at most } m \tag{2b}$$

Given a set of knots P_0, . . . , P_n and "endpoints indices" k and $k + m$, the problem of finding a polynomial $p_{k,k+m}(x)$ satisfying (2a) and (2b) will be referred to as the **polynomial interpolation problem**.

When $m = 0$, $p_{k,k}(x)$ is the zeroth-degree polynomial whose graph is the horizontal line through the one knot $P_k(x_k, y_k)$, that is,

$$p_{k,k}(x) \equiv y_k \qquad \text{(constant function)} \tag{3}$$

(Figure 6.1-2). When $m = 1$, $p_{k,k+1}(x)$ is the first-degree polynomial whose graph is the unique straight line through $P_k(x_k, y_k)$ and $P_{k+1}(x_{k+1}, y_{k+1})$, that is,

$$p_{k,k+1}(x) = y_k + \left(\frac{y_{k+1} - y_k}{x_{k+1} - x_k}\right)(x - x_k) \tag{4a}$$

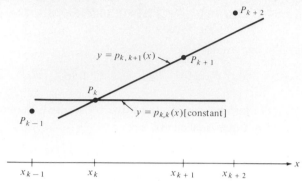

FIGURE 6.1-2　INTERPOLATING ONE KNOT $(m = 0)$ AND TWO KNOTS $(m = 1)$.

Rearranging terms in (4a) gives the symmetric expression

$$p_{k,k+1}(x) = y_k \left(\frac{x - x_{k+1}}{x_k - x_{k+1}} \right) + y_{k+1} \left(\frac{x - x_k}{x_{k+1} - x_k} \right) \tag{4b}$$

The reader has probably had experience using (4) to do **linear interpolation** $(m = 1)$. When $m > 1$ the method of undetermined coefficients can be used to convert (2a) to an $(m + 1) \times (m + 1)$ *linear* system whose solution gives the coefficients of $p_{k,k+m}(x)$. However, this method does not provide a general formula for $p_{k,k+m}(x)$ and is not well suited to hand computation if $m \geq 3$. In any case, its utility as a method for finding $p_{k,k+m}(x)$ is limited by the fact that the coefficient matrix of the system (2a) tends to become ill conditioned as m increases.

We shall use an alternative approach that does not have the drawbacks of the method of undetermined coefficients to show that *the polynomial interpolation problem always has a unique solution* $p_{k,k+m}(x)$.

6.1C　EXISTENCE OF $p_{k,k+m}(x)$; LAGRANGE'S FORM

Let us fix one node x_j from among the $m + 1$ distinct nodes $x_k, x_{k+1}, \ldots, x_{k+m}$. Then the product

$$\prod_{i \neq j} (x - x_i) = (x - x_k)(x - x_{k+1}) \cdots (x - x_{j-1})(x - x_{j+1}) \cdots (x - x_{k+m})$$

defines an mth degree polynomial that has $x_k, \ldots, x_j, x_{j+1}, \ldots, x_{k+m}$ as its m distinct roots but whose value at x_j, namely $\prod_{i \neq j} (x_j - x_i)$, is *not* zero. So if we define

$$L_j(x) = \frac{\prod_{i \neq j} (x - x_i)}{\prod_{i \neq j} (x_j - x_i)} = \frac{(x - x_k) \cdots (x - x_{j-1})(x - x_{j+1}) \cdots (x - x_{k+m})}{(x_j - x_k) \cdots (x_j - x_{j-1})(x_j - x_{j+1}) \cdots (x_j - x_{k+m})} \tag{5}$$

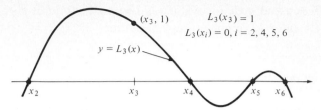

FIGURE 6.1-3 $L_3(x)$ FOR THE FIVE NODES x_2, x_3, x_4, x_5, x_6.

then $L_j(x)$ is an mth degree polynomial that "selects" x_j from among $x_k, \ldots, x_{k+m}$ in the sense that (see Figure 6.1-3)

$$L_j(x_j) = 1, \quad \text{but } L_j(x_i) = 0 \text{ for } i = k, k+1, \ldots, j-1, j+1, \ldots, k+m \qquad (6)$$

Since each of $L_k(x), \ldots, L_{k+m}(x)$ has degree m, the polynomial

$$y_k L_k(x) + y_{k+1} L_{k+1}(x) + \cdots + y_{k+m} L_{k+m}(x)$$

has degree $\leqslant m$; and by the "selecting property" (6), its value at x_j is

$$y_k \cdot 0 + y_{k+1} \cdot 0 + \cdots + y_{j-1} \cdot 0 + y_j \cdot 1 + y_{j+1} \cdot 0 + \cdots + y_{k+m} \cdot 0 = y_j$$

for $j = k, k+1, \ldots, k+m$. Thus *the polynomial interpolation problem always has at least one solution*, namely

$$\boxed{p_{k,k+m}(x) = y_k L_k(x) + y_{k+1} L_{k+1}(x) + \cdots + y_{k+m} L_{k+m}(x)} \qquad (7)$$

Note that (7) becomes (4b) when $m = 1$.

For the five knots considered in Example 6.1A, namely

$$P_0(-2, -8), \quad P_1(0, 0), \quad P_2(1, 1), \quad P_3(4, 64), \quad P_4(5, 125)$$

$p_{2,4}(x)$ can be obtained from P_2, P_3, and P_4 as follows:

$$p_{2,4}(x) = 1 \cdot L_2(x) + 64 \cdot L_3(x) + 125 \cdot L_4(x) \qquad \text{[by (7)]}$$

$$= 1 \frac{(x-4)(x-5)}{(1-4)(1-5)} + 64 \frac{(x-1)(x-5)}{(4-1)(4-5)} + 125 \frac{(x-1)(x-4)}{(5-1)(5-4)} \qquad \text{[by (5)]}$$

$$= 1\left(\frac{x^2 - 9x + 20}{12}\right) + 64\left(\frac{x^2 - 6x + 5}{-3}\right) + 125\left(\frac{x^2 - 5x + 4}{4}\right)$$

$$= 10x^2 - 29x + 20 \qquad \text{(same answer as in Section 6.1A)}$$

Terminology The expression for $p_{k,k+m}(x)$ given in (7) is called the **Lagrange form** of $p_{k,k+m}(x)$ after Joseph Louis Lagrange, who was clever enough to think of it in the late 1700s. The mth-degree polynomials $L_k(x), \ldots, L_{k+m}(x)$ defined by (5) are called the **Lagrange polynomials** for the $m+1$ nodes $x_k, x_{k+1}, \ldots, x_{k+m}$. Notice that the $L_j(x)$'s *depend only on the x_i's*. The y_i values are needed *only* in the Lagrange form of $p_{k,k+m}(x)$.

Figure 6.1-4 gives pseudocode for evaluating Lagrange's form of $p_{k,k+m}(z)$. The algorithm is quite well suited to computer implementation.

Algorithm: Lagrange Interpolation

Purpose: To evaluate the Lagrange form of $p_{k,k+m}(z)$, that is,

$$p_{k,k+m}(z) = y_k L_k(z) + y_{k+1} L_{k+1}(z) + \cdots + y_{k+m} L_{k+m}(z)$$

where $L_j(x) = \Pi_{i \neq j} (x - x_i)/(x_j - x_i)$, the jth Lagrange polynomial for the $m + 1$ knots $P_k(x_k, y_k), \ldots, P_{k+m}(x_{k+m}, y_{k+m})$, and z is a specified point near the interpolating nodes $x_k, \ldots, x_{k+m}$.

GET n, **x**, **y**,   {$\mathbf{x} = [x_0 \quad x_1 \quad \cdots \quad x_n]$, $\mathbf{y} = [y_0 \quad y_1 \quad \cdots \quad y_n]$}
   k, m,   {starting index, degree of interpolating polynomial}
   z {point at which interpolated value is desired}

$PofZ \leftarrow 0$
DO FOR $j = k$ TO $k + m$ {Form $Termj = y_j * L_j(x)$.}
  BEGIN
  $Termj \leftarrow y_j$
  DO FOR $i = k$ TO $k + m$
    IF $i \neq j$ THEN $Termj \leftarrow Termj*(z - x_i)/(x_j - x_i)$
  $PofZ \leftarrow PofZ + Termj$
  END

OUTPUT (The interpolated value $p_{k,k+m}(z)$ is $PofZ$.)

FIGURE 6.1-4   EVALUATING $p_{k,k+m}(x)$ AT $x = z$ USING LAGRANGE'S FORM.

6.1D   UNIQUENESS OF $p_{k,k+m}(x)$

Any polynomial $p(x)$ that is known to have at least the $m + 1$ distinct roots x_k, $x_{k+1}, \ldots, x_{k+m}$ can be factored as

$$p(x) = (x - x_k)(x - x_{k+1}) \cdots (x - x_{k+m})q(x) \tag{8a}$$

where $q(x)$ is a polynomial such that

$$\text{either } q(x) \equiv 0 \qquad \text{or} \qquad (\text{degree of } q) = (\text{degree of } p) - (m + 1) \tag{8b}$$

With this in mind, suppose that both $p_{k,k+m}(x)$ and $\tilde{p}_{k,k+m}(x)$ are of degree $\leq m$ and that both interpolate $P_k, P_{k+1}, \ldots, P_{k+m}$. Then

$$p(x) - p_{k,k+m}(x) - \tilde{p}_{k,k+m}(x) \text{ satisfies (8a)}$$

Since the degree of $p(x)$ is $\leqslant m$, it follows from (8b) that $q(x) \equiv 0$. So $p(x) \equiv 0$, that is, $p_{k,k+m}(x) \equiv \tilde{p}_{k,k+m}(x)$. This shows that *once we have one polynomial* $p_{k,k+m}(x)$ *of degree* $\leqslant m$ *that interpolates* P_k, . . . , P_{k+m} *(no matter how it is obtained), we have the only possible one.* We shall refer to this *unique* $p_{k,k+m}(x)$ as the **interpolating polynomial** for P_k, . . . , P_{k+m}. When $m > 2$, it is generally easier to obtain $p_{k,k+m}(x)$ using the Lagrange form (7) than using the method of undetermined coefficients.

EXAMPLE. Find **(a)** $p_{2,3}(x)$, **(b)** $p_{1,3}(x)$, and **(c)** $p_{0,3}(x)$ for

$$P_0(-2, -8), \quad P_1(0, 0), \quad P_2(1, 1), \quad P_3(4, 64), \quad P_4(5, 125) \tag{9}$$

Solution

a. For the two knots $P_2(1, 1)$ and $P_3(4, 64)$, (4b) gives

$$p_{2,3}(x) = y_2 L_2(x) + y_3 L_3(x) = 1\left(\frac{x-4}{1-4}\right) + 64\left(\frac{x-1}{4-1}\right) = 21x - 20$$

b. For the three knots $P_1(0, 0)$, $P_2(1, 1)$, and $P_3(4, 64)$, (7) gives

$$p_{1,3}(x) = 0 \cdot L_1(x) + 1 \cdot L_2(x) + 64 \cdot L_3(x)$$

where this time $L_2(x)$ and $L_3(x)$ are *quadratics*, that is,

$$p_{1,3}(x) = 0 \cdot L_1(x) + 1 \frac{(x-0)(x-4)}{(1-0)(1-4)} + 64 \frac{(x-0)(x-1)}{(4-0)(4-1)}$$

$$= 0 - \tfrac{1}{3}(x^2 - 4x) + \tfrac{16}{12}(x^2 - x) = 5x^2 - 4x$$

c. For the four knots $P_0(-2, -8)$, $P_1(0, 0)$, $P_2(1, 1)$, and $P_3(4, 64)$, (7) gives

$$p_{0,3}(x) = -8 \cdot L_0(x) + 0 \cdot L_1(x) + 1 \cdot L_2(x) + 64 \cdot L_3(x)$$

$$= -8 \frac{(x-0)(x-1)(x-4)}{(-2-0)(-2-1)(-2-4)} + 0 + 1 \frac{(x+2)(x-0)(x-4)}{(1+2)(1-0)(1-4)}$$

$$+ 64 \frac{(x+2)(x-0)(x-1)}{(4+2)(4-0)(4-1)}$$

$$= \frac{8}{36}(x^3 - 5x^2 + 4x) + 0 - \frac{1}{9}(x^3 - 2x^2 - 8x) + \frac{64}{72}(x^3 + x^2 - 2x) = x^3$$

Had we recognized in (9) that $y_k = x_k^3$ for $k = 0, 1, 2, 3$, then we could have avoided the preceding computation and simply argued as follows. Since x^3 is of degree $\leqslant 3$ and interpolates P_0, . . . , P_3, it must be the *unique* interpolating polynomial for these four knots, that is, $p_{0,3}(x) = x^3$ (see Figure 6.1-5). The same argument shows that $p_{1,4}(x) = x^3$ and $p_{0,4}(x) = x^3$.

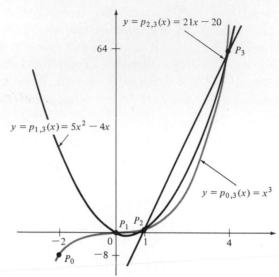

FIGURE 6.1-5 $p_{2,3}(x)$, $p_{1,3}(x)$, AND $p_{0,3}(x)$ FOR P_0, . . . , P_4 ON THE CURVE $y = x^3$.

6.2   Divided Differences and the Recursive Form of $p_{k,k+m}(x)$

We know from the preceding section that the six knots

$$P_0(-2, 69), \quad P_1(-1, 10), \quad P_2(0, 3), \quad P_3(1, 0), \quad P_4(2, 1), \quad P_5(3, 54) \tag{1}$$

can be interpolated by a unique polynomial $p_{0,5}(x)$ of degree $\leqslant 5$. But does $p_{0,5}(x)$ actually have degree < 5? The degree of $p_{0,n}(x)$ can be quite useful in trying to reconstruct the function that gave rise to $n + 1$ knots

$$P_0(x_0, y_0), \quad P_1(x_1, y_1), \quad . . . , \quad P_n(x_n, y_n) \tag{2}$$

Unfortunately, the Lagrange form of $p_{k,k+m}(x)$ given in Section 6.1C does not enable us to obtain this information efficiently. The **Newton form** of $p_{k,k+m}(x)$ to be described in this section is no harder to obtain than Lagrange's form but gives better insight into the degree of the polynomial that "best" interpolates P_0, . . . , P_n over all or part of the interpolating interval $[x_0, x_n]$.

6.2A   DIVIDED DIFFERENCES AND DIVIDED DIFFERENCE TABLES

The number

$$\Delta y_k = \frac{y_{k+1} - y_k}{x_{k+1} - x_k}, \qquad k = 0, 1, . . . , n - 1 \tag{3}$$

is called the **first divided difference** (abbreviated **1st DD**) at P_k. Geometrically, Δy_k is *the forward slope at P_k, that is, the slope of the line through P_k and P_{k+1}* (see Figure 6.2-1). Thus Δy_k is the first derivative of $p_{k,k+1}(x)$.

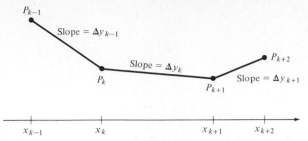

Figure 6.2-1   Geometric interpretation of $\Delta y_{k-1}, \Delta y_k, \Delta y_{k+1}$.

The **second divided difference** (abbreviated **2nd DD**) at P_k is

$$\Delta^2 y_k = \frac{\Delta y_{k+1} - \Delta y_k}{x_{k+2} - x_k}, \qquad k = 0, 1, \ldots, n-2 \tag{4}$$

Since $\Delta^2 y_k$ has units of (change in slope)/(change in x), we expect that the number $\Delta^2 y_k$ should give information about the second derivative of the interpolating quadratic for P_k, P_{k+1}, and P_{k+2}. For example, to get $\Delta^2 y_1$ for the five cubic knots

$$P_0(-2, -8), \quad P_1(0, 0), \quad P_2(1, 1), \quad P_3(4, 64), \quad P_4(5, 125)$$

we first use the coordinates of P_1, P_2, and P_3 to get the slopes

$$\Delta y_1 = \frac{y_2 - y_1}{x_2 - x_1} = \frac{1-0}{1-0} = 1 \quad \text{and} \quad \Delta y_2 = \frac{y_3 - y_2}{x_3 - x_2} = \frac{64-1}{4-1} = 21$$

and we then use these values in (4) (with $k = 1$) to get

$$\Delta^2 y_1 = \frac{\Delta y_2 - \Delta y_1}{x_3 - x_1} = \frac{21-1}{4-0} = 5$$

This positive 2nd DD indicates that $p_{1,3}(x)$ is concave up (see Figure 6.1-5).

Continuing inductively for any $m \geq 1$, we define the **mth divided difference** (abbreviated **mth DD**) at P_k to be the number†

$$\Delta^m y_k = \frac{\Delta^{m-1} y_{k+1} - \Delta^{m-1} y_k}{x_{k+m} - x_k}, \qquad k = 0, 1, \ldots, n-m \tag{5}$$

If we interpret $\Delta^0 y_k$ as y_k and $\Delta^1 y_k$ as Δy_k, then (5) becomes (3) when $m = 1$ and (4) when $m = 2$. Taking $m = 3$ gives the 3rd DD at P_k, namely

$$\Delta^3 y_k = \frac{\Delta^2 y_{k+1} - \Delta^2 y_k}{x_{k+3} - x_k}, \qquad k = 0, 1, \ldots, n-3 \tag{6}$$

† Some authors denote this mth DD by $f[x_k, x_{k+1}, \ldots, x_{k+m}]$.

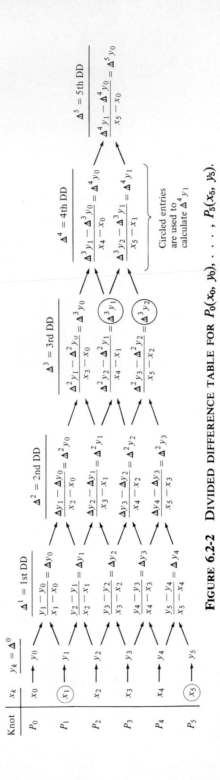

FIGURE 6.2-2 DIVIDED DIFFERENCE TABLE FOR $P_0(x_0, y_0), \ldots, P_5(x_5, y_5)$.

238

We shall see in Section 6.2D that $\Delta^3 y_k$ is related to the third derivative of $p_{k,k+3}(x)$.

Since the calculation of any mth DD requires subtracting two successive $(m-1)$st DDs, it is convenient to write the 0th, 1st, . . . , nth DDs in the columns of a triangular array called a **divided difference** (or simply **DD**) **table** as shown in Figure 6.2-2. Note that $\Delta^m y_k$ involves the coordinates of only P_k, P_{k+1}, . . . , P_{k+m}. The four numbers $\Delta^{m-1} y_{k+1}$, $\Delta^{m-1} y_k$, x_{k+m}, and x_k needed to calculate $\Delta^m y_k$ can be located by inspection by retracing the arrows terminating at the $\Delta^m y_k$ location back to the "Δ^{m-1}" and "node" columns as shown for $\Delta^4 y_1$ in Figure 6.2-2. This observation makes it unnecessary to formally substitute in (5) when making a DD table by hand.

EXAMPLE. Make a DD table for the five cubic knots

$$P_0(-2, -8), \quad P_1(0, 0), \quad P_2(1, 1), \quad P_3(4, 64), \quad P_4(5, 125)$$

Solution. The DD table is shown in Figure 6.2-3. The Δ^1, Δ^2, Δ^3, and Δ^4 columns were obtained *in that order* from the Δ^0, Δ^1, Δ^2, and Δ^3 columns, respectively. For illustrative purposes we have shown intermediate calculations on the DD table itself. From now on we shall do this on the side, putting only the numerical value of $\Delta^m y_k$ in the appropriate place in the table (i.e., *m places diagonally down from* y_k).

Pseudocode for forming a DD table in the upper triangular part of a square matrix *DD* is shown in Figure 6.2-4.

6.2B   RECURSIVE FORMULAS FOR $p_{k,k+m}(x)$

An examination of the circled entries of Figure 6.2-3 and the interpolating polynomials obtained in the examples of Sections 6.1A and 6.1D reveals that

$$\Delta^2 y_2 = 10 \text{ is the leading coefficient of } p_{2,4}(x) = 10x^2 - 29x - 20$$
$$\Delta^1 y_2 = 21 \text{ is the leading coefficient of } p_{2,3}(x) = 21x - 20$$
$$\Delta^2 y_1 = 5 \text{ is the leading coefficient of } p_{1,3}(x) = 5x^2 - 4x$$
$$\Delta^3 y_0 = 1 \text{ is the leading coefficient of } p_{0,3}(x) = x^3$$

We shall prove in Section 6.2F that for *any k* and *m*,

$$\boxed{\Delta^m y_k \text{ is the leading coefficient of } p_{k,k+m}(x)} \qquad \text{(7a)}$$

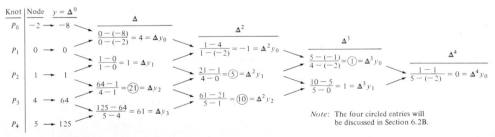

FIGURE **6.2-3**   DIVIDED DIFFERENCE TABLE FOR FIVE KNOTS ON $y = x^3$.

Algorithm: FORMDD (Forming a Divided Difference Table)

Purpose: To form the divided difference table for n given knots $P_1(x_1, y_1), \ldots,$
$P_n(x_n, y_n)$ and store it in the matrix $DD_{n \times n}$; specifically, to store $\Delta^m y_k$
in $DD(k, m + 1)$.
GET n, x, y $\{$x $= [x_1 \quad x_2 \cdots x_n]$ and y $= [y_1 \quad y_2 \cdots y_n]\}$

DO FOR $k = 1$ TO n $\{$Put Δ^0 values in col$_1 DD\}$
  $DD(k, 1) \leftarrow y_k$
DO FOR $m = 1$ TO $n - 1$ $\{$Put Δ^m values in col$_{m+1} DD\}$
  DO FOR $k = 1$ TO $n - m$
    $DD(k, m + 1) \leftarrow [DD(k + 1, m) - DD(k, m)]/(x_{k+m} - x_k)$

OUTPUT (The Δ^0, Δ^1, $\ldots$, Δ^{n-1} values are col$_1 DD$, $\ldots$, col$_n DD$)

FIGURE 6.2-4   PSEUDOPROGRAM FOR ALGORITHM FORMDD (FORMING A DD TABLE).

Put another way,

$$p_{k,k+m}(x) = \Delta^m y_k x^m + \text{a polynomial of degree} < m \tag{7b}$$

Thus the leading coefficient of $p_{k,k+m}(x)$ is located where the arrows from the "endpoint nodes" x_k and x_{k+m} meet, that is, *m entries diagonally down from y_k on a DD table for $P_0, \ldots, P_n$.*

Formula (7b) makes it possible to "build" $p_{k,k+m}(x)$ from

$$p_{\text{prev}}(x) = \text{interpolating polynomial for all but one of } P_k, \ldots, P_{k+m} \tag{8}$$

Indeed, we know that $p_{\text{prev}}(x)$ has degree $< m$. So if we let $\delta_m(x)$ denote the increment to add to $p_{\text{prev}}(x)$ to get $p_{k,k+m}(x)$, then by (7b),

$$\delta_m(x) = p_{k,k+m}(x) - p_{\text{prev}}(x) = \Delta^m y_k x^m + \text{(a polynomial of degree} < m) \tag{9}$$

But the m previously used nodes x_i are distinct roots of $\delta_m(x)$ because

$$\delta_m(x_i) = p_{k,k+m}(x_i) - p_{\text{prev}}(x_i) = y_i - y_i = 0$$

Since degree $\delta_m(x) \leq m$, it follows from (8) of Section 5.4D that

$$\delta_m(x) = C \Pi_{\text{prev}} (x - x_i) \qquad (C = \text{constant}) \tag{10}$$

where Π_{prev} denotes the product as x_i varies over the *previously used nodes*. Upon comparing (10) with (9), we see that $C = \Delta^m y_k$, proving that

$$p_{k,k+m}(x) = p_{\text{prev}}(x) + \delta_m(x), \qquad \text{where } \delta_m(x) = \Delta^m y_k \Pi_{\text{prev}}(x - x_i) \tag{11}$$

If we take $p_{\text{prev}}(x)$ to be either $p_{k,k+m-1}(x)$ or $p_{k+1,k+m}(x)$, we get the following especially useful formulas for $p_{k,k+m}(x)$:

Forward Recursive Form (added node x_{k+m} lies to the *right* of $x_k, \ldots, x_{k+m-1}$)

$$p_{k,k+m}(x) = p_{k,k+m-1}(x) + \Delta^m y_k(x - x_k)(x - x_{k+1}) \cdots (x - x_{k+m-1}) \quad \textbf{(12a)}$$

Backward Recursive Form (added node x_k lies to the *left* of $x_{k+1}, \ldots, x_{x+m}$)

$$p_{k,k+m}(x) = p_{k+1,k+m}(x) + \Delta^m y_k(x - x_{k+1})(x - x_{k+2}) \cdots (x - x_{k+m}) \quad \textbf{(12b)}$$

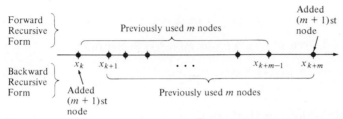

FIGURE 6.2-5   GRAPHICAL DESCRIPTION OF RECURSIVE FORMS OF $p_{k,k+m}(x)$.

These formulas, attributed to Newton, are described graphically in Figure 6.2-5. To illustrate, having obtained $p_{2,4}(x)$ $[=p_{\text{prev}}(x)]$, we can use (12a) to get

$$p_{2,5}(x) = p_{2,4}(x) + \Delta^3 y_2(x - x_2)(x - x_3)(x - x_4)$$

or we can use (12b) to get

$$p_{1,4}(x) = p_{2,4}(x) + \Delta^3 y_1(x - x_2)(x - x_3)(x - x_4)$$

When $m = 0$, $p_{k,k}(x)$ and $p_{k+1,k+1}(x)$ are the constant functions

$$p_{k,k}(x) \equiv y_k \qquad \text{and} \qquad p_{k+1,k+1}(x) \equiv y_{k+1} \quad \textbf{(13)}$$

Hence when $m = 1$, (12a) and (12b) become the familiar point-slope forms of the straight line through P_k and P_{k+1}, namely

$$p_{k,k+1}(x) = y_k + \Delta y_k(x - x_k) \qquad \text{(forward)} \quad \textbf{(14a)}$$

$$p_{k,k+1}(x) = y_{k+1} + \Delta y_k(x - x_{k+1}) \qquad \text{(backward)} \quad \textbf{(14b)}$$

We now show how to use (12) to build interpolating polynomials.

EXAMPLE. Use a DD table for the five cubic knots

$$P_0(-2, -8), \quad P_1(0, 0), \quad P_2(1, 1), \quad P_3(4, 64), \quad P_4(5, 125)$$

to get **(a)** $p_{1,2}(x)$; **(b)** $p_{1,3}(x)$; **(c)** $p_{0,3}(x)$; **(d)** $p_{1,4}(x)$; **(e)** $p_{0,4}(x)$.

Solution. For convenience, we display the nodes $x_0, \ldots, x_4$ in Figure 6.2-6. The DD table for $P_0, \ldots, P_4$ is shown in Figure 6.2-7.

FIGURE 6.2-6   NODES OF $P_0, \ldots, P_4$ ON THE CURVE $y = x^3$.

a. We can get $p_{1,2}(x)$ [for $P_1(0, 0)$ and $P_2(1, 1)$] in two ways:

$$p_{1,2}(x) = y_1 + \Delta y_1(x - x_1) = 0 + 1(x - 0) = x \qquad \text{[using (14a)]}$$

$$p_{1,2}(x) = y_2 + \Delta y_1(x - x_2) = 1 + 1(x - 1) = x \qquad \text{[using (14b)]}$$

b. To get $p_{1,3}(x)$ from $p_{1,2}(x)$, we add $P_3(4, 64)$ to the right:

$$\begin{aligned} p_{1,3}(x) &= p_{1,2}(x) + \Delta^2 y_1(x - 0)(x - 1) \qquad \text{[using (12a)]} \\ &= x + 5(x^2 - x) = 5x^2 - 4x \end{aligned}$$

c. To get $p_{0,3}(x)$ from $p_{1,3}(x)$, we add $P_0(-2, -8)$ to the left:

$$\begin{aligned} p_{0,3}(x) &= p_{1,3}(x) + \Delta^3 y_0(x - 0)(x - 1)(x - 4) \qquad \text{[using (12b)]} \\ &= (5x^2 - 4x) + 1\,(x^3 - 5x^2 + 4x) = x^3 \end{aligned}$$

d. To get $p_{1,4}(x)$ from $p_{1,3}(x)$, we add $P_4(5, 125)$ to the right:

$$\begin{aligned} p_{1,4}(x) &= p_{1,3}(x) + \Delta^3 y_1(x - 0)(x - 1)(x - 4) \qquad \text{[using (12a)]} \\ &= (5x^2 - 4x) + 1(x^3 - 5x^2 + 4x) = x^3 \end{aligned}$$

e. We can get $p_{0,4}(x)$ either from $p_{0,3}(x)$ (by adding P_4 to the right) or from $p_{1,4}(x)$ (by adding P_0 to the left). Since $\Delta^4 y_0 = 0$, either gives

$$p_{0,4}(x) = p_{0,3}(x) = p_{1,4}(x) = x^3 \qquad \text{[using (12a) or (12b)]}$$

Knot	Node	$\Delta^0 = y$	Δ^1	Δ^2	Δ^3	Δ^4
P_0	$-2 \longrightarrow$	-8				
			$4 = \Delta y_0$			
P_1	$0 \longrightarrow$	0		$-1 = \Delta^2 y_0$		
			(12b) $①= \Delta y_1$ (12a)		(12b) $①= \Delta^3 y_0$ (12a)	
P_2	$1 \longrightarrow$	$①$		$⑤ = \Delta^2 y_1$		$⓪ = \Delta^4 y_0$
			$21 = \Delta y_2$		$1 = \Delta^3 y_1$	
P_3	$4 \longrightarrow$	64		$10 = \Delta^2 y_2$		
			$61 = \Delta y_3$			
P_4	$5 \longrightarrow$	125				

Note: The circled DDs will be discussed in Section 6.2C.

FIGURE 6.2-7   DD TABLE FOR $P_0, \ldots, P_4$ ON THE CURVE $y = x^3$.

Since $P_0, \ldots, P_4$ lie on the cubic $y = x^3$, we should have expected x^3 itself to be the unique interpolating polynomial for any four or more of these five knots [cf. part (c) of the example in Section 6.1D].

6.2C LOCATING LEADING COEFFICIENTS BY INSPECTION

Let us build $p_{0,4}(x)$ starting with $x_2 = 1$ and then using (12a) and (12b) alternately to add nodes as indicated by the arrows in Figure 6.2-8. The resulting accumulated expression for $p_{0,4}(x)$ is

$$
\begin{array}{cc}
\text{(12b)} & \text{(12a)} \\
\downarrow & \downarrow
\end{array}
$$

$$p_{0,4}(x) = y_2 + \Delta^1 y_1 (x - 1) + \Delta^2 y_1 (x - 1)(x - 0)$$

$$
\begin{array}{cc}
\text{(12b)} & \text{(12a)} \\
\downarrow & \downarrow
\end{array}
$$

$$+ \Delta^3 y_0 (x - 1)(x - 4) + \Delta^4 y_0 (x - 1)(x - 0)(x - 4)(x + 2)$$

FIGURE 6.2-8   ADDING NODES USING (12a) AND (12b) ALTERNATELY.

Notice how the arrows in Figure 6.2-8 correspond to the "zigzag" path through the leading coefficients y_2, $\Delta^1 y_1$, $\Delta^2 y_1$, $\Delta^3 y_0$, $\Delta^4 y_0$ circled on the DD table of Figure 6.2-7. The correspondence is shown in Table 6.2-1.

TABLE 6.2-1   VISUALIZING (12a) AND (12b) ON A DD TABLE.

Formula	Added Node	Direction to New $\Delta^m y_k$
(12a)	to right	↘ on DD table
(12b)	to left	↗ on DD table

This correspondence makes it unnecessary to write "$= \Delta^m y_k$" on the DD table. From now on we shall enter only numerical values.

6.2D USING A DD TABLE TO RECOGNIZE POLYNOMIAL DATA

Recall from (7b) that

$$p_{k,k+m}(x) = \Delta^m y_k \, x^m + \text{a polynomial of degree} < m$$

Upon differentiating this result m times, we see that

$$\frac{d^m}{dx^m} [p_{k,k+m}(x)] \equiv m! \, \Delta^m y_k \quad \text{(constant)} \tag{15a}$$

This important result allows us to interpret $\Delta^m y_k$ as an mth derivative:

$$\Delta^m y_k = \frac{1}{m!} \frac{d^m}{dx^m} \{\text{interpolating polynomial for } P_k, \ldots, P_{k+m}\} \qquad \textbf{(15b)}$$

If $P_0, \ldots, P_n$ lie on the graph of an mth-degree polynomial $p(x)$, then

$$p_{k,k+m}(x) = p(x) \qquad \text{for any } k$$

so by (15), all mth DDs will be the constant $p^{(m)}(x)/m!$. We saw this for $p(x) = x^3$ ($m = 3$) in Figure 6.2-6. Conversely, if the mth column of a DD table is constant, then all subsequent columns will be zero (i.e., $\Delta^r y_k = 0$ for $r > m$), so it follows from the recursive forms (12) that

$$p_{k,k+r}(x) = p_{k,k+m}(x) \qquad \text{for } any \ k \text{ and all } r \geqslant m$$

In particular, $p_{0,n}(x) = p_{k,k+m}(x)$ for any k. In summary:

A DD table will have a constant Δ^m column if and only if $P_0, \ldots, P_n$ all lie on the graph of an mth-degree polynomial. This polynomial can be found as $p_{k,k+m}(x)$ using any $m + 1$ convenient knots $P_k, \ldots, P_{k+m}$.

EXAMPLE. Find the polynomial of lowest degree that interpolates

$$P_0(-2, 69), \quad P_1(-1, 10), \quad P_2(0, 3), \quad P_3(1, 0), \quad P_4(2, 1), \quad P_5(3, 54)$$

Solution. The DD table for these six knots is shown in Figure 6.2-9. The constant Δ^4 column indicates that these knots all lie on the graph of a fourth-degree polynomial $p(x)$ [see (1) above]. So any *five* knots determine $p(x)$. For example, we could add the first five nodes in their *natural order*

$$x_0 = -2, \quad x_1 = -1, \quad x_2 = 0, \quad x_3 = 1, \quad x_4 = 2$$

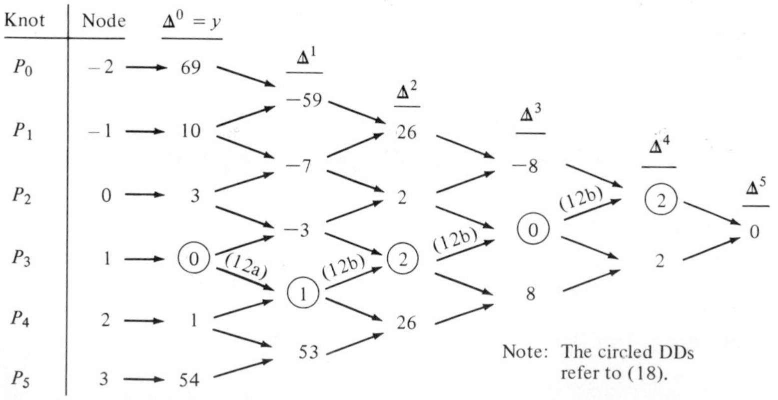

FIGURE 6.2-9 DD TABLE FOR $P_0, \ldots, P_5$.

to get $p(x)$ as $p_{0,4}(x)$ using only (12a) [**forward Newton form** of $p(x)$]:

$$p(x) = 69 - 59(x + 2) + 26(x + 2)(x + 1)$$
$$- 8(x + 2)(x + 1)x + 2(x + 2)(x + 1)x(x - 1) \qquad (16)$$

Similarly, we could add the last five nodes in their *reverse order,*

$$x_5 = 3, \quad x_4 = 2, \quad x_3 = 1, \quad x_2 = 0, \quad x_1 = -1$$

to get $p(x)$ as $p_{1,5}(x)$ using only (12b) [**backward Newton form** of $p(x)$]:

$$p(x) = 54 + 53(x - 3) + 26(x - 3)(x - 2)$$
$$+ 8(x - 3)(x - 2)(x - 1) + 2(x - 3)(x - 2)(x - 1)x \qquad (17)$$

Alternatively, we could *add nodes so as to use the most convenient DD's,* for example, $0, \pm 1, \pm 2$. One such path (circled in Figure 6.2-9) corresponds to the order shown in Figure 6.2-10. Using (12a) once and (12b) afterward gives $p(x)$ as $p_{1,5}(x)$ thus:

$$p(x) = 0 + 1(x - 1) + 2(x - 1)(x - 2)$$
$$+ 0(x - 1)(x - 2)x + 2(x - 1)(x - 2) \, x(x + 1) \qquad (18)$$

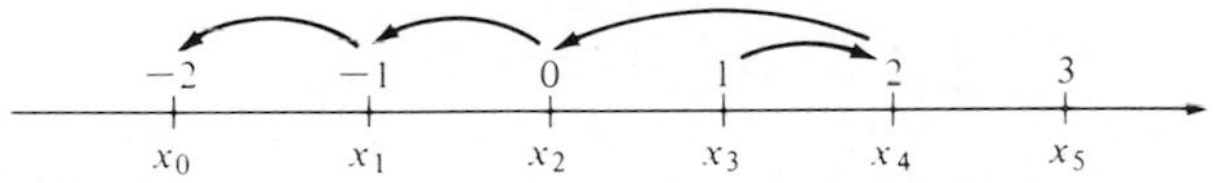

FIGURE 6.2-10   ADDING NODES IN THE ORDER x_3, x_4, x_2, x_1, x_0.

Any of (16), (17), or (18) (the latter most easily) simplifies to

$$p(x) = 2x^4 - 4x^3 - x + 3 \qquad (\text{degree} = 4) \qquad (19)$$

which, as the reader should verify, interpolates $P_0, \ldots, P_5$.

It should be noted that the three Newton forms of $p(x)$ given in (16)–(18) can be written in the **nested forms**

$$p(x) = [[[2(x - 1) - 8]x + 26](x + 1) - 59](x + 2) + 69 \qquad (20a)$$

$$p(x) = [[[2x + 8](x - 1) + 26](x - 2) + 53](x - 3) + 54 \qquad (20b)$$

$$p(x) = [[[2(x + 1) + 0]x + 2](x - 2) + 1](x - 1) + 0 \qquad (20c)$$

respectively. These can be used to evaluate $p(z)$ for a given z as easily as (19) but without having to perform the work of getting (19). For example, using (20c), we obtain

$$p(4) = [[[2(5) + 0](4) + 2](2) + 1](3) + 0 = 255$$

6.2E   DIFFERENCE TABLES FOR EQUISPACED NODES

If $x_0, x_1, \ldots, x_n$ are h-spaced, that is,

$$x_k = x_0 + kh, \qquad k = 0, 1, 2, \ldots, n \qquad (21)$$

then it is useful to define the *m*th **forward difference** at x_k by

$$\Delta^m y_k = \Delta^{m-1} y_{k+1} - \Delta^{m-1} y_k, \qquad m = 1, 2, \ldots \tag{22}$$

where the zeroth forward difference $\Delta^0 y_k$ is taken to be y_k itself. Thus

$$\Delta^1 y_k = y_{k+1} - y_k \tag{23a}$$

$$\Delta^2 y_k = \Delta^1 y_{k+1} - \Delta^1 y_k = y_{k+2} - 2y_{k+1} + y_k \tag{23b}$$

$$\Delta^3 y_k = \Delta^2 y_{k+1} - \Delta^2 y_k = y_{k+3} - 3y_{k+2} + 3y_{k+1} - y_k \tag{23c}$$

$$\Delta^4 y_k = \Delta^3 y_{k+1} - \Delta^3 y_k = y_{k+4} - 4y_{k+3} + 6y_{k+2} - 4y_{k+1} + y_k \tag{23d}$$

The (unsigned) coefficients of $y_{k+m}, \ldots, y_{k+1}, y_k$ in the expansion of $\Delta^m y_k$ can be obtained from the *m*th row of Pascal's triangle [Figure 6.2-11].

$$
\begin{array}{ccccccc}
 & & & 1 & 1 & & \\
 & & 1 & 2 & 1 & & \\
 & 1 & 3 & 3 & 1 & & \\
 1 & 4 & 6 & 4 & 1 & & \\
1 & 5 & 10 & 10 & 5 & 1 &
\end{array}
$$

FIGURE 6.2-11 **PASCAL'S TRIANGLE**

It is easy to use the definitions of $\Delta^m y_k$ and $\Delta^m y_k$ [see (22) and Section 6.2A] and the fact that $x_{k+m} - x_k = mh$ to prove by induction that forward and divided differences are related by

$$\Delta^m y_k = \frac{1}{m!\, h^m} \Delta^m y_k, \qquad m = 0, 1, 2, \ldots \tag{24}$$

So in view of (15),

$$\frac{\Delta^m y_k}{h^m} = \frac{d^m}{dx^m}[p_{k,k+m}(x)] \qquad \text{(constant)} \tag{25}$$

Consequently, $\Delta^m y_k / h^m$ can be used to approximate *m*th derivatives (cf. Section 7.2A).

Forward differences can be calculated and displayed conveniently on a **forward difference table** (often called simply a **difference table**). This is done in Figure 6.2-12 for the equispaced knots

$$P_0(-2, 69), \quad P_1(-1, 10), \quad P_2(0, 3), \quad P_4(1, 0), \quad P_5(2, 1), \quad P_6(3, 54) \tag{26}$$

which generated the DD table of Figure 6.2-9.

Knot	Node	$\Delta^0 = y$
P_0	-2	69
P_1	-1	10
P_2	0	3
P_3	1	0
P_4	2	1
P_5	3	54

Δ^1

$-59 = \Delta y_0$

$-7 = \Delta y_1$

$-3 = \Delta y_2$

$1 = \Delta y_3$

$53 = \Delta y_4$

Δ^2

$52 = \Delta^2 y_0$

$4 = \Delta^2 y_1$

$4 = \Delta^2 y_2$

$52 = \Delta^2 y_3$

Δ^3

$-48 = \Delta^3 y_0$

$0 = \Delta^3 y_1$

$48 = \Delta^3 y_2$

Δ^4

$48 = \Delta^4 y_0$

$48 = \Delta^4 y_1$

Δ^5

$0 = \Delta^5 y_0$

FIGURE 6.2-12 FORWARD DIFFERENCE TABLE FOR $P_0, \ldots, P_6$.

The recursive formulas (12) of Section 6.2B can be modified to allow efficient polynomial interpolation directly from forward difference tables (see Exercise 6-15).

The entries $\Delta^m y_k$ of a forward difference table can be viewed as **mth backward differences** $\nabla^m y_k$ or as **mth central differences** $\delta^m y_k$, where

$$\Delta^m y_k = \nabla^m y_{k+m} = \delta^m y_{k+m/2} \tag{27}$$

as shown in Figure 6.2-13. Thus the three entries diagonally down from $y_1 = 10$ on the difference Table of Figure 6.2-12 are

$$-7 = \Delta^1 y_1 = \nabla^1 y_2 = \delta^1 y_{3/2}$$

$$4 = \Delta^2 y_1 = \nabla^2 y_3 = \delta^2 y_2$$

$$0 = \Delta^3 y_1 = \nabla^3 y_4 = \delta^3 y_{5/2}$$

Viewing difference table entries as central differences makes it convenient to use formulas for what amounts to the average value of two interpolating polynomials. These

Knot	Node	$\Delta^0 = y$
P_0	x_0	y_0
P_1	x_1	y_1
P_2	x_2	y_2
P_3	x_3	y_3
P_4	x_4	y_4
P_5	x_5	y_5

∇^1

∇y_1

∇y_2

∇y_3

∇y_4

∇y_5

∇^2

$\nabla^2 y_2$

$\nabla^2 y_3$

$\nabla^2 y_4$

$\nabla^2 y_5$

∇^3

$\nabla^3 y_3$

$\nabla^3 y_4$

$\nabla^3 y_5$

∇^4

$\nabla^4 y_4$

$\nabla^4 y_5$

∇^5

$\nabla^5 y_5$

Knot	Node	$\delta^0 = y$
P_0	x_0	y_0
P_1	x_1	y_1
P_2	x_2	y_2
P_3	x_3	y_3
P_4	x_4	y_4
P_5	x_5	y_5

δ^1

$\delta y_{1/2}$

$\delta y_{3/2}$

$\delta y_{5/2}$

$\delta y_{7/2}$

$\delta y_{9/2}$

δ^2

$\delta^2 y_1$

$\delta^2 y_2$

$\delta^2 y_3$

$\delta^2 y_4$

δ^3

$\delta^3 y_{3/2}$

$\delta^3 y_{5/2}$

$\delta^3 y_{7/2}$

δ^4

$\delta^4 y_2$

$\delta^4 y_3$

δ^5

$\delta^5 y_{5/2}$

(a)   (b)

FIGURE 6.2-13 LOCATIONS OF $\nabla^m y_k$ AND $\delta^m y_k$ ON A DIFFERENCE TABLE.

central difference interpolating formulas, which include those of **Stirling, Bessel,** and **Gauss,** yield interpolated values which generally are as least as accurate as those obtained by polynomial interpolation. The improved accuracy can be useful in actuarial work (where interpolation is referred to as **collocation**); however, it is not viewed as significant enough to warrant detailed study by students of science and engineering, hence will not be pursued further here. The interested reader is referred to [20].

6.2F   PROOF THAT $\Delta^m y_k$ IS THE LEADING COEFFICIENT OF $p_{k,k+m}(x)$

Let

$$p(x) = \frac{1}{x_{k+m} - x_k} \{(x - x_k)\, p_{k+1,k+m}(x) - (x - x_{k+m})\, p_{k,k+m-1}(x)\} \qquad (28)$$

Since

$$p_{k,k+m-1}(x_i) = y_i \quad \text{for } i = k, \ldots, k+m-1$$

and

$$p_{k+1,k+m}(x_i) = y_i \quad \text{for } i = k+1, \ldots, k+m$$

we see from (28) that $p(x)$ interpolates $P_k, \ldots, P_{k+m}$:

$$p(x_k) = \frac{1}{x_{k+m} - x_k} \{0 \cdot p_{k+1,k+m}(x_k) - (x_k - x_{k+m})\, y_k\} = y_k$$

$$p(x_i) = \frac{1}{x_{k+m} - x_k} \{(x_i - x_k)\, y_i - (x_i - x_{k+m})\, y_i\} = y_i, \quad i = k+1, \ldots, k+m-1$$

$$p(x_{k+m}) = \frac{1}{x_{k+m} - x_k} \{(x_{k+m} - x_k)\, y_{k+m} - 0 \cdot p_{k,k+m-1}(x_{k+m})\} = y_{k+m}$$

Moreover, since $p_{k+1,k+m}(x)$ and $p_{k,k+m-1}(x)$ both have degree $\leq m-1$, it follows from (28) that degree $p(x) \leq m$. So, by the uniqueness of the interpolating polynomial (Section 6.1D), $p(x)$ must be $p_{k,k+m}(x)$, that is,

$$p_{k,k+m}(x) = \frac{1}{x_{k+m} - x_k} \{(x - x_k)\, p_{k+1,k+m}(x) - (x - x_{k+m})\, p_{k,k+m-1}(x)\} \qquad (29)$$

This result, due to Neville, allows us prove by induction on m that

$$\text{the coefficient of } x^m \text{ in } p_{k,k+m}(x) \text{ is } \Delta^m y_k \qquad (30)$$

We saw in (14) that (30) is true when $m = 1$. Let us assume it to be true for interpolating polynomials of degree $\leq m-1$. Then the coefficient of x^{m-1} in $p_{k+1,k+m}(x)$ and $p_{k,k+m-1}(x)$ are $\Delta^{m-1} y_{k+1}$ and $\Delta^{m-1} y_k$, respectively. In view of (29), the coefficient of x^m in $p_{k,k+m}(x)$ is $(\Delta^{m-1} y_{k+1} - \Delta^{m-1} y_k)/(x_{k+m} - x_k)$. This is the definition of $\Delta^m y_k$ and so completes the proof of (30).

Practical Strategies for Polynomial Interpolation   **6.3**

Given $n + 1$ points on the graph of f, namely

$$P_i(x_i, y_i) \qquad \text{where } y_i = f(x_i), \quad i = 0, 1, \dots, n \tag{1}$$

we can estimate $f(z)$ for a specified z as follows:

$$f(z) \approx p_{k,k+m}(z) \qquad \text{for suitably chosen } m \text{ and } k \tag{2}$$

The question is: *How do we choose m and k to ensure best accuracy?*

In view of the Polynomial Wiggle Problem (Section 5.3B) the "obvious" answer "$k = 0$ and $m = n$" (use all knots) generally will *not* give the most accuracy. So the question is not as simple as it may seem.

6.3A   STRATEGY FOR EFFICIENT POLYNOMIAL INTERPOLATION

Let m be a specified degree. Among the numbers

$$p_{0,m}(z), \quad p_{1,m+1}(z), \quad \dots, \quad p_{n-m,n}(z) \tag{3}$$

which can be used to give an mth-degree approximation of $f(z)$, it is intuitively plausible that the one most likely to approximate $f(z)$ accurately is

$$\boxed{\hat{p}_m(z) = p_{k,k+m}(z), \qquad \begin{array}{l} \text{where } k \text{ is chosen so that the interval} \\ [x_k, x_{k+m}] \text{ best centers } z \end{array}} \tag{4}$$

We shall call $\hat{p}_m(z)$ the **best mth interpolant of** $f(z)$. Analytic justification for calling it "best" will be given at the end of Section 6.3D.

To get an accurate estimate of $f(z)$ for a given z, we find

$$\hat{p}_0(z), \quad \hat{p}_1(z), \quad \hat{p}_2(z), \dots \tag{5}$$

successively, adding new nodes so as to best center z. The arrows in Figure 6.3-1 show how new nodes would be added for z_1 between x_1 and x_2 and for z_2 between x_3 and x_4. We can see from Figure 6.3-1 that if the spacing between nodes is reasonably uniform, the interpolants in (5) will be obtained by taking

$$\hat{p}_0(z) = y_k, \qquad \text{where } x_k \text{ is the node nearest } z \tag{6}$$

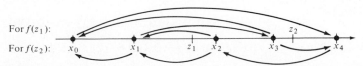

For $f(z_1)$:

For $f(z_2)$: x_0 x_1 z_1 x_2 x_3 z_2 x_4

FIGURE 6.3-1   NODES ADDED TO GET BEST INTERPOLANTS OF z_1 AND z_2.

as the best zeroth interpolant, and then *adding nodes* (*if available*) *on alternate sides
of z*. The recursive formula (11) of Section 6.2B can be written as

$$\hat{p}_m(z) = \hat{p}_{m-1}(z) + \delta_m(z), \qquad \text{where } \delta_m(z) = \Delta^m y_k \, \Pi_{\text{prev}} (z - x_i) \tag{7}$$

This formula makes it easy to find $\hat{p}_0(z)$, $\hat{p}_1(z)$, . . . successively until $\delta_m(z)$ ceases to
indicate significantly improved accuracy.

EXAMPLE. The **normalized cumulative distribution function**

$$\Phi(x) = \frac{1}{\sqrt{2\pi}} \int_{-\infty}^{x} e^{-t^2/2} \, dt \tag{8}$$

plays an important role in statistics. Since $e^{-t^2/2}$ has no antiderivative expressible in
terms of elementary functions, the values of $\Phi(x)$ must be obtained from tables such
as that shown in Table 6.3-1. From these values, we wish to estimate **(a)** $\Phi(0.52)$; **(b)**
$\Phi(0.22)$; **(c)** $\Phi(1.4)$.

TABLE 6.3-1   TABULATED
$\Phi(x)$ VALUES.

x	$\Phi(x)$ (4d)
$x_0 = 0.0$	0.5000
$x_1 = 0.2$	0.5793
$x_2 = 0.4$	0.6554
$x_3 = 0.6$	0.7257
$x_4 = 0.8$	0.7881
$x_5 = 1.0$	0.8413

Solution

a. The DD table (to 5*s*) for the six given knots is shown in Figure 6.3-2. For $z = 0.52$, the nodes for the best *m*th interpolants of $\Phi(z)$ should be added in the order
x_3, x_2, x_4, x_1, x_5, x_0, as shown in Figure 6.3-3. The leading coefficients of $\hat{p}_0(z)$, . . . ,
$\hat{p}_5(z)$ are circled in Figure 6.3-2.

   Starting with $\hat{p}_0(z) = \Phi(0.6) = 0.7257$, the recursive formula (7) gives (to 5*d*)

$$\hat{p}_1(z) = \hat{p}_0(z) + (0.3515)(z - 0.6) = 0.7257 + (-0.02812) \doteq 0.69758$$

$$\hat{p}_2(z) = \hat{p}_1(z) + (-0.09875)(z - 0.6)(z - 0.4) \doteq 0.69758 + (0.00095) = 0.69853$$

$$\hat{p}_3(z) = \hat{p}_2(z) + (-0.04375)(z - 0.6)(z - 0.4)(z - 0.8) \doteq 0.69853 + (-0.00012) = 0.69841$$

$$\hat{p}_4(z) = \hat{p}_3(z) + (0.020833)(z - 0.6)(z - 0.4)(z - 0.8)(z - 0.2) \doteq 0.69843$$

$$\hat{p}_5(z) = \hat{p}_4(z) + (0.0078123)(z - 0.6)(z - 0.4)(z - 0.8)(z - 0.2)(z - 1) \doteq 0.69843 \doteq \hat{p}_4(z)$$

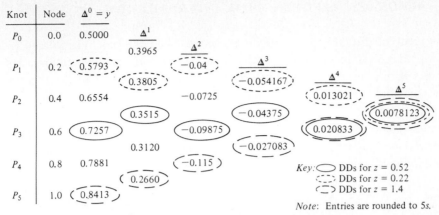

FIGURE 6.3-2 DD TABLE FOR $\Phi(x)$ DATA.

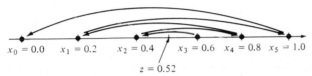

FIGURE 6.3-3   ADDING NODES TO GET THE BEST INTERPOLANTS OF $z = 0.52$.

b and c. Similarly, for $z = 0.22$ and $z = 1.4$, we add closest nodes in the following order:

$$\text{For } z = 0.22: \qquad x_1, \ x_2, \ x_0, \ x_3, \ x_4, \ x_5$$

$$\text{For } z = 1.4: \qquad x_5, \ x_4, \ x_3, \ x_2, \ x_1, \ x_0$$

The resulting best mth interpolants $\hat{p}_m(z)$ are tabulated in Table 6.3-2 together with those of $z = 0.52$. In working with these $4d$ data, we carried more than $5s$ in $\Delta^m y_k$ and $\Pi_{\text{prev}} (z - x_i)$, and gave $\delta_m(z)$ and $\hat{p}_m(z)$ to $5d$ (one "guard digit").

TABLE 6.3-2   INTERPOLATING $\Phi(z)$ AT $z = 0.52$, $z = 0.22$, AND $z = 1.4$.

	(a) $z = 0.52$, $\hat{p}_0(z) = \Phi(0.6)$			(b) $z = 0.22$, $\hat{p}_0(z) = \Phi(0.2)$			(c) $z = 1.4$, $\hat{p}_0(z) = \Phi(1.0)$		
m	New Node	$\delta_m(z)$	$\hat{p}_m(z)$	New Node	$\delta_m(z)$	$\hat{p}_m(z)$	New Node	$\delta_m(z)$	$\hat{p}_m(z)$
0	0.6	—	0.7257	0.2	—	0.5793	1.0	—	0.8413
1	0.4	-0.02812	0.69758	0.4	0.00761	0.58691	0.8	0.1064	0.94770
2	0.8	0.00095	0.69853	0.0	0.00014	0.58705	0.6	-0.0276	0.92010
3	0.2	-0.00012	0.69841	0.6	0.00004	0.58709	0.4	-0.0052	0.91490
4	1.0	0.00002	0.69843	0.8	0.00000	0.58709	0.2	0.00400	0.91890
5	0.0	0.00000	0.69843	1.0	0.00000	0.58709	0.0	0.00180	0.92070

6.3B ACCURACY OF POLYNOMIAL INTERPOLATION

The value of $\Phi(0.52)$ to $4s$ is 0.6985, not 0.6984 as the best interpolants of Table 6.3-2 would indicate. Since $5^{+}s$ were carried in the intermediate computations, this small error is not due to propagated roundoff, but rather to the fact that the *inherent error* of the tabulated values produced a slightly low value at $z = 0.52$.

When interpolating $f(z)$, the best accuracy one can realistically hope for is the accuracy of the tabulated values; and one should be prepared to accept a small error after rounding to the tabulated accuracy.

When $z = 0.22$, $\hat{p}_3(z) = 0.5871$ approximates $\Phi(0.22)$ to $4s$. However, the value of $\Phi(1.4)$ to $4s$ is 0.9192. So $\hat{p}_4(1.4) = 0.9189$ *approximates* $\Phi(1.4)$ *better than* $\hat{p}_5(1.4) = 0.9207$; and neither is as accurate as the corresponding approximations of $\Phi(0.52)$ and $\Phi(0.22)$. This should serve as a reminder that we must be most careful where the effects of the Polynomial Wiggle Problem are most evident:

For z near an endpoint of an interpolating interval and/or relatively far from the nearest node, it is especially important not to use a large m unless doing so appears to increase the number of accurate significant digits.

The word **extrapolation** is used for interpolation of $f(z)$ when either $z < x_0$ or $z > x_n$. When extrapolating, it is worthwhile to examine the DD table near the appropriate end of the interpolating interval $[x_0, x_n]$. In the example above, for instance, the nearly constant Δ^4 column suggests (correctly) that $\hat{p}_4(x)$ may give a reasonably faithful approximation of $\Phi(x)$ for $x > 1$. In any case, the large values of $\delta_m(z)$ (of the order of 10^{-3}) should have prepared us to expect significant errors in the fourth decimal place of both $\hat{p}_4(z)$ and $\hat{p}_5(z)$ when $z = 1.4$.

Extrapolation should be avoided if at all possible. If necessary, it should be performed using the *lowest degree* that appears to give reasonable accuracy, and with the expectation of poor accuracy. (See Exercise 6-18.)

6.3C ERROR PROPAGATION ON A DD TABLE

If the values of $\Phi(x)$ were given to $3d$ (rather than $4d$) in the example in Section 6.3A, then the resulting DD table (carrying $5^{+}s$ as was done in the example in Section 6.3A) would have been that shown in Figure 6.3-4.

A comparison of Figure 6.3-2 and Figure 6.3-4 reveals that the entries of the Δ^1 column differ in the third significant digit; those of the Δ^2 and Δ^3 columns differ in the second or first (i.e., leading!) significant digit; and the $\Delta^4 y_0$ entries have opposite sign! The explanation of these discrepancies is simple enough: *There is loss of significance when the nearly equal $\Phi(x)$ values are subtracted in calculating the 1st DDs, and these errors propagate to the higher DD columns, getting larger as they do.*

Knot	Node	$\Delta^0 = y$					
P_0	0.0	0.500	Δ^1				
			0.395	Δ^2			
P_1	0.2	0.579		-0.0375	Δ^3		
			0.38		-0.041667	Δ^4	
P_2	0.4	0.655		-0.0625		-0.052083	Δ^5
			0.355		-0.083333		0.15624
P_3	0.6	0.726		-0.1125		0.10416	
			0.31		0		
P_4	0.8	0.788		-0.1125			
			0.265				
P_5	1.0	0.841			*Note*: Entries are rounded to 5s.		

FIGURE 6.3-4   DD TABLE FOR $\Phi(x)$ ROUNDED TO $3d$.

For closely spaced nodes such as these, *propagated roundoff is indicated by erratic behavior down a column* such as in the Δ^3 column of Figure 6.3-4 (Exercise 6-26). *When such a column is detected, all subsequent columns should be ignored* because the random nature of roundoff error makes their entries as likely to worsen the accuracy of $\hat{p}_m(z)$ as it is to improve it!

6.3D   THE ERROR OF POLYNOMIAL INTERPOLATION

For a given z and $m + 1$ consecutive knots $P_k, \ldots, P_{k+m}$ on the graph of a function f, we wish to discuss the error of approximating $f(z)$ by $p_{k,k+m}(x)$, that is,

$$E_{k,k+m}(z) = f(z) - p_{k,k+m}(z) \tag{9}$$

Specifically, we wish to draw conclusions from the error formula

$$E_{k,k+m}(z) = \frac{f^{(m+1)}(c_{k,k+m})}{(m+1)!}(z - x_k)(z - x_{k+1}) \cdots (z - x_{k+m}) \tag{10}$$

where $c_{k,k+m}$ is a point in the smallest closed interval containing $x_k, \ldots x_{k+m}$ and z. We denote this interval by I.

The derivation of (10) will be given in Section 6.3F after we use it to show (1) why and where the worst errors of the approximation $f(z) \approx p_{k,k+m}(z)$ are likely to occur, and (2) where to locate the $m + 1$ nodes x_i so as to minimize this worst error.

Toward this end, we define the **max-norm of $f^{(m+1)}$ on I** to be

$$\|f^{(m+1)}\|_I = \text{the maximum value of } |f^{(m+1)}(x)| \text{ on } I \tag{11}$$

Since $|f^{(m+1)}(c_{k,k+1})| \leq \|f^{(m+1)}\|_I$, it follows from (10) that

$$|E_{k,k+m}(z)| \leq \frac{\|f^{(m+1)}\|_I}{(m+1)!}|z - x_0||z - x_1| \cdots |z - x_n| \tag{12}$$

Hence, for a given z and a specified m, the error of approximating $f(z)$ by $p_{k,k+m}(z)$ will be smallest when the factors $|z - x_i|$ in (12) are smallest, that is, when x_k, x_{k+1}, ..., x_{k+m} are the $m + 1$ nodes that best center z. Also, $|E_{k,k+m}(z)|$ will be largest when z is not close to any node, especially if z lies outside the interpolating interval $[x_k, x_{k+m}]$ (see Section 6.3B).

6.3E UNIFORM APPROXIMATION USING CHEBYSHEV NODES

The velocity or pressure of a gas or liquid flowing through a length of pipe can be monitored by putting measuring devices (sensors) at fixed nodes along the pipes as in Figure 6.3-5. The number of sensors used is limited by their physical size and by the

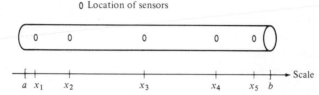

FIGURE 6.3-5 LOCATING SENSORS ALONG A LENGTH OF PIPE.

experimental error each one introduces; this number is generally determined in advance. Once we have decided to use $n + 1$ of them, the question is

Where should the sensors be (permanently) installed so that the readings at these $n + 1$ nodes can be used to interpolate the value at any other point with a uniform accuracy along the pipe?

Mathematically, our problem is this: Given an interval $[a, b]$ and a prescribed n, we wish to determine where to locate $n + 1$ nodes $x_0, x_1, \ldots, x_n$ in $[a, b]$ so as to make the interpolation error

$$E_{n+1}(z) = f(z) - p_{0,n}(z) \tag{13}$$

as uniformly small as possible as z varies over $[a, b]$. From (12),

$$|E_{n+1}(z)| \leqslant \frac{\|f^{(n+1)}\|_{[a, b]}}{(n+1)!} |\Pi_{n+1}(z)| \tag{14}$$

where $\Pi_{n+1}(x)$ is the $(n + 1)$st-degree polynomial

$$\Pi_{n+1}(x) = (x - x_0)(x - x) \cdots (x - x_n) \tag{15}$$

Since $[a, b]$ and n are fixed, we cannot control $\|f^{(n+1)}\|_{[a, b]}$ or $(n + 1)!$ So the desired nodes, which we shall denote by $\hat{x}_0, \hat{x}_1, \ldots, \hat{x}_n$, are those that minimize $\|\Pi_{n+1}\|_{[a, b]}$, where

$$\|\Pi_{n+1}\|_{[a, b]} = \text{the maximum value of } |\Pi_{n+1}(z)| \text{ for } a \leqslant z \leqslant b \tag{16}$$

The particular $\Pi_{n+1}(x)$ having these nodes as its roots will be denoted by

$$\hat{\Pi}_{n+1}(x) = (x - \hat{x}_0)(x - \hat{x}_1)\cdots(x - \hat{x}_n) \tag{17}$$

and called the **(n + 1)st minimax polynomial** for $[a, b]$. Thus, by definition,

$$\|\hat{\Pi}_{n+1}\|_{[a,\ b]} \leqslant \|\Pi_{n+1}\|_{[a,\ b]} \qquad \text{for any } \Pi_{n+1}(x) = (x - x_0)\cdots(x - x_n) \tag{18}$$

The Russian mathematician Chebyshev showed that when $[a, b]$ is $[-1, 1]$, the desired minimax polynomials are related to the Chebyshev polynomials $T_n(\xi)$ described in Section 5.4C. Specifically, he proved that for $n = 1, 2, \ldots$, the **nth minimax polynomial on** $[-1, 1]$ can be expressed as

$$\boxed{\hat{\Pi}_n(\xi) = (\tfrac{1}{2})^{n-1} T_n(\xi), \qquad \text{where } T_n(\xi) = \cos\left[n \cos^{-1}\xi\right] \quad \text{for } -1 \leqslant \xi \leqslant 1} \tag{19}$$

The $n + 1$ roots of $T_{n+1}(\xi)$ are called the **Chebyshev nodes on $[-1, 1]$** and denoted by $\hat{\xi}_0, \hat{\xi}_1, \ldots, \hat{\xi}_n$. It can be seen from Figure 5.4-3 that they are symmetrically located in $[-1, 1]$ (i.e., $\hat{\xi}_{n-i} = \hat{\xi}_i$) and most densely spaced near its endpoints.

In view of (19), the Chebyshev nodes $\hat{\xi}_0, \ldots, \hat{\xi}_n$ satisfy

$$T_{n+1}(\hat{\xi}_i) = 0 \qquad \Longleftrightarrow \qquad (n+1)\cos^{-1}\hat{\xi}_i \text{ is an odd multiple of } \pi/2$$

They are therefore given explicitly by the formula

$$\boxed{\hat{\xi}_i = \cos\left[\left(\frac{2(n-i)+1}{n+1}\right)\frac{\pi}{2}\right], \qquad i = 0, 1, \ldots, n} \tag{20a}$$

To get the desired nodes $\hat{x}_0, \ldots, \hat{x}_n$ in $[a, b]$, we simply reflect the Chebyshev nodes (15a) "proportionally" into $[a, b]$ as shown in Figure 6.3-6. Analytically,

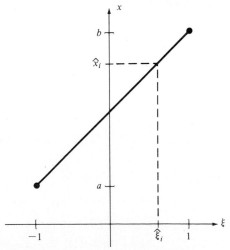

FIGURE 6.3-6   REFLECTING $\hat{\xi}_i$ INTO $\hat{x}_i$.

$$\hat{x}_i = a + \frac{b-a}{2}(\hat{\xi}_i + 1), \qquad i = 0, 1, \ldots, n \qquad \text{(20b)}$$

These $\hat{x}_i$'s will be called the $(n+1)$ **Chebyshev nodes** on $[a, b]$. Their use as nodes will be referred to as $(n+1)$st-degree **Chebyshev interpolation on** $[a, b]$.

EXAMPLE. Suppose that the pipe shown in Figure 6.3-5 is 60 meters long (i.e., $a = 0$ and $b = 60$) and we have decided to use five sensors (i.e., $n = 4$). By (20b) the five Chebyshev nodes on $[0, 60]$ are at

$$\hat{x}_i = 0 + \frac{60-0}{2}(\hat{\xi}_i + 1) = 30(\hat{\xi}_i + 1)$$

where by (20a), $\hat{\xi}_i = \cos[(9 - 2i)\,\pi/10]$, $i = 0, 1, \ldots, 4$. So the smallest possible maximum error of 5 knot interpolation will occur when the sensors are placed at

$$\hat{x}_0 = 30\left[1 + \cos\left(\frac{9\pi}{10}\right)\right] \doteq 30(1 - 0.9511) \doteq 1.47 \text{ m}$$

$$\hat{x}_1 = 30\left[1 + \cos\left(\frac{7\pi}{10}\right)\right] \doteq 30(1 - 0.5878) \doteq 12.37 \text{ m}$$

$$\hat{x}_2 = 30\left[1 + \cos\left(\frac{5\pi}{10}\right)\right] = 30(1 + 0) = 30 \text{ m}$$

$$\hat{x}_3 = 30\left[1 + \cos\left(\frac{3\pi}{10}\right)\right] \doteq 30(1 + 0.5878) \doteq 47.63 \text{ m}$$

$$\hat{x}_4 = 30\left[1 + \cos\left(\frac{\pi}{10}\right)\right] \doteq 30(1 + 0.9511) \doteq 58.53 \text{ m}$$

6.3F   DERIVATION OF THE FORMULA FOR $E_{k,k+m}(z)$

We wish to prove that

$$f(z) - p_{k,k+m}(z) = \frac{f^{(m+1)}(\xi)}{(m+1)!}\,\Pi(z) \qquad \text{for some } \xi \text{ in } I \qquad \text{(21a)}$$

where I is the smallest closed interval containing $x_k, \ldots, x_{k+m}$ and z, and

$$\Pi(x) = (x - x_k)(x - x_{k+1})\cdots(x - x_{k+m}) \qquad \text{(21b)}$$

provided that $f^{(n+1)}$ exists on the interior of I.

If z is one of the nodes $x_k, \ldots, x_{k+m}$, then $f(z) = p_{k,k+m}(z)$ and $\Pi(z) = 0$; so (21) holds trivially. Otherwise, let

$$\varphi(x) = f(x) - p_{k,k+m}(x) - \frac{\Pi(x)}{\Pi(z)} [f(z) - p_{k,k+m}(z)] \qquad (22)$$

It is easy to see that x_k, x_{k+1}, . . . , x_{k+m} and z are $m+2$ distinct zeros of $\varphi(x)$, all lying in I. So, by the generalized Rolle's theorem (see Appendix II.2D),

$$\varphi^{(m+1)} \text{ has at least one zero in } I; \quad \text{call it } \xi$$

Since degree $p_{k,k+m}(x) \leqslant m$ and $\Pi(x) = x^{m+1} + \cdots$,

$$\frac{d^{m+1}}{dx^{m+1}} p_{k,k+m}(x) \equiv 0 \quad \text{and} \quad \frac{d^{m+1}}{dx^{m+1}} \Pi(x) \equiv (m+1)! \quad \text{(constant)}$$

But z is being held fixed; so it follows easily from (22) that

$$0 = \varphi^{(m+1)}(\xi) = f^{(m+1)}(\xi) - 0 - \frac{(m+1)!}{\Pi(z)} [f(z) - p_{k,k+m}(z)]$$

from which (20) follows.

Interpolation Using Piecewise Cubic Splines   6.4

As before, suppose that we are given $n+1$ knots on the graph of f, that is,

$$P_k(x_k, y_k), \qquad \text{where } y_k = f(x_k), \quad k = 0, 1, \ldots, n \qquad (1)$$

The nodes x_k need not be equispaced, but we do assume that

$$x_0 < x_1 < \cdots < x_k < x_{k+1} < \cdots < x_n \qquad (2)$$

We saw in Figure 5.3-1 that unless the knots lie on the graph of a polynomial, $p_{0,n}(x)$ tends to "wiggle" between knots, especially near the endpoints of the interpolating interval $[x_0, x_n]$ if n is large.

A strategy that has been found to be effective for large n is to "piece together" the graphs of lower-degree polynomials $q_k(x)$, where $q_k(x)$ interpolates the two successive knots P_k and P_{k+1} for $k = 0, 1, \ldots, n-1$ as shown in Figure 6.4-1. [The fact that

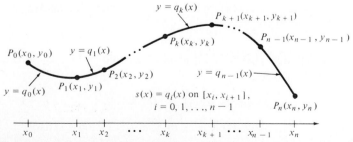

FIGURE 6.4-1   PIECEWISE POLYNOMIAL INTERPOLATION OF $P_0, \ldots, P_n$.

the "pieces" $q_k(x)$ and $q_{k+1}(x)$ are "tied together" at P_{k+1} accounts for the name "knots."] The purpose of this section is to develop computational procedures for this strategy called **piecewise polynomial interpolation.**

6.4A PIECEWISE LINEAR INTERPOLATION

The simplest piecewise polynomial strategy is to simply connect consecutive knots with straight lines as shown in Figure 6.4-2. This strategy, called **piecewise linear interpo-**

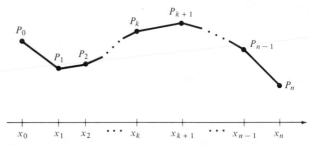

FIGURE 6.4-2   PIECEWISE LINEAR INTERPOLATION.

lation, can be described analytically using the Lagrange form of $p_{k,k+1}(x)$ to define the interpolating function $s(x)$ as follows:

$$s(x) = q_k(x) = y_k \left(\frac{x - x_{k+1}}{x_k - x_{k+1}} \right) + y_{k+1} \left(\frac{x - x_k}{x_{k+1} - x_k} \right) \qquad \text{for } x_k \leqslant x \leqslant x_{k+1} \qquad (3)$$

The resulting curve, shown in Figure 6.4-2, is continuous but is not well suited for interpolating smooth (i.e., differentiable) functions.

6.4B PIECEWISE CUBIC SPLINES

If we are to allow for the possibility that $f(x)$ has an inflection point between P_k and P_{k+1}, then $q_k(x)$ must be at least third degree (i.e., cubic). Experience has shown that for most smooth functions $f(x)$, cubic $q_k(x)$'s provide adequately accurate interpolation.

Terminology The function $s(x)$ is called **piecewise cubic** on $[x_0, x_n]$ if there exist cubics $q_0(x), \ldots, q_{n-1}(x)$ such that

$$s(x) = q_k(x) \text{ on } [x_k, x_{k+1}] \qquad \text{for } k = 0, 1, \ldots, n-1 \qquad (4)$$

In order for $s(x)$ to interpolate $P_0, \ldots, P_n$ the $q_k(x)$'s must satisfy

$$\textbf{S0:} \quad q_k(x_k) = y_k \quad \text{and} \quad q_k(x_{k+1}) = y_{k+1} \qquad \text{for } k = 0, 1, \ldots, n-1 \qquad (5a)$$

We shall call $s(x)$ in (4) a **cubic spline** (or simply a **spline**) if the "pieces" $q_k(x)$ have the *same slope* and *same concavity* at the knots where they are joined, that is, if

$$\text{S1:} \quad q'_{k-1}(x_k) = q'_k(x_k) \quad [= s'(x_k)] \qquad \text{for } k = 1, 2, \ldots, n-1 \qquad \textbf{(5b)}$$

$$\text{S2:} \quad q''_{k-1}(x_k) = q''_k(x_k) \quad [= s''(x_k)] \qquad \text{for } k = 1, 2, \ldots, n-1 \qquad \textbf{(5c)}$$

The $2n$ conditions in S0, together with the $n-1$ conditions in each of S1 and S2, ensure that $s(x)$ and both its first and second derivatives are continuous on $[x_0, x_n]$. Consequently, its graph, $y = s(x)$, is *smooth* and has a continuously turning tangent. Any $s(x)$ satisfying S0–S2 will be called an **interpolating spline** for $P_0, \ldots, P_n$.

6.4C   FINDING $q_0(x), \ldots, q_{n-1}(x)$

If $s(x)$ is piecewise cubic on $[x_0, x_n]$, then its second derivative $s''(x)$ is piecewise linear on $[x_0, x_n]$; in particular, by S2, $q''_k(x)$ is linear and interpolates $(x_k, s''(x_k))$ and $(x_{k+1}, s''(x_{k+1}))$ on $[x_k, x_{k+1}]$. So

$$q''_k(x) = s''(x_k)\left(\frac{x - x_{k+1}}{x_k - x_{k+1}}\right) + s''(x_{k+1})\left(\frac{x - x_k}{x_{k+1} - x_k}\right), \qquad k = 0, 1, \ldots, n-1 \qquad \textbf{(6)}$$

by (3). If we denote the increment from x_k to x_{k+1} by

$$h_k = x_{k+1} - x_k \qquad \text{for } k = 0, 1, \ldots, n-1 \qquad \textbf{(7)}$$

and we denote the second derivative of s at x_k by

$$\sigma_k = s''(x_k) \qquad \text{for } k = 0, 1, \ldots, n \qquad \textbf{(8)}$$

then (6) can be rewritten as

$$q''_k(x) = \frac{\sigma_k}{h_k}(x_{k+1} - x) + \frac{\sigma_{k+1}}{h_k}(x - x_k), \qquad k = 0, 1, \ldots, n-1 \qquad \textbf{(9)}$$

where the h_k's and σ_k's are constants, with the σ_k's to be determined. Integrating (9) twice with respect to x gives for $k = 0, 1, \ldots, n-1$,

$$q_k(x) = \frac{\sigma_k}{h_k}\frac{(x_{k+1} - x)^3}{6} + \frac{\sigma_{k+1}}{h_k}\frac{(x - x_k)^3}{6} + \lambda_k(x) \qquad \textbf{(10a)}$$

where $\lambda_k(x) = C_k + D_k x$. In view of the form of the σ_k and σ_{k+1} terms of (10a), $\lambda_k(x)$ is best rewritten in the alternative form

$$\lambda_k(x) = A_k(x - x_k) + B_k(x_{k+1} - x), \qquad A_k, B_k \text{ are arbitrary constants} \qquad \textbf{(10b)}$$

Putting (10) in S0, we get for $k = 0, 1, \ldots, n-1$,

$$y_k = \frac{\sigma_k}{6}h_k^2 + B_k h_k \qquad \text{and} \qquad y_{k+1} = \frac{\sigma_{k+1}}{6}h_k^2 + A_k h_k \qquad \textbf{(11)}$$

Finally, solving this for A_k and B_k and substituting in (10) gives

$$q_k(x) = \frac{\sigma_k}{6}\left[\frac{(x_{k+1}-x)^3}{h_k} - h_k(x_{k+1}-x)\right] + \frac{\sigma_{k+1}}{6}\left[\frac{(x-x_k)^3}{h_k} - h_k(x-x_k)\right]$$
$$+ y_k\left[\frac{x_{k+1}-x}{h_k}\right] + y_{k+1}\left[\frac{x-x_k}{h_k}\right], \qquad k=0,1,\ldots,n-1 \tag{12}$$

This formula can be used to evaluate $s(x)$ [as $q_k(x)$] for $x_k \leqslant x \leqslant x_{k+1}$ *once we know the values of* σ_k *and* σ_{k+1}. Thus, to be able to use $s(x)$ to approximate $f(x)$ on $[x_0, x_n]$, we must find the second derivatives

$$\sigma_0, \quad \sigma_1, \quad \ldots, \quad \sigma_n \qquad (n+1 \text{ unknowns})$$

To this end we impose S1. Differentiating (12) gives

$$q_k'(x) = \frac{\sigma_k}{6}\left[\frac{-3(x_{k+1}-x)^2}{h_k} + h_k\right] + \frac{\sigma_{k+1}}{6}\left[\frac{3(x-x_k)^2}{h_k} - h_k\right] + \Delta y_k$$

where $\Delta y_k = (y_{k+1}-y_k)/h_k$. Hence for $k=0,1,\ldots,n-1$,

$$q_k'(x_k) = \frac{\sigma_k}{6}[-2h_k] + \frac{\sigma_{k+1}}{6}[-h_k] + \Delta y_k \tag{13a}$$

$$q_k'(x_{k+1}) = \frac{\sigma_k}{6}[h_k] + \frac{\sigma_{k+1}}{6}[2h_k] + \Delta y_k \tag{13b}$$

Replacing k by $k-1$ in (13b) to get $q_{k-1}'(x_k)$, and equating to (13a) gives

$$(E_k) \quad h_{k-1}\sigma_{k-1} + 2(h_{k-1}+h_k)\sigma_k + h_k\sigma_{k+1}$$
$$= 6[\Delta y_k - \Delta y_{k-1}], \qquad k=1,\ldots,n-1 \tag{14}$$

where $\Delta y_{k-1} = (y_k - y_{k-1})/h_{k-1}$. If the x_k's are equispaced, say $h_k = h$ for all k, then (14) simplifies to

$$(E_k) \quad \sigma_{k-1} + 4\sigma_k + \sigma_{k+1} = \frac{6}{h}[\Delta y_k - \Delta y_{k-1}], \qquad k=1,\ldots,n-1 \tag{15}$$

EXAMPLE. Find (E_1)–(E_3) for the five logarithmic knots

$$P_0(1, \ln 1), \quad P_1(2, \ln 2), \quad P_2(3, \ln 3), \quad P_3(4, \ln 4), \quad P_4(6, \ln 6)$$

Solution. Here $x_0 = 1$, $x_1 = 2$, $x_2 = 3$, $x_3 = 4$, and $x_4 = 6$, hence

$$h_0 = h_1 = h_2 = 1 \quad \text{and} \quad h_3 = 6-4=2$$

Since $n = 4$, the system (14) consists of the $n-1 = 3$ equations

$$(E_1) \quad 1\sigma_0 + 2(1+1)\sigma_1 + 1\sigma_2 = 6\left[\frac{\ln\left(\frac{3}{2}\right)}{1} - \frac{\ln\left(\frac{2}{1}\right)}{1}\right] = -1.72609$$

$$(E_2) \quad 1\sigma_1 + 2(1+1)\sigma_2 + 1\sigma_3 = 6\left[\frac{\ln\left(\frac{4}{3}\right)}{1} - \frac{\ln\left(\frac{3}{2}\right)}{1}\right] = -0.70670 \qquad \textbf{(16)}$$

$$(E_3) \quad 1\sigma_2 + 2(1+2)\sigma_3 + 2\sigma_4 = 6\left[\frac{\ln\left(\frac{6}{4}\right)}{2} - \frac{\ln\left(\frac{4}{3}\right)}{1}\right] = -0.50970$$

where we have used the identity $\ln a - \ln b = \ln(a/b)$.

As seen in the preceding example, the system (14) is *linear* in the $n+1$ unknowns $\sigma_0, \ldots, \sigma_n$. However, since it has only $n-1$ equations, it is underdetermined, and hence has infinitely many solutions (Section 3.4E). Table 6.4-1 summarizes four strategies for eliminating σ_0 from (E_1) and σ_n from (E_{n-1}), yielding an $(n-1) \times (n-1)$ *tridiagonal system* (see Section 3.4D) in the variables $\sigma_1, \sigma_2, \ldots, \sigma_{n-1}$.

TABLE 6.4-1   EQUATIONS FOR IMPLEMENTING FOUR ENDPOINTS STRATEGIES.

Strategy	Endpoint Condition	Equations for Eliminating σ_0 or σ_n
I	Specify the value of $s''(x)$ at the endpoint	$\sigma_0 = s''(x_0)$ $\sigma_n = s''(x_n)$
II	Assume that $s''(x)$ is *constant* near the endpoint	$\sigma_0 = \sigma_1$ $\sigma_n = \sigma_{n-1}$
III	Assume that $s''(x)$ is *linear* near the endpoint	$\sigma_0 = \dfrac{1}{h_1}\{(h_0 + h_1)\sigma_1 - h_0\sigma_2\}$ $\sigma_n = \dfrac{1}{h_{n-2}}\{-h_{n-1}\sigma_{n-2} + (h_{n-2} + h_{n-1})\sigma_{n-1}\}$
IV	Specify the value of $s'(x)$ at the endpoint	$\sigma_0 = \dfrac{3}{h_0}[\Delta y_0 - s'(x_0)] - \dfrac{1}{2}\sigma_1$ $\sigma_n = \dfrac{3}{h_{n-1}}[s'(x_n) - \Delta y_{n-1}] - \dfrac{1}{2}\sigma_{n-1}$

It is important to note that *it is not necessary to use the same strategy at both endpoints* as long as some strategy is used at each of x_0 and x_n.

In geometric terms, *strategy I imposes a desired concavity of $s(x)$ at x_0 or x_n; strategy II imposes quadratic behavior on $s(x)$ over the "double interval"* $[x_0, x_2]$ *or* $[x_{n-2}, x_n]$; *strategy III imposes the behavior of a single cubic on $s(x)$ over* $[x_0, x_2]$ *or* $[x_{n-2}, x_n]$; and *strategy IV imposes a desired slope of $s(x)$ at x_0 or x_n.* The strategy III equations are obtained by taking $k = 1$ and $k = n-2$ in (9) and using the identities

$$x_2 - x_0 = h_0 + h_1 \quad \text{and} \quad x_n - x_{n-2} = h_{n-2} + h_{n-1} \qquad \textbf{(17)}$$

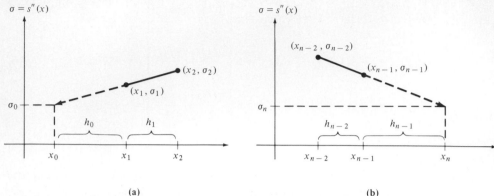

FIGURE 6.4-3 STRATEGY III: (a) AT x_0; (b) AT x_n.

(see Figure 6.4-3). The strategy IV equations are obtained by taking $k = 0$ in (13a) and $k = n - 1$ in (13b) (see Exercise 6-35).

If we use Table 6.4-1 to eliminate σ_0 from

$$(\mathrm{E}_1) \quad h_0\sigma_0 + 2(h_0 + h_1)\sigma_1 + h_1\sigma_2 = 6[\Delta y_1 - \Delta y_0]$$

[the first equation in (14)], then upon combining terms we get

$$
\begin{array}{lll}
(\mathrm{E}_1)_{\mathrm{I}} & 2(h_0 + h_1)\sigma_1 + h_1\sigma_2 & = 6[\Delta y_1 - \Delta y_0] - h_0 s''(x_0) \\[2mm]
(\mathrm{E}_1)_{\mathrm{II}} & (3h_0 + 2h_1)\sigma_1 + h_1\sigma_2 & = 6[\Delta y_1 - \Delta y_0] \\[2mm]
(\mathrm{E}_1)_{\mathrm{III}} & (h_0 + 2h_1)\sigma_1 + (h_1 - h_0)\sigma_2 & = \dfrac{6h_1}{h_0 + h_1}[\Delta y_1 - \Delta y_0] \\[3mm]
(\mathrm{E}_1)_{\mathrm{IV}} & \left(\dfrac{3}{2}h_0 + 2h_1\right)\sigma_1 + h_1\sigma_2 & = 3[2\Delta y_1 - 3\Delta y_0 + s'(x_0)]
\end{array}
\tag{18a}
$$

where the subscript on (E_1) corresponds to the endpoint strategy used to eliminate σ_0. Similarly, if we use Table 6.4-1 to eliminate σ_n from

$$(\mathrm{E}_{n-1}) \quad h_{n-2}\sigma_{n-2} + 2(h_{n-2} + h_{n-1})\sigma_{n-1} + h_{n-1}\sigma_n = 6[\Delta y_{n-1} - \Delta y_{n-2}]$$

[the last equation in (14)], then upon combining terms we get

$$
\begin{array}{ll}
(\mathrm{E}_{n-1})_{\mathrm{I}} & h_{n-2}\sigma_{n-2} + 2(h_{n-2} + h_{n-1})\sigma_{n-1} = 6[\Delta y_{n-1} - \Delta y_{n-2}] - h_{n-1} s''(x_n) \\[2mm]
(\mathrm{E}_{n-1})_{\mathrm{II}} & h_{n-2}\sigma_{n-2} + (2h_{n-2} + 3h_{n-1})\sigma_{n-1} = 6[\Delta y_{n-1} - \Delta y_{n-2}] \\[2mm]
(\mathrm{E}_{n-1})_{\mathrm{III}} & (h_{n-2} - h_{n-1})\sigma_{n-2} + (2h_{n-2} + h_{n-1})\sigma_{n-1} \\[2mm]
& \qquad\qquad\qquad = \dfrac{6h_{n-2}}{h_{n-2} + h_{n-1}}[\Delta y_{n-1} - \Delta y_{n-2}] \\[4mm]
(\mathrm{E}_{n-1})_{\mathrm{IV}} & h_{n-2}\sigma_{n-2} + \left(2h_{n-2} + \dfrac{3}{2}h_{n-1}\right)\sigma_{n-1} = 3[3\Delta y_{n-1} - 2\Delta y_{n-2} - s'(x_n)]
\end{array}
\tag{18b}
$$

Note that strategies I–IV affect *only* (E_1) and (E_{n-1}). *The "interior" equations* $(E_2)–(E_{n-2})$ *are always given by* (14).

EXAMPLE. Illustrate strategies I–IV for the five logarithmic knots

$$P_0(1, \ln 1), \quad P_1(2, \ln 2), \quad P_2(3, \ln 3), \quad P_3(4, \ln 4), \quad P_4(6, \ln 6)$$

Solution [*See* (16)]. At $x_0 = 1$, since $h_1 = h_2 = 1$, (18a) gives

$$
\begin{aligned}
(E_1)_I \quad & 2(1+1)\sigma_1 + 1\sigma_2 && = -1.72609 - 1s''(x_0) \\[6pt]
(E_1)_{II} \quad & (3 \cdot 1 + 2 \cdot 1)\sigma_1 + 1\sigma_2 && = -1.72609 \\[6pt]
(E_1)_{III} \quad & (1 + 2 \cdot 1)\sigma_1 + (1 - 1)\sigma_2 && = \frac{6 \cdot 1}{1+1}[-1.72609] \\[6pt]
(E_1)_{IV} \quad & \left(\frac{3}{2} \cdot 1 + 2 \cdot 1\right)\sigma_1 + 1\sigma_2 && = 3[2(0.40547) - 3(0.69315) + 1s'(x_0)]
\end{aligned}
\tag{19a}
$$

At $x_n = x_4 = 6$, since $h_{n-2} = h_2 = 1$ and $h_{n-1} = h_3 = 2$, (18b) gives

$$
\begin{aligned}
(E_3)_I \quad & 1\sigma_2 + 2(1+2)\sigma_3 && = -0.50970 - 2s''(x_4) \\[6pt]
(E_3)_{II} \quad & 1\sigma_2 + (2 \cdot 1 + 3 \cdot 2)\sigma_3 && = -0.50970 \\[6pt]
(E_3)_{III} \quad & (1 - 2)\sigma_2 + (2 \cdot 1 + 2)\sigma_3 && = \frac{6 \cdot 1}{(1+2)}[-0.50970] \\[6pt]
(E_3)_{IV} \quad & 1\sigma_2 + \left(2 \cdot 1 + \frac{3}{2} \cdot 2\right)\sigma_3 && = 3[2(0.20273) - 3(0.28768) - s'(x_4)]
\end{aligned}
\tag{19b}
$$

Whatever strategies are used at x_0 and x_4, the second (and only remaining) equation is given by (16), that is,

$$(E_2) \quad 1\sigma_1 + 2(1+1)\sigma_2 + 1\sigma_3 = 6[\Delta y_2 - \Delta y_1] = -0.70670 \tag{20}$$

With four choices for (E_1) in (18a) and another four for (E_{n-1}) in (18b), there are 16 possible endpoint strategy combinations, with further flexibility possible in specifying values of s'' of s' if strategy I or IV is used. So strategies I–IV offer considerable latitude in describing the endpoint behavior of $s(x)$.

6.4D FINDING $\sigma_0, \ldots, \sigma_n$

No matter which of the strategies (18) are used to eliminate σ_0 from (E_1) and σ_n from (E_{n-1}), the resulting equations can be written as

$$(E_k) \quad a_k\sigma_{k-1} + b_k\sigma_k + c_k\sigma_{k+1} = d_k, \qquad k = 1, 2, \ldots, n-1 \tag{21}$$

where $a_1 = 0$ [σ_0 is removed from (E_1)] and $c_{n-1} = 0$ [σ_n is removed from (E_{n-1})].

In matrix form, (21) is the $(n - 1) \times (n - 1)$ *tridiagonal* system

$$T\boldsymbol{\sigma} = \mathbf{d}, \qquad \text{where } \boldsymbol{\sigma} = [\sigma_1 \quad \sigma_2 \quad \cdots \quad \sigma_{n-1}]^T \text{ and } \quad T = \text{trid}(\mathbf{a}, \mathbf{b}, \mathbf{c}) \qquad \textbf{(22)}$$

[see (17a) of Section 3.4D]. Since $h_0, \ldots, h_{n-1}$ are positive, it follows from (14) and (18) that *the coefficient matrix T is diagonally dominant*; so (21) can always be solved uniquely for $\sigma_1, \ldots, \sigma_{n-1}$ using Gaussian elimination (Figure 3.4-2); Table 6.4-1 can then be used to get σ_0 and σ_n

EXAMPLE. Find $\sigma_0, \ldots, \sigma_4$ for the spline that fits

$$P_0(1, \ln 1), \quad P_1(2, \ln 2), \quad P_2(3, \ln 3), \quad P_3(4, \ln 4), \quad P_4(6, \ln 6) \qquad \textbf{(23)}$$

using strategy IV with $s'(1) = 1$ at $x_0 = 1$ and strategy III at $x_n = x_4 = 6$. Then use $s(3.7)$ to estimate $f(3.7) = \ln(3.7) \doteq 1.3083$.

Solution. From (19) and (20), the system $T\boldsymbol{\sigma} = \mathbf{d}$ that we must solve is

$$(\text{E}_1)_{\text{IV}} \quad \tfrac{7}{2}\sigma_1 + 1\sigma_2 \qquad\quad = 3[-1.26851 + 1] = -0.80553$$
$$(\text{E}_2) \quad\quad 1\sigma_1 + 4\sigma_2 + 1\sigma_3 = -0.70670$$
$$(\text{E}_3)_{\text{III}} \qquad\quad (-1)\sigma_2 + 4\sigma_3 = -0.16990$$

Using Gaussian elimination (Figure 3.4-2), we get (to $5d$)

$$[T : \mathbf{d}] \rightarrow \begin{bmatrix} \frac{7}{2} & 1 & 0 & : & -0.80553 \\ & \frac{26}{7} & 1 & : & -0.47655 \\ & & \frac{111}{26} & : & -0.29820 \end{bmatrix} \Rightarrow \begin{bmatrix} \sigma_1 \\ \sigma_2 \\ \sigma_3 \end{bmatrix} = \begin{bmatrix} -0.19887 \\ -0.10950 \\ -0.06985 \end{bmatrix} \qquad \textbf{(24a)}$$

To get σ_0 and σ_4, we use Table 6.4-1:

$$\sigma_0 = 3\left[\frac{0.69315 - 1}{1}\right] - \frac{1}{2}(-0.19887) = -0.82111$$
$$\sigma_4 = \frac{-2}{1}(-0.10950) + \frac{1 + 2}{1}(-0.06985) = 0.00945 \qquad \textbf{(24b)}$$

Having found $\sigma_0, \ldots, \sigma_4$, we can now interpolate $\ln z$ on $[x_0, x_n] = [1, 6]$. In particular, since $z = 3.7$ satisfies

$$x_2 = 3 < z = 3.7 < 4 = x_3$$

we can use formula (12) with $k = 2$ to approximate $\ln(3.7)$ as

$$s(z) = q_2(z) = \frac{\sigma_2}{6}\left[\frac{(x_3 - z)^3}{h_2} - h_2(x_3 - z)\right] + \frac{\sigma_3}{6}\left[\frac{(z - x_2)^3}{h_2} - h_2(z - x_2)\right]$$

$$+ y_2\left[\frac{x_3 - z}{h_2}\right] + y_3\left[\frac{z - x_2}{h_2}\right] \qquad \textbf{(25)}$$

$$= \frac{-0.10950}{6}\left[\frac{(0.3)^3}{1} - 1(0.3)\right] + \frac{-0.06985}{6}\left[\frac{(0.7)^3}{1} - 1(0.7)\right]$$

$$+ \ln 3\left[\frac{0.3}{1}\right] + \ln 4\left[\frac{0.7}{1}\right]$$

$$= 1.3091 \qquad (\text{Error} = 1.3083 - 1.3091 = -0.0008)$$

Notice that although the exact value $f'(1) = 1/1$ was used for $s'(1)$ in $(E_1)_{IV}$, the values of $\sigma_k = s''(x_k)$ agree with the exact values $f''(x_k) = -1/x_k^2$ to at most $2s$; and σ_4 actually has the wrong sign $[f''(6) = -1/36]$. Nevertheless, for $z = 3.7$ (near the middle of the interpolating interval $[1, 6]$), $s(z)$ approximated $f(z) = \ln z$ to almost $4s$.

6.4E SELECTING ENDPOINT STRATEGIES

Strategy I is frequently used with $\sigma_0 = \sigma_n = 0$. These so-called *free boundary conditions* result in a $y = s(x)$ curve having the shape that would be assumed by a flexible rod (such as draftsman's spline) if it were bent around pegs at the knots but allowed to maintain its natural (straight line) shape outside $[x_0, x_n]$. This $s(x)$ is therefore referred to as a **natural spline.** A free boundary condition should only be used if it is known that the curve $y = f(x)$ approaches a straight line (i.e., flattens) or has an inflection point as x approaches the endpoint.

There are situations (e.g., beam problems in civil engineering) where $s'(x_0)$ or $s'(x_n)$ are known. When these *clamped boundary conditions* are given, strategy IV should be used.

At endpoints where neither $s'(x)$ or $s''(x)$ is known, strategy II or III should be used. If the $y = f(x)$ curve appears to have an inflection point near the endpoint, strategy III (cubic behavior) is recommended; otherwise, use strategy II (quadratic behavior). This would have avoided the incorrect sign of σ_4 (at the right endpoint) in the example in Section 6.4D.

6.4F SUMMARY: ALGORITHM FOR PIECEWISE CUBIC
SPLINE INTERPOLATION

Once endpoint strategies have been selected at x_0 and x_n, proceed as in Figure 6.4-4.

As with polynomial interpolation, one should try to avoid approximating $f(z)$ for z outside $[x_0, x_n]$. If this must be done when $s(x)$ is available, one should use

$$f(z) \approx q_0(z) \quad \text{for } z < x_0 \qquad \text{and} \qquad f(z) \approx q_{n-1}(z) \quad \text{for } z > x_n \qquad (26)$$

with the understanding that $s(x)$ may not behave like $f(x)$ outside $[x_0, x_n]$.

If several values of $s(z)$ are needed [e.g., to make a table of approximate $f(z)$ values], or if derivatives or integrals of $s(x)$ are to be used to approximate those of $f(x)$, then it is worthwhile to make the substitution

$$x_{k+1} - z = (x_{k+1} - x_k) - (z - x_k) = h_k - (z - x_k) \qquad (27)$$

in $q_k(z)$ and then collect powers of $(z - x_k)$ to get

$$\boxed{q_k(z) = y_k + c_{1,k}(z - x_k) + c_{2,k}(z - x_k)^2 + c_{3,k}(z - x_k)^3} \qquad (28a)$$

Algorithm: SPLINE (Interpolation Using a Piecewise Cubic Spline)

Purpose: To evaluate $s(z)$, where s is the interpolating cubic spline for $n + 1$ given knots $P_0(x_0, y_0), \ldots, P_n(x_n, y_n)$ that satisfies specified endpoint conditions (at x_0 and x_n), and z is a specified point between x_0 and x_n.

GET n, **x**, **y**, $\{\mathbf{x} = [x_0 \quad x_1 \quad \cdots \quad x_n]$ and $\mathbf{y} = [y_0 \quad y_1 \quad \cdots \quad y_n]\}$
   z,   {point at which interpolated valued is desired}
   parameters {if needed} for endpoint conditions
DO FOR $k = 0$ TO $n - 1$
   $h_k \leftarrow x_{k+1} - x_k$

{*form* $[T : \mathbf{d}]$} Use (14) to form $(E_2), \ldots, (E_{n-2})$, (18a) to form (E_1), and (18b) to form (E_{n-1}) for the tridiagonal system $T\boldsymbol{\sigma} = \mathbf{d}$ in (22).
OUTPUT $([T : \mathbf{d}])$

{*get $\boldsymbol{\sigma}$'s*} Use Gaussian Elimination (see Figure 3.4-2) to solve $T\boldsymbol{\sigma} = \mathbf{d}$ for σ_1, $\sigma_2, \ldots, \sigma_{n-1}$; then use Table 6.4-1 to get σ_0 and σ_n.
OUTPUT $(\sigma_0, \sigma_1, \ldots, \sigma_n)$

{*interpolate*}
Find k such that $x_k \leqslant z < x_{k+1}$

$$Sof Z \leftarrow \frac{\sigma_k}{6}\left[\frac{(x_{k+1} - z)^3}{h_k} - h_k(x_{k+1} - z)\right] + \frac{\sigma_{k+1}}{6}\left[\frac{(z - x_k)^3}{h_k} - h_k(z - x_k)\right]$$
$$+ y_k\left(\frac{x_{k+1} - z}{h_k}\right) + y_{k+1}\left(\frac{z - x_k}{h_k}\right)$$

OUTPUT (The interpolated value $s(z)$ is $Sof Z$)

FIGURE 6.4-4 PSEUDOPROGRAM FOR ALGORITHM SPLINE.

where

$$c_{1,k} = \Delta y_k - \frac{h_k}{6}(\sigma_{k+1} + 2\sigma_k), \quad c_{2,k} = \frac{\sigma_k}{2}, \quad \text{and} \quad c_{3,k} = \frac{\sigma_{k+1} - \sigma_k}{6h_k} \tag{28b}$$

For example, the $k = 2$ values of the example in Section 6.4D, namely

$$h_2 = 1, \quad \Delta y_2 = \frac{\ln\left(\frac{4}{3}\right)}{1} = 0.28768, \quad \sigma_2 = -0.10950, \quad \sigma_3 = -0.06985$$

[see (24a)] could be used in (28b) to obtain

$$c_{1,2} = 0.28768 - \frac{1}{6}[-0.06985 + 2(-0.10950)] \doteq 0.33582$$

$$c_{2,2} = \frac{1}{2}(-0.10950) = -0.05475 \qquad\qquad (29)$$

$$c_{3,2} = \frac{-0.06985 - (-0.10950)}{6 \cdot 1} = 0.00661$$

from which (28a) (in nested form) with $z - x_k = 3.7 - 3.0 = 0.7$ gives

$$q_2(3.7) = \{[c_{3,2}(0.7) + c_{2,2}](0.7) + c_{1,2}\}(0.7) + \ln 3 = 1.3091 \qquad (30)$$

in agreement with the value obtained in (25).

6.4G POLYNOMIAL VERSUS CUBIC SPLINE INTERPOLATION

For hand calculation of an approximation of $f(z)$, polynomial interpolation as described in Section 6.3A [i.e., finding best mth interpolants $\hat{p}_0(z)$, $\hat{p}_1(z)$, . . . until the $\delta_m(z)$'s stop decreasing] is the preferred method. A computer program that does this is a bit easier to use than one for cubic spline interpolation because there is no need to select endpoint strategies.

If a single smooth curve is to interpolate a large number of knots (say $n > 6$), cubic splines are preferable because they are not as prone to "wiggle" between knots. Consequently, of the two approximations

$$f'(z) \approx \hat{p}'_m(z) \qquad \text{and} \qquad f'(z) \approx s'(z) \qquad\qquad (31)$$

the latter is generally more accurate and, if (28) is used, easy to obtain. Similarly, once the $c_{i,k}$'s in (28) are found, the approximation

$$\int_a^b f(x)\, dx \approx \int_a^b s(x)\, dx \qquad \text{for } x_0 \le a < b \le x_n \qquad (32)$$

can be used to obtain accurate results easily (see Exercise 6-34).

However, since $s''(x)$ is only piecewise linear, it cannot be expected to be very accurate no matter what endpoint strategies are used. If a second- or higher-order derivative is needed, the best general strategy is to *fit* (rather than interpolate) a suitable curve as in Section 5.2 or Section 5.3 and then use its derivatives to approximate those of f.

For a more extensive discussion of spline approximations, see [10].

Exercises

Section 6.1

6-1. For the cubic knots $P_0(0, 0)$, $P_1(1, 1)$, $P_2(2, 8)$, $P_3(3, 27)$, find $p_{1,3}(x)$ two ways:
   (a) Use the method undetermined coefficients (Section 6.1A).
   (b) Use the Lagrange form of $p_{1,3}(x)$ (Section 6.1C).

6-2. For the knots $P_0(-2, -15)$, $P_1(-1, -2)$, $P_2(0, 1)$, $P_3(2, 1)$, $P_4(3, 10)$ find the Lagrange form (do not simplify) of

    (a) $p_{2,3}(x)$ **(b)** $p_{2,4}(x)$ **(c)** $p_{1,4}(x)$ **(d)** $p_{0,4}(x)$

6-3. For the knots $P_0(-3, 1)$, $P_1(0, 9)$, $P_2(2, 1)$, $P_3(3, 1)$, $P_4(5, 81)$, find the Lagrange form (do not simplify) of

    (a) $p_{1,2}(x)$ **(b)** $p_{0,2}(x)$ **(c)** $p_{0,3}(x)$ **(d)** $p_{0,4}(x)$

6-4. Let $L_0(x), \ldots, L_4(x)$ denote the Lagrange polynomials for $P_0, \ldots, P_4$.

    (a) For $P_0, \ldots, P_4$ of Exercise 6-2, use the "selecting property" (6) of Section 6.1C to evaluate *by inspection*

$$\text{(i) } L_2(3) \quad \text{(ii) } L_2(0) \quad \text{(iii) } L_3(3) \quad \text{(iv) } L_3(2) \quad \text{(v) } L_2(2)$$

    (b) Repeat part (a) for $P_0, \ldots, P_4$ of Exercise 6-3.

6-5. Let $x_0, x_1, \ldots, x_n$ denote any $n + 1$ distinct nodes. Use the uniqueness of $p_{0,n}(x)$ to show that their Lagrange polynomials $L_0(x), \ldots, L_n(x)$ must satisfy

    (a) $L_0(x) + L_1(x) + \cdots + L_n(x) \equiv 1$ (constant) for all x.

    (b) $x_0 L_0(x) + x_1 L_1(x) + \cdots + x_n L_n(x) = x$ for all x.

You do *not* have to write out the $L_j(x)$'s. Consider $f(x) = 1$ in part (a) and $f(x) = x$ in part (b).

Section 6.2

6-6. What (if anything) can you conclude about the knots P_2, P_3, P_4, P_5 if $\Delta^3 y_2 = 0$? If $\Delta^2 y_3 = 0$?

6-7. Consider the knots $P_0(-3, 1)$, $P_1(-1, 9)$, $P_2(0, 1)$, $P_3(3, 1)$, $P_4(5, -39)$.

    (a) Form a DD table for $P_0, \ldots, P_4$ and use it in (b)–(d).

    (b) What are the values of $\Delta^1 y_3$, $\Delta^3 y_1$, $\Delta^4 y_0$, $\Delta^2 y_1$, and $\Delta^2 y_2$?

    (c) Find (in the order given): $p_{1,2}(x)$, $p_{1,3}(x)$, $p_{0,3}(x)$, $p_{0,4}(x)$.

    (d) Find (in the order given): $p_{2,3}(x)$, $p_{1,3}(x)$, $p_{1,4}(x)$, $p_{0,4}(x)$.

6-8. Complete the following DD table up to the Δ^3 column.

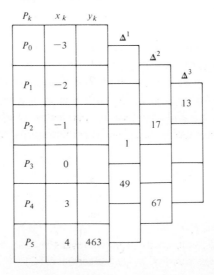

P_k	x_k	y_k	Δ^1	Δ^2	Δ^3
P_0	-3				
P_1	-2				13
P_2	-1			17	
P_3	0		1		
P_4	3		49	67	
P_5	4	463			

6-9. For the DD table shown, form [without simplifying, as in (17) in Section 6.2D] $p_{0,5}(x)$ by adding nodes in the following orders:

(a) $x_0, x_1, x_2, x_3, x_4, x_5$ [forward: use only (12a) of Section 6.2B]

(b) $x_5, x_4, x_3, x_2, x_1, x_0$ [backward: use only (12b) of Section 6.2B]

(c) $x_2, x_1, x_3, x_4, x_5, x_0$

(d) $x_3, x_2, x_1, x_4, x_0, x_5$

Circle the leading coefficients used (see Figure 6.2-6).

Knot	Node	y	Δ	Δ^2	Δ^3	Δ^4	Δ^5
P_0	-2	21					
			-14				
				4			
P_1	-1	7			-1		
			-6			0	
				1			1
P_2	0	1			-1		
			-4			5	
				-2			
P_3	1	-3			19		
			-8				
				55			
P_4	2	-11					
			102				
P_5	3	91					

6-10. For (a)–(d) of Exercise 6-9, form $p_{0,5}(x)$ in nested form, and use it to evaluate $p_{0,5}(-3)$. [See (20) of Section 6.2D.]

6-11. By inspection of the DD table in Exercise 6-9, find the leading coefficient of $p_{1,3}(x)$, $p_{2,5}(x)$, and $p_{0,4}(x)$.

6-12. Form a DD table for the six knots

$$P_0(-3, 200), \quad P_1(-2, 46), \quad P_2(-1, 6), \quad P_3(0, 2), \quad P_4(2, 30), \quad P_5(3, 146)$$

and use it to determine the degree of $p_{0,5}(x)$.

6-13. For $P_0, \ldots, P_5$ of Exercise 6-12, find $p_{0,5}(x)$ as indicated in (a)–(d) of Exercise 6-9. Use any nested form to evaluate $p_{0,5}(1)$.

6-14. Make a forward difference table for the knots used in Exercise 6-9 (see Figure 6.2-12). Verify that $\Delta^m y_k = h^m m! \, \Delta^m y_k$ for $\Delta^3 y_0$, $\Delta^4 y_1$, and $\Delta^2 y_2$.

6-15. (a) Show that the entries of a forward difference table with h-spaced nodes can be used to get the forward recursive formula

$$p_{k,k+m}(x) = p_{k,k+m-1}(x) + \frac{\Delta^m y_k}{m! h^m}(x - x_k)(x - x_{k+1}) \cdots (x - x_{k+m-1})$$

(b) Deduce the **Newton forward difference formula** for $m \geqslant 1$:

$$p_{k,k+m}(x) = y_k + \frac{\Delta y_k}{1! h}(x - x_k) + \frac{\Delta^2 y_k}{2! h^2}(x - x_k)(x - x_k - h)$$

$$+ \cdots + \frac{\Delta^m y_k}{m! h^m} \prod_{j=0}^{m-1}(x - x_k - jh)$$

(c) Conjecture a *backward* difference formula for $p_{k,k+m}(x)$.

6-16. Make a forward difference table for the following data:

$$P_0(1, 263), \quad P_1(1.5, 230), \quad P_2(2, 200), \quad P_3(2.5, 174), \quad P_4(3, 150)$$

Use it to find the Newton forward difference formula for $p_{0,4}(x)$.

Section 6.3

6-17. Using the $5s$ DD Table of Figure 6.3-2, set up a "Worksheet Table" as in Figure 6.3-3 for getting $\hat{p}_0(z), \ldots, \hat{p}_5(z)$ when z is
(a) 0.1   (b) 0.75.
NOTE: When z is the midpoint of $[x_k, x_{k+1}]$, take either y_k or y_{k+1} as $\hat{p}_0(z)$.

6-18. Using the $5s$ DD Table of Figure 6.3-2, estimate $\Phi(-0.5) \doteq 0.3085$ two ways:
(a) Extrapolate: Find $\hat{p}_m(-0.5)$, $m = 0, 1, \ldots, 5$.
(b) Use the fact that $\Phi(-z) = 1 - \Phi(z)$.
Which of parts (a) and (b) is more accurate? Did you expect this? Was the most accurate $\hat{p}_m(z)$ in part (a) the one with for which $\delta_m(z)$ is smallest? Can you suggest a "rule of thumb" for which $\hat{p}_m(z)$ to use when $\delta_m(z)$ stops shrinking substantially as m is increased?

6-19. Estimate (a) $\Phi(0.52)$, (b) $\Phi(0.22)$, and (c) $\Phi(1.4)$ using the DD table in Figure 6.3-4; compare your accuracy with that obtained in Table 6.3-2.

6-20. In (a)–(c), use a $7d$ DD table based on the $6d$ values of $\sinh x = \frac{1}{2}(e^x - e^{-x})$ shown in the accompanying table.

x	$\sinh x$
0.2	0.201336
0.4	0.410752
0.6	0.636654
0.8	0.888106
1.0	1.175201

(a) With $z = 0.55$, find the best interpolants $\hat{p}_0(z)$, $\hat{p}_1(z)$, $\hat{p}_2(z)$, $\ldots$, stopping when either $\delta_m(z) = 0$ or $|\delta_{m+1}(z)| > |\delta_m(z)|$.
(b) Repeat part (a) with $z = 0.86$.
(c) Repeat part (a) with $z = 1.3$ (extrapolation).
(d) Discuss the accuracy of the approximations $\sinh z \approx \hat{p}_m(z)$ obtained in (a)–(c). Did you expect some to be more accurate than others? Explain.

6-21. Replace the values of $\sinh x$ given in Exercise 6-20 by those of $\ln x$ (to $6s$). Then do (a)–(d) of Exercise 6-20.

6-22. Consider the five logarithmic knots

$$P_0(\tfrac{1}{2}, \ln \tfrac{1}{2}), \quad P_1(1, 0), \quad P_2(2, \ln 2), \quad P_3(5, \ln 5), \quad P_4(10, \ln 10)$$

(a) Let $z = 7$. Make a table for $\hat{p}_0(z)$, $\hat{p}_1(z)$, $\ldots$, $\hat{p}_4(z)$ as in Table 6.3-2. Is $\hat{p}_4(z)$ the most accurate approximation of $\ln z$? Could you have guessed the most accurate $\hat{p}_m(z)$ from the $\delta_m(z)$ values? Explain the causes of inaccuracy.
(b) Sketch the graphs of $p_{2,4}(x)$ and $p_{0,4}(x)$. How do these graphs help explain your results in part (a)?

6-23. Repeat parts (a) and (b) of Exercise 6-22 but for the knots

$$P_0(0, 0), \quad P_1(1, 1), \quad P_2(4, 2), \quad P_3(9, 3), \quad P_4(16, 4)$$

on the curve $y = \sqrt{x}$, and with $z = 13$ replacing $z = 7$.

6-24. (a) Find the five Chebyshev nodes $\hat{x}_0, \ldots, \hat{x}_4$ for $[0, 16]$.

(b) Make a DD table for $P_0(\hat{x}_0, \sqrt{\hat{x}_0}), \ldots, P_4(\hat{x}_4, \sqrt{\hat{x}_4})$ and use it to get $\hat{p}_0(13), \ldots, \hat{p}_4(13)$ to approximate $\sqrt{13}$ as in Table 6.3-2. Compare the accuracy to that obtained in Exercise 6-23(a).

6-25. (a) Find the four Chebyshev nodes $\hat{x}_0, \ldots, \hat{x}_3$ for $[\frac{1}{2}, 10]$.

(b) Make a DD table for $P_0(\hat{x}_0, \ln \hat{x}_0), \ldots, P_3(\hat{x}_3, \ln \hat{x}_3)$ and use it to get $\hat{p}_0(7), \ldots, \hat{p}_3(7)$ to approximate $\ln 7$ as in Table 6.3-2. Compare the accuracy to that obtained in Exercise 6-22(a).

6-26. Suppose that ϵ_k, the error of y_k, is zero except at x_3 where $\epsilon_3 = \epsilon \neq 0$. Make a forward difference table for $(x_0, \epsilon_0), \ldots, (x_5, \epsilon_5)$ to show how the error in y_3 propagates to higher differences. Can you explain why alternating signs in a column of a difference table indicate that roundoff error is dominating the entries?

6-27. Make a DD table (up to the Δ^3 column) for $P_1, \ldots, P_8$ of Exercise 5-13. Can you deduce that the data can be fit well by a quadratic? Explain.

6-28. Make as many DD table columns as you think are necessary to determine the degree of a polynomial that should fit the data of Exercise 5-14 well. Justify your choice of degree.

Section 6.4

6-29. Four cubic splines are to be passed through the points

$$P_0(-2, -8), \quad P_1(0, 0), \quad P_2(1, 1), \quad P_3(2, 8)$$

on the curve $y = x^3$. The four sets of endpoint conditions are

(I) Strategy I with $s''(-2) = -12$, $s''(2) = +12$ [exactly $d^2(x^3)/dx^2$]

(II) Strategy II at both endpoints

(III) Strategy III at both endpoints

(IV) Strategy IV with $s'(-2) = 12 = s'(2)$ [exactly $d(x^3)/dx$]

(a) Which of (I)–(IV) will result in $s(x) = x^3$ on $[-2, 2]$? Explain.

(b) Set up the equations in σ_1 and σ_2 imposed by each of (I)–(IV).

(c) Solve the four systems in part (b) and get $\sigma_0, \ldots, \sigma_3$ for each of (I)–(IV). For which of (I)–(IV) is σ_k exactly $d^2(x^3)/dx^2$ at x_k, $k = 0, 1, 2, 3$?

6-30. Consider the following five knots on the curve $y = \sqrt{x}$:

$$P_0(0, 0), \quad P_1(1, 1), \quad P_2(4, 2), \quad P_3(9, 3), \quad P_4(16, 4)$$

(a) Find $\sigma_0, \ldots, \sigma_4$ for the interpolating cubic spline $s(x)$ with the "natural" endpoint conditions $s''(0) = s''(16) = 0$.

(b) Use your answer to part (a) to approximate $\sqrt{z}$ by $s(z)$ when $z = \frac{1}{2}$ and $z = 13$. Discuss the accuracy obtained and compare with Exercise 6-23 for $z = 13$.

6-31. Repeat parts (a) and (b) of Exercise 6-30, but impose the endpoint slopes $s'(0) = 20$, $s'(16) = \frac{1}{8}$.

6-32. Repeat parts (a) and (b) of Exercise 6-30, but impose strategy III at $x_0 = 0$ and strategy II at $x_4 = 16$.

6-33. Express the indicated $q_k(x)$ as $y_k + c_{1,k}(x - x_k) + c_{2,k}(x - x_k)^2 + c_{3,k}(x - x_k)^3$ [see (28) of Section 6.4F].

(a) $q_1(x)$ $(0 \leqslant x \leqslant 1)$ for $s(x)$ in (I) of Exercise 6-29.

(b) $q_0(x)$ $(-2 \leqslant x \leqslant 0)$ for $s(x)$ in (III) of Exercise 6-29.

(c) $q_2(x)$ $(4 \leqslant x \leqslant 9)$ for $s(x)$ in Exercise 6-30(a).

(d) $q_3(x)$ $(9 \leqslant x \leqslant 16)$ for $s(x)$ in Exercise 6-32(a).

6-34. Suppose that $s(x) = q_k(x)$ for $x_k \leqslant x \leqslant x_{k+1}$, where

$$q_k(x) = y_k + c_{1,k}(x - x_k) + c_{2,k}(x - x_k)^2 + c_{3,k}(x - x_k)^3$$

as in (28) of Section 6.4F for $k = 0, 1, \ldots, n - 1$. Derive formulas involving x_k, y_k, $c_{i,k}$, z, a, and b for

(a) $s'(z)$ if $x_0 \leqslant z \leqslant x_n$ (b) $\int_a^b f(x)\, dx$ if $x_0 \leqslant a < b \leqslant x_n$

6-35. Use Figure 6.4-3 to obtain the strategy III equations of Table 6.4-1.

Computer and Programming Exercises

6-36. Write a FUNCTION subprogram LAGR(n, **x**, **y**, k, m, z) that uses the n ($n \leqslant 7$) components of **x** and **y** to form the Lagrange form of $p_{k,k+m}(z)$ (Figure 6.1-4) and return it as LAGR. Test it by evaluating $p_{2,3}(-1)$, $p_{1,4}(1)$, and $p_{1,4}(2)$ for the data of Exercise 6-2.

6-37. Write a subroutine DDTABL(n, **x**, **y**, *DD*) that forms a DD table in the upper-triangular part of the $n \times n$ matrix *DD* where $n \leqslant 7$ (Figure 6.2-4). Test it using the data in the example in Section 6.3A.

6-38. Write a FUNCTION subprogram NEWTON(n, **x**, **y**, k, m, *DD*, z) that uses the matrix *DD* formed by DDTABL in Exercise 6-37 to find $p_{k,k+m}(z)$ using only the forward recursive form (12a) of Section 6.2B and return it as NEWTON. Test it as in Exercise 6-36.

6-39. Write a subroutine SPLINE (n, **x**, **y**, C) that forms a $3 \times n$ matrix C ($n \leqslant 100$) as in (29) of Section 6.4F. (NOTE: This requires first finding $\sigma_0, \ldots, \sigma_n$ as in Figure 6.4-4. If done in FORTRAN, use TRIDAG of Figure 3.4-3.) Test it using the example in Section 6.4D.

6-40. Write a FUNCTION subprogram S(n, **x**, **y**, C, z) that uses the matrix C of Exercise 6-39 to return $s(z)$ as S using (28) of Section 6.4F. Test it by obtaining $s(3.7) = q_2(3.7)$ in (31) of Section 6.4F.

6-41. Use any spline program available to interpolate the knots given in Figure 5.3-1. Get enough values to plot the spline. Does $s(x)$ look more like the generating curve in Figure 5.3-2?

7

Numerical Methods for Differentiation and Integration

Introduction **7.0**

Although we have used calculus techniques to help obtain some of the numerical methods considered so far, the problems themselves (namely, *solving equations, fitting curves,* and *interpolating*) were *algebraic* in that *they could be posed without the idea of a limit.* For such problems, efficient, practical procedures could be obtained by considering only the effects of *roundoff error.*

We now turn our attention to numerical procedures for approximating the two fundamental quantities of calculus, namely *the derivative of f at x,* defined as the limit

$$f'(x) = \lim_{h \to 0} \frac{\Delta f(x)}{h}, \qquad \text{where } \frac{\Delta f(x)}{h} = \frac{f(x+h) - f(x)}{h} \tag{1}$$

that is, $\Delta f(x)/h$ is the **difference quotient of f at x,** and the *definite integral of f over* [a, b], given by the limit

$$\int_a^b f(x) \, dx = \lim_{h \to 0} R[h], \qquad \text{where } R[h] = \sum_{k=1}^{n} f(x_{k-1}) h \tag{2}$$

that is, $R[h]$ is the **left-endpoint Riemann sum** for n subintervals of equal length $h = (b - a)/n$ (see Appendix II.4A).

The need for accurate derivative estimates arises when dealing with tabulated data and in the solution of differential equations. Methods for approximating derivatives are given in Sections 7.1 and 7.2.

The need for accurate estimates of $\int_a^b f(x) \, dx$ arises when the integrand turns out to be either a function such as

$$f(x) = e^{-x^2} \quad \text{or} \quad f(x) = \frac{\sin x}{x} \tag{3}$$

which has no antiderivative expressible in terms of elementary functions, or one whose value is known only at certain tabulated values of x. Methods for approximating *proper integrals* are given in Sections 7.3 and 7.4. Strategies are then given for approximating *improper integrals* (Section 7.5) and *double integrals* (Section 7.6).

A formula due to Richardson can be used to produce an improved estimate from two known estimates. This important formula is described in Section 7.1D; it is applied to the approximations of derivatives and integrals in this chapter, and to the solution of differential equations in Chapter 8.

7.1   Formulas for $f'(x)$; Richardson's Formula

In order to discuss the truncation error of formulas for derivatives and integrals, we shall need the important terminology and notation described next.

7.1A "BIG O" NOTATION FOR DESCRIBING TRUNCATION ERRORS

Both $f'(x)$ and $\int_a^b f(x)\,dx$ are special cases of numerical quantities Q which are defined or can be expressed as

$$Q = \lim_{h \to 0} F[h], \qquad \text{where } F[h] \text{ is an approximating formula} \tag{1a}$$

In the absence of roundoff error, the value of such a Q can be obtained to any desired accuracy using the approximation

$$Q \approx F[h], \qquad \text{where } h \text{ is sufficiently small (but not zero)} \tag{1b}$$

The error of primary interest for this approximation is

$$\boxed{\tau[h] = Q - F[h] = \text{the \textbf{truncation error} of approximating } Q \text{ by } F[h]} \tag{1c}$$

Thus *the truncation error is the error inherent in the approximation formula $F[h]$ itself* in the absence of roundoff error.

In assessing the desirability of $F[h]$ as an approximating formula for Q, it is important to know the rate at which $\tau[h]$ shrinks as $h \to 0$. This is done by finding the leading terms of the Maclaurin series for $\tau[h]$, specifically by expressing $\tau[h]$ as

$$\tau[h] = Ch^n + Dh^m + \cdots \qquad \text{where } n < m \tag{2}$$

When this holds, $F[h]$ is called an *n*th **order** approximating formula for Q.

To illustrate, suppose that we wanted to approximate the exact value of a function f at a point $x + h$ near the (fixed) point x. The obvious approximation is the nth Taylor polynomial $P_n(x + h)$, which satisfies

$$\underbrace{f(x + h)}_{Q} = \underbrace{f(x) + f'(x)h + \frac{f''(x)}{2!} h^2 + \cdots + \frac{f^{(n)}(x)}{n!} h^n}_{F[h] = P_n(x + h)} + \underbrace{R_n(x + h)}_{\tau[h]} \qquad \textbf{(3a)}$$

In this case the truncation error for the approximation $f(x + h) \approx P_n(x + h)$ (obtained by truncating the Taylor series after the h^n term) is the nth remainder, that is,

$$\tau[h] = R_n(x + h) = \frac{f^{(n+1)}(x)}{(n + 1)!} h^{n+1} + \frac{f^{(n+2)}(x)}{(n + 2)!} h^{n+2} + \cdots \qquad \textbf{(3b)}$$

Since $f^{(n+1)}(x)$ is constant (x is fixed), $P_n(x + h)$ is often referred to as the **$(n + 1)$st order Taylor approximation** of $f(x + h)$.

When the approximation $Q \approx F[h]$ is nth order, that is, when Ch^n is the leading term of the Maclaurin series for $\tau[h]$, we shall write

$$\boxed{\tau[h] = O(h^n) \qquad \text{or} \qquad Q = F[h] + O(h^n)} \qquad \textbf{(4a)}$$

One should read "$O(h^n)$" as "a quantity that gets small like Ch^n." This is because when (2) holds,

$$\tau[h] = Ch^n \{1 + (D/C)h^{m-n} + \text{higher-order terms}\}$$

and

$$\{1 + (D/C)h^{m-n} + \cdots\} \to 1 \qquad \text{as } h \to 0.$$

So, when $C \neq 0$,

$$\tau[h] = O(h^n) \quad \Rightarrow \quad \tau[h] \approx Ch^n \qquad \text{when } h \approx 0 \qquad \textbf{(4b)}$$

We illustrate with some nth Taylor approximations (see Table 5.4-1):

$$e^h = 1 + h + \frac{h^2}{2} + \frac{h^3}{6} + O(h^4), \qquad \text{that is, } \tau[h] = R_3(0 + h) = O(h^4)$$

$$\sin h = h - \frac{h^3}{6} + O(h^5), \qquad \text{that is, } \tau[h] = R_4(0 + h) = O(h^5) \qquad \textbf{(5)}$$

$$\sqrt{1 + h} = 1 + \frac{h}{2} + O(h^2), \qquad \text{that is, } \tau[h] = R_1(1 + h) = O(h^2)$$

Also, we shall often describe (2) by simply writing

$$\tau[h] = Ch^n + O(h^m) \qquad \text{or} \qquad Q = F[h] + Ch^n + O(h^m) \qquad \textbf{(6)}$$

To illustrate the significance of the order of an approximation, let us see how the accuracy of $F[h]$ improves when we replace h by h/r, where $r > 1$. If $\tau[h] \approx Ch^n$, then $\tau[h/r] \approx Ch^n/r^n$ for small h. Thus

$$\boxed{F[h] \text{ is } O(h^n) \;\Rightarrow\; \tau\left[\frac{1}{r}h\right] \approx \left(\frac{1}{r}\right)^n \tau[h] \quad \text{for small } h} \qquad (7)$$

Hence, if $F[h]$ is $O(h^n)$ and, for a particular h, $F[h]$ approximates Q to about $2d$ (i.e., $|\tau[h]| \approx \frac{1}{2}10^{-2}$), then replacing h by $h/10$ results in

$$Q - F\left[\frac{h}{10}\right] = \tau\left[\frac{1}{10}h\right] \approx \left(\frac{1}{10}\right)^n \tau[h] \approx \frac{1}{2}\cdot 10^{-(n+2)} \qquad (8)$$

So $F[h/10]$ will be accurate to about $3d$ if $n = 1$; $4d$ if $n = 2$; $6d$ if $n = 4$; and so on. Thus *the larger the order n, the faster F[h] will approach Q as h $\to$ 0.*

EXAMPLE. Verify that the approximation $\sin h \approx h - \dfrac{h^3}{3!}$ is $O(h^5)$.

Solution. Starting with $h = 0.4$, the result of halving h twice is shown in Table 7.1-1.

TABLE 7.1-1 VERIFICATION THAT $h - h^3/3!$ IS AN $O(h^5)$ APPROXIMATION OF $\sin h$.

h	$Q = \sin h$	$F[h] = h - \dfrac{h^3}{6}$	$\tau[h] = Q - F[h]$	$\dfrac{\tau[\frac{1}{2}h]}{\tau[h]}$
0.4	0.38941834	0.38933333	0.8501E−4	$\dfrac{\tau[0.2]}{\tau[0.4]} \approx \dfrac{1}{32}$
0.2	0.19866933	0.19866667	0.2664E−5	
0.1	0.09983341	0.09983333	0.8331E−7	$\dfrac{\tau[0.1]}{\tau[0.2]} \approx \dfrac{1}{32}$

From the last column, $\tau[\frac{1}{2}h] \approx (\frac{1}{2})^5\tau[h]$, indicating that $\tau[h] = O(h^5)$.

The more rapid shrinking of $\tau[h]$ for larger n is shown graphically in Figure 7.1-1. If two approximations are both $O(h^n)$, the one with the smaller **convergence constant** C will be more accurate for given h. It is possible that for a *particular h*, a higher-order truncation error can be larger than a lower-order one; however, as h is decreased, the higher-order truncation error will eventually get (and then stay) smaller than the lower-order one (see Exercise 7-2).

The effect of multiplying, adding, and scaling truncation errors $\tau_1[h]$ and $\tau_2[h]$ is described concisely as follows (see Exercise 7-3):

If $\tau_1[h] = O(h^m)$ and $\tau_2[h] = O(h^n)$, and r and s are nonzero scalars, then

$$\tau_1[h]\tau_2[h] = O(h^{m+n}); \text{ in particular } h^m \tau_2[h] = O(h^{m+n}) \qquad \textbf{(9a)}$$

$$r\tau_1[h] + s\tau_2[h] = O(h^{\text{smaller of } m,n}) \qquad \textbf{(9b)}$$

$$\tau_1[rh] \text{ is } O(h^m) \text{ (although its } C \text{ is } r^m \text{ times that of } \tau_1[h]) \qquad \textbf{(9c)}$$

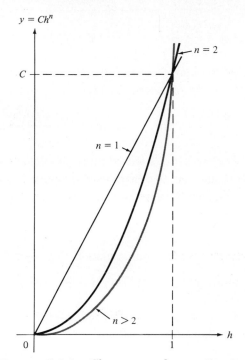

FIGURE 7.1-1 Ch^n VERSUS h FOR $C > 0$.

7.1B   USING $\Delta f(x)/h$ TO APPROXIMATE $f'(x)$

The derivative of f at the point x (held fixed) is the limit as $h \to 0$ of

$$\boxed{\frac{\Delta f(x)}{h} = \frac{f(x+h) - f(x)}{h} = \text{the \textbf{difference quotient} of } f \text{ at } x} \qquad \textbf{(10a)}$$

We wish to use (2) to determine the order of the approximation

$$\boxed{f'(x) \approx \frac{\Delta f(x)}{h}, \qquad \text{where } h \approx 0} \qquad \textbf{(10b)}$$

To get the Maclaurin expansion of its truncation error, we begin with

$$f(x+h) = f(x) + \frac{f'(x)}{1!} h + \frac{f''(x)}{2!} h^2 + \frac{f'''(x)}{3!} h^3 + \frac{f^{(iv)}(x)}{4!} h^4 + \cdots \qquad \textbf{(11)}$$

Subtracting $f(x)$ and then dividing by h gives the desired expansion:

$$f'(x) = \frac{f(x+h) - f(x)}{h} - \frac{f''(x)}{2}h - \frac{f'''(x)}{6}h^2 - \frac{f^{(iv)}(x)}{24}h^3 + \cdots \qquad (12)$$

$$\underbrace{\qquad}_{Q} \quad \underbrace{F[h] = \frac{\Delta f(x)}{h}}_{} \qquad \underbrace{\tau[h] = f'(x) - \frac{\Delta f(x)}{h}}_{}$$

It follows that *the approximation* $f'(x) \approx \Delta f(x)/h$ *is exact* (i.e., *equality*) *when* $f(x)$ *is linear* (in which case $f'' \equiv 0$); otherwise, by (4),

$$f'(x) = \frac{\Delta f(x)}{h} + \tau[h], \qquad \text{where } \tau[h] \approx \frac{-f''(x)}{2}h = O(h) \qquad (13)$$

The approximation of $f'(x)$ by $\Delta f(x)/h$ will be called the $O(h)$ **forward difference approximation** of $f'(x)$ if $h > 0$, and the $O(h)$ **backward difference approximation** if $h < 0$. If it happens that $f''(x) = 0$, then the approximation becomes $O(h^2)$ [see (12) and Exercise 7-4].

EXAMPLE. Discuss the error of the approximation $f'(x) \approx \Delta f(x)/h$ when

$$f(x) = e^x \quad \text{and} \quad x = 1 \qquad [\text{Exact } f'(x) = f''(x) = e^1 \doteq 2.718282]$$

Solution. The results for $h = \pm 0.2$, ± 0.02, and ± 0.0002 are shown in Table 7.1-2. The underlined digits of the $\Delta f(x)/h$ column are those that would be in error *after* rounding. The *actual* error $\epsilon[h]$ is the combined effect of truncation and roundoff error. The last two columns shows that for $0.002 \leq |h| \leq 0.2$, the truncation error estimate in (13) can be used to estimate the actual error, that is,

$$-\tfrac{1}{2}f''(x)h = -\tfrac{1}{2}eh \approx \tau[h] \approx \epsilon[h]$$

Also, dividing h by 10 produces about one more accurate decimal place (i.e., $\tau[h/10] \approx \tau[h]/10$), confirming that $\Delta f(x)/h$ is an $O(h)$ approximation $f'(x)$, (i.e., $n = 1$).

TABLE 7.1-2   USING $F[h] = \Delta f(x)/h$ TO APPROXIMATE $d(e^x)/dx = e^x$ WHEN $x = 1$.

h	Approximation $F[h]$ $\dfrac{\Delta f(x)}{h} = \dfrac{e^{1+h} - e^1}{h}$	Actual Error $\epsilon[h] = e^1 - \dfrac{\Delta f(x)}{h}$	Approximate Truncation Error $-\tfrac{1}{2}eh \approx \tau[h]$
0.2	3.009175	−0.290893	−0.271828
0.02	2.745650	−0.027368	−0.027183
0.002	2.721000	−0.002718	−0.002718
−0.002	2.715500	0.002782	0.002718
−0.02	2.691300	0.026982	0.027183
−0.2	2.463705	0.254577	0.271828

7.1C ROUNDOFF VERSUS TRUNCATION ERROR: THE STEPSIZE DILEMMA

Unfortunately, the improved accuracy of $\Delta f(x)/h$ with decreasing h does *not* continue indefinitely. Indeed, if we continue to reduce h to $h/10$ and use $7s$ arithmetic (as we did in Table 7.1-2), we get the results shown in Table 7.1-3. Clearly, the truncation error estimate $-\frac{1}{2}f''(x)h$ has ceased to approximate $\epsilon[h]$. The reason is simple: The *actual error $\epsilon[h]$ is dominated by roundoff error rather than truncation error.* What is happening is that when $h \approx 0$, there is loss of significance in $\Delta f(x, = e^{1+h} - e^1$, which gets magnified when divided by h. *This effect gets worse as h gets smaller.* When $h = 0.0000002$, $1 + h \doteq 1$ (to $7s$); hence $\Delta f(x) \doteq 0$, giving the absurd estimate in the last row of Table 7.1-3.

TABLE 7.1-3 USING 7S ARITHMETIC TO CALCULATE $\Delta f(x)/h$ FOR SMALL h

		Actual Error	Approximate Truncation Error
h	$\dfrac{\Delta f(x)}{h} = \dfrac{e^{1+h} - e^1}{h}$	$\epsilon[h] = e^1 - \dfrac{\Delta f(x)}{h}$	$-\frac{1}{2}eh \approx \tau[h]$
0.0002	2.7200	-0.01718	$-2.7\text{E}{-4}$
0.00002	2.7000	$+0.01828$	$-2.7\text{E}{-5}$
0.000002	2.5000	$+0.21828$	$-2.7\text{E}{-6}$
0.0000002	0.0000 !!!	$+2.7183$	$-2.7\text{E}{-7}$

This phenomenon occurs any time we try to approximate the behavior of f at (or near) a fixed x using only the values of f at $x + \Delta x$, where Δx is a multiple of a small stepsize h. In such a situation

$$\epsilon[h] = \tau[h] + \rho[h] \tag{14}$$

$$\underbrace{\quad}_{\text{actual error}} \quad \underbrace{\quad}_{\text{truncation error}} \quad \underbrace{\quad}_{\text{roundoff error}}$$

where $\tau[h] = O(h^n)$, whereas $\rho[h]$ tends to grow as $h \to 0$ (see Figure 7.1-2). As a result, there will be an $h_{\tau=\rho}$ for which $\tau[h] = \rho[h]$, with $\rho[h]$ being the dominant term in (14) for $h < h_{\tau=\rho}$.

The problem of finding a stepsize h small enough so that $\tau[h]$ is small yet large enough so that $\rho[h]$ does not dominate the error (i.e., $h \approx h_{\tau=\rho}$) will be referred to as **the Stepsize Dilemma.**

It may turn out that $E_{\min}$ of Figure 7.1-2 is unacceptably large. For example, Tables 7.1-2 and 7.1-3 show that *when $f(x) = e^x$ and $x = 1$ and $7s$ arithmetic is used, the $O(h)$ approximation $\Delta f(x)/h$ is incapable of approximating $f'(x)$ to $6s$;* in fact, for the h values shown, the best accuracy achieved was only $3s$! Figure 7.1-2 suggests two ways to reduce the size of $E_{\min}$ when it is not sufficiently small.

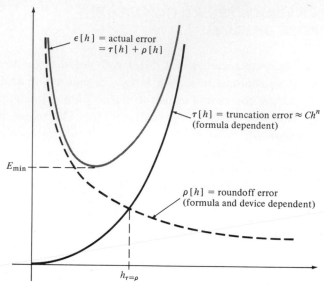

FIGURE 7.1-2   ACTUAL ERROR = TRUNCATION ERROR + ROUNDOFF ERROR.

Remedy 1. *Use a higher-order formula (i.e., increase n). This will reduce E_{min} by lowering the $\tau[h]$ curve for small h.*

Remedy 2. *Use a higher-precision arithmetic. This will reduce E_{min} by moving the $\rho[h]$ curve down and to the left.*

Both of these remedies have a serious shortcoming: *They require repeating the calculation.* And remedy 2 may require a different digital device as well.

If the order of the approximation (i.e., n) is known, then it may not be necessary to use either remedy 1 or remedy 2. Instead, *one can get improved approximations from the available $O(h^n)$ approximations themselves* in much the same way that the Aitken formula of Section 2.3B was used to accelerate linear convergence; this important technique is described next.

7.1D   RICHARDSON'S IMPROVEMENT FORMULA

Consider again the general approximation of Q by an $O(h^n)$ formula $F[h]$. Suppose that we know in fact that the truncation error is of the form

$$\tau[h] = Ch^n + O(h^m), \qquad \text{where } C \neq 0 \text{ and } m > n \tag{15a}$$

so that

$$Q = F[h] + Ch^n + O(h^m) \tag{15b}$$

If we use the approximation formula F with a particular h and also with a larger h and we let r denote the ratio

$$r = \frac{h_{\text{larger}}}{h}, \qquad \text{so that } h_{\text{larger}} = rh, \quad \text{where } r > 1 \qquad (16)$$

then $\tau[h_{\text{larger}}] = \tau[rh] = C(rh)^n + O((rh)^m) = Cr^n h^n + O(h^m)$ [by (9c)]. So

$$Q = F[h_{\text{larger}}] + Cr^n h^n + O(h^m) \qquad (17)$$

Subtracting (17) from $r^n \cdot$ (15b) to eliminate the h^n term gives

$$r^n Q - Q = r^n F[h] - F[h_{\text{larger}}] + O(h^m) \qquad (18)$$

[see (9b)]. Finally, dividing by $r^n - 1$ gives the desired result.†

Richardson's Improvement Formula Suppose that $F[h]$ is an $O(h^n)$ approximation of Q and we use it to get two approximations $F[h]$ and $F[h_{\text{larger}}]$. Then an improved approximation of Q is given by the formula

$$F_1[h] = \frac{r^n F[h] - F[h_{\text{larger}}]}{r^n - 1}, \qquad \text{where } r = \frac{h_{\text{larger}}}{h} \qquad (19a)$$

If it is known that $\tau[h] = Ch^n + O(h^m)$, then $F_1[h]$ is mth order, that is,

$$Q - F_1[h] = Dh^m + (\text{higher-order terms}) = O(h^m) \qquad (19b)$$

In this case we can use (19a) to get still higher-order approximations,

$$F_2[h] = \frac{r^m F_1[h] - F_1[h_{\text{larger}}]}{r^m - 1}, \qquad \text{where again } r = \frac{h_{\text{larger}}}{h} \qquad (19c)$$

The Richardson formula (19a) shows how to form a weighted sum of two $O(h^n)$ approximations to get a higher-order (and presumably more accurate) approximation. In (19a), n depends only on the approximating formula F[h], whereas r depends only on the two stepsizes used.

Note that (19a) can be used whenever we know n, even if we do not know m. For example, suppose that $F[h]$ is an $O(h^3)$ approximation of Q and we know that $F[0.2]$ and $F[0.8]$. Then (19a), with $r = (0.8)/(0.2) = 4$, $h = 0.2$, and $n = 3$, gives the improved (at least fourth-order) approximation

$$Q \approx F_1[0.2] = \frac{4^3 F[0.2] - F[0.8]}{4^3 - 1} = \frac{64 F[0.2] - F[0.8]}{63}$$

---

† The use of (19) is also referred to as **Richardson extrapolation** or the **deferred approach to the limit**.

7.1E   USING RICHARDSON'S FORMULA TO REMEDY THE STEPSIZE DILEMMA

Let us take $Q = f'(x)$ and $F[h] = \Delta f(x)/h$. We know from (12) that

$$f'(x) = \underbrace{\frac{\Delta f(x)}{h}}_{F[h]} + \underbrace{Ch + Dh^2 + Eh^3 + \cdots}_{\tau[h]} \qquad \text{so that } \tau[h] = Ch^1 + O(h^2) \qquad \text{(20)}$$

$$\underbrace{}_{Q}$$

So Richardson's formula applies with $n = 1$ and $m = 2$. For the values

$$F[0.2] = 3.009175, \qquad F[0.02] = 2.745650, \qquad F[0.002] = 2.721000 \qquad \text{(21)}$$

obtained in Table 7.1-2, $h_{\text{larger}} = 10h$, that is, $r = 10$; and by (20), $n = 1$ and $m = 2$. So the improved approximations (19a) and (19c) of $f'(x)$ are

$$F_1[h] = \frac{10^1 F[h] - F[10h]}{9} \qquad \text{and} \qquad F_2[h] = \frac{10^2 F_1[h] - F_1[10h]}{99} \qquad \text{(22)}$$

Using the values (21) in these formulas yields the **Richardson table** shown in Table 7.1-4. As before, underlined digits are those that would be in error after rounding. [Recall that $Q = f'(x) = e^1 \doteq 2.718282$.] Typical calculations of $F_1[h]$ and $F_2[h]$ are

$$F_1[0.002] = \frac{10(2.721) - 2.74565}{9} \qquad \text{and} \qquad F_2[0.002] = \frac{100(2.718261) - 2.716369}{99}$$

TABLE 7.1-4   RICHARDSON TABLE FOR IMPROVING $F[h] = \Delta f(x)/h$.

h	$F[h] = \Delta f(x)/h$ $\{\tau[h] = O(h)\}$	$F_1[h]$ in (22) $\{\tau[h] = O(h^2)\}$	$F_2[h]$ in (22) $\{\tau[h] = O(h^3)\}$
$r = 10 \begin{cases} 0.2 \\ \\ 0.02 \end{cases}$	3.0<u>09175</u> 2.7<u>45650</u>	2.716369	
$r = 10 \begin{cases} 0.002 \end{cases}$	2.72<u>1000</u>	2.718261	2.71828<u>0</u>

Notice that although $F[0.002]$ was only accurate to 3s, $F_2[0.002]$ is accurate to 6s! Notice, too, that since $F_1[0.002]$ and $F_2[0.002]$ agree to about 6s, *we could have deduced that $F_2[0.002]$ approximates $f'(x)$ to 6s even if we did not know the exact value of $f'(x)$.* This shows how easily Richardson improvement can be used to get a desired accuracy (in this case 6s), and why *it should be tried before either remedy 1 or 2 of* Section 7.1C.

7.1F   THE $O(h^2)$ CENTRAL DIFFERENCE APPROXIMATION $f'(x) \approx \delta f(x)/2h$

Subtracting

$$f(x-h) = f(x) - f'(x)h + \frac{f''(x)}{2!}h^2 - \frac{f'''(x)}{3!}h^3 + \cdots + \frac{f^{(vi)}(x)}{6!}h^6 + \cdots \quad \text{(23a)}$$

from

$$f(x+h) = f(x) + f'(x)h + \frac{f''(x)}{2!}h^2 + \frac{f'''(x)}{3!}h^3 + \cdots + \frac{f^{(vi)}(x)}{6!}h^6 + \cdots \quad \text{(23b)}$$

cancels the even powers of h and gives

$$f'(x) = \underbrace{\frac{f(x+h) - f(x-h)}{2h}} - \underbrace{\frac{f'''(x)}{6}h^2 - \frac{f^{(v)}(x)}{120}h^4 - \frac{f^{(vii)}(x)}{5040}h^6 - \cdots} \quad \text{(24)}$$

$$\underbrace{}_{Q} \quad \underbrace{F[h] = \frac{\delta f(x)}{2h}} \qquad \qquad \underbrace{\tau[h] = f'(x) - \frac{\delta f(x)}{2h}}$$

So if we define

$$\boxed{\frac{\delta f(x)}{2h} = \frac{f(x+h) - f(x-h)}{2h}, \qquad \text{the \textbf{central difference quotient} of } f \text{ at } x} \quad \text{(25)}$$

then the **central difference approximation** $f'(x) \approx \delta f(x)/(2h)$ is $O(h^2)$, that is,

$$\boxed{f'(x) = \frac{\delta f(x)}{2h} + \tau[h], \qquad \text{where } \tau[h] \approx \frac{-f'''(x)}{6}h^2 = O(h^2)} \quad \text{(26)}$$

Note that the value of $\delta f(x)/(2h)$ is not changed when h is replaced by $-h$.

We see from (24) that $\delta f(x)/(2h)$ *approximates* $f'(x)$ *exactly (i.e.,* $\tau[h] = 0$) *when* $f(x)$ *is quadratic.* That $\delta f(x)/(2h)$ generally approximates $f'(x)$ more accurately than $\Delta f(x)/h$ is evident geometrically (Figure 7.1-3).

For a quantitative comparison of the $O(h)$ formula $\Delta f(x)/h$ and the $O(h^2)$ formula $\delta f(x)/(2h)$, compare Tables 7.1-1 and 7.1-2 to Table 7.1-5, where we continue to use $7s$ arithmetic. The last two columns of Table 7.1-5 indicate that roundoff error has a slight effect when $h = 0.002$, and rapidly becomes bigger than $\tau[h]$ for $h < 0.002$. However, *as long as truncation error dominates* (here $h \geqslant 0.002$), *the central difference approximation* $\delta f(x)/(2h)$ *is more accurate than* $\Delta f(x)/h$ *for a given h and satisfies*

$$\epsilon\left[\frac{h}{10}\right] \approx \frac{1}{100}\epsilon[h] \quad \text{(27)}$$

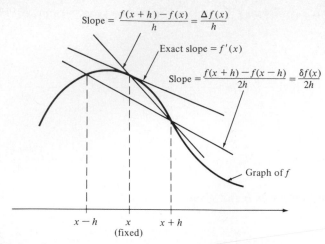

Slope $= \dfrac{f(x+h)-f(x)}{h} = \dfrac{\Delta f(x)}{h}$

Exact slope $= f'(x)$

Slope $= \dfrac{f(x+h)-f(x-h)}{2h} = \dfrac{\delta f(x)}{2h}$

Graph of f

$x-h \qquad x \qquad x+h$
(fixed)

FIGURE 7.1-3 **GEOMETRIC INTERPRETATION OF** $\Delta f(x)/h$ **AND** $\delta f(x)/(2h)$.

TABLE 7.1-5 **USING** $7s$ **ARITHMETIC TO APPROXIMATE** $f'(x) = e^1$ **BY** $\delta f(x)/(2h)$.

h	$\dfrac{\delta f(x)}{2h} = \dfrac{e^{1+h}-e^{1-h}}{2h}$	$\epsilon[h] = f'(x) - \dfrac{\delta f(x)}{2h}$	$\dfrac{-1}{6}eh^2 \approx \tau[h]$
0.2	2.736440	-0.018158	$-1.8\text{E}{-2}$
0.02	2.718475	-0.000193	$-1.8\text{E}{-4}$
0.002	2.718250	-0.000032	$-1.8\text{E}{-6}$
0.0002	2.720000	-0.001718	$-1.8\text{E}{-8}$
0.00002	2.725000	-0.006718	$-1.8\text{E}{-10}$
0.000002	2.750000	-0.031718	$-1.8\text{E}{-12}$
0.0000002	0.000000	2.718282	$-1.8\text{E}{-14}$

7.1G DESIRABLE STEPSIZES FOR RICHARDSON'S FORMULA

In view of (24), the central difference approximation satisfies

$$f'(x) = \underbrace{\frac{\delta f(x)}{2h}}_{\substack{Q \quad F[h]}} + \underbrace{Ch^2 + Dh^4 + O(h^6)}_{\tau[h]} \qquad (n=2 \text{ and } m=4) \qquad \textbf{(28)}$$

Taking $r = 10$ in (19a) and (19c) for this approximation, we get

$$F_1[h] = \frac{10^2 F[h] - F[10h]}{99} \quad \text{and} \quad F_2[h] = \frac{10^4 F_1[h] - F_1[10h]}{9999} \qquad \textbf{(29)}$$

Using (29) with the $h = 0.2$, $h = 0.02$, and $h = 0.002$ values of $F[h]$ of Table 7.1-5 gives the Richardson table shown in Table 7.1-6.

TABLE 7.1-6   RICHARDSON TABLE FOR IMPROVING $F[h] = \delta f(x)/(2h)$.

h	$F[h] = \delta f(x)/2h$ $\{\tau[h] = O(h^2)\}$	$F_1[h]$ in (29) $\{\tau[h] = O(h^4)\}$	$F_2[h]$ in (29) $\{\tau[h] = O(h^6)\}$
$r = 10 \left\{ \begin{array}{c} 0.2 \\ 0.02 \end{array} \right.$	2.736440		
	2.718475	2.718294	
$r = 10 \left\{ \begin{array}{c} \\ 0.002 \end{array} \right.$	2.718250	2.718248	2.718248

Notice that $F_1[0.02] = 2.71894$ is more accurate than both $F_1[0.002]$ and $F_2[0.002]$! This is because $F[0.002]$ had the slight roundoff error noted at the end of Section 7.1E, and since both formulas in (29) weight the erroneous $h = 0.002$ value much more than the $10h = 0.02$ value, *the error simply propagated!* The importance of the following remark should now be evident:

Richardson's formula works best when the smallest h value used is near but larger than $h_{\tau=\rho}$ of Figure 7.1-2. The accuracy deteriorates when h values get smaller than $h_{\tau=\rho}$.

If it is expected that Richardson improvement may be used on the results of a higher-order formula (say $n \geq 2$), then, if possible, r should be taken smaller than 10 (say $r = 4$ or $r = 2$) to make it easier to discern when roundoff error is beginning to dominate the error of $F[h]$. This will be done from now on.

Approximation Formulas for kth Derivatives   7.2

7.2A   THE $O(h)$ APPROXIMATION $f^{(k)}(x) \approx \Delta^k f(x)/h^k$

Consider the Taylor expansion

$$f(x + h) = f(x) + f'(x)h + \frac{f''(x)}{2}h^2 + \frac{f'''(x)}{6}h^3 + \frac{f^{(iv)}(x)}{24}h^4 + \cdots \tag{1}$$

Replacing h by $2h$ gives

$$f(x + 2h) = f(x) + 2f'(x)h + 2f''(x)h^2 + \frac{4f'''(x)}{3}h^3 + \frac{2f^{(iv)}(x)}{3}h^4 + \cdots \tag{2}$$

To eliminate the $f'(x)h$ terms, we form $2*(1) - (2)$:

$$2f(x + h) - f(x + 2h) = f(x) - f''(x)h^2 - f'''(x)h^3 + \frac{7}{12}f^{(iv)}(x)h^4 + \cdots \tag{3}$$

Upon solving this for $f''(x)$, we see that

$$f''(x) = \frac{f(x) - 2f(x+h) + f(x+2h)}{h^2} - f'''(x)h + \frac{7}{12}f^{(iv)}(x)h^2 + \cdots \qquad (4)$$

If we denote $f(x) - 2f(x+h) + f(x+2h)$ by $\Delta^2 f(x)$, then (4) implies that

$$f''(x) \approx \frac{\Delta^2 f(x)}{h^2} = \frac{f(x) - 2f(x+h) + f(x+2h)}{h^2}, \qquad \tau[h] \approx -f'''(x)h = O(h) \qquad (5)$$

We shall call the three-point formula $\Delta^2 f(x)/h^2$ **the $O(h)$ forward difference approxima-tion** of $f''(x)$ if $h > 0$, and **the $O(h)$ backward difference approximation** of $f''(x)$ if $h < 0$. It can be seen from (4) that $\Delta^2 f(x)/h^2$ *is exact for quadratics* (which satisfy $f''' \equiv 0$).

To see why $\Delta^2 f(x)/h^2$ should only be an $O(h)$ approximation of $f''(x) = df'(x)/dx$, note that it can be obtained by replacing $d\{\cdot\}/dx$ by $\Delta\{\cdot\}/h$ thus:

$$f''(x) \approx \frac{\Delta f'(x)}{h} = \frac{f'(x+h) - f'(x)}{h}$$

$$\approx \frac{\dfrac{f(x+2h) - f(x+h)}{h} - \dfrac{f(x+h) - f(x)}{h}}{h} = \frac{\Delta^2 f(x)}{h^2} \qquad (6)$$

Similarly, one can get an $O(h)$ approximation of $f'''(x) = df''(x)/dx$:

$$f'''(x) \approx \frac{\Delta f''(x)}{h} = \frac{f''(x+h) - f''(x)}{h} \approx \frac{1}{h}\left[\frac{\Delta^2 f(x+h)}{h^2} - \frac{\Delta^2 f(x)}{h^2}\right]$$

This last expression is denoted by $\Delta^3 f(x)/h^3$. Replacing the $\Delta^2\{\cdot\}/h^2$ terms by (5) gives the four-point formula

$$f'''(x) \approx \frac{\Delta^3 f(x)}{h^3} = \frac{-f(x) + 3f(x+h) - 3f(x+2h) + f(x+3h)}{h^3}, \qquad \tau[h] = O(h) \qquad (7)$$

Continuing inductively, starting with $\Delta^0 f(x) = f(x)$, we get for any $k \geq 1$:

$$f^{(k)}(x) \approx \frac{\Delta^k f(x)}{h^k} = \frac{1}{h}\left[\frac{\Delta^{k-1} f(x+h)}{h^{k-1}} - \frac{\Delta^{k-1} f(x)}{h^{k-1}}\right], \qquad \tau[h] = O(h) \qquad (8)$$

Formula (8) is called **the $O(h)$ forward** or **backward difference approximation of** $f^{(k)}(x)$ according as $h > 0$ or $h < 0$. *It is exact whenever $f(x)$ is a polynomial of degree $\leq k$* [see (25) of Section 6.2E].

It is not necessary to memorize the coefficients of

$$f(x+h), \quad f(x+2h), \ldots, \quad f(x+kh)$$

in the $(k+1)$-term expansion of $\Delta^k f(x)/h^k$. Instead, one can simply read them from the kth row of Pascal's triangle (Figure 6.2-11), remembering to alternate signs so that the coefficient of $f(x + kh)$ is $+1$. For example, the $O(h)$ approximation of $f^{(v)}(x)$ is

$$\frac{\Delta^5 f(x)}{h^5} = \frac{-f(x) + 5f(x + h) - 10f(x + 2h) + 10f(x + 3h) - 5f(x + 4h) + f(x + 5h)}{h^5} \quad (9)$$

EXAMPLE. With $f(x) = e^x$, $x = 1$, and $h = \pm 0.1$, find
(a) the $O(h)$ forward difference approximation of $f''(x)$.
(b) the $O(h)$ backward difference approximation of $f^{(v)}(x)$.

Solution
a.

$$f''(1) \approx \frac{1}{(0.1)^2} \{e^{1.0} - 2e^{1.1} + e^{1.2}\} \doteq 3.0067 \quad (10)$$

b.

$$f^{(v)}(1) \approx \frac{1}{(-0.1)^5} \{-e^{1.0} + 5e^{0.9} - 10e^{0.8} + 10e^{0.7} - 5e^{0.6} + e^{0.5}\} \doteq 2.1214 \quad (11)$$

Since $f''(1) = f^{(v)}(1) = e^1 \doteq 2.7183$, we see that *for a given h, the $O(h)$ approximation $f^{(k)}(x) \approx \Delta^k f(x)/h^k$ generally becomes less accurate as k increases.* Greater accuracy can be achieved by using Richardson's formula (with $n = 1$) to get improved $O(h^2)$ approximations

$$f^{(k)}(x) \approx F_1[h] = \frac{rF[h] - F[rh]}{r - 1}, \quad \text{where } F[h] = \frac{\Delta^k f(x)}{h^k} \text{ and } r > 1 \quad (12)$$

Alternatively, the higher-order formulas described next can be used directly.

7.2B HIGHER-ORDER FORMULAS FOR $f^{(k)}(x)$

We begin with $f'(x)$. Taking $F[h]$ to be the $O(h)$ approximation $\Delta f(x)/h$ and $r = 2$ in (12) gives the $O(h^2)$ approximation

$$f'(x) \approx F_1[h] = \frac{2F[h] - F[2h]}{2 - 1} = 2\frac{f(x + h) - f(x)}{h} - \frac{f(x + 2h) - f(x)}{2h}$$

Simplifying gives the three-point forward/backward difference formula

$$f'(x) \approx \frac{1}{2h}[-3f(x) + 4f(x + h) - f(x + 2h)], \quad \tau[h] = O(h^2) \quad (13)$$

Similarly, applying Richardson's formulas with $r = 2$ to the $O(h^2)$ approximation $F[h] = \delta f(x)/2h$ gives the $O(h^4)$ approximation

$$f'(x) \approx F_1[h] = \frac{2^2 F[h] - F[2h]}{2^2 - 1} = \frac{1}{3}\left[4\frac{f(x + h) - f(x - h)}{2h} - \frac{f(x + 2h) - f(x - 2h)}{4h}\right]$$

Simplifying gives the four-point central difference formula

$$f'(x) \approx \frac{1}{12h} [f(x-2h) - 8f(x-h) + 8f(x+h) - f(x+2h)], \qquad \tau[h] = O(h^4) \quad (14)$$

If we add the series for $f(x+h)$ and $f(x-h)$ [see (23) of Section 7.1F] to eliminate odd powers of h and then solve for $f''(x)$, we get the $O(h^2)$ **central difference formula**

$$f''(x) \approx \frac{\delta^2 f(x)}{h^2} = \frac{f(x-h) - 2f(x) + f(x+h)}{h^2}, \qquad \tau[h] = \frac{-h^2}{12} f^{(iv)}(x) + O(h^4) \quad (15)$$

Applying Richardson with $r=2$ to this important $O(h^2)$ formula gives

$$f''(x) \approx \frac{1}{12h^2} [-f(x-2h) + 16f(x-h) - 30f(x)$$

$$+ 16f(x+h) - f(x+2h)], \qquad \tau[h] = O(h^4) \tag{16}$$

Other higher-order formulas can be obtained by substituting $O(h)$ formulas (together with a suitable number of truncation error terms) in a Taylor approximation of $f(x+h)$. For example, to get an $O(h^3)$ approximation of $f'(x)$, we first substitute (4) for $f''(x)$ in the $O(h^4)$ Taylor approximation of $f(x+h)$:

$$f(x+h) = f(x) + hf'(x) + \frac{h^2}{2} \left[\frac{f(x) - 2f(x+h) + f(x+2h)}{h^2} - hf'''(x) + O(h^2) \right]$$

$$- \frac{h^3}{6} f'''(x) + O(h^4)$$

Combining like terms, substituting $\Delta^3 f(x)/h^3 + O(h)$ for $f'''(x)$, and solving for $f'(x)$ gives the four-point forward/backward difference formula

$$f'(x) \approx \frac{1}{6h} [-11f(x) + 18f(x+h) - 9f(x+2h) + 2f(x+3h)], \qquad \tau[h] = O(h^3) \quad (17)$$

The techniques described above can be used to get the $O(h^2)$ formulas in (18) and (19) and the $O(h^4)$ formulas in (20). Those in (18) are *forward* or *backward* difference formulas depending upon whether $h > 0$ or $h < 0$.

Note: In (18)–(20), $f_{\pm j}$ are abbreviations for $f(x \pm jh)$ so that

$$f_0 = f(x), \quad f_1 = f(x+h), \quad f_{-1} = f(x-h), \quad f_2 = f(x+2h), \cdots$$

$O(h^2)$ Forward/Backward Difference Formulas

$$f'(x) \approx \frac{1}{2h}\,[-3f_0 + 4f_1 - f_2] \tag{18a}$$

$$f''(x) \approx \frac{1}{h^2}\,[2f_0 - 5f_1 + 4f_2 - f_3] \tag{18b}$$

$$f'''(x) \approx \frac{1}{2h^3}\,[-5f_0 + 18f_1 - 24f_2 + 14f_3 - 3f_4] \tag{18c}$$

$$f^{(\mathrm{iv})}(x) \approx \frac{1}{h^4}\,[3f_0 - 14f_1 + 26f_2 - 24f_3 + 11f_4 - 2f_5] \tag{18d}$$

$O(h^2)$ Central Difference Formulas

$$f'(x) \approx \frac{1}{2h}\,[-f_{-1} + 0f_0 + f_1] = \frac{\delta f(x)}{2h} \tag{19a}$$

$$f''(x) \approx \frac{1}{h^2}\,[f_{-1} - 2f_0 + f_1] = \frac{\delta^2 f(x)}{h^2} \tag{19b}$$

$$f'''(x) \approx \frac{1}{2h^3}\,[-f_{-2} + 2f_{-1} + 0f_0 - 2f_1 + f_2] \tag{19c}$$

$$f^{(\mathrm{iv})}(x) \approx \frac{1}{h^4}\,[f_{-2} - 4f_{-1} + 6f_0 - 4f_1 + f_2] \tag{19d}$$

$O(h^4)$ Central Difference Formulas

$$f'(x) \approx \frac{1}{12h}\,[f_{-2} - 8f_{-1} + 0f_0 + 8f_1 - f_2] \tag{20a}$$

$$f''(x) \approx \frac{1}{12h^2}\,[-f_{-2} + 16f_{-1} - 30f_0 + 16f_1 - f_2] \tag{20b}$$

$$f'''(x) \approx \frac{1}{8h^3}\,[f_{-3} - 8f_{-2} + 13f_{-1} + 0f_0 - 13f_1 + 8f_2 - f_3] \tag{20c}$$

$$f^{(\mathrm{iv})}(x) \approx \frac{1}{6h^4}\,[-f_{-3} + 12f_{-2} - 39f_{-1} + 56f_0 - 39f_1 + 12f_2 - f_3] \tag{20d}$$

When forming a Richardson table when $F[h]$ is one of the formulas in (18)–(20), you should assume that *each improvement of* (18) *increases the order by* 1 [see the derivation of (13)], whereas *each improvement of* (19) *or* (20) *increases the order by* 2 [see the derivation of (15) and (16)].

EXAMPLE. Let $f(x) = e^x$. Get accurate estimates of $f''(1) = e^1 \doteq 2.718281$.

Solution. The $O(h^2)$ formula $\delta^2 f(x)/h^2$ [i.e., (19b)] with $h = 0.1$ gives

$$f''(1) \approx \frac{1}{(0.1)^2} [e^{0.9} - 2e^{1.0} + e^{1.1}] = 2.720548 \qquad (21)$$

The $3s$ accuracy of this three-point central difference formula compares quite favorably with the $1s$ accuracy obtained using a three-point forward difference formula with the same h in (10) above. Using $\delta^2 f(x)/h^2$ with $h = 0.05$ gives

$$f''(1) \approx \frac{1}{(0.05)^2} [e^{0.95} - 2e^{1.0} + e^{1.05}] = 2.718848 \qquad (22)$$

which is accurate to about $4s$. For still more accuracy, we can improve (22) using (21) and Richardson's formula with $r = (0.1)/(0.05) = 2$ and $n = 2$:

$$f''(1) \approx \frac{2^2(2.718848) - (2.720548)}{2^2 - 1} = 2.718281 \qquad (23)$$

This $O(h^4)$ approximation is accurate to all $7s$ shown! In view of (16), it could have been obtained directly using $h = 0.05$ in (20b).

Note: The $(n + 1)$-point formulas in (18)–(20) could have been obtained as

$$f^{(k)}(x) \approx p^{(k)}(x), \qquad k = 1, 2, 3, 4 \qquad (24)$$

where $p(x)$ is the interpolating polynomial for the $(n + 1)$ knots corresponding to the $(n + 1)$ sampled function values (see Exercise 7-20). Hence *the $(n + 1)$-point formulas (18)–(20) are exact for polynomials of degree $\leq n$.*

When the nodes x_i are equally spaced, the Polynomial Wiggle Problem of Section 5.3B is most pronounced near the endpoints of the interpolating interval. Consequently, when x is one of these endpoints, as it is in a forward/backward difference formula, the approximation (24) can be very inaccurate. *We therefore recommend the use of central difference formulas* (for which x is the midpoint of the interpolating interval) whenever it is possible to evaluate $f(x_i)$ as needed on both sides of x.

Warning: The Stepsize Dilemma (Section 7.1C) is also a factor with higher-order formulas. *Taking h too small may result in less accuracy!*

7.3   Introduction to Numerical Integration (Quadrature)

Our objective in this section is to show how to approximate definite integrals using formulas of the form

$$\int_a^b f(x) \, dx \approx w_0 f(x_0) + w_1 f(x_1) + \cdots + w_n f(x_n) = \sum_{k=0}^n w_k f(x_k) \qquad (1)$$

where the **sample points** $x_0, x_1, \ldots, x_n$ are (not necessarily equispaced) points in or near $[a, b]$. In words, *we wish to approximate the number $\int_a^b f(x)\, dx$ by a weighted sum of the values of the integrand at certain points x_k in or near the interval of integration.* Such a weighted sum is called an $(n + 1)$-**point quadrature formula**; it is a **closed formula** if both a and b are sample points, and an **open formula** if neither is.

The left endpoint Riemann sum $R[h]$ in (2) of Section 7.0 has a but not b as a sample point, and hence is neither open nor closed. Since $R[h]$ is only $O(h)$ (see Exercise 7-31), we see that the "obvious" strategy of taking equispaced sample points and uniform weights ($w_k = h$ for all k) is not very effective. The straightforward strategy given next is guaranteed to produce $(n + 1)$-point quadrature formulas that are at least $O(h^n)$.

7.3A   USING INTERPOLATING POLYNOMIALS TO OBTAIN QUADRATURE FORMULAS

Suppose that $n + 1$ sample points $x_0, \ldots, x_n$ have been selected for use in the quadrature formula (1). Let $p_{0,n}(x)$ be the unique interpolating polynomial for the $n + 1$ knots

$$P_0(x_0, f(x_0)), \quad P_1(x_1, f(x_1)), \quad \ldots, \quad P_n(x_n, f(x_n)) \tag{2}$$

The reasoning behind most quadrature formulas is this:

$$\text{If } f(x) \approx p_{0,n}(x) \text{ on } [a, b], \qquad \text{then} \int_a^b f(x)\, dx \approx \int_a^b p_{0,n}(x)\, dx \tag{3}$$

Note that the Polynomial Wiggle Problem (Section 5.3B), which causes problems when estimating derivatives [see (24) of Section 7.2B] is a less serious concern here because of the likelihood that the effects of successive wiggles will partly cancel each other (see Figure 7.3-1).

Sample weights that make (1) exact for polynomials of degree $\leq n$ are easily obtained from the Lagrange form of $p_{0,n}(x)$ [see (7) of Section 6.1C]. Indeed,

$$\int_a^b p_{0,n}(x)\, dx = \int_a^b \left[\sum_{k=0}^n f(x_k) L_k(x) \right] dx = \sum_{k=0}^n \left[\int_a^b L_k(x)\, dx \right] f(x_k) \tag{4}$$

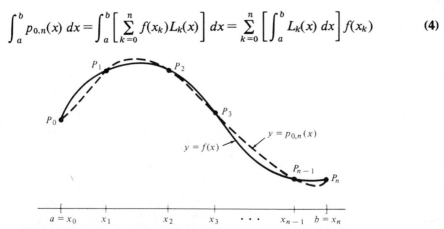

FIGURE 7.3-1   APPROXIMATING $\int_a^b f(x)\, dx$ BY $\int_a^b p_{0,n}(x)\, dx.$

The last equality used the fact that the integral of a weighted sum of functions is the weighted sum of their integrals. Since $f(x) = p_{0,n}(x)$ whenever $f(x)$ is a polynomial of degree $\leqslant n$, we see from (4) that *the quadrature formula*

$$\int_a^b f(x)\,dx \approx w_0 f(x_0) + w_1 f(x_1) + \cdots + w_n f(x_n) = \sum_{k=0}^n w_k f(x_k) \qquad \textbf{(5a)}$$

will be exact (i.e., *equality*) *for polynomials of degree $\leqslant n$ if we take*

$$w_k = \int_a^b L_k(x)\,dx, \qquad \text{where } L_k(x) = \prod_{i \neq k}\left(\frac{x - x_i}{x_k - x_i}\right) \qquad \textbf{(5b)}$$

EXAMPLE. Find weights $w_0, w_1, \ldots, w_n$, which make the following formulas exact for polynomials of degree $\leqslant n$.

a. $\displaystyle\int_a^b f(x)\,dx \approx w_0 f\left(\frac{a+b}{2}\right)$ $\qquad\qquad$ [$n = 0$; sample only the midpoint]

b. $\displaystyle\int_a^b f(x)\,dx \approx w_0 f(a) + w_1 f(b)$ $\qquad\qquad$ [$n = 1$; sample only the endpoints]

c. $\displaystyle\int_0^1 f(x)\,dx \approx w_0 f(-1) + w_1 f(0) + w_2 f(2)$ $\qquad$ [$n = 2$]

Then use (a)–(c) to estimate $\displaystyle\int_0^1 x\,dx$ and $\displaystyle\int_0^1 x^2\,dx$.

Solution
a. To be exact for polynomials of degree $\leqslant 0$, formula (a) must be exact when $f(x) \equiv 1$ (constant); by imposing this condition we get

$$b - a = \int_a^b 1\,dx = w_0 \cdot 1, \qquad \text{that is, } w_0 = b - a$$

The resulting simplest of *open* formulas is

$$\int_a^b f(x)\,dx \approx (b - a)f\left(\frac{a+b}{2}\right) \qquad \textbf{[Midpoint Rule]} \qquad \textbf{(6)}$$

b. The Lagrange polynomials for $x_0 = a$, $x_1 = b$ are

$$L_0(x) = \frac{x - b}{a - b} \qquad \text{and} \qquad L_1(x) = \frac{x - a}{b - a} \qquad \textbf{(7)}$$

In view of (5b) the desired weights for (b) are

$$w_0 = \int_a^b L_0(x)\,dx = \frac{(x-b)^2}{2(a-b)}\Big]_a^b = \frac{b-a}{2}\,; \qquad w_1 = \int_a^b L_1(x)\,dx = \frac{(x-a)^2}{2(b-a)}\Big]_a^b = \frac{b-a}{2}$$

The resulting simplest of *closed* formulas is

$$\boxed{\int_a^b f(x)\,dx \approx \frac{b-a}{2}[f(a)+f(b)] \qquad \textbf{[Trapezoidal Rule]}} \qquad (8)$$

Formulas (6) and (8) are illustrated graphically in Figure 7.3-2; note from part (a) of the figure that the Midpoint Rule is actually exact when the graph of f is a straight line; so *both* (6) *and* (8) *are exact for polynomials of degree* ≤ 1. Consequently, both are accurate when $f(x) \approx$ linear on $[a,\ b]$ (e.g., when $a \approx b$).

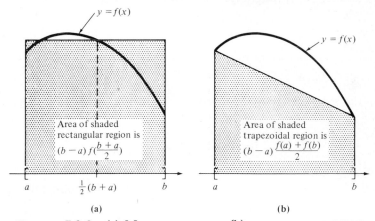

FIGURE 7.3-2   (a) MIDPOINT RULE; (b) TRAPEZOIDAL RULE.

c. The Lagrange polynomials for $x_0 = -1$, $x_1 = 0$, $x_2 = 2$ are

$$L_0(x) = \frac{(x-0)(x-2)}{(-1-0)(-1-2)}\,; \qquad L_1(x) = \frac{(x+1)(x-2)}{(0+1)(0-2)}\,; \qquad L_2(x) = \frac{(x+1)(x-0)}{(2+1)(2-0)} \qquad (9)$$

Simplifying and using (5b), we get

$$w_0 = \int_0^1 L_0(x)\,dx = \frac{1}{3}\left(\frac{x^3}{3}-x^2\right)\Big]_0^1 = \frac{-2}{9}\,; \quad w_1 = \int_0^1 L_1(x)\,dx = \frac{13}{12}\,; \quad w_2 = \int_0^1 L_2(x)\,dx = \frac{5}{36}$$

So the desired formula, which is neither open nor closed, is

$$\int_0^1 f(x)\,dx \approx \frac{-2}{9}f(-1) + \frac{13}{12}f(0) + \frac{5}{36}f(2) \qquad (10)$$

Using (6), (8), and (10) with $f(x) = x$, then $f(x) = x^2$ on $[0,\ 1]$ gives

(a) $\displaystyle\int_0^1 x\,dx \approx (1-0)\left(\frac{1}{2}\right) = \frac{1}{2}\,; \qquad\qquad \int_0^1 x^2\,dx \approx (1-0)\left(\frac{1}{2}\right)^2 = \frac{1}{4}$

(b) $\int_0^1 x\,dx \approx \dfrac{1-0}{2}[0+1]=\dfrac{1}{2}$; $\int_0^1 x^2\,dx \approx \dfrac{1-0}{2}[0^2+1^2]=\dfrac{1}{2}$

(c) $\int_0^1 x\,dx \approx -\dfrac{2}{9}(-1)+\dfrac{13}{12}0+\dfrac{5}{36}2=\dfrac{1}{2}$; $\int_0^1 x^2\,dx \approx -\dfrac{2}{9}(-1)^2+\dfrac{13}{12}0^2+\dfrac{5}{36}2^2=\dfrac{1}{3}$

All are exact for $f(x)=x$ (degree 1), but only (c) is exact for $f(x)=x^2$ (degree 2). It is interesting to note that the one-point Midpoint Rule estimated $\int_0^1 x^2\,dx=\frac{1}{3}$ more accurately than the two-point Trapezoidal Rule.

7.3B   FORMULAS FOR EQUISPACED POINTS

Let $L_{i,n}(t)$ denote the ith Lagrange polynomial for the $(n+1)$ *integer* nodes $t_i = i$, $i = 0, 1, \ldots , n$.

$$t \quad (11)$$

For example, the second Lagrange polynomial for $t_0 = 0, \ldots , t_3 = 3$ is the cubic

$$L_{2,3}(t) = \frac{(t-0)(t-1)(t-3)}{(2-0)(2-1)(2-3)} = \frac{-1}{2}(t^3 - 4t^2 + 3t)$$

Other $L_{i,n}(t)$'s, obtained similarly, are shown in Table 7.3-1.

These special $L_{i,n}(t)$'s can be used to get quadrature formulas for *any* $(n+1)$ h-spaced sample points $x_{j+i} = x_j + ih$, $i = 0, 1, \ldots , n$.

$$x \quad (12)$$

General $(n+1)$-Point Quadrature Formula for h-spaced points. If $a = x_j + t_a h$ and $b = x_j + t_b h$, then the approximation

$$\int_a^b f(x)\,dx \approx h\{W_0 f(x_j) + W_1 f(x_{j+1}) + \cdots + W_n f(x_{j+n})\} \tag{13a}$$

will be exact for polynomials of degree $\leqslant n$ if

$$W_i = \int_{t_a}^{t_b} L_{i,n}(t)\,dt, \qquad i = 0, 1, \ldots , n \tag{13b}$$

Before deriving (13), let us show how easily it can be used to obtain useful formulas. If we take $n = 3$, $t_a = 0$ ($a = x_j$) and $t_b = 3$ ($b = x_{j+3}$) in (13a), we get

$$\int_{x_j}^{x_{j+3}} f(x)\,dx = h\{W_0 f(x_j) + W_1 f(x_{j+1}) + W_2 f(x_{j+2}) + W_3 f(x_{j+3})\} \tag{14a}$$

where the weights, obtained from Table 7.3-1 using (13b), are

$$W_0 = \int_0^3 L_{0,3}(t)\, dt = -\frac{1}{6}\left(\frac{t^4}{4} - 2t^3 + \frac{11t^2}{2} - 6t\right)\Big]_0^3 = \frac{3}{8} \tag{14b}$$

TABLE 7.3-1 $L_{i,n}(t)$'s FOR $n = 2, 3, 4$.

$n = 2$ $\quad L_{0,2}(t) = \frac{1}{2}(t^2 - 3t + 2)$
$\quad\quad\quad L_{1,2}(t) = -1(t^2 - 2t)$
$\quad\quad\quad L_{2,2}(t) = \frac{1}{2}(t^2 - t)$

$n = 3$ $\quad L_{0,3}(t) = -\frac{1}{6}(t^3 - 6t^2 + 11t - 6)$
$\quad\quad\quad L_{1,3}(t) = \frac{1}{2}(t^3 - 5t^2 + 6t)$
$\quad\quad\quad L_{2,3}(t) = -\frac{1}{2}(t^3 - 4t^2 + 3t)$
$\quad\quad\quad L_{3,3}(t) = \frac{1}{6}(t^3 - 3t^2 + 2t)$

$n = 4$ $\quad L_{0,4}(t) = \frac{1}{24}(t^4 - 10t^3 + 35t^2 - 50t + 24)$
$\quad\quad\quad L_{1,4}(t) = -\frac{1}{6}(t^4 + 9t^3 + 26t^2 - 24t)$
$\quad\quad\quad L_{2,4}(t) = \frac{1}{4}(t^4 - 8t^3 + 19t^2 - 12t)$
$\quad\quad\quad L_{3,4}(t) = -\frac{1}{6}(t^4 - 7t^3 + 14t^2 - 8t)$
$\quad\quad\quad L_{4,4}(t) = \frac{1}{24}(t^4 - 6t^3 + 11t^2 - 6t)$

and similarly $W_1 = W_2 = \frac{9}{8}$ and $W_3 = \frac{3}{8}$. The resulting formula, which is exact for polynomials of degree ≤ 3, is given in (16a). A similar argument yields the important formulas in (15a), (17a), and (18a).

SIMPSON'S $\frac{1}{3}$-RULE:

$$\int_{x_j}^{x_{j+2}} f(x)\, dx \approx \frac{h}{3}\{f(x_j) + 4f(x_{j+1}) + f(x_{j+2})\} \tag{15a}$$

$$\tau[h] = \frac{-1}{90}h^5 f^{(iv)}(\xi) \qquad \text{where } x_j \leq \xi \leq x_{j+2} \tag{15b}$$

SIMPSON'S $\frac{3}{8}$-RULE:

$$\int_{x_j}^{x_{j+3}} f(x)\, dx \approx \frac{3h}{8}\{f(x_j) + 3f(x_{j+1}) + 3f(x_{j+2}) + f(x_{j+3})\} \tag{16a}$$

$$\tau[h] = \frac{-3}{80} h^5 f^{(iv)}(\xi), \qquad \text{where } x_j \leqslant \xi \leqslant x_{j+3} \tag{16b}$$

ADAMS $O(h^5)$ PREDICTOR:

$$\int_{x_j}^{x_{j+1}} f(x) \, dx \approx \frac{h}{24} \{-9f(x_{j-3}) + 37f(x_{j-2}) - 59f(x_{j-1}) + 55f(x_j)\} \tag{17a}$$

$$\tau[h] = \frac{251}{720} h^5 f^{(iv)}(\xi), \qquad \text{where } x_{j-3} \leqslant \xi \leqslant x_{j+1} \tag{17b}$$

ADAMS $O(h^5)$ CORRECTOR:

$$\int_{x_j}^{x_{j+1}} f(x) \, dx \approx \frac{h}{24} \{f(x_{j-2}) - 5f(x_{j-1}) + 19f(x_j) + 9f(x_{j+1})\} \tag{18a}$$

$$\tau[h] = -\frac{19}{720} h^5 f^{(iv)}(\xi), \qquad \text{where } x_{j-2} \leqslant \xi \leqslant x_{j+1} \tag{18b}$$

In the diagrams following the formula names, the shaded interval is the interval of integration ($[a, b]$ of (13a)) and the circled number above the sample point x_{j+i} is the sample weight W_i.

The truncation errors given in (15b)–(18b) are all special cases of

$$\tau[h] = \underbrace{\int_a^b f(x) \, dx}_{\text{exact value}} - \underbrace{h \sum_i W_i f(x_i)}_{\text{quadrature formula (13)}} \tag{19}$$

They will be derived in Section 7.3C. It can be seen from (15b)–(18b) that *all four formulas (15a)–(18a) are exact for cubics* [for which $f^{(iv)} \equiv 0$]. Moreover, since $f^{(iv)}(\xi) \approx$ constant for small h, we see that (15a)–(18a) are $O(h^5)$ formulas.

To derive (13), we first use the change of variables

$$\left\{ \begin{array}{l} x = x_j + th \\ dx = h \, dt \end{array} \right\} \quad \text{so that} \quad \left\{ \begin{array}{l} t = \frac{1}{h}(x - x_j) \\ dt = \frac{1}{h} \, dx \end{array} \right\} \tag{20a}$$

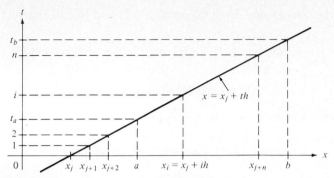

FIGURE 7.3-3 GRAPHICAL REPRESENTATION OF $x = x_j + th$.

(see Figure 7.3-3) to get

$$\int_{x=a}^{b} f(x)\,dx = \int_{t=t_a}^{t_b} f(x_j + th) \cdot h\,dt$$

$$= h\int_{t_a}^{t_b} \phi(t)\,dt, \qquad \text{where } \phi(t) = f(x_j + th)$$

Since $\phi(i) = f(x_j + ih) = f(x_i)$ for $i = 0, 1, \ldots, n$, formula (13) is obtained by simply applying strategy (5) to the quadrature formula

$$\int_{t_a}^{t_b} \phi(t)\,dt = W_0\,\phi(0) + W_1\,\phi(1) + \cdots + W_n\,\phi(n) \tag{20b}$$

If $f(x)$ is a polynomial of degree $\leq n$ in x, then $\phi(t) = f(x_j + th)$ is a polynomial of degree $\leq n$ in t. (Why?) In this case (20b), therefore (13a) is exact. The derivation of (13) is now complete.

EXAMPLE. Use the formulas discussed so far to approximate

a. $\displaystyle\int_{0.1}^{0.3} e^x\,dx$ [Exact answer is $e^{0.3} - e^{0.1} \doteq 0.244687$.]

b. $\displaystyle\int_{0.3}^{0.4} e^x\,dx$ [Exact answer is $e^{0.4} - e^{0.3} \doteq 0.141966$.]

c. $\displaystyle\int_{0}^{0.5} e^x\,dx$ [Exact answer is $e^{0.5} - e^0 \doteq 0.648721$.]

Solution

a. The Midpoint Rule (6) on [0.1, 0.3] gives

$$\int_{0.1}^{0.3} e^x\,dx \approx (0.3 - 0.1)\,f\!\left(\frac{0.1 + 0.3}{2}\right) = 0.2e^{0.2} = 0.244280 \tag{21}$$

$$(\text{Error} \doteq 0.244687 - 0.244280 = 0.000407)$$

Alternatively, the Trapezoidal Rule (8) on [0.1, 0.2] and [0.2, 0.3] gives

$$\int_{0.1}^{0.3} e^x \, dx \approx \frac{0.1}{2} [e^{0.1} + e^{0.2}] + \frac{0.1}{2} [e^{0.2} + e^{0.3}] \doteq 0.244892$$

(22)

$$(\text{Error} \doteq 0.244687 - 0.244892 = -0.000205)$$

Finally, Simpson's $\frac{1}{3}$-rule (15a) on [0.1, 0.3] ($h = 0.1$) gives

$$\int_{0.1}^{0.3} e^x \, dx \approx \frac{0.1}{3} [e^{0.1} + 4e^{0.2} + e^{0.3}] \doteq 0.244688$$

(23)

$$(\text{Error} \doteq 0.244687 - 0.244688 = -0.000001)$$

The considerably greater accuracy of (23) over (22) reflects the geometrically evident fact that the interpolating quadratic on [0.1, 0.3] approximates e^x better than the interpolating straight lines on [0.1, 0.2] and [0.2, 0.3]. Note that (21), which used only one sample point, is almost as accurate as (23), which used three.

b. With $x_j = 0.3$ and $h = 0.1$, the Adams predictor formula (17a) gives

$$\int_{0.3}^{0.4} e^x \, dx \approx \frac{0.1}{24} [-9e^0 + 37e^{0.1} - 59e^{0.2} + 55e^{0.3}] \doteq 0.141962$$

(24)

$$(\text{Error} = 0.141966 - 0.141962 = 0.000004)$$

whereas the Adams corrector formula (18a) gives

$$\int_{0.3}^{0.4} e^x \, dx \approx \frac{0.1}{24} [e^{0.1} - 5e^{0.2} + 19e^{0.3} + 9e^{0.4}] \doteq 0.141966$$

(25)

$$(\text{Error} = 0 \text{ to } 6s)$$

The better accuracy of (25) reflects the fact that the integration interval [0.3, 0.4] lies *within* the interpolation interval [0.1, 0.4] (where $p_{0,3}(x)$ best approximates $f(x)$) in (25) but lies *outside* the interpolation interval [0, 0.3] in (24).

c. Simpson's $\frac{1}{3}$-rule on [0, 0.2] and the $\frac{3}{8}$-rule on [0.2, 0.5] give

$$\int_{0}^{0.5} e^x \, dx \approx \frac{0.1}{3} [e^0 + 4e^{0.1} + e^{0.2}] + \frac{0.3}{8} [e^{0.2} + 3e^{0.3} + 3e^{0.4} + e^{0.5}]$$

(26)

$$\doteq 0.221403 + 0.427319 = 0.648722 \qquad (\text{Error} = -0.000001)$$

Alternatively, Simpson's $\frac{3}{8}$-rule on [0, 0.3] and the $\frac{1}{3}$-rule on [0.3, 0.5] give

$$\int_{0}^{.5} e^x \, dx \approx \frac{0.3}{8} [e^0 + 3e^{0.1} + 3e^{0.2} + e^{0.3}] + \frac{0.1}{3} [e^{0.3} + 4e^{0.4} + e^{0.5}]$$

(27)

$$\doteq 0.349859 + 0.298863 = 0.648722 \qquad (\text{Error} = -0.000001)$$

In both (26) and (27), the small error came from the rightmost integration where $f^{(iv)}(\xi) = e^{\xi}$ is largest [see (15b) and (16b)].

The Trapezoidal Rule (8) and the Simpson rules (15a) and (16a) are all closed quadrature formulas that integrate $f(x)$ over $[a, b] = [x_j, x_{j+n}]$ using as sample points the $n + 1$ points that subdivide $[a, b]$ into n subintervals of equal length. The general formula of this type is the following:

$(n + 1)$-Point Newton–Cotes Formula

$$\int_{a=x_j}^{b=x_{j+n}} f(x) \, dx \approx h[W_0 f(x_j) + W_1 f(x_{j+1}) + \cdots + W_n f(x_{j+n})] \qquad \text{(28a)}$$

$$\tau[h] = \begin{cases} K_n f^{(n+2)}(\xi) \, h^{n+3} & \text{if } n \text{ is even} \\ K_n f^{(n+1)}(\xi) \, h^{n+2} & \text{if } n \text{ is odd} \end{cases} \qquad \text{(28b)}$$

In (28b), K_n is a constant that depends on n, and ξ is an (unknown) point in $[x_j, x_{j+n}]$; from (28b) we see that:

The $(n + 1)$-point Newton–Cotes formula is exact when $f(x)$ is a polynomial of degree $\leqslant$ n if $n = 1, 3, 5, \ldots$, and of degree $\leqslant n + 1$ if $n = 2, 4, 6, \ldots$.

In particular, this "bonus" extra degree of exactness when $n = 2$ accounts for the widespread popularity of the three-point Simpson's $\frac{1}{3}$-rule.

7.3C   TRUNCATION ERROR OF QUADRATURE FORMULAS

To illustrate the derivation of useful expressions for the truncation error of a quadrature formula, consider the Trapezoidal Rule

$$\int_{x_j}^{x_{j+1}} f(x) \, dx \approx \frac{h}{2}[f(x_j) + f(x_{j+1})], \qquad \text{where } h = x_{j+1} - x_j \qquad \text{(29)}$$

[see (8)]. To begin, we introduce the indefinite integral

$$I(x) = \int_{x_j}^{x} f(u) \, du, \qquad \text{for which } I(x_j) = 0 \quad \text{and} \quad I'(x) = \frac{dI(x)}{dx} = f(x) \qquad \text{(30)}$$

[see Appendix II.4B]. The Taylor series for $I(x_j + h)$ is

$$I(x_{j+1}) = I(x_j) + I'(x_j) h + \frac{I''(x_j)}{2!} h^2 + \frac{I'''(x_j)}{3!} h^3 + \cdots$$

In view of (30), this can be written as

$$\int_{x_j}^{x_{j+1}} f(x)\, dx = 0 + f(x_j)\, h + \frac{f'(x_j)}{2!}\, h^2 + \frac{f''(x_j)}{3!}\, h^3$$

$$+ \frac{f'''(x_j)}{4!}\, h^4 + \frac{f^{(iv)}(x_j)}{5!} h^5 + \cdots \tag{31}$$

If we replace $f'(x_j)$ by $\Delta f(x_j)/h + \tau[h]$, that is, by

$$f'(x_j) = \frac{f(x_{j+1}) - f(x_j)}{h} - \frac{f'(x_j)}{2}\, h - \frac{f''(x_j)}{6}\, h^2 - \frac{f^{(iv)}(x_j)}{24}\, h^3 - \cdots \tag{32}$$

[see (12) of Section 7.1B] and we then combine powers of h, we get

$$\int_{x_j}^{x_{j+1}} f(x)\, dx - \frac{h}{2}\, [f(x_{j+1}) + f(x_j)] \quad \text{(Trucation error of Trapezoidal Rule)}$$

$$\tag{33}$$

$$= -\frac{h^3}{12} f''(x_j) - \frac{h^4}{24} f'''(x_j) - \frac{h^5}{80} f^{(iv)}(x_j) + O(h^6)$$

To get expressions for the truncation error of the Midpoint Rule and Simpson $\frac{1}{3}$-rule, we first replace h by $-h$ in (31) to get

$$\int_{x_j}^{x_{j-1}} f(x)\, dx = 0 - f(x_j)\, h + \frac{f'(x_j)}{2!}\, h^2 - \frac{f''(x_j)}{3!}\, h^3$$

$$+ \frac{f'''(x_j)}{4!}\, h^4 - \frac{f^{(iv)}(x_j)}{5!} h^5 + \cdots \tag{34}$$

Subtracting (34) from (31) gives

$$\int_{x_{j-1}}^{x_{j+1}} f(x)\, dx = 2f(x_j)\, h + \frac{f''(x_j)}{3}\, h^3 + \frac{f^{(iv)}(x_j)}{60}\, h^5 + O(h^7) \tag{35}$$

Taking $x_{j-1} = a$, $x_{j+1} = b$ and $x_j = x_{\text{mid}}$, so that $h = (b - a)/2$, we get

$$\boxed{\int_a^b f(x)\, dx = \underbrace{(b - a)\, f(x_{\text{mid}})}_{\text{Midpoint Rule}} + \underbrace{\frac{f''(x_{\text{mid}})}{24}\, (b - a)^3 + O(b - a)^5}_{\text{Truncation Error}}} \tag{36}$$

Alternatively, if we replace $f''(x_j)$ in (35) by $\delta^2 f(x_j)/h^2 + \tau[h]$, that is, by

$$f''(x_j) = \frac{f(x_{j-1}) - 2f(x_j) + f(x_{j+1})}{h^2} - \frac{h^2}{12} f^{(iv)}(x_j) + O(h^4) \tag{37}$$

[see (15) of Section 7.2B] and then combine powers of h, we get

$$\int_{x_{j-1}}^{x_{j+1}} f(x)\,dx = \underbrace{\frac{h}{3}\left[f(x_{j-1}) + 4f(x_j) + f(x_{j+1})\right]}_{\text{Simpson's rule on } [x_{j-1},\, x_{j+1}]} \underbrace{- \frac{h^5}{90}f^{(iv)}(x_j) + O(h^7)}_{\text{Truncation Error}} \qquad (38)$$

Had we used the Lagrange form of the remainder involving $f^{(iv)}(\xi)$ in (35) and (37), we would have obtained $\tau[h]$ as in (15b). The truncation error of the other formulas given in Section 7.3B are obtained similarly.

The Newton–Cotes formulas (28a) are generally not used for $n > 4$ because the K_n's in (28b) tend to get large as n increases. Intuitively, the Polynomial Wiggle Problem of Section 5.3B makes the higher degree $p_{j,j+n}(x)$'s poor candidates for reliably estimating $f(x)$ on $[a, b]$. A better strategy is described next.

Composite Rules and Romberg Integration   7.4

Suppose that we partition $[a, b]$ into n **panels** of equal length h.

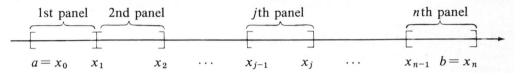

The $n + 1$ equispaced x_j's are given by

$$x_j = a + jh, \quad \text{where } h = \frac{b-a}{n}, \quad \text{for } j = 0, 1, 2, \ldots, n \qquad (1)$$

7.4A   COMPOSITE TRAPEZOIDAL AND SIMPSON RULES: $T[h]$ AND $S[h]$

If we use the Trapezoidal Rule (29) of Section 7.3C to approximate the integral of f over each panel, we get

$$\int_a^b f(x)\,dx \approx \frac{h}{2}\left[f(a) + f(x_1)\right] + \frac{h}{2}\left[f(x_1) + f(x_2)\right] + \cdots + \frac{h}{2}\left[f(x_{n-1}) + f(b)\right]$$

Combining $f(x_j)$ terms, $j = 1, \ldots, n - 1$ gives the **Composite Trapezoidal Rule**

$$\int_a^b f(x)\,dx \approx T[h] = h\left\{\frac{f(a) + f(b)}{2} + \sum_{j=1}^{n-1} f(x_j)\right\} \qquad (2a)$$

$$\tau_T[h] = \int_a^b f(x)\,dx - T[h] = \frac{-h^2}{12}(b-a)f''(\xi) = O(h^2) \qquad (2b)$$

The truncation error given in (2b), in which ξ is some unknown point of $[a, b]$, will be derived in Section 7.4B. Notice that although the per-panel truncation error of the Trapezoidal Rule is $O(h^3)$ [see (33) of Section 7.3C], the cumulative error over n panels is one order less, namely $O(h^2)$.

To get a composite Simpson's rule, *we must take n to be an even integer* so that we can use Simpson's $\frac{1}{3}$-rule [(15) of Section 7.1B] over the $n/2$ *double panels*

$$[a, x_2], \quad [x_2, x_4], \quad [x_4, x_6], \quad \ldots, \quad [x_{n-2}, b]$$

(see Figure 7.4-1). The resulting formula is the **Composite Simpson's Rule**

$$\int_a^b f(x)\, dx \approx S[h] = \frac{h}{3}\left\{ f(a) + f(b) + 4 \sum_{\text{odd}}[h] + 2 \sum_{\text{even}}[h] \right\} \tag{3a}$$

$$\tau_S[h] = \int_a^b f(x)\, dx - S[h] = \frac{-h^4}{180}(b-a)\, f^{(\text{iv})}(\xi) = O(h^4) \tag{3b}$$

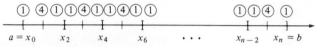

$$a = x_0 \qquad x_2 \qquad x_4 \qquad x_6 \qquad \cdots \qquad x_{n-2} \qquad x_n = b$$

FIGURE 7.4-1   DERIVATION OF THE COMPOSITE SIMPSON'S RULE $S[h]$.

In (3a), $\sum_{\text{odd}}[h]$ and $\sum_{\text{even}}[h]$ denote the sums over the *interior* sample points having odd and even subscripts respectively, that is,

$$\sum_{\text{odd}}[h] = f(x_1) + f(x_3) + \cdots + f(x_{n-3}) + f(x_{n-1}) \tag{4a}$$

$$\sum_{\text{even}}[h] = f(x_2) + f(x_4) + \cdots + f(x_{n-4}) + f(x_{n-2}) \tag{4b}$$

(Recall that n is *even*.) So summing over the *interior* x_j's can be viewed as

$$\sum_{\text{interior}}[h] = \sum_{\text{odd}}[h] + \sum_{\text{even}}[h] = \sum_{j=1}^{n-1} f(x_j) \tag{4c}$$

EXAMPLE. From Table 7.4-1, estimate $\int_1^{2.2} \ln x\, dx$ using the composite rules $T[h]$ and $S[h]$ with **(a)** 6 panels; **(b)** 12 panels.

Solution [*Note:* The exact number is 0.534606 (6s).]

a. Here $a = 1$ and $b = 2.2$ so that (to 5d)

$$f(a) + f(b) = \ln 1 + \ln 2.2 = 0 + 0.78846 = 0.78846 \tag{5a}$$

For $n = 6$ panels, $h = (2.2 - 1)/6 = 0.2$, and the seven sample points are

From (4) and the left side of table 7.4-1,

$$\sum_{\text{odd}}[0.2] = \ln(1.2) + \ln(1.6) + \ln(2.0) \doteq 1.34547 \tag{5b}$$

$$\sum_{\text{even}}[0.2] = \ln(1.4) + \ln(1.8) \doteq 0.92426 \tag{5c}$$

TABLE 7.4-1 VALUES OF $\ln x$ (5s).

x	$f(x) = \ln x$	x	$f(x) = \ln x$
1.0	0.00000	1.1	0.095310
1.2	0.18232	1.3	0.26236
1.4	0.33647	1.5	0.40547
1.6	0.47000	1.7	0.53063
1.8	0.58779	1.9	0.64185
2.0	0.69315	2.1	0.74194
2.2	0.78846		

So the Composite Trapezoidal Rule (2a) [and (4c)] gives

$$T[0.2] = (0.2)\left\{\frac{0.78846}{2} + (1.34547 + 0.92426)\right\} \doteq 0.532792 \tag{6a}$$

$$\tau_T[0.2] = 0.534606 - 0.532792 = 0.001814 \tag{6b}$$

whereas the composite Simpson's rule (3a) gives

$$S[0.2] = \frac{(0.2)}{3}\{0.78846 + 4(1.34547) + 2(0.92426)\} \doteq 0.534591 \tag{7a}$$

$$\tau_S[0.2] = 0.534606 - 0.534591 = 0.000015 \tag{7b}$$

Notice that $S[0.2]$ is more accurate than $T[0.2]$ by about $2d$!

b. Now $h = 0.1$. The six "new" sample points (marked with an "$\times$" in the sketch) have *odd* subscripts. From the right side of Table 7.4-1,

$$\sum_{\text{odd}}[0.1] = \ln(1.1) + \ln(1.3) + \ln(1.5) + \ln(1.7) + \ln(1.9) + \ln(2.1) = 2.67756 \tag{8a}$$

On the other hand, the sum over the interior *even* subscripts is

$$\sum_{\text{even}}[0.1] = \sum_{\text{interior}}[0.2] \doteq 1.34547 + 0.92426 = 2.26973 \tag{8b}$$

[See (5b) and (5c).] So (2a) and (3a) give

$$T[0.1] = (0.1) \left\{ \frac{0.78846}{2} + (2.67756 + 2.26973) \right\} \doteq 0.534152 \quad (\tau_T[0.1] \doteq 0.000454) \quad \textbf{(9a)}$$

$$S[0.1] = \frac{0.1}{3} \{0.78846 + 4(2.67756) + 2(2.26973)\} \doteq 0.534605 \quad (\tau_S[0.1] \doteq 0.000001) \quad \textbf{(9b)}$$

Notice that the truncation errors of $T[h]$ and $S[h]$ satisfy, respectively,

$$\tau_T[0.1] \approx (\tfrac{1}{2})^2 \, \tau_T[0.2] \qquad \text{and} \qquad \tau_S[0.1] \approx (\tfrac{1}{2})^4 \, \tau_S[0.2]$$

indicating that $T[h]$ is $O(h^2)$ and $S[h]$ is $O(h^4)$ [cf. (2b) and (3b)]. We shall prove this in Section 7.4B. The proof will use the fact that when n is doubled (h is halved), the sample points of $\Sigma_{\text{odd}}\,[h/2]$ are "new" whereas those of $\Sigma_{\text{even}}\,[h/2]$ have been used previously; specifically,

$$\boxed{\Sigma_{\text{even}}[h/2] = \Sigma_{\text{odd}}[h] + \Sigma_{\text{even}}[h] = \Sigma_{\text{interior}}[h]} \qquad \textbf{(10)}$$

[See (8b) and the sketch above.] So, if we record (or store) $\Sigma_{\text{odd}}[h]$ and $\Sigma_{\text{even}}[h]$, then the only *new* summation needed to get $T[h/2]$ or $S[h/2]$ is $\Sigma_{\text{odd}}[h/2]$. In fact, by (2a) and (10),

$$T[h/2] = \frac{h}{2} \left\{ \frac{f(a) + f(b)}{2} + \Sigma_{\text{odd}}[h/2] + \Sigma_{\text{interior}}[h] \right\}$$

So in view of (2a) again, we see that

$$\boxed{T[h/2] = \tfrac{1}{2}\{T[h] + h \, \Sigma_{\text{odd}}[h/2]\}} \qquad \textbf{(11)}$$

This **recursive form of the Composite Trapezoidal Rule** makes it easy to get $T[h/2]$ from $T[h]$. For example, (6a) and (8a) give

$$T[0.1] = \tfrac{1}{2}\{T[0.2] + (0.2)\,\Sigma_{\text{odd}}[0.1]\} = \tfrac{1}{2}\{0.532792 + (0.2)(2.67756)\} \doteq 0.534152$$

in agreement with $T[0.1]$ obtained directly in (9a).

7.4B   TRUNCATION ERROR OF $T[h]$ AND $S[h]$

Let us show that $T[h]$ is $O(h^2)$. In view of (33) of Section 7.3C,

$$\tau_T[h] = \int_a^b f(x) \, dx - T[h]$$

$$= \sum_{j=1}^{n} \{\text{truncation error of Trapezoidal Rule on } [x_{j-1}, x_j]\}$$

$$= \sum_{j=1}^{n} \left\{ \frac{-h^3}{12} f''(\xi_j) \right\} = \frac{-h^3}{12} \left\{ \sum_{j=1}^{n} f''(\xi_j) \right\} \tag{12}$$

where ξ_j lies in the jth panel $[x_{j-1}, x_j]$ for $j = 1, 2, \ldots, n$. If f'' is continuous on $[a, b]$, then by Appendix II.1C,

$$\sum_{j=1}^{n} f''(\xi_j) = n f''(\xi) \qquad \text{for some } \xi \text{ in } [a, b]$$

Replacing n by $(b - a)/h$ gives (2b), that is,

$$\tau_T[h] = \frac{-h^2}{12} (b - a) f''(\xi) = O(h^2) \tag{13a}$$

A similar analysis, based on (38) of Section 7.3C, shows that the truncation error of the composite Simpson's rule is given by (3b), that is,

$$\tau_S[h] = \frac{-h^4}{180} (b - a) f^{(iv)}(\xi) = O(h^4) \tag{13b}$$

where, as in (13a), ξ is some (unknown) point in $[a, b]$.

7.4C OBTAINING $S[h]$ FROM $T[h]$ AND $T[2h]$

If we apply the Richardson formula (19a) of Section 7.1D to the two trapezoidal estimates

$$T[h] \quad \text{and} \quad T[2h] \qquad (\text{so that } r = 2)$$

then, since $T[h]$ is $O(h^2)$ (i.e., $n = 2$), we get

$$T_1[h] = \frac{2^2 T[h] - T[2h]}{2^2 - 1} \tag{14a}$$

$$= \frac{1}{3} \left\{ 4h \left(\frac{f(a) + f(b)}{2} + \Sigma_{\text{odd}}[h] + \Sigma_{\text{even}}[h] \right) \right.$$

$$\left. - 2h \left(\frac{f(a) + f(b)}{2} + \Sigma_{\text{even}}[h] \right) \right\}$$

where (10) was used to replace $\Sigma_{\text{interior}}[2h]$ by $\Sigma_{\text{even}}[h]$ in $T[2h]$. Simplifying,

$$T_1[h] = \frac{h}{3} \left\{ f(a) + f(b) + 4 \sum_{\text{odd}}[h] + 2 \sum_{\text{even}}[h] \right\} = S[h]$$

In words, *applying Richardson's formula with $r = 2$ to the Composite Trapezoidal Rule gives the composite Simpson's rule.*

7.4D ROMBERG INTEGRATION

Since $T_1[h] = S[h]$ is $O(h^4)$ [see (13b)], we can apply Richardson's formula with $n = 4$ and $r = 2$ to get

$$T_2[h] = S_1[h] = \frac{2^4 S[h] - S[2h]}{2^4 - 1} = \frac{16 T_1[h] - T_1[2h]}{15}$$ (14b)

This formula can be shown to be $O(h^6)$ [cf. (38) of Section 7.3C]. In fact, it can be shown that the Maclaurin series for the truncation error of the Composite Trapezoidal Rule is of the form

$$\tau_T[h] = Ch^2 + Dh^4 + Eh^6 + Fh^8 + \cdots$$ (15)

so that from the trapezoidal estimates

$$T[h_0], \quad T[\tfrac{1}{2} h_0], \quad T[\tfrac{1}{4} h_0], \quad T[\tfrac{1}{8} h_0], \quad \ldots \quad (r = 2)$$

we can get the Richardson Table shown in Table 7.4-2. When Richardson improvement is used this way, the procedure is called **Romberg integration** and the resulting table is called a **Romberg table.**

TABLE 7.4-2 ROMBERG TABLE.

k	h	$T_0 = T(n=2)$	$T_1 = S(n=4)$	$T_2 (n=6)$	$T_3 (n=8)$	$T_4 (n=10)$
0	h_0	$T[h_0]$				
1	$\tfrac{1}{2} h_0$	$T[\tfrac{1}{2} h_0]$	$T_1[\tfrac{1}{2} h_0]$			
2	$(\tfrac{1}{2})^2 h_0$	$T[\tfrac{1}{4} h_0]$	$T_1[\tfrac{1}{4} h_0]$	$T_2[\tfrac{1}{4} h_0]$		
3	$(\tfrac{1}{2})^3 h_0$	$T[\tfrac{1}{8} h_0]$	$T_1[\tfrac{1}{8} h_0]$	$T_2[\tfrac{1}{8} h_0]$	$T_3[\tfrac{1}{8} h_0]$	
4	$(\tfrac{1}{2})^4 h_0$	$T[\tfrac{1}{16} h_0]$	$T_1[\tfrac{1}{16} h_0]$	$T_2[\tfrac{1}{16} h_0]$	$T_3[\tfrac{1}{16} h_0]$	$T_4[\tfrac{1}{16} h_0]$

If $T_0[h]$ is the leftmost entry of the kth row of a Romberg table, then the other entries of the row are obtained as

$$\boxed{T_i[h] = \frac{4^i T_{i-1}[h] - T_{i-1}[2h]}{4^i - 1}, \qquad i = 1, 2, \ldots, k}$$ (16)

A suitable termination test for Romberg integration is to take $T_k[h]$ (the last entry of row$_k$) as the desired approximation of $\int_a^b f(x) \, dx$ when it is sufficiently close to the preceding entry of row$_k$, that is, when

$$T_k[h] - T_{k-1}[h] \text{ is sufficiently close to zero}$$ (17)

EXAMPLE. Use Romberg integration to find $\int_1^{2.2} \ln x \, dx$ to 5s.

Solution. Since $\ln x$ has no "wiggles" (i.e., inflection points) on $[1, 2.2]$, we take a rather large h_0, say $h_0 = 0.4$ in formula (2a) for $T[h]$:

$$k = 0: \qquad T[0.4] = 0.4 \left\{ \frac{\ln 2.2 + \ln 1}{2} + \ln(1.4) + \ln(1.8) \right\} \doteq 0.527395.$$

$k = 1$: Putting $h = h_0 = 0.4$ in the recursive form (11) gives

$$T[0.2] = \tfrac{1}{2}\{T[0.4] + (0.4)[\ln(1.2) + \ln(1.6) + \ln(2.0)]\} \doteq 0.532792$$

[cf. (6a)]. So (16) with $i = 1$ [this is (14a)] gives

$$T_1[0.2] = \frac{4T[0.2] - T[0.4]}{3} = \frac{4(0.532792) - (0.527395)}{3} \doteq 0.534591$$

[cf. (7a)]. Since $T_1[0.2]$ and $T[0.2]$ do not agree to 5s, we form another row.

$k = 2$: Putting $h = \tfrac{1}{2}h_0 = 0.2$ in the recursive form (11) gives

$$T[0.1] = \tfrac{1}{2}\{T[0.2] + (0.2) \textstyle\sum_{\text{odd}}[0.1]\}$$

$$= \tfrac{1}{2}\{0.532792 + (0.2)(2.67756)\} = 0.534152$$

[cf. (9a)]. So (16) with $i = 1$ gives

$$T_1[0.1] = \frac{4T[0.1] - T[0.2]}{3} = \frac{4(0.534152) - (0.532792)}{3} \doteq 0.534605$$

[cf. (9b)], and with $i = 2$ [this is (14b)] gives

$$T_2[0.1] = \frac{16 T_1[0.1] - T_1[0.2]}{15} = \frac{16(0.534605) - (0.534591)}{15} = 0.534606$$

Since $T_2[0.1]$ and $T_1[0.1]$ agree to 5s, we take $T_2[0.1]$ as accurate to 5s, i.e.,

$$\int_1^{2.2} \ln x \, dx \doteq 0.534606 \qquad (5s)$$

In fact, this approximation is accurate to all six digits shown!

Table 7.4-3 is the Romberg table for the calculations just performed. Note that $T[0.1] = 0.534152$ is only accurate to 3s! This demonstrates the rapid convergence and accuracy that can be achieved using Romberg integration when the integrand is sufficiently smooth. In fact,

TABLE 7.4-3 ROMBERG TABLE FOR FINDING $\int_1^{2.2} \ln x \, dx$ TO 5s.

k	h	$T_0 = T(n = 2)$	$T_1 = S(n = 4)$	$T_2(n = 6)$
0	0.4	0.527395		
1	0.2	0.532792	0.534591	
2	0.1	0.534152	0.534605	0.534606

Algorithm: Romberg Integration

Purpose: To find $\int_a^b f(x) \, dx$ to *NumSig* significant digits. The matrix T is the Romberg table, with the kth iteration ($h = h_0/2^k$) yielding

$$\text{row}_k \, T = [T_{k,0}, \quad T_{k,1} \quad \cdots \quad T_{k,k-1} \quad T_{k,k}]$$

for $k = 0, 1, \ldots , MaxRows.$

{initialize}
GET $a, b,$ {endpoints of the interval of integration}
   $n,$ {initial number of panels}
   MaxRows, NumSig   {termination parameters}
$h \leftarrow (b - a)/n$ {This is h_0}

$T_{0,0} \leftarrow h\left(\dfrac{f(a) + f(b)}{2} + \Sigma_{\text{interior}}[h]\right)$ {Composite Trapezoidal Rule}

$RelTol \leftarrow 10^{-NumSig}$

{iterate}
DO FOR $k = 1$ TO *MaxRows* UNTIL **termination test** is satisfied
   BEGIN
   $h \leftarrow h/2$ {h is now $h_0/2^k$}
   $T_{k,0} \leftarrow \frac{1}{2}(T_{k-1,0} + 2h\,\Sigma_{\text{odd}}[h])$ {Recursive Trapezoidal Rule}
   DO FOR $i = 1$ TO k {Get ith entry of row$_k$ T}
      $T_{k,i} \leftarrow (4^i T_{k,i-1} - T_{k-1,i-1})/(4^i - 1)$ {This is $T_i[h]$}
   {**termination test:** $|T_{k,k} - T_{k,k-1}| \leqslant RelTol*|T_{k,k}|$}
   END

IF **termination test** succeeded

   THEN OUTPUT ($\int_a^b f(x) \, dx$ is $T_{k,k}$ to *NumSig* significant digits.)
   ELSE OUTPUT (*MaxRows* iterations did not yield the desired accuracy.)

FIGURE 7.4-2   PSEUDOPROGRAM FOR ROMBERG INTEGRATION.

$$\boxed{T_i[h] \text{ is exact for polynomials of degree} \le 2i + 1} \qquad (18)$$

Romberg integration will converge to $I = \int_a^b f(x)\, dx$ even if f is not particularly smooth; all that is required is for $T_0[h_0/2k]$ to approach I as $k \to \infty$ (see [29]).

The pseudoprogram shown in Figure 7.4-2 puts the $k + 1$ entries

$$T_0[h], \quad T_1[h], \quad T_2[h], \quad \ldots, \quad T_k[h] \qquad (19a)$$

in the kth row of a matrix T using the subscripts

$$T_{k,0}, \quad T_{k,1}, \quad T_{k,3}, \quad \ldots, \quad T_{k,k} \qquad (19b)$$

An upper limit, *MaxRows* (typically about 7), has been placed on the number of rows formed. The initial h, h_0, should be small enough so that $T[h_0]$ is reasonably accurate (based on a sketch of f on $[a, b]$ if necessary) yet large enough so that $T[h_0/2^{MaxRows}]$ may be calculated without serious accumulated roundoff error. If this termination test is not satisfied in *MaxRows* iterations, a check should be made to see if f has a singularity on $[a, b]$. If a singularity is detected, the integral is improper and a strategy of Section 7.6 should be used. If not, the Romberg algorithm should be repeated with a *larger* h_0 if roundoff error is evident, and a *smaller* h_0 otherwise.

Gauss Quadrature **7.5**

The quadrature formulas considered so far were of the form

$$\int_a^b f(x)\, dx \approx w_1 f(x_1) + w_2 f(x_2) + \cdots + w_n f(x_n) \qquad (1)$$

where the sample points were selected in advance. In general, such formulas are exact for polynomials having n coefficients (i.e., of degree $\le n - 1$) (see Section 7.3A). What Gauss was clever enough to realize was that by treating *both* the n sample points *and* the n weights as variables, one should be able to make (1) exact for polynomials having $2n$ coefficients (i.e., of degree $\le 2n - 1$). Formulas resulting from this strategy are called **Gauss–Legendre** (or simply **Gauss**) **quadrature formulas.**

7.5A GAUSS QUADRATURE ON $[-1, 1]$

We first restrict consideration to the "normalized" interval $[-1, 1]$. For any $n \ge 1$, our objective is to find n sample points

$$\xi_1, \xi_2, \ldots, \xi_n \qquad \text{in } [-1, 1] \qquad (2a)$$

and n corresponding weights

$$\gamma_1, \gamma_2, \ldots, \gamma_n \tag{2b}$$

such that the *n*-point Gauss quadrature formula on [−1, 1], namely

$$\int_{-1}^{1} f(\xi)\, d\xi \approx \gamma_1 f(\xi_1) + \gamma_2 f(\xi_2) + \cdots + \gamma_n f(\xi_n) \tag{3}$$

is exact for polynomials of degree $\leq 2n - 1$. We shall call the ξ_k's in (2a) **Gaussian sample points** of [−1, 1], and the γ_k's in (2b) their **Gaussian weights.**

Making (3) exact for $f(\xi) = 1, \xi, \xi^2, \ldots, \xi^{2n-1}$, yields $2n$ equations

$$(E_k) \quad \gamma_1 \xi_1^{k-1} + \gamma_2 \xi_2^{k-1} + \cdots + \gamma_n \xi_n^{k-1} = \int_{-1}^{1} \xi^{k-1}\, d\xi, \qquad k = 1, 2, \ldots, 2n \tag{4a}$$

where the kth equation (E_k) imposes the exactness of (3) for $f(\xi) = \xi^{k-1}$. From elementary calculus

$$\int_{-1}^{1} \xi^{k-1}\, d\xi = \frac{\xi^k}{k} \Bigg]_{-1}^{1} = \begin{cases} 0 & \text{if } k \text{ is even} \\ 2/k & \text{if } k \text{ is odd} \end{cases} \tag{4b}$$

The system (4) is nonlinear in the $2n$ variables $\xi_1, \ldots, \xi_n, \gamma_1, \ldots, \gamma_n$. Its solution generally requires a numerical procedure such as NRSYS (Section 4.6).

EXAMPLE. Derive the two-point Gauss quadrature formula on [−1, 1].

Solution. Taking $n = 2$ in (4) yields a nonlinear system in $\xi_1, \xi_2, \gamma_1, \gamma_2$:

$$f(\xi) = 1: \quad (E_1) \quad \gamma_1 1 + \gamma_2 1 \quad = \int_{-1}^{1} 1\, d\xi = \frac{2}{1}$$

$$f(\xi) = \xi: \quad (E_2) \quad \gamma_1 \xi_1 + \gamma_2 \xi_2 \quad = \int_{-1}^{1} \xi\, d\xi = 0 \tag{5}$$

$$f(\xi) = \xi^2: \quad (E_3) \quad \gamma_1 \xi_1^2 + \gamma_2 \xi_2^2 = \int_{-1}^{1} \xi^2\, d\xi = \frac{2}{3}$$

$$f(\xi) = \xi^3: \quad (E_4) \quad \gamma_1 \xi_1^3 + \gamma_2 \xi_2^3 = \int_{-1}^{1} \xi^3\, d\xi = 0$$

This *nonlinear* system can be solved analytically if we argue as follows: Since the interval [−1, 1] is *symmetric* about 0, formula (3) should give equal importance to the values of f on [−1, 0] and [0, 1]; that is, we should have

$$\xi_1 = -\xi_2 \quad \text{and} \quad \gamma_2 = \gamma_1$$

It then follows from (E_1) that $\gamma_1 = \gamma_2 = 1$, and from (E_3) that

$$1(\xi_1)^2 + 1(-\xi_1)^2 = \frac{2}{3} \iff \xi_1^2 = \frac{1}{3} \iff \xi_1 = -\frac{1}{\sqrt{3}}, \quad \xi_2 = \frac{1}{\sqrt{3}}$$

So the **two-point Gauss quadrature formula on [−1, 1]** is simply

$$\int_{-1}^{1} f(\xi)\, d\xi \approx f\left(-\frac{1}{\sqrt{3}}\right) + f\left(\frac{1}{\sqrt{3}}\right), \quad \text{where } \frac{1}{\sqrt{3}} \doteq 0.5773502692 \tag{6}$$

By construction [see (5)], (6) is exact for polynomials of degree ≤ 3.

Similarly, the **three-point Gauss quadrature formula on [−1, 1]** is

$$\int_{-1}^{1} f(\xi)\, d\xi \approx \tfrac{1}{9}[5f(-\sqrt{0.6}) + 8f(0) + 5f(\sqrt{0.6})], \quad \text{where } \sqrt{0.6} \doteq 0.7745966692 \tag{7}$$

This formula is exact for polynomials of degree $\leq 2 \cdot 3 - 1 = 5$.

A table of Gauss sample points ξ_k and their weights γ_k for $n = 2, 3, 4, 5, 6$ is given in Table 7.5-1.

TABLE 7.5-1 $\quad \xi_k$ AND γ_k FOR $\displaystyle\int_{-1}^{1} f(\xi)\, d\xi \approx \sum_{k=1}^{n} \gamma_k f(\xi_k), \ n = 2, \ldots, 6.$

n	ξ_k	γ_k	n	ξ_k	γ_k
2	$\pm 1/\sqrt{3}$	1	5	± 0.9061798459	0.2369268850
				± 0.5384693101	0.4786286705
3	$\pm \sqrt{0.6}$	5/9		0	0.5688888889
	0	8/9			
			6	± 0.9324695142	0.1713244924
4	± 0.8611363116	0.3478548451		± 0.6612093865	0.3607615730
	± 0.3399810436	0.6521451549		± 0.2386191861	0.4679139346

Notice from Table 7.5-1 that (i) the Gaussian sample points ξ_k are symmetrically located in the *open* interval $(-1, 1)$ so that (3) *is an open formula*, (ii) the density of the Gaussian sample points ξ_k is greatest near the endpoints of $(-1, 1)$, and (iii) the γ_k's are all positive. More extensive tables and properties of the ξ_k's and γ_k's can be found in [34].

7.5B   GAUSS QUADRATURE ON [a, b]

To use Gauss–Legendre quadrature to integrate $f(x)$ over the arbitrary closed interval $[a, b]$, we simply map the ξ-interval $[-1, 1]$ into the x-interval $[a, b]$ using the linear transformation

$$x = a + \frac{b-a}{2}(\xi + 1), \qquad dx = \frac{b-a}{2}\, d\xi \tag{8}$$

(see Figure 6.3-6). Making this substitution in $\int_a^b f(x)\, dx$ gives

$$\int_{x=a}^b f(x)\, dx = \int_{\xi=-1}^1 f\left(a + \frac{b-a}{2}(\xi + 1)\right) \cdot \frac{b-a}{2}\, d\xi \tag{9}$$

$$= \frac{b-a}{2} \int_{\xi=-1}^1 f\left(a + \frac{b-a}{2}(\xi + 1)\right) d\xi$$

If we use a Gauss formula on $[-1, 1]$ to approximate this last integral, we get

$$\boxed{\int_{x=a}^b f(x)\, dx \approx \frac{b-a}{2}\{\gamma_1 f(x_1) + \gamma_2 f(x_2) + \cdots + \gamma_n f(x_n)\}} \tag{10a}$$

where γ_k is the tabulated Gaussian weight associated with the tabulated Gaussian sample point ξ_k in $[-1, 1]$, and x_k is obtained from ξ_k as follows:

$$\boxed{x_k = a + \frac{b-a}{2}(\xi_k + 1), \qquad k = 1, 2, \ldots, n} \tag{10b}$$

These x_k's will be referred to as the n **Gaussian sample points of** $[a, b]$; **n-point Gauss quadrature on** $[a, b]$ thus consists of two steps:

STEP 1: Use (10b) to get the n sample points $x_1, \ldots, x_n$.
STEP 2: Put $x_1, \ldots, x_n$ in (10a) to get the desired integral.

EXAMPLE. Use Gauss quadrature to approximate

$$\text{(a)} \int_0^{0.5} e^x\, dx \qquad \text{(b)} \int_1^{2.2} \ln x\, dx$$

Solution
a. From (10b), the Gaussian sample points on $[0, 0.5]$ are

$$x_k = 0 + \frac{0.5 - 0}{2}(\xi_k + 1) = \frac{1}{4}(\xi_k + 1), \qquad k = 1, 2, \ldots, n \tag{11a}$$

Since e^x has no inflection points, it can be approximated well by a cubic on the "thin" interval $[0, 0.5]$; so we expect n-point Gauss quadrature to give good accuracy when $2n - 1 = 3$ (i.e., $n = 2$). From (11a) and Table 7.5-1,

$$x_1 = \frac{1}{4}\left(-\frac{1}{\sqrt{3}} + 1\right) \doteq 0.105662 \qquad \text{and} \qquad x_2 = \frac{1}{4}\left(\frac{1}{\sqrt{3}} + 1\right) \doteq 0.394338 \tag{11b}$$

Taking these values in the general Gauss formula (10a), we get

$$\int_0^{0.5} e^x \, dx \approx \frac{0.5 - 0}{2} \left\{ 1e^{x_1} + 1e^{x_2} \right\}$$

$$\doteq 0.648712 \quad (\text{Error} = 0.648721 - 0.648712 = 0.000009)$$

This open two-point Gauss formula gives almost $5s$ accuracy, comparable to the six-point Simpson's rule calculations in (c) of the example in Section 7.3B!

b. From (10b), the Gauss sample points on [1, 2.2] are

$$x_k = 1 + \frac{2.2 - 1}{2} (\xi_k + 1) = 1 + 0.6(\xi_k + 1) = 1.6 + 0.6\xi_k \qquad \textbf{(12a)}$$

Again $f(x)$ has no inflection points. However, [1, 2.2] is not a "thin" interval; so we shall use the three-point formula. From Table 7.5-1 and (12a),

$$x_1 \doteq 1.6 + 0.6(-\sqrt{0.6}) \doteq 1.135242, \qquad x_2 = 1.6, \qquad x_3 \doteq 1.6 + 0.6(\sqrt{0.6}) \doteq 2.064758$$

Hence, by the general Gauss quadrature formula (10a),

$$\int_1^{2.2} \ln x \, dx \approx \frac{2.2 - 1}{2} \left\{ \frac{5}{9} \ln x_1 + \frac{8}{9} \ln x_2 + \frac{5}{9} \ln x_3 \right\}$$

$$\doteq 0.534622 \qquad (\text{Error} = 0.534606 - 0.534622 = -0.000016) \qquad \textbf{(12b)}$$

This open three-point Gauss formula gives accuracy comparable to the seven-point estimate $S[0.2]$ obtained in (7) of the example in Section 7.4A. It should be evident that *Gauss quadrature can attain a specified accuracy using about half as many sample points as the Newton–Cotes-based methods of* Section 7.4. This reflects the fact that the degree of exact polynomial fit of an n-point Gauss formula is about twice that of an n-point Newton–Cotes formula.

7.5C   CHOOSING A METHOD FOR ESTIMATING A PROPER INTEGRAL

The method used to evaluate a proper integral $\int_a^b f(x) \, dx$ depends on the situation.

Situation I: The number of sample points n is specified, but their location can be determined by the user.

Such situations arise when sensors that read the *rate of flow* of a liquid or gas are to be *permanently* installed along a fixed length of uniform pipe or tubing as in Figure 6.3-5 and what is wanted is the *volume* through the pipe (i.e., the *integral* of the rate along the pipe). *For maximum accuracy in such a situation, Gaussian quadrature should be used;* for the tubing problem, the sensors should be put at the Gaussian sample points along the pipe, and their readings weighted as in the Gauss quadrature formula (10a). (Exercise 7-38).

Situation II: The function values are known only at a discrete set of x's.
Such situations arise when dealing with tabulated functions or values generated by a computer printout. *In such situations, one has no choice but to use the method of Section 7.3A if the x_k's are unevenly spaced, or the composite rules of Section 7.4 if they are equispaced.* [See also Exercise 7-27(e).]

Situation III: $f(x)$ can be evaluated wherever necessary to determine $\int_a^b f(x)\,dx$ to a specified accuracy.

In this commonly occurring situation, one should first draw a sketch if necessary to ensure that the integral is proper (i.e., that $f(x)$ has no singularities on $[a, b]$).

In order to determine that the desired accuracy has been achieved, it is necessary to obtain at least one additional, more accurate approximation. It is here that the greater accuracy of the Gauss formulas is offset by the fact that, *unlike Romberg integration, one cannot reuse previous sample values.* Thus to test the accuracy of an n-point Gauss formula on $[a, b]$, the reasonable approach of bisecting $[a, b]$ and using the formula over each half requires $2n$ *additional* evaluations, more than twice as many as the $n - 1$ "new" evaluations needed to get $T[h/2]$ for Romberg integration [see (11) of Section 7.4A]. And Romberg integration does not require transforming ξ_k into x_k. So, *in this situation, Romberg integration is generally preferable for hand calculation*; programs for both methods are about as easy to write and use.

7.6   Discontinuities and Improper Integrals

The accuracy of all quadrature formulas considered so far rests on the ability to approximate the integrand $f(x)$ by a polynomial on the interval of integration $[a, b]$. Since polynomials are continuous for all x, special care is needed to obtain accurate estimates of $\int_a^b f(x)\,dx$ when $f(x)$ has discontinuities on $[a, b]$. Indeed, quadrature formulas that are generally $O(h^n)$ converge much more slowly as $h \to 0$ if $f(x)$ has singularities on $[a, b]$. *It is therefore important to examine the integrand carefully to see if it has any discontinuities on $[a, b]$ before using any numerical integration method.* Similarly, special care is needed if the interval of integration is unbounded, that is $[a, \infty)$, $(-\infty, b]$, or $(-\infty, \infty)$.

7.6A   REMOVABLE DISCONTINUITIES ON $[a, b]$

Suppose that f is continuous on the open interval (a, b) but has a **removable discontinuity** at a and/or b, that is, $f(a)$ and/or $f(b)$ are not defined but *both*

$$f(a^+) = \lim_{x \to a^+} f(x) \qquad \text{and} \qquad f(b^-) = \lim_{x \to b^-} f(x) \tag{1}$$

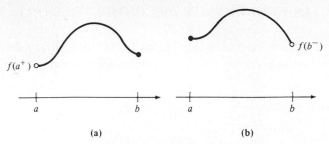

(a)   (b)

FIGURE 7.6-1   REMOVABLE SINGULARITY: (a) AT $x = a$; (b) AT $x = b$.

exist [Figure 7.6-1(a) and (b)]. *When this occurs, closed quadrature formulas can still be used to approximate $\int_a^b f(x)\,dx$ accurately, provided that $f(a^+)$ and $f(b^-)$ are used for $f(a)$ and $f(b)$.*

For example, it is known from calculus that (with x in radians)

$$f(x) = \frac{\sin x}{x} \quad \Rightarrow \quad f(0^+) = \lim_{x \to 0^+} \frac{\sin x}{x} = 1 \tag{2}$$

So Simpson's $\frac{1}{3}$-rule on $[0, 1]$ [see (15a) of Section 7.3B] gives

$$\int_0^1 \frac{\sin x}{x}\,dx \approx \frac{\frac{1}{2}}{3}\left\{ f(0^+) + f(1) + 4f\!\left(\frac{1}{2}\right) \right\} = \frac{1}{6}\left\{ 1 + \frac{\sin 1}{1} + 4\frac{\sin \frac{1}{2}}{\frac{1}{2}} \right\} \doteq 0.946146$$

Alternatively, two-point Gauss quadrature on $[0, 1]$ [see (10) of Section 7.5B] gives

$$\int_0^1 \frac{\sin x}{x}\,dx \approx \frac{1-0}{2}\left\{ f\!\left(\frac{1-1/\sqrt{3}}{2}\right) + f\!\left(\frac{1+1/\sqrt{3}}{2}\right) \right\} \doteq 0.946041 \tag{3}$$

The exact value of $\int_0^1 (\sin x)/x\,dx$ is 0.946083 (6s). So the open two-point Gauss formula achieved about the same accuracy as the closed three-point Simpson formula but *without requiring* $f(0^+)$. It should be clear that Gauss formulas, being open, are especially useful when f has a removable discontinuity at a or b or, more generally, when $f(x)$ is **piecewise continuous** (i.e., has only finitely many discontinuities, each being a *removable* or *finite jump discontinuity*). For example, if $f(x)$ is as shown in Figure 7.6-2, then

$$\int_a^b f(x)\,dx = \int_a^c f(x)\,dx + \int_c^d f(x)\,dx + \int_d^b f(x)\,dx \tag{4}$$

where the integrals over $[a, c]$, $[c, d]$, and $[d, b]$ can be obtained using Gauss quadrature *without finding one-sided limits* as we did in (2).

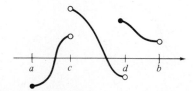

FIGURE 7.6-2   A PIECEWISE CONTINUOUS FUNCTION.

7.6B   INTEGRALS WITH INFINITE DISCONTINUITIES ON $[a, b]$

If the graph of f has a vertical asymptote on $[a, b]$, then $\int_a^b f(x)\,dx$ cannot exist as a proper integral; instead, one defines it as an **improper integral** as follows:

$$\text{If } \lim_{x \to a^+} |f(x)| = \infty, \quad \text{then } \int_a^b f(x)\,dx = \lim_{\epsilon \to 0^+} \int_{a+\epsilon}^b f(x)\,dx \tag{5a}$$

$$\text{If } \lim_{x \to b^-} |f(x)| = \infty, \quad \text{then } \int_a^b f(x)\,dx = \lim_{\epsilon \to 0^+} \int_a^{b-\epsilon} f(x)\,dx \tag{5b}$$

An improper integral is called **convergent** if the appropriate limit as $\epsilon \to 0^+$ converges (to a real number), and **divergent** otherwise.

Unlike the situation in Section 7.6A, there is no way that a polynomial can approximate $f(x)$ on $[a, b]$ if $|f(x)| \to \infty$ somewhere on $[a, b]$. A strategy that can always be employed when this occurs is to **"isolate" the singularity** by evaluating $\int_a^b f(x)\,dx$ as

$$\int_a^b f(x)\,dx = \int_a^{a+\epsilon} f(x)\,dx + \int_{a+\epsilon}^b f(x)\,dx \qquad \text{if } \lim_{x \to a^+} |f(x)| = \infty \tag{6a}$$

or as

$$\int_a^b f(x)\,dx = \int_a^{b-\epsilon} f(x)\,dx + \int_{b-\epsilon}^b f(x)\,dx \qquad \text{if } \lim_{x \to b^-} |f(x)| = \infty \tag{6b}$$

with Gauss quadrature used over the thin ϵ-interval near the singularity, that is, $[a, a + \epsilon]$ in (6a) or $[b - \epsilon, b]$ in (6b). Any convenient method (e.g., Romberg integration) can be used for the remaining *proper* integral (see Figure 7.6-3). For convergent integrals, the integral over the ϵ-interval will approach zero as $\epsilon \to 0^+$.

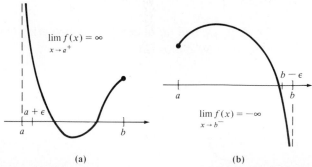

(a)   (b)

FIGURE 7.6-3   ISOLATING A SINGULARITY: (a) AT $x = a$; (b) AT $x = b$.

EXAMPLE. Find (a) $I_1 = \int_0^{\pi/2} \tan x \, dx$ and (b) $I_2 = \int_0^1 dx/\sqrt{x}$ (if they converge).

Solution

a. Since $\tan x \to \infty$ as $x \to \pi/2^-$, (6b) gives

$$I_1 = \int_0^{\beta_1} \tan x \, dx + \int_{\beta_1}^{\pi/2} \tan x \, dx, \qquad \beta_1 = \pi/2 - 0.01 \doteq 1.5607963$$

The (proper) first integral is 4.605187 (6d); five-point Gauss on $[\beta_1, \pi/2]$ gives

$$\int_{\beta_1}^{\pi/2} \tan x \, dx \approx \frac{0.01}{2} \left[\sum_{i=1}^{5} \gamma_i \tan \left(\beta_1 + \frac{0.01}{2} (\xi_i + 1) \right) \right] \doteq 4.566650 \qquad (7)$$

Since (7) is comparable in size to $\int_0^{\beta_1} \tan x \, dx$, we suspect that the given integral may diverge. To check this, we further "isolate" $\pi/2$:

$$\int_{\beta_1}^{\pi/2} \tan x \, dx = \underbrace{\int_{\beta_1}^{\beta_2} \tan x \, dx}_{\doteq 4.605153} + \underbrace{\int_{\beta_2}^{\pi/2} \tan x \, dx}_{\approx 4.566667}, \qquad \beta_2 = \frac{\pi}{2} - 0.0001 \doteq 1.5706963 \quad (8)$$

where five-point Gauss was used for the integral on $[\beta_2, \pi/2]$. We conclude from (7) and (8) that $\int_{\pi/2-\epsilon}^{\pi/2} \tan x \, dx$ does *not* approach 0 as $\epsilon \to 0^+$, and hence that $\int_0^{\pi/2} \tan x \, dx$ diverges. In fact, by the definition (5b),

$$I_1 = \int_0^{\pi/2} \tan x \, dx = \lim_{\epsilon \to 0^+} \left\{ \int_0^{\pi/2-\epsilon} \tan x \, dx \right\} = \lim_{\epsilon \to 0^+} \left\{ -\ln \left| \cos \left(\frac{\pi}{2} - \epsilon \right) \right| \right\} = +\infty.$$

b. Since $1/\sqrt{x} \to \infty$ as $x \to 0^+$,

$$I_2 = \int_0^1 \frac{dx}{\sqrt{x}} = \int_0^{0.01} \frac{dx}{\sqrt{x}} + \int_{0.01}^1 \frac{dx}{\sqrt{x}}$$

The (proper) integral over [0.01, 1] is 1.8; five-point Gauss on [0, 0.01] gives

$$\int_0^{0.01} \frac{dx}{\sqrt{x}} \approx \frac{0.01}{2} \left\{ \sum_{i=1}^{5} \gamma_i \frac{1}{\sqrt{0.005(\xi_i + 1)}} \right\} \doteq 0.184160$$

To check the apparent convergence, we further "isolate" the singularity:

$$\int_0^{0.01} \frac{dx}{\sqrt{x}} = \int_0^{0.0001} \frac{dx}{\sqrt{x}} + \int_{0.0001}^{0.01} \frac{dx}{\sqrt{x}}$$

$$\doteq 0.018416 + 0.18 \quad \text{(using five-point Gauss on [0, 0.0001])}$$

Clearly, the integral is convergent and its value is approximately

$$I_2 \approx 1.8 + 0.18 + 0.018416 = 1.9984616$$

In fact, we can use definition (5a) to see that $I_2 = \int_0^1 dx/\sqrt{x} = 2$. The poor accuracy of five-point Gauss quadrature on [0, 0.0001] results from the poor fit of a polynomial of degree $\leqslant 2 \cdot 5 - 1 = 9$ to $f(x) = 1/\sqrt{x}$ near $x = 0$.

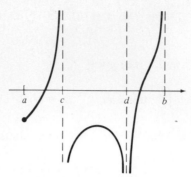

FIGURE 7.6-4 SINGULARITIES AT INTERIOR POINTS OF $[a, b]$.

If f has a singularity at an interior point of $[a, b]$, say as in Figure 7.6-4, then (4) can be used, with (6) applied over each of the subintervals. This improper integral will diverge if any one of $\int_a^c$, $\int_c^d$, or $\int_d^b$ diverges.

7.6C INTEGRALS OVER $[a, \infty)$, $(-\infty, b]$, AND $(-\infty, \infty)$

Definite integrals of a continuous $f(x)$ over the unbounded intervals $[a, \infty)$ and $(-\infty, b]$ cannot be proper, but are defined as the following **improper integrals**

$$\int_a^\infty f(x)\, dx = \lim_{b \to \infty} \int_a^b f(x)\, dx \tag{9a}$$

$$\int_{-\infty}^b f(x)\, dx = \lim_{a \to -\infty} \int_a^b f(x)\, dx \tag{9b}$$

Such an improper integral is **convergent** if the appropriate limit of the proper integral exists (as a real number); otherwise, it is **divergent.**

Two general strategies for evaluating (9) are

Strategy I (Transformation): Make a substitution such as

$$x = u^{-n} \quad \text{so that} \quad dx = -nu^{-(n+1)}\, du \tag{10}$$

or

$$u = e^{nx} \quad \text{so that} \quad x = \frac{\ln u}{n}, \quad dx = \frac{du}{nu} \tag{11}$$

to transform (9) into a u-integral over a bounded interval; then use methods of Sections 7.6A or 7.6B as appropriate.

Strategy II (Isolation) [For $\int_a^\infty f(x)\, dx$]: Sketch $f(x)$ to determine intervals

$$[a, b_1], \quad [b_1, b_2], \quad [b_2, b_3], \quad \ldots \tag{12a}$$

over which f(x) appears to behave like a polynomial. Then evaluate the integral of f(x)
over these intervals in sequence, stopping when it seems clear that

$$\int_a^{b_1} f(x)\,dx + \int_{b_1}^{b_2} f(x)\,dx + \cdots + \int_{b_{n-1}}^{b_n} f(x)\,dx \tag{12b}$$

either has the accuracy that is desired or is diverging. An analogous procedure applies
to $\int_{-\infty}^b f(x)\,dx$.

Integrals over $(-\infty, \infty)$ can be separated into integrals over $(-\infty, c)$ and (c, ∞) for some convenient c. Such integrals converge if and only if both $\int_{-\infty}^c$ and $\int_c^\infty$ converge.

EXAMPLE. Evaluate to 5s: **(a)** $I_1 = \int_1^\infty x^2 e^{-x^2}\,dx$; **(b)** $I_2 = \int_0^\infty \sqrt{x}\,e^{-x}\,dx$.

Solution
a. We try the substitution $u = 1/x^2$ $(x = 1/\sqrt{u},\ dx = -\tfrac{1}{2}u^{-3/2}\,du)$:

$$I_1 = \int_{x=1}^\infty x^2 e^{-x^2}\,dx = \int_{u=1}^0 \frac{1}{u} e^{-1/u}\left(-\frac{1}{2}u^{-3/2}\,du\right) = \frac{1}{2}\int_0^1 \frac{e^{-1/u}}{u^{5/2}}\,du \tag{13}$$

Using L'Hospital's rule, one can show that

$$f(u) = \frac{e^{-1/u}}{u^{5/2}} \quad \Rightarrow \quad f(0^+) = \lim_{u \to 0^+} \frac{e^{-1/u}}{u^{5/2}} = 0 \tag{14}$$

hence that $f(u)$ has a *removable* discontinuity at $u = 0$. One can therefore use any method described in Section 7.6A to get $I_1 \doteq 0.25364$.
    Alternatively, strategy II could have been used to get

$$I_1 = \int_1^3 x^2 e^{-x^2}\,dx + \int_3^{10} x^2 e^{-x^2}\,dx + \int_{10}^{50} x^2 e^{-x^2}\,dx + \cdots$$

$$\doteq 0.253446 + 0.000195 + 0 \doteq 0.25364 \tag{15}$$

with Romberg integration used over the subintervals.
b. We try the substitution $u = e^{-x}$ $(du = -e^{-x}\,dx,\ x = -\ln u)$:

$$I_2 = \int_{x=0}^\infty \sqrt{x}\,e^{-x}\,dx = \int_{u=1}^0 \sqrt{-\ln u}\,(-du) = \int_0^1 \sqrt{\ln(1/u)}\,du \tag{16}$$

This time $f(u) = \sqrt{\ln(1/u)} \to \infty$ as $u \to 0^+$; so the transformed I_2 is improper. Isolating the singularity at 0^+ as in Section 7.6B, we get

$$I_2 = \int_{0.01}^1 \sqrt{\ln\left(\frac{1}{u}\right)}\,du + \int_{0.0001}^{0.01} \sqrt{\ln\left(\frac{1}{u}\right)}\,du + \int_0^{0.0001} \sqrt{\ln\left(\frac{1}{u}\right)}\,du$$

$$\doteq 0.862649 + 0.023273 + 0.000319 \doteq 0.88624 \ (5s) \tag{17}$$

Alternatively, I_2 could have been obtained to $5s$ by integrating $\sqrt{x}\ e^{-x}$ to $6s$ over $[0, 2]$, $[2, 10]$, and $[10, 50]$ (strategy II).

An entertaining presentation of strategies for evaluating improper integrals is given in [1].

7.7 Multiple Integration

We know from calculus that if $f(x, y)$ is continuous over a bounded region R such as that of Figure 7.7-1, then the **double integral over** R is defined as the limit of the Riemann sums:

$$\iint_R f(x, y)\ dA = \lim_{\text{all } \Delta A_i \to 0} \left(\sum_i f(x_i, y_i)\ \Delta A_i \right) \tag{1}$$

where the index i varies over all rectangles that intersect R.

If the **region of integration** R can be described as

$$R = \{(x, y) : a \leqslant x \leqslant b, \quad F_1(x) \leqslant y \leqslant F_2(x) \qquad \text{for each } fixed\ x\} \tag{2}$$

(Figure 7.7-2), then the double integral (1) can be evaluated more easily as the **iterated integral**

$$\iint_R f(x, y)\ dA = \int_{x=a}^b \left[\int_{y=F_1(x)}^{F_2(x)} f(x, y)\ dy \right] dx \tag{3a}$$

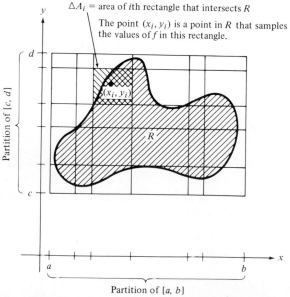

ΔA_i = area of ith rectangle that intersects R

The point (x_i, y_i) is a point in R that samples the values of f in this rectangle.

FIGURE 7.7-1 DOUBLE INTEGRATION.

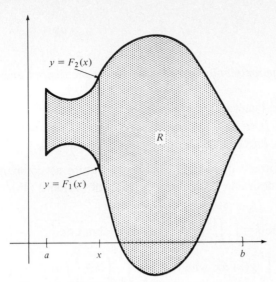

FIGURE 7.7-2 ITERATED INTEGRATION.

The **inner integral** with respect to y [in square brackets in (3a)] is carried out with x held fixed, so its value generally depends on this fixed x. We express this dependence explicitly by rewriting the iterated integral in (3a) as

$$\int_a^b \int_{F_1(x)}^{F_2(x)} f(x, y)\, dy\, dx = \int_a^b g(x)\, dx, \qquad \text{where } g(x) = \int_{y=F_1(x)}^{F_2(x)} f(x, y)\, dy \qquad \textbf{(3b)}$$

This suggests the following procedure.

7.7A GENERAL NUMERICAL PROCEDURE FOR APPROXIMATING
$I = \int_a^b \int_{F_1(x)}^{F_2(x)} f(x, y)\, dy\, dx$

Step I: *Sketch the region R by inspection of*

$$\int_{x=a}^b \int_{y=F_1(x)}^{F_2(x)}$$

Step II: *After assessing how much $g(x)$ in (3b) may vary over $[a, b]$, select a quadrature formula for the x-integral:*

$$I = \int_a^b g(x)\, dx \approx w_1 g(x_1) + \cdots + w_n g(x_n) \qquad \textbf{(4a)}$$

Step III: *For $k = 1, \ldots, n$, assess how much $f(x_k, y)$ (viewed as a function of y) varies over $[F_1(x_k), F_2(x_k)]$, and use a suitable quadrature formula to approximate*

$$g(x_k) = \int_{y=F_1(x_k)}^{F_2(x_k)} f(x_k, y)\, dy \tag{4b}$$

Step IV: Put the approximations (4b) in (4a) to get the desired approximation.

Note 1: Different quadrature formulas may be used for different k's in (4b), depending on the behavior of $f(x_k, y)$ for $F_1(x_k) \le y \le F_2(x_k)$. In particular, the Midpoint Rule often suffices when $F_1(x_k) \approx F_2(x_k)$.

Note 2: The accuracy of n-point Gauss quadrature as compared to other n-point formulas makes it desirable for hand calculation of (4a) and (4b).

EXAMPLE. Estimate $I = \int_0^1 \int_1^{e^x} \left(x + \dfrac{1}{y}\right) dy\, dx$ to about 4s.

Solution. Here $I = \int_0^1 g(x)\, dx$, where $g(x) = \int_1^{e^x} \left(x + \dfrac{1}{y}\right) dy$.

STEP I: The region of integration is shown shaded in Figure 7.7-3.

STEP II: Since $g(x)$ involves e^x and x, which vary like low-degree polynomials for $0 \le x \le 1$, we try three-point Gauss quadrature for the x-integral. By (7) and (10) of Section 7.5B,

$$I = \int_0^1 g(x)\, dx \approx \left(\frac{1-0}{2}\right)\left[\frac{5}{9} g(x_1) + \frac{8}{9} g(x_2) + \frac{5}{9} g(x_3)\right] \tag{5a}$$

where x_1, x_2, and x_3 are the three Gauss sample points on $[0, 1]$, that is,

$$x_1 = \tfrac{1}{2}(1 - \sqrt{0.6}) \doteq 0.11270, \qquad x_2 = \tfrac{1}{2}, \qquad x_3 = \tfrac{1}{2}(1 + \sqrt{0.6}) \doteq 0.88730 \tag{5b}$$

STEP III: Since $1/y$ varies slowly for $1 \le y \le e^{x_k}$, $k = 1, 2, 3$, we approximate (5a) by obtaining $g(x_1)$, $g(x_2)$, and $g(x_3)$, as follows:

$$g(x_1) = \int_1^{e^{x_1}} \left(x_1 + \frac{1}{y}\right) dy: \qquad \text{use the Midpoint Rule}$$

$$g(x_2) = \int_1^{e^{x_2}} \left(x_2 + \frac{1}{y}\right) dy: \qquad \text{use two-point Gauss quadrature}$$

$$g(x_3) = \int_1^{e^{x_3}} \left(x_3 + \frac{1}{y}\right) dy: \qquad \text{use two-point Gauss quadrature}$$

The five required sample points of R are shown in Figure 7.7-3, where

$$y_{11} = \text{midpoint of } [1, e^{x_1}] = \frac{e^{x_1} + 1}{2} \doteq 1.05965$$

y_{21} and y_{22} are the two Gauss sample points of $[1, e^{x_2}]$, that is,

$$y_{21} = 1 + \frac{e^{x_2} - 1}{2}\left(1 - \frac{1}{\sqrt{3}}\right) = 1.13709, \quad y_{22} = 1 + \frac{e^{x_2} - 1}{2}\left(1 + \frac{1}{\sqrt{3}}\right) \doteq 1.51163$$

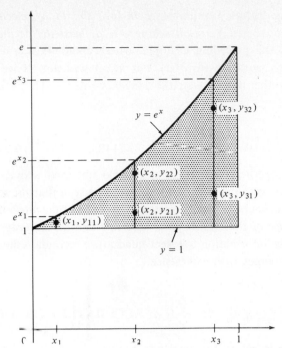

FIGURE 7.7-3 $R = \{(x, y): 0 \le x \le 1, 1 \le y \le e^x \text{ FOR EACH FIXED } x\}.$

and y_{31} and y_{32} are the two Gauss sample points of $[1, e^{x_3}]$, that is,

$$y_{31} = 1 + \frac{e^{x_3} - 1}{2}\left(1 - \frac{1}{\sqrt{3}}\right) = 1.30189, \quad y_{32} = 1 + \frac{e^{x_3} - 1}{2}\left(1 + \frac{1}{\sqrt{3}}\right) \doteq 2.12667$$

[see (10b) of Section 7.5B]. So the Midpoint Rule on $[1, e^{x_1}]$ gives

$$g(x_1) \approx (e^{x_1} - 1)\left(x_1 + \frac{1}{y_{11}}\right) \doteq 0.126026 \qquad \text{[Exact value} \doteq 0.126145]$$

and two-point Gauss quadrature on $[1, e^{x_2}]$ and $[1, e^{x_3}]$ gives

$$g(x_2) \approx \frac{e^{x_2} - 1}{2}\left[\left(x_2 + \frac{1}{y_{21}}\right) + \left(x_2 + \frac{1}{y_{22}}\right)\right] \doteq 0.824192 \qquad \text{[Exact value} = 0.824361]$$

$$g(x_3) \approx \frac{e^{x_3} - 1}{2}\left[\left(x_3 + \frac{1}{y_{31}}\right) + \left(x_3 + \frac{1}{y_{32}}\right)\right] \doteq 2.15208 \qquad \text{[Exact value} = 2.15486]$$

STEP IV: Putting these values in (5), we get $I \approx 0.999115$. The exact value is

$$I = \int_0^1 \left(xy + \ln y\right)\Big]_{y=1}^{e^x} dx = \int_0^1 xe^x \, dx = (x - 1)e^x \Big]_0^1 = 0e^1 - (-1)e^0 = 1.0000$$

The accuracy of Gauss quadrature made it possible to get almost $3s$ accuracy using the values of $f(x, y)$ at only five sample points of R.

In general, *the quadrature formulas used in* (4b) *should be selected so as to try to ensure that* $g(x_1), \ldots, g(x_n)$ *are all accurate to at least the decimal place accuracy expected in* (4a). In the preceding example, where about 4s was desired, $g(x_1)$ and $g(x_2)$ were sufficiently accurate (to 3^+d), but $g(x_3)$ was not. If we used three-point Gauss quadrature (rather than 2) on the longer y-interval $[1, e^{x_3}]$, we would have obtained

$$g(x_3) = \frac{e^{x_3} - 1}{2} \left[\frac{5}{9}\left(x_3 + \frac{1}{1.16001}\right) + \frac{8}{9}\left(x_3 + \frac{1}{1.71428}\right) + \frac{5}{9}\left(x_3 + \frac{1}{2.26756}\right) \right] \doteq 2.15473$$

Putting this $g(x_3)$, together with $g(x_1)$ and $g(x_2)$ obtained above, in (5) gives $I \approx 0.999851$, which is accurate to almost 4s. It can thus be seen that *the selection of quadrature formulas for* (4b) *should take into account the lengths of the intervals* $[F_1(x_k), F_2(x_k)]$ *as well as the behavior of* $f(x_k, y)$ *on these intervals and the accuracy expected in* (4a). The ability to use this information to select quadrature formulas efficiently when doing a hand computation comes with experience.

7.7B GETTING $I = \int_a^b \int_{F_1(x)}^{F_2(x)} f(x, y)\, dy\, dx$ ACCURATELY ON A COMPUTER

If a subroutine for Romberg integration is available, it can be used as follows:

Romberg Integration for Evaluating $I = \displaystyle\int_a^b \int_{F_1(x)}^{F_2(x)} f(x, y)\, dy\, dx$

Step 1: Write a FUNCTION *subprogram that uses Romberg integration to evaluate*

$$g(x) = \int_{F_1(x)}^{F_2(x)} f(x, y)\, dy \qquad \text{for any fixed } x$$

to a bit more than the prescribed accuracy.

Step 2: Evaluate $I = \displaystyle\int_a^b g(x)\, dx$ *to the desired accuracy using Romberg integration.*

EXAMPLE. Suppose that we wanted the value of the iterated integral I of the preceding example to 5s. Using the Composite Trapezoidal Rule $T[h]$ [see (2a) and (11) of Section 7.4A] with $n = 2, 4, 8$ panels to approximate $I = \int_0^1 g(x)\, dx$ [with Romberg integration used to get the $g(x_k)$'s to 6s], we get

$$n_0 = 2: \quad T\left[\frac{1}{2}\right] = \frac{1}{2}\left\{\frac{g(0) + g(1)}{2} + g\left(\frac{1}{2}\right)\right\} \doteq \frac{1}{2}\{2.18350\} = 1.09175$$

$$2n_0 = 4: \quad T\left[\frac{1}{4}\right] = \frac{1}{2}\left\{1.09175 + \frac{1}{2}\sum_{\text{odd}}\left[\frac{1}{4}\right]\right\} \doteq \frac{1}{2}\{2.04614\} = 1.02307$$

$$4n_0 = 8: \quad T\left[\frac{1}{8}\right] = \frac{1}{2}\left\{1.02307 + \frac{1}{4}\sum_{\text{odd}}\left[\frac{1}{8}\right]\right\} = \frac{1}{2}\{2.01155\} = 1.00578$$

The Romberg table for I is given in Table 7.7-1.

TABLE 7.7-1 ROMBERG TABLE FOR $I = \int_0^1 g(x)\,dx$.

h	$T[h]$	$T_1[h] = S[h]$	$T_2[h]$
$\frac{1}{2}$	1.09175		
$\frac{1}{4}$	1.02307	1.00018	
$\frac{1}{8}$	1.00578	1.00002	1.00001

It is clear from the last row that $I \doteq 1.0000$ (5s).

If Steps 1 and 2 are implemented in a language such as Pascal or PL/I, which allows a subroutine to call itself (such calls are called **recursive** calls), only one Romberg integration subprogram is needed. However, if implemented in FORTRAN (which does not allow recursive calls), separate Romberg integration algorithms are needed for Steps 1 and 2.

Exercises

Section 7.1

7-1. Find the $O(h^{n+1})$ approximation of $f(h)$ [see (5) of Section 7.1A].
  (a) $n = 3$, $f(h) = \ln(1 + h)$ **(b)** $n = 5$, $f(h) = \cos h$
  (c) $n = 3$, $f(h) = \sqrt{1 + h}$ **(d)** $n = 2$, $f(h) = 1/(1 + h)$

7-2. Let $f(x) = \ln x$ and $x = 1$. Show that when $h = 0.95$, $\Delta f(x)/h$ approximates $\ln'(x) = 1/x = 1$ more accurately than $\delta f(x)/2h$. Does this mean that the $O(h)$ formula $\Delta f(x)/h$ is more accurate than the $O(h^2)$ formula $\delta f(x)/(2h)$ for this $f(x)$ and x? Explain.

7-3. Use definition (2) to prove (9a), (9b), and (9c) of Section 7.1A.

7-4. The $E[H]$ column of Figure 1.1-2 gives the truncation error of using $\Delta f(x)/h$ to approximate $\sin'(x)$ when $x = 0$. Notice that $E[\frac{1}{2}H] \approx \frac{1}{4}E[H]$, indicating that $E[H]$ is $O(h^2)$, *not* $O(h)$! Explain.

7-5. Suppose you know that the truncation error of the formula $F[h]$ is of the form $\tau[h] = h^2 + O(h^5)$ and you have the estimates

$$F[0.5] = 2, \qquad F[0.1] = 1, \qquad F[0.05] = 0.4$$

Use Richardson's formula to find
  (a) $F_1[0.1]$ **(b)** $F_1[0.05]$ **(c)** $F_2[0.05]$.

In Exercises 7-6 through 7-11, do parts (a) and (b) for the given formula $F[h]$.
  (a) Approximate the indicated derivative by $F[h]$ and $F[h/r]$. Then determine if $\tau[h/r] \approx \tau[h]/r^n$ where n is the order of $F[h]$. If not, explain.

(b) Perform one Richardson improvement and discuss the accuracy of $F_1[h/r]$. (NOTE: h will be larger than h/r. So take h as h_{larger} in the formula.)

7-6. $d(x^2 - 2x)/dx$, $x = 0$, $h = 0.6$, $r = 3$; $F[h] = \Delta f(x)/h$.

7-7. $d^2(\ln x)/dx^2$, $x = 1$, $h = 0.2$, $r = 4$; $F[h] = \delta^2 f(x)/h^2$.

7-8. $d^3(e^{-x})/dx^3$, $x = 1$, $h = -0.1$, $r = 5$; $F[h]$ is (18c) of Section 7.2B.

7-9. $d(\sqrt{x})/dx$, $x = 0.2$, $h = 0.2$, $r = 2$; $F[h] = \delta f(x)/2h$.

7-10. $d(x^4)/dx$, $x = 1$, $h = 1$, $r = 2$; $F[h] = \delta f(x)/2h$.

7-11. $d^2(\cos x)/dx^2$, $x = 0$, $h = \pi/3$, $r = 3$; $F[h]$ is (20b) of Section 7.2B.

7-12. Let $f(x) = e^x$, $x = 0$, and $F[h] = \Delta f(x)/h$.
  (a) Approximate $f'(x)$ by $F[h]$ with $h = 0.5$, 0.1, and 0.05.
  (b) Make a Richardson table as in Section 7.1E for $F[0.5]$, $F[0.1]$, and $F[0.05]$. Note that the r-ratios 0.5/0.1 and 0.1/0.05 are *not* the same.

7-13. Repeat Exercise 7-12 but with $F[h] = \delta f(x)/2h$ as in Section 7.1F. Compare the accuracy of $F_2[0.05]$ with that of Exercise 7-12. Explain your result.

7-14. Repeat Exercise 7-12 but with $f(x) = x^{3/2}$. Compare the accuracy of $F_2[0.05]$ with that of Exercise 7-12. Try to explain your result.

Section 7.2

In Exercises 7-15 and 7-16, sketch the tabulated points, then use the formulas of Section 7.2 (together with Richardson improvement if possible) to get estimates of the indicated derivatives from the tabulated points.

7-15.

x	0	0.5	1.0	1.5	2.0	2.5	3.0	3.5	4.0
$f(x)$		3.96	1.00	0.74	2.04	4.00	5.96	7.50	8.44	8.44

  (a) $f'(0^+) = \lim\limits_{x \to 0^+} f'(x)$ **(b)** $f''(1.5)$ **(c)** $f'(3)$

  (d) $f''(4^-) = \lim\limits_{x \to 4^-} f''(x)$ **(e)** $f^{(iv)}(2)$ **(f)** $f'''(1)$

7-16.

x	0	2	4	6	8	10	12	14	16	18	20
$f(x)$		150	149	142	123	86	25	99	137	151	153	155

Assume that $f(x)$ is *not* differentiable at $x = 10$, that is, $f'(10^-) \neq f'(10^+)$.

  (a) $f''(0^+) = \lim\limits_{x \to 0^+} f''(x)$ **(b)** $f'(4)$ **(c)** $f'''(8)$

  (d) $f'(20^-) = \lim\limits_{x \to 20^-} f'(x)$ **(e)** $f^{(iv)}(10^+)$ **(f)** $f''(14)$

7-17. Obtain formula (9) of Section 7.2A from (7) and (8).

7-18. Carry out the details of deriving **(a)** (16) of Section 7.2B, **(b)** (17) of Section 7.2B.

7-19. **(a)** Let $f(x) = \sqrt{x}$, $x = 3$, and $h = -1$. Estimate $f'(x) = \frac{1}{2}x^{-1/2}$ using:
  (i) the $O(h^2)$ backward difference formula (13) of Section 7.2B.
  (ii) the $O(h^3)$ backward difference formula (17) of Section 7.2B.

(b) Explain why (ii) is less accurate than (i) although it uses more points and is higher order (see Exercise 5-19).

7-20. **Using Lagrange polynomials to derive finite difference formulas,** suppose that the $(n + 1)$-point formula

$$f^{(k)}(x) \approx C_0 f(x_0) + C_1 f(x_1) + \cdots + C_n f(x_n)$$

is known to be exact for polynomials of degree $\leqslant n$. Prove:

(a) The "weight" C_i can be obtained as the kth derivative at x of the ith Lagrange polynomial for $x_0, \ldots, x_n$, that is, as

$$C_i = L_i^{(k)}(x), \qquad i = 0, 1, \ldots, n$$

(b) The "weights" must sum to zero, that is, $C_0 + C_1 + \cdots + C_n = 0$.
[HINT: Consider $f(x) = L_i(x)$ for (a), and $f(x) \equiv 1$ for (b).]

7-21. Use the formula $C_i = L_i^{(k)}(x)$ to find C_0, C_1, and C_2 in the formula

$$f^{(k)}(x) \approx C_0 f(x - h) + C_1 f(x) + C_2 f(x + h)$$

(a) when $k = 1$ [cf. $\delta f(x)/2h$]   **(b)** when $k = 2$ [cf. $\delta^2 f(x)/h^2$]

Section 7.3

7-22. Find the weights that make the quadrature formula

$$\int_0^3 f(x)\, dx \approx w_1 f(-1) + w_2 f(0) + w_3 f(2) + w_4 f(4)$$

exact for cubics. [See part (c) of the example in Section 7.3A.]

7-23. Using the $L_{i,n}(t)$'s of Table 7.3-1 and (13) of Section 7.3B, derive
(a) Simpson's $\frac{1}{3}$-rule (15a) of Section 7.3B.
(b) The Adams $O(h^5)$ predictor (17a) of Section 7.3B.
(c) The Adams $O(h^5)$ corrector (18a) of Section 7.3B.

7-24. Show that if an $(n + 1)$-point quadrature formula of the form

$$\int_a^b f(x)\, dx \approx w_0 f(x_0) + w_1 f(x_1) + \cdots + w_n f(x_n)$$

is exact for polynomials of degree $\leqslant n$, then $w_0 + w_1 + \cdots + w_n = b - a$.

7-25. Verify that Simpson's $\frac{1}{3}$-rule is exact for $f(x) = x^3$ on $[0, 2]$.

Section 7.4

7-26. Using the values tabulated in Exercise 7-15, estimate
(a) $\int_0^3 f(x)\, dx$ using the Midpoint Rule on $[0, 1]$, $[1, 2]$, and $[2, 3]$.
(b) $\int_0^3 f(x)\, dx$ using $T[h]$ with $h = 1$ (three panels).
(c) $\int_0^3 f(x)\, dx$ using $S[h]$ with $h = \frac{1}{2}$ (six panels).
(d) $\int_0^3 f(x)\, dx$ using Romberg integration starting with three panels.
(e) $\int_0^4 f(x)\, dx$ using Romberg integration starting with one panel.
(f) $\int_0^{3.5} f(x)\, dx$ using $S[h]$ on $[0, 2]$ and Simpson's $\frac{3}{8}$-rule on $[2, 3.5]$.

7-27. Using the $f(x)$ values tabulated in Exercise 7-16, estimate

(a) $\int_2^{10} f(x)\,dx$ using Romberg integration starting with one panel.

(b) $\int_{18}^{20} f(x)\,dx$ using the Adams corrector (18a) of Section 7.3B.

(c) $\int_0^2 f(x)\,dx$ using the Adams corrector (with $h = -2$).

(d) $\int_8^{12} f(x)\,dx$ as accurately as you can. Bear in mind that $f(x)$ *is not differentiable at $x = 10$.*

(e) $\int_0^{20} f(x)\,dx$ using a combination of Simpson's $\frac{1}{3}$- and $\frac{3}{8}$-rules on each of $[0, 10]$ and $[10, 20]$.

7-28. Evaluate to $5s$ using Romberg integration starting with n_0 panels.

(a) $\int_{-4}^0 x^5\,dx,\ n_0 = 1$ (b) $\int_0^1 e^{-x}\,dx,\ n_0 = 2$

(c) $\int_{-1/2}^{1/2} e^{-x^2}\,dx,\ n_0 = 1$ (d) $\int_{-2}^2 (x^4 - x)\,dx,\ n_0 = 1$

(e) $\int_0^{\pi/4} \tan x\,dx,\ n_0 = 1$ (f) $\int_{-\pi/4}^{\pi/2} \cos x\,dx,\ n_0 = 3$

7-29. Which row of a Romberg table yields $\int_a^b f(x)\,dx$ exactly if $f(x)$ is a polynomial of degree 7? Verify for $\int_0^2 x^7\,dx$; start with one panel.

7-30. Use Romberg integration for $I = \int_0^4 \sqrt{x}\,dx$; start with one panel ($h = 4$) and halve h five times. Can you explain the slow convergence to $I = \frac{16}{3}$?

7-31. (a) From (31) of Section 7.3C, deduce that for the left endpoint approximation,

$$\int_{x_{j-1}}^{x_j} f(x)\,dx \approx f(x_{j-1})h, \qquad \tau[h] = \frac{f'(\xi_j)}{2!}\,h^2, \quad \text{where } x_{j-1} < \xi_j < x_j$$

(b) Argue as in Section 7.4B that the left endpoint Riemann sum $R[h]$ in (2) of Section 7.0 has an $O(h)$ truncation error.

Section 7.5

7-32. Show that making the one-point Gauss quadrature formula

$$\int_{-1}^1 f(\xi)\,d\xi \approx \gamma_1 f(\xi_1) \qquad \text{exact for } f(\xi) \equiv 1 \text{ and } f(\xi) = \xi$$

yields the *Midpoint Rule* (i.e., $\gamma_1 = 2$, $\xi_1 = 0$) (cf. the example in Section 7.5A). (This helps explain why it is exact for polynomials of degree $2 \cdot 1 - 1 = 1$.)

7-33. The nth **Legendre polynomial** $P_n(\xi)$ is defined by the **three-term recurrence relation**

$$P_0(\xi) \equiv 1, \quad P_1(\xi) = \xi, \quad P_{n+1}(\xi) = \frac{1}{n+1}\,[(2n + 1)\,\xi P_n(\xi) - n P_{n-1}(\xi)]$$

(a) Find $P_2(\xi)$, $P_3(\xi)$, . . . , $P_6(\xi)$.

(b) Deduce from the recurrence relation that $P_n(1) = 1$ for all n.

(c) Verify that the tabulated ξ's in Table 7.5-1 are the roots of $P_n(\xi)$ for $n = 2, 3$, and 4.

7-34. (a) What is the smallest n for which n-point Gauss quadrature is exact for seventh-degree polynomials?

(b) Verify your answer to part (a) for $\int_0^2 x^7\,dx$.

7-35. Use n-point Gauss quadrature to approximate the given integral.

(a) $\int_0^3 x^3\,dx,\ n = 2$ (b) $\int_{-1}^2 e^{-x^2} \cos x\,dx,\ n = 3$ (c) $\int_{-1}^1 e^{-x^2} \sin x\,dx,\ n = 4$

7-36. Use $(n_0 + 2)$-point Gauss quadrature for the integrals in Exercise 7-28, (a)–(f).

7-37. Estimate $I = \int_0^4 \sqrt{x}\, dx$ using (a) three-point and (b) five-point Gauss quadrature. Why is the improvement so slight? (Cf. Exercise 7-30.)

7-38. Assuming that the tubing shown in Figure 6.3-5 is 60 m long, describe (i) where you would position the five sensors, and (ii) how you would weight the readings to get accurate estimates of the *integral* of the sampled quantity along the tube.

Section 7.6

7-39. In (a)–(g) sketch the graph of f over $[a, b]$ and verify that f is either continuous or piecewise continuous on $[a, b]$. Then:

(i) Subdivide $[a, b]$ into one or more subintervals so that $f(x)$ appears polynomial-like over the interior of each subinterval.

(ii) Integrate $f(x)$ as indicated ($n_0 =$ initial number of panels) over each subinterval, then add your answers to get $I = \int_a^b f(x)\, dx$ to the stated desired accuracy. (See Section 7.6A.)

	$f(x)$	a	b	Method	Accuracy of I
(a)	$(e^x - 1)/x$	0	2	Romberg ($n_0 = 1$)	$4s$
(b)	$\lvert x^3 - 1 \rvert$	0	2	Three-point Gauss	Exact
(c)	$(1 - \cos x)/x^2$	0	1	Romberg ($n_0 = 1$)	$4s$
(d)	e^{-x^2} (Be careful!)	0	50	Romberg ($n_0 = 2$)	$4s$
(e)	$(x^3 - 5x - 1)\operatorname{sgn}(x)$	-1	1	Two-point Gauss	Exact
(f)	$(x^4 - 1)/(x + 1)$	-1	0	Romberg ($n_0 = 1$)	Exact

7-40. In (a)–(d), state why the integral is improper and describe in detail one or more strategies for determining either that it diverges or its value to $4s$.

(a) $\displaystyle\int_0^\pi \frac{\sin x}{x^{3/2}}\, dx$
(b) $\displaystyle\int_0^1 \frac{e^x}{x^2}\, dx$
(c) $\displaystyle\int_0^1 \frac{\ln x\, dx}{\sqrt{1 - x^2}}$
(d) $\displaystyle\int_0^1 \frac{e^x}{\sqrt[3]{x}}\, dx$

7-41. Repeat Exercise 7-40 but for the following integrals:

(a) $\displaystyle\int_0^\infty \frac{dx}{e^x + e^{-x}}$
(b) $\displaystyle\int_1^\infty \frac{dx}{\sqrt{x}\,(1 + x)}$
(c) $\displaystyle\int_0^\infty e^{-x^2} \ln x\, dx$

(d) $\displaystyle\int_{-\infty}^\infty \left(\frac{\cos x}{e^{-x}}\right)^2 dx$

Section 7.7

7-42. Approximate as $\int_a^b g(x)\, dx$ as indicated, showing the sample points on a sketch of R as in Figure 7.7-3.

(a) $\displaystyle\int_{-1}^1 \int_0^1 (e^{3x} - y)\, dy\, dx$
$\left\{ \begin{array}{l} \text{Use four-point Gauss for } \int_{-1}^1 \cdot\ dx; \\ \text{two-point Gauss for } g(x_i). \end{array} \right.$

(b) $\displaystyle\int_{-1}^1 \int_0^{\pi/3} e^x \tan y\, dy\, dx$
$\left\{ \begin{array}{l} \text{Use two-point Gauss for } \int_{-1}^1 \cdot\ dx; \\ \text{the Midpoint Rule for } g(x_1), g(x_2). \end{array} \right.$

(c) $\int_{2}^{4}\int_{1/2}^{\sqrt{x}} xy\, dy\, dx$ $\left\{\begin{array}{l} \text{Use two-point Gauss for } \int_{2}^{4} \cdot\, dx; \\ \text{the Midpoint Rule for } g(x_1),\ g(x_2). \end{array}\right.$

(d) $\int_{0}^{4}\int_{x^2/2}^{2x} (e^x - y)\, dy\, dx$ $\left\{\begin{array}{l} \text{Use three-point Gauss for } \int_{0}^{4} \cdot\, dx; \text{ Simpson's} \\ \tfrac{1}{3}\text{-rule for } g(x_2); \text{ the Midpoint Rule for } g(x_1),\ g(x_2). \end{array}\right.$

(e) $\int_{0}^{\pi/2}\int_{\tan\,(x/2)}^{\sin\,x} (x + y)\, dy\, dx$ $\left\{\begin{array}{l} \text{Use Simpson's } \tfrac{3}{8}\text{-rule for } \int_{0}^{\pi/2} \cdot\, dx; \\ \text{Simpson's } \tfrac{1}{3}\text{-rule for } g(x_1) \text{ and } g(x_2). \end{array}\right.$

NOTE: Here $g(x_0) = g(0) = 0$, and $g(x_3) = g(\pi/2) = 0$. (Verify.)

(f) $\int_{0}^{1}\int_{x^2}^{x} e^{xy}\, dy\, dx$ {Try to get $2s$ accuracy.}

(g) $\int_{0}^{2}\int_{1-x}^{e^{-x}} \sqrt{x + y}\, dy\, dx$ {Try to get $2s$ accuracy.}

Computer and Programming Exercises

7-43. Assume that the truncation error of $F[h]$ satisfies

$$\tau[h] = Ch^{n_0} + Dh^{n_0+\Delta n} + Eh^{n_0+2\Delta n} + Fh^{n_0+3\Delta n} + \cdots$$

(a) Write a subroutine EXTRAP(k, *F0*, **row**, *NextF0*, r, n, Δn) that uses the $(k-1)$st row of a Richardson table stored as

$$[F0 : \textbf{row}] = [F_0[h] : F_1[h] \quad F_2[h] \quad \cdots \quad F_{k-1}[h]]$$

and the scalar *NextF0* to form the kth row as

$$[NextF0 : \textbf{row}] = [F_0[h/r] : F_1[h/r] \quad F_2[h/r] \quad \cdots \quad F_k[h/r]]$$

(b) Let F(h, other parameters) be a FUNCTION subprogram that forms $F[h]$ (to approximate Q). Use F and EXTRAP of part (a) as follows in a FUNCTION subprogram

$$\text{APPROX(F, } MaxRows,\ n_0,\ \Delta n,\ h_0,\ r,\ \text{other parameters)}$$

which returns APPROX as the kth entry of the array **row** as follows:

```
{initialize}
GET MaxRows, termination test parameters,
      n0, Δn, h0, r, other parameters
h ← h0
F0 ← F(h, other parameters)   {This is F0[h0].}

{iterate}
DO FOR k = 1 TO MaxRows UNTIL termination test is satisfied
   BEGIN
   h ← h/r
```

NextF0 ← F(h, other parameters) {This is $F_0[h_0/r^k]$.}
{**get next row**} Invoke EXTRAP(k, F_0, **row**, *NextF0*, r, n_0, Δn).
{**update**} *F0* ← *NextF0*
{**termination test:** |**row**(k) − **row**(k − 1)| ≈ 0}
END

{If **termination test** succeeded, then **row**(k) approximates the quantity Q to the desired accuracy}

(c) Write a FUNCTION subprogram F(h, f, x) that returns $\Delta f(x)/h$. Use it with $f(x) = e^x$, $h_0 = 0.2$, and $r = 10$ [as in Section 7.1B] to test your subprogram of part (b).

(d) *Romberg Integration:* Write a subprogram F(h, f, a, b, *PrevTrap*) to form $F = T[h]$ from *PrevTrap* $= T[2h]$ using the Recursive Form

$$T[h] = \tfrac{1}{2}\{T[2h] + 2h \sum_{odd}[h]\}$$

Use this F in your subprogram of part (b) to get the results of the example in Section 7.4D.

7-44. Write a FUNCTION subprogram GAUSS(f, a, b) that returns the result of using five-point Gauss quadrature to integrate $f(x)$ over [a, b]. Test it with $f(x) = e^x$ on [0, 1].

7-45. For (a)–(d) of Exercise 7-40, use any available programs to evaluate the integral to $5s$ or to determine that it is divergent.

7-46. Same as Exercise 7-45 but for (a)–(d) of Exercise 7-41.

7-47. (a) Write a pseudocode incorporating the subprogram in Exercise 7-43(d) to evaluate

$$\int_a^b \int_{F_1(x)}^{F_2(x)} f(x, y)\, dy\, dx$$

as described in Section 7.7B.

(b) Use your pseudocode in part (a) as the basis for a FUNCTION subprogram

DBLINT(f, a, b, F_1, F_2, termination test parameters)

(Those readers who are familiar with recursive subroutine calls may find this to be an interesting exercise.)

8

Numerical Methods for Ordinary Differential Equations

Introduction 8.0

The world rarely reveals itself to us as observable relationships among the relevant variables. What it does make evident are relationships that describe how both the *variables and their rates of change* (i.e., *derivatives*) affect each other (i.e., **differential equations**).

Given a differential equation involving one or more physical quantities (e.g., displacement, temperature, voltage, concentration, population, etc.), the problem of interest is to find the relationship it imposes upon the variables themselves (i.e., to find its *solution*). There are special differential equations for which explicit analytic solutions can be found; unfortunately, however, these are unlikely to arise in nontrivial engineering and scientific applications. Consequently, it is important to know how to solve differential equations *numerically*.

Our attention will be confined to systems for which all dependent variables (denoted by y's) depend on a *single* independent variable (denoted by t), that is, *ordinary differential equations*. The simple *initial value problem* (IVP)

$$\frac{dy}{dt} = f(t, y), \qquad y = y_0 \quad \text{when } t = t_0$$

is considered first in Sections 8.1–8.3. The two major classes of methods, *Runge–Kutta* and *Predictor–Corrector,* are described and compared, and practical software is presented and used.

Then, in Section 8.4, matrix notation is used to generalize these methods to coupled *systems of n first-degree differential equations* involving n dependent variables, and this in turn is used to solve nth-order IVPs of the form

$$y^{(n)} = f(t, y, \ldots, y^{(n-1)}), \qquad y^{(k)}(t_0) = y_{0k}, \quad k = 0, 1, \ldots, n-1$$

Finally, in Section 8.5 we describe the *Shooting Method* and *Finite Difference Method* for solving the two-point *Boundary Value Problem* (BVP)

$$y'' = f(t, y, y'), \qquad y(a) = \alpha, \quad y(b) = \beta$$

Unlike the preceding chapters, a programmable device is a virtual necessity if accurate numerical solutions of ordinary differential equations are to be found without an inordinate amount of work.

8.1   Introduction to Solving the Initial Value Problem (IVP)

In this section we lay the groundwork for efficient numerical methods for solving the general **first-order initial value problem**

$$\text{(IVP)} \quad \boxed{\frac{dy}{dt} = f(t, y) \qquad \text{subject to} \qquad y = y_0 \ \text{ when } t = t_0} \tag{1}$$

8.1A   EXISTENCE AND UNIQUENESS OF SOLUTIONS

A **solution** of (IVP) is a function $y(t)$ that satisfies

$$\frac{d}{dt}[y(t)] = f(t, y(t)) \qquad \text{and} \qquad y(t_0) = y_0 \tag{2}$$

In words, $y(t)$ is a solution of (IVP) if the function of t obtained by replacing y by $y(t)$ in $f(t, y)$ is the derivative of $y(t)$, and $y = y(t)$ satisfies the **initial condition:** $y = y_0$ when $t = t_0$. Geometrically, the graph of a solution satisfies

1. Its slope at the point (t, y) is $f(t, y)$.
2. It goes through the point (t_0, y_0) in the ty-plane.

as shown in Figure 8.1-1. The fact that the graph of a solution is "nailed down" at (t_0, y_0) and gets traced with slope precisely $f(t, y)$ at each point (t, y) on it suggests that for any "reasonable" $f(t, y)$ and any "reasonable" initial condition $y(t_0) = y_0$, (IVP) will have a unique solution. To see the extent to which this is true, let us examine three examples.

EXAMPLE 1. Discuss the existence and uniqueness of $y(t)$ for the IVP

$$\frac{dy}{dt} = -ty^2 \qquad \text{subject to} \qquad y = 1 \quad \text{when } t = 2 \tag{3}$$

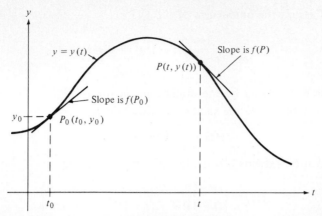

FIGURE 8.1-1   GRAPH OF THE SOLUTION OF (IVP): $y' = f(t, y)$, $y(t_0) = y_0$.

Solution. Upon separating variables and integrating, we see that any solution $y = y(t)$ must satisfy

$$-\int \frac{dy}{y^2} = \int t \, dt \quad \Leftrightarrow \quad \frac{1}{y} = \frac{1}{2} t^2 + C \quad \Leftrightarrow \quad y = \frac{2}{t^2 + 2C} \tag{4}$$

where C is an arbitrary constant. However, to satisfy the initial condition $y(2) = 1$, C must be -1. So

$$y(t) = \frac{2}{t^2 - 2} \tag{5}$$

is the only possible solution for $t > \sqrt{2}$. This $y(t)$ is a solution of the IVP in (3) because

$$\frac{d}{dt}[y(t)] = \frac{-4t}{(t^2 - 2)^2} = -t[y(t)]^2 = f(t, y(t)) \quad \text{and} \quad y(2) = \frac{2}{4 - 2} = 1$$

However, the initial condition at $t = 2$ does *not* "nail down" the solution to the left of $t = \sqrt{2}$. In fact $y(t)$ can be extended to the left of $t = \sqrt{2}$ using *any* value of C in (4) for $t < \sqrt{2}$ (see Figure 8.1-2).

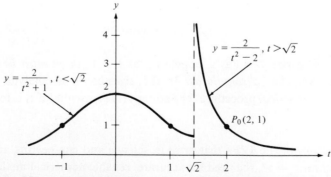

FIGURE 8.1-2   NONUNIQUENESS OF A SOLUTION ACROSS A SINGULARITY OF $y(t)$.

EXAMPLE 2. Discuss the uniqueness of the IVP

$$\frac{dy}{dt} = \frac{2y}{t-1} + (t-1)^2, \qquad y(2) = 3 \tag{6}$$

Solution. After multiplying by the integrating factor $\mu = (t-1)^{-2}$, it is easy to see that for $t > 1$ the only possible solution of this IVP is

$$y(t) = (t-1)^3 + 2(t-1)^2 \tag{7}$$

This solution can be extended to the left of $t = 1$ by taking

$$y(t) = \begin{cases} (t-1)^3 + 2(t-1)^2 & \text{for } t > 1 \\ (t-1)^3 + C(t-1)^2 & \text{for } t \leq 1 \end{cases} \tag{8}$$

where C can be *any* real number. Note that $y(t)$ in (8) will be differentiable at $t = 0$ for any choice of C (Exercise 8-2).

The preceding examples show that we cannot be assured of a *unique* solution across a singularity of *either* $y(t)$ ($t = \sqrt{2}$ in Example 1) or $f(t, y)$ ($t = 1$ in Example 2). However, for most IVPs encountered, the following is true.

> The solution $y(t)$ exists and is unique over any subinterval of the t-axis that contains t_0 and over which *both* $y(t)$ and $f(t, y)$ remain continuous. (9)

We shall assume this to be true of all IVPs considered. More precise existence and uniqueness statements can be found in [5].

EXAMPLE 3. Discuss the existence and uniqueness of the IVP

$$y' = t^2 + y^2, \qquad y(0) = 1 \tag{10}$$

Solution. Despite the simplicity of $f(t, y)$ [the slope at (t, y) is the square of its distance to the origin], there is no formula in terms of the elementary functions for $y(t)$! However, since $f(t, y) = t^2 + y^2$ is continuous for all (t, y), $y(t)$ exists and is unique over any interval containing $t_0 = 0$ and over which $y(t)$ is continuous. And since $t^2 \geq 0$, we know from (10) that the slope at (t, y) must satisfy $y'(t) \geq y^2$ for all $t \geq 0$. So whatever $y(t)$ is, for $t \geq 0$ it must satisfy

$$y(t) \geq \hat{y}(t) = \frac{1}{1-t}, \qquad [\hat{y}(t) \text{ is the solution of } y' = y^2, \quad y(0) = 1]$$

(see Figure 8.1-3). Since $\hat{y}(t)$ has a singularity at $t = 1$, *there must be a t_s between 0 and 1 at which $y(t)$ has a singularity.* In the absence of an analytic expression for $y(t)$, an accurate *numerical* procedure for finding $y(t)$ is essential if t_s is to be determined to say $4s$.

Since the $f(t, y)$'s of the IVPs that arise in science and engineering are considerably more complex than $t^2 + y^2$, the need for accurate, reliable numerical methods for solving (IVP) should be clear.

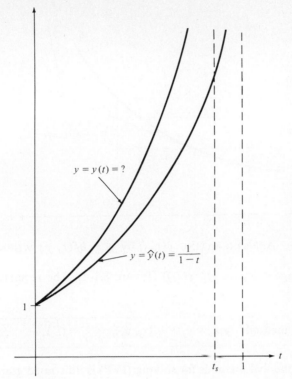

FIGURE 8.1-3   GRAPHS OF $y(t)$ AND $\hat{y}(t) = 1/(1 - t)$.

8.1B   EULER'S METHOD

Let $[t_0, t_F]$ be an interval over which we want the solution $y(t)$ of

$$\text{(IVP)} \quad \frac{dy}{dt} = f(t, y), \quad y(t_0) = y_0$$

If we subdivide $[t_0, t_F]$ into n intervals using a **stepsize**

$$h = \frac{t_F - t_0}{n} \tag{11}$$

we get the points $t_1, \ldots, t_{n-1}$ shown in the following grid:

$$\tag{12}$$

A numerical method for solving (IVP) will start with $y_0 = y(t_0)$ and then generate values $y_1, \ldots, y_n$ such that

$$y_j \text{ approximates the exact value } y(t_j) \quad \text{for } j = 1, \ldots, n \tag{13}$$

For small h, the solution curve $y = y(t)$ can be approximated on the interval

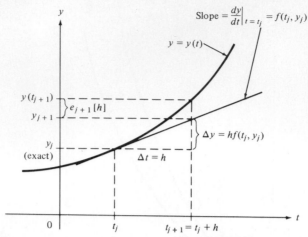

FIGURE 8.1-4   APPROXIMATING $y(t_{j+1})$ BY $y_j + hf(t_j, y_j)$ WHEN $y_j = y(t_j)$.

$[t_j, t_{j+1}]$ by the tangent line at $(t_j, y(t_j))$ (Figure 8.1-4). The recursive formula based on this strategy is

$$\boxed{\textbf{Euler's method}\quad y_{j+1} = y_j + hf(t_j, y_j), \qquad j = 0, 1, \ldots, n-1} \qquad \textbf{(14)}$$

This simplest of numerical methods for solving (IVP) is illustrated graphically in Figure 8.1-5 together with

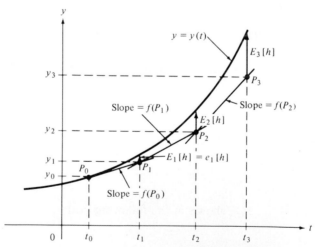

FIGURE 8.1-5   EULER'S METHOD, SHOWING $E_1[h]$, $E_2[h]$, $E_3[h]$.

$$\boxed{E_{j+1}[h] = y(t_{j+1}) - y_{j+1} = \text{the \textbf{accumulated truncation error} at } t_{j+1}} \qquad \textbf{(15)}$$

The error $E_{j+1}[h]$ is also called the **global truncation error** at t_{j+1}. It results from the combined effects of the error of the tangent line approximation (shown as $e_{j+1}[h]$ in

Figure 8.1-4) and the fact that for $j \geq 1$ the slope $f(t_j, y_j)$ used in (14) is generally *not* the exact slope $f(t_j, y(t_j))$.

EXAMPLE. Use Euler's method on [2, 3] for the IVP

$$\frac{dy}{dt} = -ty^2, \qquad y(2) = 1$$

first with $h = 0.1$, then with $h = 0.05$. Discuss the accuracy attained.

Solution. Since $f_j = -t_j y_j^2$, the Euler formula (14) for this IVP is

$$y_{j+1} = y_j + h[-t_j y_j^2] \approx y(t_{j+1}), \qquad t_{j+1} = 2 + (j+1)h \qquad \textbf{(16)}$$

Starting with $t_0 = 2$ and $y_0 = 1$ and taking $h = 0.1$, we get to 4s.

$j = 0$: $\quad y_1 = y_0 - h[t_0 y_0^2] = 1 - 0.1\,[2 \cdot 1^2] = 0.8000 \approx y(2.1)$
$j = 1$: $\quad y_2 = y_1 - h[t_1 y_1^2] = 0.8000 - 0.1\,[(2.1)(0.8000)^2] = 0.6656 \approx y(2.2)$
$j = 2$: $\quad y_3 = y_2 - h[t_2 y_2^2] = 0.6656 - 0.1\,[(2.2)(0.6656)^2] \doteq 0.5681 \approx y(2.3)$
$j = 3$: $\quad y_4 = y_3 - h[t_3 y_3^2] = 0.5681 - 0.1\,[(2.3)(0.5681)^2] \doteq 0.4939 \approx y(2.4)$

Similarly, taking $h = 0.05$ in (16) gives 4s.

$j = 0$: $\quad y_1 = 1 - 0.05\,[2 \cdot 1^2] = 0.9000 \approx y(2.05)$
$j = 1$: $\quad y_2 = 0.9000 - 0.05\,[(2.05)(0.9000)^2] = 0.8170 \approx y(2.1)$
$j = 2$: $\quad y_3 = 0.8170 - 0.05\,[(2.10)(0.8170)^2] \doteq 0.7469 \approx y(2.15)$
$j = 3$: $\quad y_4 = 0.7469 - 0.05\,[(2.15)(0.7469)^2] \doteq 0.6869 \approx y(2.2)$

The results are tabulated for $t_j = 2, 2.1, 2.2, \ldots, 3$ in the $h = 0.1$ and $h = 0.05$ columns of Table 8.1-1. The exact $y(t_j)$ values were obtained from the solution $y(t)$ shown in (5), that is, as

$$y(t_j) = \frac{2}{t_j^2 - 2}$$

Intermediate calculations were done in 13s arithmetic. So the errors shown are entirely due to accumulated truncation error.

An examination of the $E[0.1]$ and $E[0.05]$ columns of Table 8.1-1 reveals that halving h approximately halves $E[h]$. This suggests that for Euler's method, $E[h]$ is $O(h)$. Assuming this to be true (see Section 8.1C), we can apply Richardson's formula [(19) of Section 7.1D] with

$$F[h] = y_j[h], \quad h = 0.05, \quad n = 1, \quad \text{and} \quad r = \frac{0.1}{0.05} = 2$$

to get the improved approximations

$$y_j[0.05]_{\text{improved}} = \frac{2y_j[0.05] - y_j[0.1]}{2 - 1} = 2y_j[0.05] - y_j[0.1]$$

The resulting values, shown in the rightmost column of Table 8.1-1, are more accurate than the $y_j[0.05]$ values by at least one decimal place.

TABLE 8.1-1 EULER'S METHOD VALUES FOR $y' = -ty^2$, $y(2) = 1$.

t_j	Exact $y(t_j)$	Using $h = 0.1$		Using $h = 0.05$		Richardson ($n = 1$)
		$y_j[0.1]$	$E_j[0.1]$	$y_j[0.05]$	$E_j[0.05]$	$y_j[0.05]_{improved}$
$t_0 = 2.0$	1	1	0	1	0	1
2.1	0.8299	0.8000	0.0299	0.8170	0.0129	0.8340
2.2	0.7042	0.6656	0.0386	0.6869	0.0173	0.7082
2.3	0.6079	0.5681	0.0398	0.5879	0.0182	0.6113
2.4	0.5319	0.4939	0.0380	0.5142	0.0177	0.5345
2.5	0.4706	0.4354	0.0352	0.4539	0.0167	0.4742
2.6	0.4202	0.3880	0.0322	0.4048	0.0154	0.4216
2.7	0.3781	0.3488	0.0292	0.3640	0.0141	0.3792
2.8	0.3425	0.3160	0.0265	0.3297	0.0128	0.3434
2.9	0.3120	0.2880	0.0240	0.3003	0.0117	0.3126
$t_F = 3.0$	0.2857	0.2640	0.0217	0.2751	0.0106	0.2862

8.1C THE ORDER OF A NUMERICAL METHOD

In discussing the accuracy of any numerical method, it is useful to distinguish two errors at t_{j+1}:

$$e_{j+1}[h] = y(t_{j+1}) - y_{j+1} \text{ assuming that } y_j \text{ is } exactly \ y(t_j) \tag{17a}$$

$$E_{j+1}[h] = y(t_{j+1}) - y_{j+1} \text{ assuming that } y_j \text{ has accumulated error} \tag{17b}$$

The error $e_{j+1}[h]$ is called the **local** or **per-step truncation error** of the method at t_{j+1}. For Euler's method (see Figure 8.1-4), $e_{j+1}[h]$ is simply the remainder of the first Taylor approximation

$$y(t_j + h) \approx y(t_j) + hy'(t_j), \qquad \text{where } y'(t_j) = f(t_j, y(t_j)) \tag{18}$$

In view of Lagrange's form of this remainder [see (2a) of Section 7.1],

$$e_{j+1}[h] = \frac{y''(t_j + \theta h)}{2} h^2, \qquad \text{where } 0 < \theta < 1 \tag{19}$$

Thus, although the per-step truncation error of Euler's method is $O(h^2)$, its accumulated error is only $O(h)$. More generally:

> If the local truncation error $e_j[h]$ of a method is $O(h^{n+1})$,
> then for any (IVP) such that $y^{(n+1)}(t) \approx$ constant on $[t_0, t_F]$, $\qquad$ (20)
> the accumulated truncation error $E_j[h]$ will be $O(h^n)$.

To see why this is so, consider $t_j = t_0 + jh$. Clearly,

$$j \text{ } h\text{-steps are required to get from } t_0 \text{ to } t_j$$

If h is reduced to h/r (r a positive integer), then

$$rj \, \frac{h}{r}\text{-steps are required to go from } t_0 \text{ to } t_j$$

But if $e[h]$ is $O(h^{n+1})$, then [see (7) of Section 7.1A]

$$e_i\left[\frac{h}{r}\right] \approx \frac{1}{r^{n+1}} \, e_i[h] \qquad \text{for } t_0 \leqslant t_i \leqslant t_j \tag{21}$$

Since the number of steps from t_0 to t_j is multiplied by r while each per-step error is divided by r^{n+1}, we expect the *accumulated* error at t_j to satisfy

$$E_j\left[\frac{h}{r}\right] \approx r\left(\frac{1}{r^{n+1}}\right) E_j[h] = \frac{1}{r^n} E_j[h] \tag{22}$$

A numerical method is called **nth order** if $E[h]$ is $O(h^n)$, that is, if $e[h]$ is $O(h^{n+1})$. Since $e[h]$ for Euler's method is $O(h^2)$, we see that

Euler's method is a first-order method.

To see the importance of a higher-order method, consider the r needed to produce two extra digits of accuracy. In view of (22), r must satisfy

$$E_j\left[\frac{h}{r}\right] \leqslant 10^{-2} E_j[h] \qquad \Leftrightarrow \qquad \frac{1}{r^n} \leqslant \frac{1}{100} \qquad \Leftrightarrow \qquad r^n \geqslant 100$$

Consequently, r should be about 100 if $n = 1$, 10 if $n = 2$, 5 if $n = 3$, and 3 if $n = 4$. For example, the $E_j[0.05]$ column of Table 8.1-1 shows that 20 steps ($h = 0.05$) produced about $2d$ accuracy on $[2, 3]$. Since Euler's method is only first order (i.e., $n = 1$), $20 \cdot 100 = 2000$ steps (i.e., $h = 0.0005$) would be needed to increase the accuracy to about $4d$. Aside from the time and/or expense that this entails, there is the risk that human and/or accumulated roundoff error may offset some or all of the reduced truncation error! This risk would be lessened substantially if the method were fourth order, in which case only $20 \cdot 3 = 60$ steps (i.e., $h \doteq 0.017$) would increase the accuracy to about $4d$.

We now present some effective higher-order methods.

Self-Starting Methods: Taylor and Runge–Kutta   **8.2**

Euler's method can be obtained from the $O(h^2)$ Taylor approximation

$$y(t_{j+1}) = y(t_j + h) \approx y(t_j) + hy'(t_j) \tag{1}$$

by replacing the unknown exact values of $y(t_j)$ and $y'(t_j)$ by the available current approximations

$$y(t_j) \approx y_i \qquad \text{and} \qquad y'(t_j) \approx f_j = f(t_j, y_j) \tag{2}$$

The resulting formula for this first-order method can be written as

$$y_{j+1} = y_j + h\phi_{T,1}, \qquad \text{where } \phi_{T,1} = f_j \tag{3}$$

8.2A TAYLOR'S METHOD

The natural extension of (3) to an nth-order method is to start with the $O(h^{n+1})$ Taylor approximation

$$y(t_{j+1}) \approx y(t_j) + hy'(t_j) + \frac{h^2}{2!}y''(t_j) + \cdots + \frac{h^n}{n!}y^{(n)}(t_j) \tag{4}$$

and replace $y''(t_j), \ldots, y^{(n)}(t_j)$ by computable approximations $y_j'', \ldots, y_j^{(n)}$; the result is the **nth-order Taylor's method** formula

$$y_{j+1} = y_j + h\phi_{T,n}, \qquad \text{where } \phi_{T,n} = f_j + \frac{h}{2!}y_j'' + \cdots + \frac{h^{n-1}}{n!}y_j^{(n)} \tag{5}$$

To get the desired computable approximations, we use the Chain Rule for functions of two variables (see Appendix II.5E) to differentiate

$$y' = f(t, y), \qquad \text{where } y = y(t) \tag{6}$$

with respect to t. One differentiation gives

$$y'' = \frac{d}{dt} f(t, y(t)) = f_t + f_y y' = f_t + f_y f \tag{7}$$

where $f_t = \partial f(t, y)/\partial t$, $f_y = \partial f(t, y)/\partial y$, and $f = f(t, y)$. Similarly,

$$y''' = \frac{d}{dt}(f_t) + \frac{d}{dt}(f_y y') = (f_{tt} + f_{ty}y') + [f_y y'' + (f_{yt} + f_{yy}y')y']$$

Assuming continuous partials, we obtain $f_{ty} = f_{yt}$ (see Appendix II.5B). So

$$y''' = f_{tt} + 2f_{ty}y' + f_{yy}(y')^2 + f_y y'' \tag{8a}$$

In view of (6) and (7), this can be rewritten as

$$y''' = f_{tt} + 2f_{ty}f + f_{yy}f^2 + f_y[f_t + f_y f] \tag{8b}$$

It should be evident that any derivative $y^{(k)}$ can be expressed solely in terms of f and its partials (although such expressions become increasingly unwieldy as k increases). These expressions can then be used to approximate $y^{(k)}(t_j)$ in (5). For example, from (7), $y''(t_j)$ can be approximated by

$$y_j'' = [f_t + f_y f]_j = f_t(t_j, y_j) + f_y(t_j, y_j)f(t_j, y_j) \tag{9}$$

Putting this in (5) with $n = 2$ gives the **second-order Taylor's method** formula

$$y_{j+1} = y_j + h\phi_{T,2}, \qquad \text{where } \phi_{T,2} = f_j + \frac{h}{2}[f_t + f_y f]_j \qquad \textbf{(10)}$$

Similarly, we can get the **third-order Taylor's method** formula

$$y_{j+1} = y_j + h\phi_{T,3}, \qquad \text{where } \phi_{T,3} = \phi_{T,2} + \frac{h^2}{6} y_j''' \qquad \textbf{(11)}$$

with y_j''' obtained by evaluating (8a) or (8b) at (t_j, y_j).

EXAMPLE. Use the second-order Taylor's method on [2, 3] for the IVP

$$\frac{dy}{dt} = -ty^2, \qquad y(2) = 1 \qquad \textbf{(12)}$$

Take $h = 0.1$; then $h = 0.05$ as in the example in Section 8.1B.

Solution. For $f(t, y) = -ty^2$ the first partial derivatives are

$$f_t = -y^2 \qquad \text{and} \qquad f_y = -2ty$$

So the second-order Taylor's method formula (10) becomes

$$y_{j+1} = y_j + h\left\{-t_j y_j^2 + \frac{h}{2}[-y_j^2 + (-2t_j y_j)(t_j y_j^2)]\right\}$$

$$= y_j + hy_j^2\left\{-t_j + \frac{h}{2}[-1 + 2t_j^2 y_j]\right\}$$

Taking $h = 0.1$ and starting with $t_0 = 2$, $y_0 = 1$, we get (to 5s)

$$j = 0: \quad y(t_1) = y(2.1) \approx y_1 = y_0 + hy_0^2\left\{-t_0 + \frac{h}{2}[-1 + 2t_0^2 y_0]\right\}$$

$$y(t_1) \approx 1 + 0.1(1)^2\{-2 + 0.05[-1 + 2(2)^2 1]\} = 0.835$$

$$j = 1: \quad y(t_2) = y(2.2) \approx y_2 = y_1 + hy_1^2\left\{-t_1 + \frac{h}{2}[-1 + 2t_1^2 y_1]\right\}$$

$$y(t_2) \approx 0.835 + 0.1(0.835)^2\{-2.1 + 0.05[-1 + 2(2.1)^2(0.835)]\} \doteq 0.71077$$

Similarly, taking $h = 0.05$ and starting with $t_0 = 2$, $y_0 = 1$ gives (to 5s)

$$j = 0: \quad y(t_1) = y(2.05) \approx y_1 = 1 + 0.05(1)^2\{-2 + 0.025[-1 + 2(2)^2 1]\} = 0.90875$$

$$j = 1: \quad y(t_2) = y(2.1) \approx y_2 = y_1 + 0.05y_1^2\{-2.05 + 0.025[-1 + 2(2.05)^2 y_1]\} \doteq 0.83096$$

and so on. The resulting approximations of $y(2.0)$, $y(2.1)$, . . . , $y(3.0)$ are shown in Table 8.2-1. Since we are using a second-order method, the improved values were obtained using $n = 2$ in the Richardson formula, that is, as

$$y_j[0.05]_{\text{improved}} = \frac{2^2 y_j[0.05] - y_j[0.1]}{2^2 - 1} = \frac{4y_j[0.05] - y_j[0.1]}{3} \tag{13}$$

These improved values are accurate to almost $4\,d$.

Comparing the second-order Taylor values of Table 8.2-1 to the first-order Euler values of Table 8.1-1, we see that the second-order values are more accurate for a given h, and show better improvement when h is halved ($E_j[0.05] \approx \frac{1}{4} E_j[0.1]$).

TABLE 8.2-1 SECOND-ORDER TAYLOR'S METHOD VALUES FOR $y' = -ty^2$, $y(2) = 1$.

t_j	Exact $y(t_j)$	Using $h = 0.1$		Using $h = 0.05$		Richardson
		$y_j[0.1]$	$E_j[0.1]$	$y_j[0.05]$	$E_j[0.05]$	$y_j[0.05]_{\text{improved}}$
$t_0 = 2.0$	1	1	0	1	0	1
2.1	0.8299	0.835	-0.0051	0.8310	-0.0011	0.8297
2.2	0.7042	0.7108	-0.0065	0.7056	-0.0014	0.7039
2.3	0.6079	0.6145	-0.0066	0.6093	-0.0014	0.6076
2.4	0.5319	0.5380	-0.0061	0.5332	-0.0013	0.5316
2.5	0.4706	0.4761	-0.0055	0.4718	-0.0012	0.4704
2.6	0.4202	0.4250	-0.0049	0.4212	-0.0010	0.4199
2.7	0.3781	0.3823	-0.0043	0.3790	-0.0009	0.3779
2.8	0.3425	0.3462	-0.0037	0.3433	-0.0008	0.3423
2.9	0.3120	0.3153	-0.0033	0.3127	-0.0007	0.3118
$t_F = 3.0$	0.2857	0.2886	-0.0029	0.2862	-0.0006	0.2855

The problem with programming Taylor's method is that one must (correctly) find and then write code for suitable partial derivatives of $f(t, y)$. From the user's point of view, *a preferable method is one that requires code for only $f(t, y)$ itself.* The Runge–Kutta methods described next do precisely this.

8.2B SECOND-ORDER RUNGE–KUTTA METHODS

The formula for the second-order Taylor method is

$$y_{j+1} = y_j + h\phi_{T,2}, \qquad \text{where } \phi_{T,2} = f_j + \frac{h}{2}[f_t(t_j, y_j) + f_j f_y(t_j, y_j)] \tag{14}$$

At the end of the nineteenth century, the German mathematician Runge observed that this expression for $\phi_{T,2}$ looks like the $O(h^2)$ Taylor approximation

$$f(t_j + ph, y_j + qhf_j) \approx f_j + phf_t(t_j, y_j) + qhf_j f_y(t_j, y_j) \tag{15}$$

See Appendix II.5C. Indeed, comparing (14) to (15) with $p = q = \frac{1}{2}$ reveals that

$$\phi_{T,2} \approx f(t_j + \tfrac{1}{2}h, y + \tfrac{1}{2}hf_j) \qquad \text{with an } O(h^2) \text{ error} \tag{16}$$

Substituting (16) in (14) gives the formula for the

> **Modified Euler method:** $y_{j+1} = y_j + hf(t_j + \tfrac{1}{2}h, y_j + \tfrac{1}{2}hf_j)$ $\qquad$ (17)

Since (16) is $O(h^2)$, the y_{j+1} in (17) differs from that of (14) by $h \cdot O(h^2) = O(h^3)$. But $e_{j+1}[h]$ for (14) is $O(h^3)$. It follows that the per-step truncation error of the Modified Euler's method is also $O(h^3)$; that is, *the modified Euler method is a second-order method.* It requires sampling $f(t, y)$ at (t_j, y_j) then at $(t_j + \tfrac{1}{2}h, y_j + \tfrac{1}{2}hf_j)$ at each step.

In (17), the latter sample slope $f(t_j + \tfrac{1}{2}h, y_j + \tfrac{1}{2}hf_j)$ is used in place of $\phi_{T,2}$. Still other second-order methods can be obtained by approximating $\phi_{T,2}$ by a *weighted sum* of sample slopes, that is, as

$$\phi_{T,2} \approx a_1 f(t_j, y_j) + a_2 f(t_j + ph, y_j + qhf_j) \tag{18}$$

where the "weights" a_1 and a_2 and the "scale factors" p and q are determined so that this approximation is $O(h^2)$. Algorithms based on this strategy are called **Runge–Kutta methods.**

Substituting (15) for $f(t_j + ph, y_j + qhf_j)$ in (18), then equating coefficients of $f_t(t_j, y_j)$ and $f_y(t_j, y_j)$ with those in (10) gives

$$a_1 + a_2 = 1 \qquad \text{and} \qquad a_2 p = a_2 q = \tfrac{1}{2}$$

It can be seen that a_2 can be chosen arbitrarily, with

$$a_1 = 1 - a_2 \quad \text{and} \quad p = q = \frac{1}{2a_2} \qquad (a_2 \neq 0) \tag{19}$$

Taking $a_2 = 1$ gives the modified Euler method (13). Taking $a_2 = \tfrac{1}{2}$ (so that $a_1 = \tfrac{1}{2}$, $p = q = 1$) gives the formula for

> **Huen's method:** $y_{j+1} = y_j + \dfrac{h}{2} [f_j + f(t_j + h, y_j + hf_j)]$ $\qquad$ (20)

When $f(t, y)$ depends only on t, (17) and (20) amount to approximating the integral of $y'(t)$ from t_j to t_{j+1} by the Midpoint and Trapezoidal Rules, respectively. Since both rules are $O(h^3)$ [see (33) and (36) of Section 7.3C], we have further confirmation that the modified Euler and Huen methods are both second order.

EXAMPLE. With $h = 0.1$, find y_1 and y_2 for

$$\text{(IVP)} \quad y' = -ty^2, \qquad y(2) = 1$$

using (a) the modified Euler method and (b) Huen's method.

Solution

a. For $f(t, y) = -ty^2$, the modified Euler method formula (17) is

$$y_{j+1} = y_j - 0.1(t_j + 0.05)[y_j + 0.05f_j]^2, \qquad \text{where } f_j = -t_j y_j^2 \qquad (21)$$

j = 0: Here $t_0 = 2$ and $y_0 = 1$; so $f_0 = -2(1)^2 = -2$. By (21)

$$y_1 = 1 - 0.1(2 + 0.05)[1 + 0.05(-2)]^2$$
$$= 0.83395 \qquad (E_1[0.1] \doteq -0.0041)$$

j = 1: Now $t_1 = 2.1$ and $y_1 = 0.83395$; so $f_1 = -t_1 y_1^2 \doteq -1.46049$, hence

$$y_2 = 0.83395 - 0.1(2.1 + 0.05)[0.83395 + 0.05(-1.46049)]^2$$
$$\doteq 0.70946 \qquad (E_2[0.1] \doteq -0.0053)$$

b. For this problem, the Huen's method formula (20) is

$$y_{j+1} = y_j + 0.05[f_j - (t_j + 0.1)(y_j + 0.1f_j)^2], \qquad \text{where } f_j = -t_j y_j^2 \qquad (22)$$

j = 0: With $t_0 = 2$, $y_0 = 1$, and $f_0 = -2$, (22) gives

$$y_1 = 1 + 0.05[(-2) - (2 + 0.1)(1 + 0.1(-2))^2]$$
$$\doteq 0.83280 \qquad (E_1[0.1] \doteq -0.0029)$$

j = 1: Now $t_1 = 2.1$ and $y_1 = 0.83280$; so $f_1 = -t_1 y_1^2 \doteq -1.45647$, hence

$$y_2 = 0.83280 + 0.05[(-1.45647) - (2.1 + 0.1)(0.83280 + 0.1(-1.45647))^2]$$
$$\doteq 0.70804 \qquad (E_2[0.1] \doteq -0.0042)$$

Comparing these values to those obtained in Table 8.2-1, we see that the second-order Runge–Kutta formulas (17) and (20) do indeed give accuracy comparable to the second-order Taylor method without requiring partial derivatives.

8.2C HIGHER-ORDER RUNGE–KUTTA METHODS

To get fourth-order Runge–Kutta formulas, one starts with the fourth-order Taylor's method formula

$$y_{j+1} = y_j + h\phi_{T,4}, \qquad \text{where } \phi_{T,4} = f_j + \frac{h}{2} y_j'' + \frac{h^2}{6} y_j''' + \frac{h^3}{24} y_j^{(iv)} \qquad (23)$$

and then approximates $\phi_{T,4}$ by a weighted sum

$$w_1 m_1 + w_2 m_2 + w_3 m_3 + w_4 m_4 \qquad (24a)$$

where the **sample slopes** m_1, m_2, m_3, and m_4 are defined recursively by

$$\begin{aligned} m_1 &= f(t_j, y_j) = f_j \\ m_2 &= f(t_j + p_2 h, y_j + h[q_{21} m_1]) \\ m_3 &= f(t_j + p_3 h, y_j + h[q_{31} m_1 + q_{32} m_2]) \\ m_4 &= f(t_j + h, y_j + h[q_{41} m_1 + q_{42} m_2 + q_{43} m_3]) \end{aligned} \qquad (24b)$$

The weights w in (24a) and the scale factors p and q in (24b) are determined by replacing the expressions for the sample slopes m_2, m_3, and m_4 in (24b) by their (rather complex) $O(h^4)$ Taylor polynomial approximations [cf. (15)] then equating the coefficients of the partials of f at (t_j, y_j) in (24a) with those in (23). The messy details can be found in [29] and will be omitted. We merely note that the w's and q's can be determined from p_2 and p_3, which can be chosen arbitrarily. The most commonly used **fourth-order Runge–Kutta formula** results from taking $p_2 = p_3 = \frac{1}{2}$; it is

$$y_{j+1} = y_j + \frac{h}{6}\{m_1 + 2(m_2 + m_3) + m_4\} \qquad \text{(25a)}$$

where
$$
\begin{aligned}
m_1 &= f(t_j, y_j) \\
m_2 &= f(t_j + \tfrac{1}{2}h,\ y_j + \tfrac{1}{2}hm_1) \\
m_3 &= f(t_j + \tfrac{1}{2}h,\ y_j + \tfrac{1}{2}hm_2) \\
m_4 &= f(t_j + h,\ y_j + hm_3)
\end{aligned}
\qquad \text{(25b)}
$$

The method resulting from this formula will be abbreviated as simply **RK4.**

The "sample slopes" $m_1, \ldots, m_4$ are the values of f at the "sample points" $P_1, \ldots, P_4$ shown in Figure 8.2-1. If $f(t, y)$ depends only on t, say $f(t, y) = g(t)$, then (25) amounts to using Simpson's rule to integrate $y'(t) = g(t)$ from t_j to t_{j+1}.

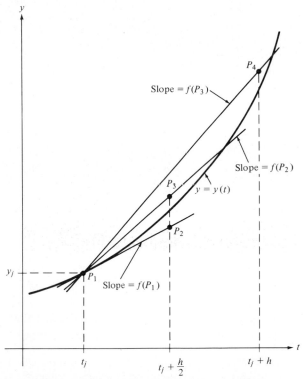

FIGURE 8.2-1   Sample points used to get t_{j+1} by RK4 when y_j is exact.

EXAMPLE. Use RK4 with $h = 0.1$ on [2, 3] for the IVP

$$y' = -ty^2, \quad y(2) = 1 \qquad \left[\text{Exact solution:} \quad y(t) = \frac{2}{t^2 - 2} \right]$$

Solution. Starting with $t_0 = 2$, $y_0 = 1$, (25) gives

$$m_1 = f(2.0, \ 1) = -(2)(1)^2 = -2$$
$$m_2 = f(2.05, \ 1 + 0.05(-2)) = -(2.05)(.9)^2 = -1.6605$$
$$m_3 = f(2.05, \ 1 + 0.05(-1.6605)) = -(2.05)(0.916975)^2 \doteq -1.72373$$
$$m_4 = f(2.1, \ 1 + 0.1(-1.72373)) = -(2.1)(0.82763)^2 \doteq -1.43843$$
$$y_1 = y_0 - \frac{0.1}{6} \{2 + 2(1.6605 + 1.72373) + 1.43843\} \doteq 0.829885$$

Table 8.2-2 shows both the RK4 values and the exact values of $y(2.0)$, $y(2.1)$, . . . , $y(3.0)$ rounded to 6 d. The RK4 values y_j were obtained using the FORTRAN program shown in Figure 8.2-2.

TABLE 8.2-2   RK4 VALUES FOR
$y' = -ty^2$, $y(2) = 1$ ($h = 0.1$).

t_j	y_j	$y(t_j)$
2.0	1.000000	1.000000
2.1	0.829885	0.829876
2.2	0.704237	0.704225
2.3	0.607914	0.607903
2.4	0.531924	0.531915
2.5	0.470596	0.470588
2.6	0.420175	0.420168
2.7	0.378078	0.378072
2.8	0.342471	0.342466
2.9	0.312017	0.312012
3.0	0.285718	0.285714

The reasons for the popularity of RK4 are evident from Table 8.2-2 and Figure 8.2-2. Clearly RK4 is accurate.† Moreover SUBROUTINE RK4, which yielded this accuracy, is short, straightforward, and easy to use. (To change (IVP), one need only modify the function statement in line 2200. Any other changes are made during execution.)

There are, however, some shortcomings of RK4. One is the fact that four slope values must be sampled at each step. This shortcoming can be serious when the slope function

---

† If $f(t, y)$ is a polynomial of degree $\leqslant 4$ in t and y (e.g., $-ty^2$), then the $O(h^5)$ Taylor approximation of $f(t, y)$ is exact; hence RK4 will give exceptionally accurate values for $y(t_{j+1})$, as happened in this case.

```
00100  C  * * * * * * * *  CALRK4  * * * * * * * * * * * * * *
00200  C  CALLING PROGRAM FOR 4TH ORDER RUNGE-KUTTA METHOD
00300        DOUBLE PRECISION Y0
00400        EXTERNAL FTEST
00500        DATA IW, IR /5, 5/
00600  C
00700        WRITE(IW,1)
00800      1 FORMAT('0INPUT (SEPARATED BY COMMAS) T0, TF, Y0')
00900        READ(IR,*) T0, TF, Y0
01000        WRITE(IW,2)
01100      2 FORMAT('0INPUT # STEPS, NPRINT')
01200        READ(IR,*) NSTEPS, NPRINT
01300        WRITE(IW, 3)
01400      3 FORMAT(6X,'T',12X,'Y')
01500  C
01600        CALL RK4(FTEST, T0, TF, NSTEPS, NPRINT, Y0, IW)
01700  C
01800        STOP
01900        END
02000
02100        FUNCTION FTEST(T,Y)
02200            FTEST = -T*Y*Y
02300        RETURN
02400        END


00100        SUBROUTINE RK4(F, T, TF, NSTEPS, NPRINT, Y, IW)
00200        REAL M1, M2, M3, M4
00300        DOUBLE PRECISION Y
00400  C - - - - - - - - - - - - - - - - - - - - - - - - - - - C
00500  C  THIS SUBROUTINE INTEGRATES FROM T0 TO TF THE 1ST ORDER IVP  C
00600  C       Y' = F(T,Y)     Y(T0) = Y0  (INITIAL T,Y)         C
00700  C  USING NSTEPS STEPS OF THE 4TH ORDER RUNGE-KUTTA METHOD.    C
00800  C  IF NPRINT>0, IT PRINTS T AND Y EVERY NPRINT STEPS.        C
00900  C  NOTE:  F MUST BE DECLARED EXTERNAL IN THE CALLING PROGRAM  C
01000  C - - - - - - - - - - - - - - - - - - VERSION 1:  5/1/81 C
01100        IF (NPRINT .GT. 0) WRITE (IW,1) T, Y
01200      1 FORMAT (F10.3, 3X, E14.7)
01300  C
01400        H = (TF - T)/NSTEPS
01500        DO 10 J=1,NSTEPS
01600            M1 = F(T,Y)
01700            M2 = F(T + 0.5*H, Y + 0.5*H*M1)
01800            M3 = F(T + 0.5*H, Y + 0.5*H*M2)
01900            M4 = F(T + H, Y + H*M3)
02000            T = T + H
02100            Y = Y + H*(M1 + 2*(M2 + M3) + M4)/6
02200            IF (NPRINT .GT. 0 .AND. MOD(J,NPRINT) .EQ. 0)
02300        &        WRITE(IW,1) T, Y
02400     10 CONTINUE
02500        RETURN
02600        END
```

FIGURE 8.2-2 A FORTRAN PROGRAM FOR SOLVING $y' = -ty^2$, $y(2) = 1$ BY RK4.

is complicated or the time available to calculate y_{j+1} is limited. An "obvious" remedy for this is to pause every few steps and *repeat the numerical solution from t_j to t_{j+1} using RK4 with the stepsize halved.* The difference in the two approximations of $y(t_{j+1})$ can then be used to estimate the error and, if appropriate, change the stepsize. However,

Algorithm: RKF4 (Fourth-Order Runge–Kutta–Fehlberg Method)

Purpose: To solve to a prescribed accuracy on $[t_0, \ t_F]$ the IVP

$$y' = f(t, y), \qquad y = y_0 \text{ when } t = t_0$$

{*initialize*}
GET $t_0, \ t_F, \ y_0,$ {parameters of IVP}
      $Rmax,$ {accuracy control parameter}
         ScaleMin, ScaleMax   {stepsize control parameters}
$h \leftarrow (Rmax)^{1/4}$ {initial stepsize}
$Hmin \leftarrow h * 10^{-4}$ {minimum allowable stepsize}
$t \leftarrow t_0; \quad y \leftarrow y_0$ {(t, y) is current (t_j, y_j)}

{*iterate*}
DO UNTIL **termination test** is satisfied
  BEGIN
  If $t + h > t_F$ THEN $h \leftarrow t_F - t$ {stepsize for final step}
  {**estimate next $e[h]$**}
  $k_1 \leftarrow hf(t_j, \ y_j)$

  $k_2 \leftarrow hf(t_j + \frac{1}{4}h, \ y_j + \frac{1}{4}k_1)$

  $k_3 \leftarrow hf(t_j + \frac{3}{8}h, \ y_j + \frac{3}{32} k_1 + \frac{9}{32} k_2)$

  $k_4 \leftarrow hf(t_j + \frac{12}{13}h, \ y_j + \frac{1932}{2197} k_1 - \frac{7200}{2197} k_2 + \frac{7296}{2197} k_3)$

  $k_5 \leftarrow hf(t_j + h, \ y_j + \frac{439}{216} k_1 - 8k_2 + \frac{3680}{513} k_3 - \frac{845}{4104} k_4)$

  $k_6 \leftarrow hf(t_j + \frac{1}{2}h, \ y_j - \frac{8}{27} k_1 + 2k_2 - \frac{3544}{2565} k_3 + \frac{1859}{4104} k_4 - \frac{11}{40} k_5)$

  $ErrorEstimate \leftarrow \frac{1}{360} k_1 - \frac{128}{4275} k_3 - \frac{2097}{75.240} k_4 + \frac{1}{50} k_5 + \frac{2}{55} k_6$ {$\approx e[h]$}
  {**accuracy test**}
  $Ratio \leftarrow |ErrorEstimate|/h$
  IF $Ratio \leq Rmax$ THEN   {accuracy of next y is acceptable}
    BEGIN
    $t \leftarrow t + h$ {$t = t_F$ for final step}
    $y \leftarrow y + \frac{25}{216} k_1 + \frac{1408}{2565} k_3 + \frac{2197}{4104} k_4 - \frac{1}{5} k_5$ {Now $y \approx y(t)$.}
    OUTPUT (t, h, y)
    END

  {**set next h:** $h* ScaleMin \leq$ next $h \leq h * ScaleMax$}
  $ScaleFactor \leftarrow 0.84*(Rmax/Ratio)^{1/4}$
  If $ScaleFactor < ScaleMin$ THEN $ScaleFactor \leftarrow ScaleMin$
  If $ScaleFactor > ScaleMax$ THEN $ScaleFactor \leftarrow ScaleMax$
  $h \leftarrow ScaleFactor*h$
  {**termination test:** $t = t_F$ or $h < Hmin$}
  END

IF $t = t_F$ THEN OUTPUT (current y approximates $y(t_F)$ to the desired accuracy)
         ELSE OUTPUT ($h < Hmin$ occurred; apparent singularity near current t)

FIGURE 8.2-3 PSEUDOPROGRAM FOR THE RUNGE–KUTTA–FEHLBERG (RKF4) METHOD.

eight additional evaluations per "check" (and a considerable amount of additional code) are needed to do this.

An alternative remedy is to sample more than four (but less than eight) $f(t, y)$ values per step and to use this extra information to get two estimates of $y(t_{j+1})$. To be a fourth-order method, the first estimate, used for y_{j+1}, should have $e_{j+1}[h] = O(h^5)$. The second, a higher-order formula [usually having $e[h] = O(h^6)$], is used to get a computable estimate

$$ErrorEstimate \approx \text{local truncation error of } y_{j+1} \qquad (26)$$

This estimate of $e_{j+1}[h]$ can be used to reassess the stepsize h for the next step. The objective is to take a larger step if $y'(t)$ varies slowly for $t \approx t_j$, and a smaller step if $y'(t)$ varies rapidly [due to oscillation or a vertical asymptote of $y(t)$] for $t \approx t_j$.

Of the many fourth-order methods using this strategy, one of the most effective, due to Fehlberg [14], uses six iterations per step. It is known as the fourth-order **Runge–Kutta–Fehlberg method** (abbreviated **RKF4**). The details of the RKF4 algorithm are given in Figure 8.2-3.

In the **accuracy test** steps, t is incremented by the current h only if *Ratio* ($\approx |e[h]/h|$) is no larger than *Rmax* (an accuracy control parameter provided by the user). Otherwise (i.e., if $Ratio > Rmax$), another attempt is made to get a y that approximates $y(t + h)$ but with the smaller stepsize $0.84h(Rmax/Ratio)^{1/4}$. The parameters *ScaleMin* and *ScaleMax* (also provided by the user) control the rate at which h can be allowed to vary. Typical values of the user-provided parameters are

$$Rmax = 10^{-4}, \qquad ScaleMin = 0.1, \qquad \text{and } ScaleMax = 4.0 \qquad (27)$$

These values will be used throughout the remainder of this text.

Figure 8.2-4 shows the result of replacing SUBROUTINE RK4 of Figure 8.2-2 by a subroutine that performs the fourth-order Runge–Kutta–Fehlberg method. Notice how h increases as $y(t)$ "levels off" near $t_F = 4$. (The smaller final value of h was adjusted so that $t_9 = t_F = 4$ exactly.)

Figure 8.2-5 illustrates the behavior of RKF4 when the solution has a singularity at some value t_s between t_0 and t_F. Notice how h decreases as the graph becomes more vertical. Even if we did not anticipate a singularity (see Figure 8.1-3), the output shows that $t_s \doteq 0.97$.

It should be clear that RKF4 *is generally to be preferred to RK4 unless there is a need to use a constant value of h.* One such situation occurs when "starting" a multistep method, as described in Section 8.3A.

J	T	H	Y
0	2.0000	0.1000000E+00	0.1000000E+01
1	2.1000	0.1000000E+00	0.8298735E+00
2	2.2115	0.1114898E+00	0.6918740E+00
3	2.3496	0.1381092E+00	0.5680786E+00
4	2.5204	0.1708108E+00	0.4595052E+00
5	2.7342	0.2137747E+00	0.3652411E+00
6	3.0050	0.2707763E+00	0.2844991E+00
7	3.3529	0.3478943E+00	0.2164084E+00
8	3.8076	0.4547751E+00	0.1600242E+00
9	4.0000	0.1923698E+00	0.1428565E+00

FIGURE 8.2-4 RKF4 VALUES FOR $y' = -ty^2$, $y(2) = 1$ ON $[2, 4]$.

J	T	H	Y
0	0.0000	0.1000000E+00	0.1000000E+01
1	0.1000	0.1000000E+00	0.1111464E+01
2	0.3010	0.2010294E+00	0.1441911E+01
3	0.4351	0.1340828E+00	0.1810051E+01
4	0.5314	0.9625394E-01	0.2219264E+01
5	0.6030	0.7165717E-01	0.2666464E+01
6	0.6579	0.5491116E-01	0.3149553E+01
7	0.7010	0.4309238E-01	0.3667271E+01
8	0.7355	0.3449929E-01	0.4218920E+01
9	0.7636	0.2809059E-01	0.4804112E+01
10	0.7868	0.2320410E-01	0.5422593E+01
	⋮		
20	0.9023	0.5579488E-02	0.1479329E+02
30	0.9341	0.1986123E-02	0.2802866E+02
40	0.9475	0.9523264E-03	0.4474236E+02
50	0.9544	0.5311221E-03	0.6488248E+02
60	0.9585	0.3252021E-03	0.8829552E+02
	⋮		
130	0.9667	0.3264732E-04	0.3205916E+03
140	0.9670	0.3227802E-04	0.3589668E+03
150	0.9673	0.3278130E-04	0.3923074E+03
160	0.9675	0.8484543E-05	0.4285446E+03

APPARENT SINGULARITY NEAR T = 0.967E+00

FIGURE 8.2-5   USING RKF4 TO FIND t_s FOR $y' = t^2 + y^2$, $y(0) = 1$.

8.2D   PARTIAL EXTENDED PRECISION

When using a formula of the form

$$y_{j+1} = y_j + h\phi, \qquad \phi = \text{a linear combination of } y\text{'s and } f(t, y)\text{'s} \tag{28}$$

the $h\phi$ term is often much smaller than y_j. Consequently, there is the risk of "negligible addition" in forming y_{j+1} (see Section 1.4C). An efficient remedy for this is to *store the current y_j in extended precision (to make room for the small increment $h\phi$), with all other calculations performed in single precision*. This form of **partial extended precision** can significantly improve the accuracy of *any* method when a large number of steps are taken.

8.3   Multistep Methods (Predictor–Corrector Strategies)

For the methods considered so far (Taylor and Runge–Kutta), all $f(t, y)$ evaluations needed for the calculation of y_{j+1} are made *after* y_j is obtained. Methods with this property are called **self-starting** because they can be applied starting with the initial value y_0. Unfortunately, such methods do not take advantage of previously obtained values such as

$$\ldots, \quad y_{j-4}, \quad y_{j-3}, \quad y_{j-2}, \quad y_{j-1}, \qquad \text{where } y_i \approx y(t_i) \tag{1a}$$

$$\ldots, \quad f_{j-4}, \quad f_{j-3}, \quad f_{j-2}, \quad f_{j-1}, \qquad \text{where } f_i = f(t_i, y_i) \approx y'(t_i) \tag{1b}$$

Methods that make use of information about $y(t)$ and $y'(t)$ for $t < t_j$ in calculating y_{j+1} are called **multistep methods.**

Since the values (1) are not available when $j = 0$, *multistep methods are not self-starting.* We shall soon see, however, that once started they can be used to get y_1, y_2, $\ldots$, to a desired accuracy with fewer $f(t, y)$ evaluations at each step than a self-starting method.

Formulas for both self-starting and multistep methods can be obtained from the Fundamental Theorem of Calculus. Indeed, it yields the following integral formula for getting from $y(t_j)$ to $y(t_{j+1})$:

$$y(t_{j+1}) = y(t_j) + \int_{t_j}^{t_{j+1}} f(t, y(t)) \, dt \tag{2}$$

(see Figure 8.3-1). Since we generally do not know $y(t)$ (if we did, there would be no need for a numerical method!), we cannot use (2) directly.

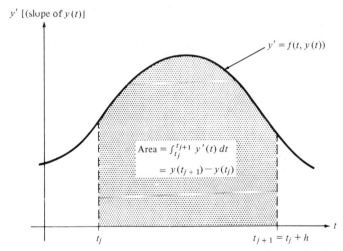

FIGURE 8.3-1   INTEGRATING $y'(t) = f(t, y(t))$ TO GET $y(t_{j+1}) - y(t_j)$.

However, once we have values of $y_j \approx y(t_j)$ and $f_j \approx y'(t_j)$, we can use them in a quadrature formula for the integral in (2) to obtain $y_{j+1} \approx y(t_{j+1})$. The result will be a formula of the form

$$y_{j+1} = y_j + h\phi(h, t_j, y_j, f_j, \text{ and perhaps other } y\text{'s and } f(t, y)\text{'s}) \tag{3}$$

$$O(h^{n+1}) \text{ formula for integrating } f(t, y) \text{ on } [t_j, t_{j+1}]$$

The $O(h^{n+1})$ error of the quadrature formula $h\phi$ is the error of y_{j+1} when y_j is exactly $y(t_j)$, that is, the per-step truncation error $e_{j+1}[h]$. Therefore, the use of an $(n+1)$st-order quadrature formula in (3) yields an nth-order method.

8.3A   THE ADAMS PREDICTOR–CORRECTOR METHOD (APC4)

Taking $h\phi$ in (3) to be the $O(h^5)$ Adams formulas [(17) and (18) of Section 7.3B] gives

Adams Predictor

$$p_{j+1} = y_j + \frac{h}{24}\left[-9f_{j-3} + 37f_{j-2} - 59f_{j-1} + 55f_j\right] \tag{4a}$$

$$e_{j+1}[h]_p = y(t_{j+1}) - p_{j+1} = \frac{251}{720}y^{(v)}(\xi_p)h^5, \qquad \text{where } t_{j-3} \leqslant \xi_p \leqslant t_{j+1} \tag{4b}$$

Adams Corrector

$$c_{j+1} = y_j + \frac{h}{24}\left[f_{j-2} - 5f_{j-1} + 19f_j + 9f_{j+1}\right] \tag{5a}$$

$$e_{j+1}[h]_c = y(t_{j+1}) - c_{j+1} = \frac{-19}{720}y^{(v)}(\xi_c)h^5, \qquad \text{where } t_{j-2} \leqslant \xi_c \leqslant t_{j+1} \tag{5b}$$

The geometric meaning of (4a) and (5a) is shown in Figure 8.3-2.

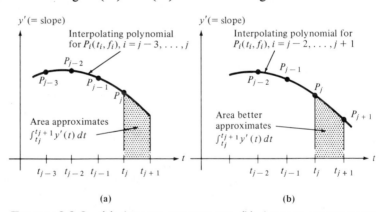

(a)   (b)

FIGURE 8.3-2   (a) ADAMS PREDICTOR; (b) ADAMS CORRECTOR.

Both p_{j+1} and c_{j+1} are obtained by integrating an interpolating cubic from t_j to t_{j+1}. Notice that $[t_j, t_{j+1}]$ lies *within* the interpolating interval used for c_{j+1} but *outside* the one used for p_{j+1}. We should therefore expect c_{j+1} to approximate y_{j+1} more accurately than p_{j+1}. [See (4b) and (5b).] However, formula (5a) for c_{j+1} is an *implicit* formula: It involves $f_{j+1} = f(t_{j+1}, y_{j+1})$, which *cannot be evaluated without knowing y_{j+1}.*

An explicit formula such as (4a) can be used to extrapolate a *predicted* estimate p_{j+1}; $f(t_{j+1}, p_{j+1})$ can then be used for f_{j+1} in an implicit formula such as (5a) to obtain the *corrected* estimate c_{j+1}. Methods incorporating this strategy are called **Predictor–Corrector (PC)** methods.

If the formulas for p_{j+1} and c_{j+1} are the same order, then the values of p_{j+1} and c_{j+1} can be used to estimate the local truncation error of c_{j+1}. For example, if h in (4b) and (5b) is small enough so that $y^{(v)}$ is nearly constant on $[t_{j-3}, t_{j+1}]$, then

$$19[y(t_{j+1}) - p_{j+1}] + 251[y(t_{j+1}) - c_{j+1}] \approx 0$$

Solving this for $y(t_{j+1})$ gives

$$y(t_{j+1}) \approx c_{j+1} - \tfrac{19}{270}[c_{j+1} - p_{j+1}] \tag{6}$$

Upon comparing (6) with (5b), we see that

$$\boxed{\delta_{j+1} = -\tfrac{19}{270}[c_{j+1} - p_{j+1}] \text{ is a computable estimator of } e_{j+1}[h]_c} \tag{7}$$

If δ_{j+1} indicates that c_{j+1} is not accurate enough, we can recompute c_{j+1} with $f(t_{j+1}, c_{j+1})$ used as a more accurate estimate of f_{j+1}. The predictor–corrector method that does this using (4) and (5) will be called the **fourth-order Adams method**† and abbreviated as **APC4**.

EXAMPLE. Use APC4 on $[2, 3]$ with $h = 0.1$ for the IVP

$$y' = -ty^2, \quad y(2) = 1 \quad \left[\text{Exact solution is } y(t) = \frac{2}{t^2 - 2}\right]$$

Try to get about four significant digits. To start the method, use the following exact values (to $7s$):

$t_0 = 2.0$:	$y_0 = y(2.0) = 1.000000,$	$f_0 = -t_0 y_0^2 = -2.000000$
$t_1 = 2.1$:	$y_1 = y(2.1) \doteq 0.8298755,$	$f_1 = -t_1 y_1^2 \doteq -1.446256$
$t_2 = 2.2$:	$y_2 = y(2.2) \doteq 0.7042254,$	$f_2 = -t_2 y_2^2 \doteq -1.091053$
$t_3 = 2.3$:	$y_3 = y(2.3) \doteq 0.6079027,$	$f_3 = -t_3 y_3^2 \doteq -0.8499552$

Solution

$$j = 3: \quad p_4 = y_3 + \frac{h}{24}\{-9f_0 + 37f_1 - 59f_2 + 55f_3\} \doteq 0.5333741$$

$$y_4 = y_3 + \frac{h}{24}\{f_1 - 5f_2 + 19f_3 + 9(-t_4 p_4^2)\} \doteq 0.5317149 \ (= c_4)$$

$$\delta_4 = -\frac{19}{270}\{y_4 - p_4\} \doteq 0.0001144$$

Since δ_4 indicates possible inaccuracy in the fourth decimal place (which is the fourth significant digit) of y_4, we take y_4 as an improved p_4 to get an improved y_4 as follows:

$$y_4 = y_3 + \frac{h}{24}\{f_1 - 5f_2 + 19f_3 + 9[-t_4(0.5317149)^2]\} \doteq 0.5318739$$

† APC4 is also called the **Adams–Bashforth** or **Adams–Moulton** method.

The local truncation error estimate of this y_4 is

$$\delta_4 = -\tfrac{19}{270} \{0.5318739 - 0.5317149\} \doteq -0.0000112$$

indicating that y_4 should be accurate to about 5s.

$$j = 4: \quad f_4 = f(t_4, y_4) = -(2.4)(0.5318739)^2 \doteq -0.6789358$$

$$p_5 = y_4 + \frac{h}{24} \{-9f_1 + 37f_2 - 59f_3 + 55f_4\} \doteq 0.4712642$$

$$y_5 = y_4 + \frac{h}{24} \{f_2 - 5f_3 + 19f_4 - 9(-t_5 p_5^2)\} \doteq 0.4704654 \, (= c_5)$$

$$\delta_5 = -\frac{19}{270} \{y_5 - p_5\} \doteq 0.0000562$$

As before, δ_5 indicates possible inaccuracy in the fourth significant digit of y_5. So we get an improved y_5 as

$$y_5 = y_4 + \frac{h}{24} \{f_2 - 5f_3 + 19f_4 - 9[-t_5(0.4704654)^2]\} \doteq 0.4705358$$

The local truncation error estimate for this y_5 is

$$\delta_5 = -\tfrac{19}{270} \{0.4705358 - 0.4704654\} \doteq -0.0000050$$

indicating that this y_5 should be accurate to about 5s.

In fact, as shown in Table 8.3-1, y_4 and y_5 are accurate only to about 4s. Moreover, had we "corrected" y_4 a second time (with 0.531874 taken as p_4), the resulting y_4 would have been *less* accurate than 0.531874! More generally, experience has shown that:

TABLE 8.3-1 APC4 AND RK4 VALUES FOR $y' = -ty^2$, $y(2) = 1$ $(h = 0.1)$.

t_j	Exact $y(t_j)$	Using APC4 $(h = 0.1)$		Using RK4 $(h = 0.1)$	
		y_j	$E_j[h]$	y_j	$E_j[h]$
$t_0 = 2.0$	1.000000	Exact	—	Exact	—
2.1	0.829876	Exact	—	0.829885	−0.000009
2.2	0.704225	Exact	—	0.704237	−0.000012
2.3	0.607903	Exact	—	0.607914	−0.000011
2.4	0.531915	0.531874	0.000041	0.531924	−0.000009
2.5	0.470588	0.470536	0.000052	0.470596	−0.000008
2.6	0.420168	0.420114	0.000054	0.420175	−0.000007
2.7	0.378072	0.378020	0.000052	0.378078	−0.000006
2.8	0.342466	0.342419	0.000047	0.342471	−0.000005
2.9	0.312012	0.311971	0.000041	0.312017	−0.000005
$t_F = 3.0$	0.285714	0.285674	0.000040	0.285718	−0.000004

The values obtained by performing at most one correction of y_{j+1} are as likely to be accurate as those obtained using any general strategy for iterating the corrector formula. If more than one correction appears necessary, decrease the stepsize.

In Table 8.3-1, three $f(t, y)$ evaluations [one at (t_j, y_j) to get p_{j+1}, one at (t_{j+1}, p_{j+1}) to get y_{j+1}, and one at (t_{j+1}, y_{j+1}) to get a corrected y_{j+1}] were used at all steps except the last, which used only two. For this problem, APC4 requires a stepsize smaller than $h = 0.1$ to achieve $5s$ accuracy. The stepsize $h = 0.1$ was suitable for RK4 because $f(t, y) = -ty^2$ is a polynomial of degree ≤ 4 in t and y. APC4 will be more accurate than RK4 (in fact *exact*) when $y(t)$ is a polynomial of degree ≤ 4 in t. (Why?)

Pseudocode for the APC4 algorithm is given in Figure 8.3-3. *MaxIt* is usually set to 2. The method used to start a PC method should be at least the same order as the PC method itself. RK4 is usually used to start APC4.

8.3B STEPSIZE CONTROL OF PREDICTOR–CORRECTOR METHODS

The error indicator δ_{j+1} can be used to exercise stepsize control in much the same way that *ErrorEstimate* was used in Figure 8.2-3 (Section 8.2C). However, since the method must be restarted each time h is changed, h should not be changed too frequently. A strategy currently recommended for an nth-order method is

$$Ratio \leftarrow |\delta_{j+1}|/h$$
$$\text{IF } Ratio > BigRatio \quad \text{or} \quad Ratio < SmallRatio \tag{8}$$
$$\text{THEN } h \leftarrow h\left(\frac{DesiredRatio}{Ratio}\right)^{1/n}$$

In (8), *DesiredRatio* is chosen as $C*10^{-s}$, where s is the desired number of significant digits. The effect of (8) is to decrease h when *Ratio* is getting unacceptably large, and to increase h when *Ratio* shows h to be needlessly small.

If the time or expense of restarting a fourth-order PC method is a critical factor, one can save f_{j-4} in addition to the f_i's needed to get y_{j+1} and then either double or halve h as follows:

HALVING H: Use the interpolating quartic for the five nodes (t_{j-4}, f_{j-4}), . . . , (t_j, f_j) to get the bisecting values

$$f_{j-1/2} = \tfrac{1}{128}\left[-5f_{j-4} + 28f_{j-3} - 70f_{j-2} + 140f_{j-1} + 35f_j\right] \tag{9a}$$
$$f_{j-3/2} = \tfrac{1}{64}\left[3f_{j-4} - 16f_{j-3} + 54f_{j-2} + 24f_{j-1} - f_j\right] \tag{9b}$$

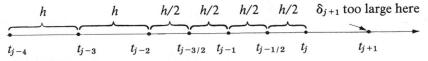

Then proceed from (t_j, y_j) with stepsize $h/2$.

Algorithm: APC4 (Adams Fourth-Order Predictor–Corrector Method)

Purpose: To solve, on the interval $[t_0, t_F]$, the IVP

$$y' = f(t, y), \quad y = y_0 \text{ when } t = t_0$$

using a specified number of steps to obtain *NumSig* significant digit accuracy. The three preceding slope values f_{j-1}, f_{j-2}, and f_{j-3} will be stored as simply f_{-1}, f_{-2}, and f_{-3}.

{*initialize*}
GET $t_0, t_F, y_0,$ {parameters of IVP}
        NumberOfSteps,   {from t_0 to t_F; at the jth step, $t_j = t_0 + jh$}
        NumSig, MaxIt   {maximum number of iterations of corrector}
$h \leftarrow (t_F - t_0)/NumberOfSteps; \quad RelTol \leftarrow 10^{-NumSig}$
$t \leftarrow t_0; \quad y \leftarrow y_0$ {(t, y) is the current (t_j, y_j).}
DO FOR $j = 0$ TO 2   {Initialize f_{-3}, f_{-2}, f_{-1}.}
  BEGIN
  $f_{j-3} \leftarrow f(t, y)$
  Use a self-starting method to get *Ynew*   {*Ynew* approximates $y(t + h)$.}
  $t \leftarrow t + h; \quad y \leftarrow Ynew$
  OUTPUT $(j + 1, t, y, f_{j-3})$
  END
{Now $t = t_3$, $y = y_3$, and f_{-3}, f_{-2}, f_{-1} are slope values at t_0, t_1, t_2 respectively.}
$f \leftarrow f(t, y)$ {f is f_j, the slope at (t_j, y_j).}

{*iterate*}
DO FOR $j = 3$ TO (*NumberOfSteps* $- 1$)
  BEGIN

  {**predict**} $p \leftarrow y - \dfrac{h}{24}[-9f_{-3} + 37f_{-2} - 59f_{-1} + 55f]$

  DO FOR $k = 1$ TO *MaxIt* UNTIL **termination test** is satisfied
    BEGIN

    {**correct**} $c \leftarrow y + \dfrac{h}{24}[f_{-2} - 5f_{-1} + 19f + 9f(t + h, p)]$

    $Delta \leftarrow -\frac{19}{270}(c - p)$ {estimate of $e_c[h]$}
    $p \leftarrow c$ {prepare for another iteration}
    {**termination test:** $|Delta| \leqslant RelTol*|c|$}
    END
  IF **termination test** was not satisfied
    THEN OUTPUT (Smaller stepsize may be needed for desired accuracy.)
  {**update**}
  $t \leftarrow t + h; \quad y \leftarrow c$
  $f_{-3} \leftarrow f_{-2}; \quad f_{-2} \leftarrow f_{-1}; \quad f_{-1} \leftarrow f; \quad f \leftarrow f(t, y)$
  OUTPUT $(j + 1, t, y, f)$
  END

IF **termination test** was satisfied at each step
  THEN OUTPUT (The y values should be accurate to *NumSig* significant digits.)

FIGURE 8.3-3 PSEUDOPROGRAM FOR THE FOURTH-ORDER ADAMS PREDICTOR–CORRECTOR (APC4) METHOD.

DOUBLING H: Take one more h-step to get to t_{j+2}. Then use f_{j-4}, f_{j-2}, f_j and f_{j+2} to proceed from (t_{j+2}, y_{j+2}) with stepsize $2h$.

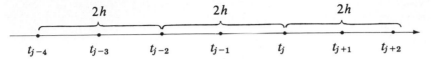

8.3C STABILITY

A formula of the form

$$y_{j+1} = y_j + h\,\phi \tag{10}$$

can generally be viewed as the result of replacing y' in an IVP by a finite difference approximation. Although it is not immediately apparent, such replacements can introduce **parasitic terms** of the form

$$Ce^{\nu t_j} \quad \text{and/or} \quad (-1)^j Ce^{\nu t_j} \tag{11}$$

into the calculated solution that have no relation to the exact solution. If $\nu > 0$, they grow exponentially in magnitude as t_j increases, in which case the method is called **unstable** for the IVP. Intuitively, instability means that a small error at one step can cause considerably worsened errors several steps later.

The stability of a method can be determined by examining the step sizes h for which the method gives accurate solutions to three test problems:

$$\text{(I)} \quad y' \equiv 0, \quad y(0) = 1 \quad \text{[Exact solution is } y(t) \equiv 1\text{]} \tag{12}$$

$$\text{(II)} \quad y' \equiv 1, \quad y(0) = 0 \quad \text{[Exact solution is } y(t) = t\text{]} \tag{13}$$

$$\text{(III)} \quad y' = \lambda y, \quad y(0) = 1 \quad \text{[Exact solution is } y(t) = e^{\lambda t}\text{]} \tag{14}$$

Methods that exhibit instability for Test Problems I or II for some values of h are called **strongly unstable**; those that exhibit instability for some values of λ in Test Problem III are called **weakly unstable**.

EXAMPLE. The **midpoint predictor** formula

$$y_{j+1} = y_{j-1} + 2hf_j, \qquad j = 1, 2, 3, \ldots \tag{15}$$

can be obtained form the exact IVP constraint at t_j, namely

$$y'(t_j) = f(t_j, y(t_j)), \qquad j = 1, 2, \ldots$$

by replacing $y'(t_j)$ and $f(t_j, y(t_j))$, respectively, by

$$\frac{y_{j+1} - y_{j-1}}{2h} \quad \text{and} \quad f_j = f(t_j, y_j) \qquad \text{for } j = 1, 2, \ldots \tag{16}$$

Examine the weak stability of (15) by applying it to Test Problem III.

Solution. Taking $f_j = \lambda y_j$ in (15) gives the **finite difference equation**

$$y_{j+1} - 2\lambda h y_j - y_{j-1} = 0, \qquad j = 1, 2, \ldots \tag{17}$$

It can be shown (see [19]) that its general solution is

$$y_j = C_1 r^j + C_2 s^j, \qquad \text{where } C_1 + C_2 = y_0 = 1 \tag{18a}$$

and r and s are the roots of its **characteristic equation**

$$x^2 - 2\lambda h x - 1 = 0 \tag{18b}$$

By the quadratic formula, these roots can be expressed as

$$r = \lambda h + \sqrt{1 + \lambda^2 h^2} \qquad \text{and} \qquad s = \lambda h - \sqrt{1 + \lambda^2 h^2} \tag{19}$$

Replacing $\sqrt{1 + u}$ by the binomial approximation $1 + \frac{1}{2} u + O(u^2)$, $u = \lambda^2 h^2$, gives

$$r = \lambda h + [1 + \tfrac{1}{2}\lambda^2 h^2 + O(h^4)] = e^{\lambda h} + O(h^3) \qquad \text{and} \qquad s = -e^{-\lambda h} + O(h^3) \tag{20}$$

[See (6b) of Section 7.1A.] So (18a) can be rewritten as

$$y_j = (1 - C_2)(e^{\lambda h})^j + C_2(-1)^j (e^{-\lambda h})^j + O(h^3) \tag{21}$$

Since $hj = 0 + jh = t_j$,

$$y_j = \underbrace{e^{\lambda t_j}}_{\text{exact } y(t_j)} - \underbrace{[C_2 e^{\lambda t_j} + C_2(-1)^j e^{-\lambda t_j}]}_{\text{parasitic terms}} + \underbrace{O(h^3)}_{\text{truncation error}} \tag{22}$$

Generally, $C_2 \approx 0$. However, the parasitic terms will affect the solution unless C_2 happens to be *exactly* zero. When $\lambda > 0$ [in which case $y(t) \to \infty$ as $t \to \infty$], they introduce only a small relative error. But when $\lambda < 0$ [in which case $y(t) \to 0$ as $t \to \infty$], the oscillatory $(-1)^j e^{-\lambda t_j}$ term eventually *dominates* y_j. So *the midpoint predictor is weakly unstable.*

More generally, exponentially growing oscillations in y_j should alert the user to the possibility of instability.

In Test Problem III, $\partial f/\partial y = \partial(\lambda y)/\partial y = \lambda$. Once the stability of a method for Test Problem III is known, it can be used as follows:

Find the values of $\bar{h} = h\lambda$ for which the method is stable for Test Problem III. Then the method should be stable for the IVP

$$y' = f(t, y), \qquad y(t_0) = y_0$$

if one uses stepsizes h for which the product $h \cdot \partial f/\partial y$ is an acceptable $\bar{h}$ along the solution curve.

Thus the stepsizes h for which a particular method will give a stable solution of a particular IVP depend upon (i) the values of f_y along the solution curve $y = y(t)$, and (ii) the values of $\bar{h} = h\lambda$ for which the method is stable for Test Problem III.

Investigations have shown all Runge–Kutta methods to be stable for reasonably small h. A stability analysis of Predictor–Corrector methods is more complex, as it must take into account the combined effects of both the predictor and corrector formulas. The APC4 method of Section 8.3A is generally accepted as stable hence suitable for use in general-purpose IVP-solving programs. For more details, the reader is referred to [9].

8.3D   COMPARING RK AND PC METHODS

The general-purpose IVP solvers discussed so far are summarized in Table 8.3-2. Taylor's method, although useful in some special situations, is not easily automated, and hence is not included. All methods shown are stable for sufficiently small h.

TABLE 8.3-2   IVP SOLVERS COMPARED.

Method (Section)	Self-Starting?	Local Error	Global Error	$f(t, y)$ eval./step	Stepsize Control
Euler (8.1B)	Yes	$O(h^2)$	$O(h)$	1	Possible
Modified Euler (8.2B)	Yes	$O(h^3)$	$O(h^2)$	2	Possible
Huen (8.2B)	Yes	$O(h^3)$	$O(h^2)$	2	Possible
RK4 (8.2C)	Yes	$O(h^5)$	$O(h^4)$	4	Possible
RKF4 (8.2D)	Yes	$O(h^5)$	$O(h^4)$	6	Easy
APC4 (8.3A)	No	$O(h^5)$	$O(h^4)$	2–3	Awkward

If a singularity of $y(t)$ is a possibility on $[t_0, t_F]$, then a method with convenient stepsize control such as RKF4 is recommended. If $f(t, y)$ is expensive to evaluate, then the APC4 method might be preferable. Finally, in a **real-time** situation (e.g., a missile guidance system) where one has a fixed (*short*) amount of time in which to calculate y_{j+1}, Euler's method (modified if time permits) might be the method of choice.

One final word about PC methods. It may have occurred to the reader that since δ_{j+1} is an estimate of $e_{j+1}[h]_c$ (the local truncation error of c_{j+1}), one can add it to c_{j+1} to get an "improved corrector" $c_{j+1} + \delta_{j+1}$. Although this strategy is enticing, empirical tests have shown that methods incorporating it tend to be unstable, and hence not generally desirable.

This concludes our discussion of general IVP solvers. More extensive discussions can be found in [21 and 22]. Methods that are effective in certain specific situations are discussed in Section 8.4E.

8.4 First-Order Systems and nth-Order IVPs

Physical systems generally require several variables to describe their state at any time t. For example, the **state variables** of a *thermodynamic system* might include temperature, pressure, volume, and entropy; the state variables of a *mechanical system* might include the displacements of certain points; and the state variables of an *electrical circuit* might include the voltages and currents that determine the energy delivered to certain critical components.

8.4A NOTATION AND TERMINOLOGY

Our "neutral" notation for the state variables of a complex system will be y_1, y_2, . . . , y_n, where each varies with a *single* variable t (usually time) according to the applicable physical laws. Frequently, these laws take the form of n first-order initial value problems as follows:

$$
\textbf{(IVP)}_n
\quad
\begin{aligned}
y_1' &= \frac{dy_1}{dt} = f_1(t, y_1, y_2, \ldots, y_n), & y_1(t_0) &= y_{01} \\[2mm]
y_2' &= \frac{dy_2}{dt} = f_2(t, y_1, y_2, \ldots, y_n), & y_2(t_0) &= y_{02} \\
&\ \ \vdots & &\ \ \vdots \\
y_n' &= \frac{dy_n}{dt} = f_n(t, y_1, y_2, \ldots, y_n), & y_n(t_0) &= y_{0n}
\end{aligned}
\tag{1}
$$

In words, we know the **initial state** at some t_0, and we know the rate at which each state variable changes when the system is in a particular state. An example of such a system is

$$
\begin{aligned}
y_1' &= 3ty_2 + y_1 y_2, & y_1(0) &= -1 \\[2mm]
y_2' &= 2 \ln(1 + y_2^2) + \frac{1}{y_3}, & y_2(0) &= 1 \\[2mm]
y_3' &= y_3^2 - y_1 e^{y_2} + 1, & y_3(0) &= 1
\end{aligned}
\tag{2}
$$

Notice that the rates at which y_1, y_2, or y_3 change at time t depend on the values of *all three* state variables at that t. For this reason $(\text{IVP})_n$ is often referred to as a **coupled system** of first-order equations.

A **solution** of $(\text{IVP})_n$ consists of n functions

$$
y_1 = y_1(t), \quad y_2 = y_2(t), \quad \ldots, \quad y_n = y_n(t)
\tag{3a}
$$

which satisfy $(\text{IVP})_n$ in the sense that for $i = 1, 2, \ldots, n$,

$$
y_i'(t) = f_i(t, y_1(t), \ldots, y_n(t)) \quad \text{and} \quad y_i(t_0) = y_{0i}
\tag{3b}
$$

As in Section 8.1A, we assume solutions of $(\text{IVP})_n$ to be uniquely determined on any interval containing t_0 on which all $y_i(t)$'s and all f_i's remain continuous.

8.4B   VECTOR FORMULATION OF NUMERICAL METHODS FOR SOLVING $(\text{IVP})_n$

If we let

$$\mathbf{y} = \mathbf{y}(t) = [y_1 \quad y_2 \quad \cdots \quad y_n]^T = \text{the } \textbf{state-variable vector} \tag{4a}$$

then $(\text{IVP})_n$ can be put in the **vector form**

$$\boxed{(\text{IVP})_n \quad \mathbf{y}' = \mathbf{f}(t, \mathbf{y}), \qquad \mathbf{y}(t_0) = \mathbf{y}_0} \tag{4b}$$

where $\mathbf{y}'$, $\mathbf{f}(t, \mathbf{y})$, and $\mathbf{y}_0$ are defined by

$$\mathbf{y}' = \begin{bmatrix} y_1' \\ y_2' \\ \vdots \\ y_n' \end{bmatrix}, \quad \mathbf{f}(t, \mathbf{y}) = \begin{bmatrix} f_1(t, \mathbf{y}) \\ f_2(t, \mathbf{y}) \\ \vdots \\ f_n(t, \mathbf{y}) \end{bmatrix}, \quad \text{and} \quad \mathbf{y}_0 = \begin{bmatrix} y_{01} \\ y_{02} \\ \vdots \\ y_{0n} \end{bmatrix} \tag{4c}$$

For example, the vector form of the $(\text{IVP})_3$ in (2) is

$$\underbrace{\begin{bmatrix} y_1' \\ y_2' \\ y_3' \end{bmatrix}}_{\mathbf{y}'} = \underbrace{\begin{bmatrix} 3ty_2 + y_1 y_2 \\ 2\ln(1 + y_2^2) + \dfrac{1}{y_3} \\ y_3^2 - y_1 e^{y_2} + 1 \end{bmatrix}}_{\mathbf{f}(t,\ \mathbf{y})}, \qquad \underbrace{\begin{bmatrix} y_1(0) \\ y_2(0) \\ y_3(0) \end{bmatrix}}_{\mathbf{y}(0)} = \underbrace{\begin{bmatrix} -1 \\ 1 \\ 1 \end{bmatrix}}_{\mathbf{y}_0}$$

A **numerical solution** of $(\text{IVP})_n$ on the interval $[t_0, \ t_F]$ is a sequence of vectors $\mathbf{y}_0$, $\mathbf{y}_1, \ldots, \mathbf{y}_F$, where

$$\boxed{\mathbf{y}_j \text{ approximates the exact solution } \mathbf{y}(t_j) \qquad \text{for } j = 0, 1, \ldots, F} \tag{5}$$

It can be seen from (4b) that (IVP) becomes $(\text{IVP})_n$ if we replace the scalars y, y', $f(t, y)$, and y_0 by the vectors $\mathbf{y}$, $\mathbf{y}'$, $\mathbf{f}(t, \mathbf{y})$, and $\mathbf{y}_0$. *Performing these replacements in the formulas of an IVP-solver results in a formula for an $(\text{IVP})_n$-solver.* In particular, RK4 becomes the following set of *vector* equations, which we shall refer to as $\textbf{RK4}_n$:

$$\mathbf{y}_{j+1} = \mathbf{y}_j + \frac{h}{6}\{\mathbf{m}_1 + 2(\mathbf{m}_2 + \mathbf{m}_3) + \mathbf{m}_4\} \tag{6a}$$

where the "slope vectors" $\mathbf{m}_1$, $\mathbf{m}_2$, $\mathbf{m}_3$, and $\mathbf{m}_4$ are obtained recursively as

$$\mathbf{m}_1 = \mathbf{f}(t_j, \mathbf{y}_j)$$

$$\mathbf{m}_2 = \mathbf{f}\left(t_j + \frac{h}{2}, \mathbf{y}_j + \frac{h}{2}\mathbf{m}_1\right) \tag{6b}$$

$$\mathbf{m}_3 = \mathbf{f}\left(t_j + \frac{h}{2}, \mathbf{y}_j + \frac{h}{2}\mathbf{m}_2\right)$$

$$\mathbf{m}_4 = \mathbf{f}(t_j + h, \mathbf{y}_j + h\mathbf{m}_3)$$

EXAMPLE. Use $RK4_n$ to find $\mathbf{y}_1 \approx \mathbf{y}(0.2)$ for the coupled system

$$\frac{dy_1}{dt} = y_2, \qquad y_1(0) = 1 \qquad [f_1(t, \mathbf{y}) = y_2, \qquad y_{01} = 1]$$

$$\frac{dy_2}{dt} = y_1 + t, \quad y_2(0) = -1 \quad [f_2(t, \mathbf{y}) = y_1 + t, \, y_{02} = -1] \tag{7a}$$

Solution. The vector form of this $(IVP)_2$ is

$$\underbrace{\begin{bmatrix} y_1' \\ y_2' \end{bmatrix}}_{\mathbf{y}'} = \underbrace{\begin{bmatrix} y_2 \\ y_1 + t \end{bmatrix}}_{\mathbf{f}(t, \mathbf{y})}, \quad \underbrace{\begin{bmatrix} y_1(0) \\ y_2(0) \end{bmatrix}}_{\mathbf{y}(0)} = \underbrace{\begin{bmatrix} 1 \\ -1 \end{bmatrix}}_{\mathbf{y}_0} \tag{7b}$$

Since $t_0 = 0$ and $t_1 = t_0 + h = 0.2$, h must be 0.2. So, by (6b),

$$\mathbf{m}_1 = \mathbf{f}(t_0, \mathbf{y}_0) = \begin{bmatrix} y_{02} \\ y_{01} + t_0 \end{bmatrix} = \begin{bmatrix} -1 \\ 1 \end{bmatrix}; \qquad\qquad \mathbf{y}_0 + \frac{h}{2}\mathbf{m}_1 = \begin{bmatrix} 1 \\ -1 \end{bmatrix} + \frac{0.2}{2}\begin{bmatrix} -1 \\ 1 \end{bmatrix} = \begin{bmatrix} 0.9 \\ -0.9 \end{bmatrix}$$

$$\mathbf{m}_2 = \mathbf{f}\left(t_0 + \frac{h}{2}, \mathbf{y}_0 + \frac{h}{2}\mathbf{m}_1\right) = \begin{bmatrix} -0.9 \\ 0.9 + 0.1 \end{bmatrix} = \begin{bmatrix} -0.9 \\ 1.0 \end{bmatrix}; \qquad \mathbf{y}_0 + \frac{h}{2}\mathbf{m}_2 = \begin{bmatrix} 0.91 \\ -0.9 \end{bmatrix}$$

$$\mathbf{m}_3 = \mathbf{f}\left(t_0 + \frac{h}{2}, \mathbf{y}_0 + \frac{h}{2}\mathbf{m}_2\right) = \begin{bmatrix} -0.9 \\ 0.91 + 0.1 \end{bmatrix} = \begin{bmatrix} -0.9 \\ 1.01 \end{bmatrix}; \qquad \mathbf{y}_0 + h\mathbf{m}_3 = \begin{bmatrix} 0.82 \\ -0.798 \end{bmatrix}$$

$$\mathbf{m}_4 = \mathbf{f}(t_0 + h, \mathbf{y}_0 + h\mathbf{m}_3) = \begin{bmatrix} -0.798 \\ 0.82 + 0.2 \end{bmatrix} = \begin{bmatrix} -0.798 \\ 1.02 \end{bmatrix}$$

Hence, by (6a), the desired approximation of $\mathbf{y}(0.2)$ is

$$\mathbf{y}_1 = \begin{bmatrix} 1 \\ -1 \end{bmatrix} + \frac{0.2}{6}\left\{\begin{bmatrix} -1 \\ 1 \end{bmatrix} + 2\left(\begin{bmatrix} -0.9 \\ 1.0 \end{bmatrix} + \begin{bmatrix} -0.9 \\ 1.01 \end{bmatrix}\right) + \begin{bmatrix} -0.798 \\ 1.02 \end{bmatrix}\right\} \doteq \begin{bmatrix} 0.820067 \\ -0.798667 \end{bmatrix}$$

It is easy to verify that the exact solution of (7) is[†]

$$\mathbf{y}(t) = \begin{bmatrix} \cosh t - t \\ \sinh t - 1 \end{bmatrix} \quad \text{so that } \mathbf{y}(0.2) \doteq \begin{bmatrix} 0.820067 \\ -0.798665 \end{bmatrix} \tag{8}$$

[†] Recall that $\cosh t = \frac{1}{2}(e^t + e^{-t})$ and $\sinh t = \frac{1}{2}(e^t - e^{-t})$.

Thus for this simple $\mathbf{f}(t, \mathbf{y})$ (f_1 and f_2 are linear in t, y_1, and y_2), $5s$ accuracy was achieved with a rather large stepsize, $h = 0.2$.

8.4C   SOLVING AN *n*th-ORDER IVP

There are many real-world situations that are naturally described not as a first-order coupled system but as a single ***n*th-order IVP** whose general form, after solving for the highest derivative, is

$$y^{(n)} = f(t, y, y', y'', \ldots, y^{(n-1)}) \qquad \textbf{(9a)}$$

subject to n initial conditions at $t = t_0$:

$$y(t_0) = y_0, \quad y'(t_0) = y_0', \quad \ldots, \quad y^{(n-1)}(t_0) = y_0^{(n-1)} \qquad \textbf{(9b)}$$

To be an *initial value problem,* all the initial conditions must be specified at the *same* t_0.[†]

The general approach to solving the nth-order IVP (9) is to *convert it to an equivalent system of n first-order equations.* To do this, one simply takes the ith state variable to be the $(i-1)$st derivative of y, that is, form the state variable vector

$$\mathbf{y} = \begin{bmatrix} y_1 \\ y_2 \\ \vdots \\ y_{n-1} \\ y_n \end{bmatrix}, \quad \text{where} \quad \begin{matrix} y_1 & = y \\ y_2 & = y' \\ \vdots \\ y_{n-1} & = y^{(n-2)} \\ y_n & = y^{(n-1)} \end{matrix} \qquad \textbf{(10a)}$$

Substituting this in (9) and noting that $y_n' = d(y^{(n-1)})/dt = y^{(n)}$ gives the equivalent first-order coupled system

$$\begin{aligned} y_1' &= y_2, & y_1(t_0) &= y_0 \\ y_2' &= y_3, & y_2(t_0) &= y_0' \\ &\vdots & &\vdots \\ y_{n-1}' &= y_n, & y_{n-1}(t_0) &= y_0^{(n-2)} \\ y_n' &= f(t, y_1, y_2, \ldots, y_n), & y_n(t_0) &= y_0^{(n-1)} \end{aligned} \qquad \textbf{(10b)}$$

This is now of the form $\mathbf{y}' = \mathbf{f}(t, \mathbf{y})$, $\mathbf{y}(t_0) = \mathbf{y}_0$; hence it can be solved by any of the methods of Section 8.4B.

[†] When these conditions involve more than one t, the problem becomes a *boundary value problem.* These are considered in Section 8.5.

EXAMPLE 1. Convert the following third-order IVP to (IVP)$_3$.

$$ty''' + t^2y' + yy'' = 2te^{-3t} \tag{11a}$$

$$y(1) = -2, \qquad y'(1) = 1, \qquad y''(1) = 0 \tag{11b}$$

Solution. We must first solve for the highest derivative,

$$y''' = 2e^{-3t} - ty' - \frac{1}{t}yy''$$

Taking $y_1 = y$, $y_2 = y'$, $y_3 = y''$ gives the desired system,

$$
\begin{aligned}
y_1' &= y_2, & y_1(1) &= -2 \\
y_2' &= y_3, & y_2(1) &= 1 \\
y_3' &= 2e^{-3t} - ty_2 - \frac{1}{t}y_1y_3, & y_3(1) &= 0
\end{aligned}
\tag{12}
$$

As another example, the reader should verify that (IVP)$_2$ given in the example in Section 8.4B results from taking $y_1 = y$, $y_2 = y'$ in the second-order IVP

$$y'' = y + t, \qquad y(0) = 1, \qquad y'(0) = -1 \tag{13}$$

When an (IVP)$_n$ solver is used to solve (10b), *the first component of* $\mathbf{y}_j$ *is the desired approximation of* $y(t_j)$ [see (10a)]. Approximations of $y'(t_j), \ldots, y^{(n-1)}(t_j)$ are obtained *gratis* as the remaining components of $\mathbf{y}_j$.

EXAMPLE 2. Consider the second-order IVP

$$y'' = \frac{-y'}{y^2}, \qquad y(2) = 2, \qquad y'(2) = \frac{1}{2} \tag{14}$$

Its exact solution, as the reader can verify, is

$$y(t) = \sqrt{2t}; \qquad \text{so that } y'(t) = \frac{1}{\sqrt{2t}} = \frac{1}{y(t)} \tag{15}$$

Starting with the exact values at $t = 2, 2.1, 2.2, 2.3$, use the Adams predictor–corrector equations to get estimates of $y(2.4)$ and $y'(2.4)$.

Solution. For reference, we note that the use of APC4 to solve

$$(\text{IVP})_n \qquad \mathbf{y}' = \mathbf{f}(t, \mathbf{y}), \qquad \mathbf{y}(t_0) = \mathbf{y}_0$$

requires the following **APC4**$_n$ equations:

Predict: $\qquad \mathbf{p}_{j+1} = \mathbf{y}_j + \dfrac{h}{24}\{-9\mathbf{f}_{j-3} + 37\mathbf{f}_{j-2} - 59\mathbf{f}_{j-1} + 55\mathbf{f}_j\}$ $\qquad$ (16a)

Correct: $\qquad \mathbf{c}_{j+1} = \mathbf{y}_j + \dfrac{h}{24}\{\mathbf{f}_{j-2} - 5\mathbf{f}_{j-1} + 19\mathbf{f}_j + 9\mathbf{f}(t_{j+1}, \mathbf{p}_{j+1})\}$ $\qquad$ (16b)

Error Estimate: $\boldsymbol{\delta}_{j+1} = \dfrac{-19}{270}\{\mathbf{c}_{j+1} - \mathbf{p}_{j+1}\}$ $\qquad$ (16c)

Putting $y_1 = y$, $y_2 = y'$ transforms (14) to the following (IVP)$_2$:

$$\underbrace{\begin{bmatrix} y_1' \\ y_2' \end{bmatrix}}_{\mathbf{y'}} = \underbrace{\begin{bmatrix} y_2 \\ -\dfrac{y_2}{y_1^2} \end{bmatrix}}_{\mathbf{f}(t,\,\mathbf{y})}, \qquad \underbrace{\begin{bmatrix} y_1(2) \\ y_2(2) \end{bmatrix}}_{\mathbf{y}(2)} = \underbrace{\begin{bmatrix} 2 \\ 1 \\ 2 \end{bmatrix}}_{\mathbf{y_0}} \tag{17}$$

Using (15), we get $\mathbf{y}_j$ as $\mathbf{y}(t_j) = \mathbf{y}(2 + 0.1j)$ to $7s$, $j = 0, 1, 2, 3$:

$$\mathbf{y_0} = \begin{bmatrix} 2 \\ 0.5 \end{bmatrix}, \quad \mathbf{y_1} = \begin{bmatrix} 2.049390 \\ 0.4879500 \end{bmatrix}, \quad \mathbf{y_2} = \begin{bmatrix} 2.097618 \\ 0.4767313 \end{bmatrix}, \quad \mathbf{y_3} = \begin{bmatrix} 2.144761 \\ 0.4662524 \end{bmatrix} \tag{18a}$$

Since $\mathbf{f}_j = [\, y_{2j} \quad -y_{2j}/y_{1j}^2 \,]^T$, where $\mathbf{y}_j = [\, y_{1j} \quad y_{2j} \,]^T$,

$$\mathbf{f_0} = \begin{bmatrix} 0.5 \\ -0.125 \end{bmatrix}, \quad \mathbf{f_1} = \begin{bmatrix} 0.4879500 \\ -0.1161786 \end{bmatrix}, \quad \mathbf{f_2} = \begin{bmatrix} 0.4767313 \\ -0.1083480 \end{bmatrix}, \quad \mathbf{f_3} = \begin{bmatrix} 0.4662524 \\ -0.1013592 \end{bmatrix}$$

$$\tag{18b}$$

With $h = 0.1$ and $t_3 = 2.3$, we get $\mathbf{y_4}$ as follows:

$$\mathbf{p_4} = \mathbf{y_3} + \frac{h}{24}\{-9\mathbf{f_0} + 37\mathbf{f_1} - 59\mathbf{f_2} + 55\mathbf{f_3}\} \doteq \begin{bmatrix} 2.190890 \\ 0.4564364 \end{bmatrix}$$

So

$$\mathbf{f}(t_4, \mathbf{p_4}) = \begin{bmatrix} 0.4564364 \\ \dfrac{-0.4564364}{(2.190890)^2} \end{bmatrix} \doteq \begin{bmatrix} 0.4564364 \\ -0.09509094 \end{bmatrix}$$

hence

$$\mathbf{y_4} = \mathbf{c_4} = \mathbf{y_3} + \frac{h}{24}\{\mathbf{f_1} - 5\mathbf{f_2} + 19\mathbf{f_3} + 9\mathbf{f}(t_4, \mathbf{p_4})\} \doteq \begin{bmatrix} 2.190890 \\ 0.4564354 \end{bmatrix}$$

$$\boldsymbol{\delta}_4 = -\tfrac{19}{270}\{\mathbf{c_4} - \mathbf{p_4}\} = -\tfrac{19}{270}\left\{ \begin{bmatrix} 2.190890 \\ 0.4564354 \end{bmatrix} - \begin{bmatrix} 2.190890 \\ 0.4564364 \end{bmatrix} \right\} \doteq \begin{bmatrix} 0 \\ 7.0\,\text{E}{-}8 \end{bmatrix}$$

It appears that this $\mathbf{y_4}$, without further iteration, is accurate to about $7s$. In fact, by (15) the exact components of $\mathbf{y}(t_4)$ are

$$y(t_4) = \sqrt{2(2.4)} \doteq 2.1908902 \qquad \text{and} \qquad y'(t_4) = \frac{1}{y(t_4)} \doteq 0.45643546 \tag{19}$$

The excellent accuracy attained in the preceding example should not be too surprising because $\mathbf{y}(t) = [\sqrt{2t} \quad 1/\sqrt{2t}]^T$ varies slowly on $[t_0, t_4] = [2.0, 2.4]$. More generally, given a suitable h, APC4$_n$ can usually be expected to solve (IVP)$_n$ about as accurately as RK4$_n$; and it will do so with between $2n$ and $3n$ scalar function evaluations [of $f_i(t, \mathbf{y})$] per step, compared to $4n$ for RK4$_n$.

8.4D SOLVING (IVP)$_n$ ON A COMPUTER

Most computer installations have in their libraries at least one program for solving

$$(\text{IVP})_n \quad \mathbf{y'} = \mathbf{f}(t, \mathbf{y}), \qquad \mathbf{y}(t_0) = \mathbf{y_0}$$

The program DIFSUB in the IMSL package is a rather sophisticated, variable-stepsize and variable-order predictor–corrector method, which has proved to be especially reliable.

To illustrate a general-purpose $(IVP)_n$-solver, we shall use the less sophisticated but still reliable FORTRAN SUBROUTINE RKF4 shown in Figure 8.4-1. This subroutine is based on the pseudoprogram for the Runge–Kutta–Fehlberg Method given in Figure 8.2-3. The **estimate next** $e[h]$ steps are performed by calling SUBROUTINE SUMK (Figure 8.4-2) to put $k_1, \ldots, k_6$ in columns $1, \ldots, 6$ of the matrix K. RATIO is then set to the largest (in magnitude) component of ERREST (lines 3600–4100) and then used in line 4400 to determine whether the array Y calculated in line 4600 will be a sufficiently accurate approximation of $y(T + H)$ [**accuracy test** steps], and in line 5300 to set the size of the next h [**set h** steps]. Note that the array Y is stored in extended precision to guard against the accumulated effects of negligible addition (Section 8.2D).

The user of RKF4 must provide SUBROUTINE EVALF(T, Y, F) to form the REAL array F $(= \mathbf{f}(t, \mathbf{y}))$ from T $(= t)$ and the DOUBLE PRECISION array Y $(= \mathbf{y})$.

RKF4 was used with $n = 1$ to obtain the values shown in Figures 8.2-4 and 8.2-5. An application when $n = 2$ is described in Section 8.5A.

8.4E   STIFF DIFFERENTIAL EQUATIONS

Differential equations or systems whose general solution involves exponential terms of the form

$$e^{-\lambda_i t}, \qquad \text{where } 0 < |\lambda_i|_{\min} \ll |\lambda_i|_{\max} \tag{20}$$

arise frequently when dealing with chemical reactions, process control, circuit theory, and vibrations. Such differential equations, called **stiff,** present serious numerical difficulties because *a small step size is needed to "track" the contribution of the rapidly decaying* $e^{-(\lambda_i)_{\max}}$ *term accurately,* whereas the resulting *accumulated roundoff error tends to undo the accuracy achieved* (see Section 8.2D). None of the methods considered so far can be expected to perform well in this situation.

EXAMPLE. Consider the linear, second-order IVP

$$y'' - 49.9y' - 5y = -45.9e^{-t}$$

The reader can verify that the general solution is

$$y(t) = Ce^{50t} + De^{-0.1t} - e^{-t} \tag{21a}$$

If we impose the initial conditions

$$y(0) = 5, \quad y'(0) = 0.4 \tag{21b}$$

then the desired solution, as the reader can verify, is

$$y(t) = 6e^{-0.1t} - e^{-t} \quad (C = 0, \ D = 6) \tag{21c}$$

```
00100          SUBROUTINE RKF4(RMAX, SCAMIN, SCAMAX, NPRINT, IW)
00200          REAL K(10,6)
00300          DOUBLE PRECISION Y(10)
00400          COMMON N, T, TF, Y
00500          COMMON /KCALC/ H, K
00600   C - - - - - - - - - - - - - - - - - - - - - - - - - - - - - - - C
00700   C THIS SUBROUTINE USES THE 4TH ORDER RUNGE-KUTTA-FEHLBERG ALGORITHM C
00800   C TO INTEGRATE N (N < 11) COUPLED FIRST ORDER IVPS, I.E.           C
00900   C        Y' = F(T,Y)   Y(TO) = YO    (TO,YO ARE INITIAL T,Y)       C
01000   C FROM TO TO TF, WHERE TF CAN BE TO THE LEFT OF TO.                C
01100   C VALUES OF T, H, AND VECTOR Y ARE PRINTED EVERY NPRINT ITERATIONS. C
01200   C IF NPRINT = 0, NOTHING IS PRINTED (UNLESS H BECOMES TOO SMALL).  C
01300   C - - - - - - - - - - - - - - - - - - - - - - -  VERSION 1: 5/1/81 C
01400   C INITIALIZE STEPSIZE, MINIMUM ALLOWABLE STEPSIZE, AND COUNTER:
01500          H = SIGN(RMAX**.25, TF-T)
01600          HMIN = 0.5E-4*H
01700          ITER = 0
01800   C
01900          IF (NPRINT.GT.0) WRITE(IW,1) ITER, T, H, (Y(I),I=1,N)
02000        1 FORMAT(I6, F9.4, E15.7, E15.7, 9E15.7)
02100   C
02200   C ITERATE:
02300   C      **BEGIN LOOP BY SETTING H TO TF-T IF T+H PASSES TF
02400       10   IF ( H*(T+H-TF) .GE. 0.) H = TF - T
02500   C
02600   C      **PUT VECTOR KJ IN JTH COLUMN OF MATRIX K, J=1,..,6
02700          CALL SUMK(1, 0., 0., 0., 0., 0., 0.)
02800          CALL SUMK(2, .25, .25, 0., 0., 0., 0.)
02900          CALL SUMK(3, .375, 3./32, 9./32, 0., 0., 0.)
03000          CALL SUMK(4, 12./13, 1932./2197, -7200./2197, 7296./2197, 0.,0.)
03100          CALL SUMK(5, 1., 439./216, -8., 3680./513, -845./4104, 0.)
03200          CALL SUMK(6, .5, -8./27, 2., -3544./2565, 1859./4104, -11./40)
03300   C
03400   C      **FORM ERREST = ESTIMATE OF ERROR OF NEXT Y(I) FOR I = 1,..,N
03500   C      **AND FIND RATIO = THE LARGEST OF THE ERREST/H RATIOS
03600          RATIO = 0.
03700          DO 20 I=1,N
03800             ERREST = K(I,1)/360 - 128*K(I,3)/4275 - 2197*K(I,4)/75240
03900        &            + K(I,5)/50 + 2*K(I,6)/55
04000             RATIO = AMAX1(RATIO,ABS(ERREST/H))
04100       20   CONTINUE
04200   C
04300   C      **TEST ACCURACY OF NEXT Y.  IF OK, UPDATE T, Y AND ITER
04400          IF (RATIO .GT. RMAX) GOTO 30
04500             T = T + H
04600             CALL SUMK(0, 0., 25./216, 0., 1408./2565, 2197./4104, -0.2)
04700             ITER = ITER + 1
04800   C
04900             IF (NPRINT.GT.0 .AND. (MOD(ITER,NPRINT).EQ.0 .OR. T.EQ.TF))
05000        &       WRITE(IW,1) ITER, T, H, (Y(I), I=1,N)
05100   C
05200   C      **SET SCALE (BETWEEN SCAMIN AND SCAMAX) AND UPDATE H
05300       30   SCALE = 0.84*(RMAX/RATIO)**.25
05400          IF (SCALE .LT. SCAMIN) SCALE = SCAMIN
05500          IF (SCALE .GT. SCAMAX) SCALE = SCAMAX
05600          H = SCALE*H
05700   C
05800   C      **TERMINATION TESTS
05900          IF (T .EQ. TF) RETURN
06000          IF (ABS(H) .GT. HMIN) GOTO 10
06100   C      **END OF LOOP
06200   C
06300          WRITE(IW,2) T
06400        2 FORMAT('0APPARENT SINGULARITY NEAR T =',E10.3)
06500          RETURN
06600          END
```

FIGURE 8.4-1 SUBROUTINE RKF4.

```
00100         SUBROUTINE SUMK(J, P, Q1, Q2, Q3, Q4, Q5)
00200         REAL K(10,6), F(10)
00300         DOUBLE PRECISION Y(10), SUM(10)
00400         COMMON N, T, TF, Y
00500         COMMON /KCALC/ H, K
00600   C - - - - - - - - - - - - - - - - - - - - - - - - - - - - - - - - - C
00700   C        THIS SUBROUTINE EVALUATES THE N-VECTOR               C
00800   C                                                            C
00900   C        SUM = Y + Q1*ROW1(K) + ... + Q5*ROW5(K)             C
01000   C                                                            C
01100   C        IF J = 0, IT SETS Y = SUM.                          C
01200   C        IF 1 <= J <= 6, IT PUTS F(T+P*H,SUM) IN JTH COLUMN OF K    C
01300   C - - - - - - - - - - - - - - - - - - - - - - - - - - - - - - - - - C
01400         DO 10 I=1,N
01500           SUM(I) = Y(I) + DBLE(Q1)*K(I,1) + DBLE(Q2)*K(I,2) +
01600      &            DBLE(Q3)*K(I,3) + DBLE(Q4)*K(I,4) + DBLE(Q5)*K(I,5)
01700           IF (J .EQ. 0) Y(I) = SUM(I)
01800    10   CONTINUE
01900         IF (J .EQ. 0) RETURN
02000
02100         CALL EVALF(T+P*H, SUM, F)
02200         DO 20 I=1,N
02300           K(I,J) = H*F(I)
02400     20    CONTINUE
02500         RETURN
02600         END


00100   C * * * CALLING PROGRAM FOR SUBROUTINE RKF4 * * *
00200         DOUBLE PRECISION Y0(10)
00300         COMMON N, T0, TF, Y0
00400         DATA IW, IR /5, 5/
00500         DATA SCAMIN, SCAMAX, RMAX /0.1, 4.0, 1.E-4/
00600   C
00700         WRITE(IW,1)
00800       1 FORMAT('0INPUT N, T0, TF, NPRINT')
00900         READ(IR,*) N, T0, TF, NPRINT
01000   C
01100         WRITE(IW,2) N
01200       2 FORMAT(' INPUT',I2,' COMPONENTS OF Y0')
01300         READ(IR,*) (Y0(I), I=1,N)
01400   C
01500         WRITE(IW,3) T0, TF, NPRINT
01600       3 FORMAT('0INTEGRATING FROM',F8.4,' TO',F8.4,
01700      &       ',  PRINTING EVERY',I5,' STEPS'//5X,
01800      &       'J',6X,'T',10X,'H',8X,'-----Y------>')
01900   C
02000         CALL RKF4(RMAX, SCAMIN, SCAMAX, NPRINT, IW)
02100   C
02200         STOP
02300         END


00100         SUBROUTINE EVALF(T,Y,F)
00200         DIMENSION F(1)
00300         DOUBLE PRECISION Y(1)
00400   C
00500         F(1) = -T*Y(1)*Y(1)
00700   C
00800         RETURN
00900         END
```

FIGURE 8.4-2   SUBROUTINE SUMK.

T	EXACT Y(T)	YJ [H=0.1]	YJ [H=0.01]	YJ [H=0.001]
0.0000	0.5000000E+01	0.5000000E+01	0.5000000E+01	0.5000000E+01
0.1000	0.5035462E+01	0.5035230E+01	0.5035461E+01	0.5035462E+01
0.2000	0.5062461E+01	0.5047111E+01	0.5062383E+01	0.5062462E+01
0.3000	0.5081855E+01	0.4078148E+01	0.5070195E+01	0.5081908E+01
0.4000	0.5094417E+01	-0.6052312E+02	0.3366885E+01	0.5102299E+01
0.5000	0.5100846E+01	-0.4284646E+04	-0.2508466E+03	0.6270727E+01
0.6000	0.5101776E+01	-0.2804371E+06	-0.3791554E+05	0.1787274E+03
0.7000	0.5097778E+01	-0.1833390E+08	-0.5618237E+07	0.2577343E+05
0.8000	0.5089369E+01	-0.1198579E+10	-0.8323871E+09	0.3824363E+07
0.9000	0.5077017E+01	-0.7835712E+11	-0.1233247E+12	0.5675849E+09
1.0000	0.5061145E+01	-0.5122596E+13	-0.1827154E+14	0.8423705E+11

FIGURE 8.4-3   (RK4)$_n$ RESULTS FOR A STIFF SECOND-ORDER IVP.

Figure 8.4-3 shows the RK4 solution at $t = 0, 0.1, \ldots, 1$ using stepsizes $h = 0.1$, 0.01, and 0.001. The errors near $t = 1$ are intolerable. Here roundoff error put (t_1, y_1) on a solution curve (21a) for which $C \approx 0$ but $C \neq 0$, and the Ce^{50t} term eventually dominates the numerical solution. (Note that $C < 0$ when $h = 0.1$ and 0.01, but $C > 0$ when $h = 0.001$.)

Among the many stiff IVP solvers developed in recent years, the following method due to Gear [17] has proved to be particularly reliable. It is a predictor–corrector method, based on $O(h^6)$ formulas, which uses the result of the y_{j+1} calculation to improve the previously obtained values of both y_j and y_{j-1}. The iterative formulas for **Gear's method** for solving (IVP)$_n$ are

$$
\begin{aligned}
&p_{j+1} \leftarrow 10y_{j-2} + 9y_{j-1} - 18y_j + 3hf_{j-2} + 18hf_{j-1} + 9hf_j \\
&c_{j+1} \leftarrow 33y_{j-2} + 24y_{j-1} - 57y_j + 10hf_{j-2} + 57hf_{j-2} + 24hf_j \\
&\delta_{j+1} \leftarrow c_{j+1} - hf(t_{j+1}, p_{j+1}) \qquad \{\text{error indicator}\} \\
&y_{j+1} \leftarrow p_{j+1} - \tfrac{95}{288}\delta_{j+1} \qquad \{y_{j+1} \text{ before improvement}\} \\
&y_j \leftarrow y_j + \tfrac{3}{160}\delta_{j+1} \qquad \{\text{partially improved } y_j\} \\
&y_{j-1} \leftarrow y_{j-1} - \tfrac{11}{1440}\delta_{j+1} \qquad \{\text{improved } y_{j-1}\} \\
&hf_{j+1} \leftarrow c_{j+1} - \delta_{j+1}
\end{aligned}
\qquad (22)
$$

Notice that this method requires only three starting values, y_0, y_1, and y_2.

The DVOGER subroutine of the IMSL library implements a variable-stepsize method based on Gear's method and has proven to be effective for stiff differential equations.

It should be noted that the **trapezoidal corrector**

$$
y_{j+1} = y_j + \frac{h}{2}\{f_j + f(t_{j+1}, y_{j+1})\}
\qquad (23)
$$

has also been used successfully for stiff equations. Since it is an *implicit* formula, one generally has to predict y_{j+1}, say using the **midpoint predictor**

$$
y_{j+1} = y_{j-1} + 2\,hf(t_j, y_j)
\qquad (24)
$$

and then iterate (23) until y_{j+1} is sufficiently accurate. Further details can be found in [13 and 33].

A criterion for determining whether $y' = f(t, y)$ is stiff is described in the note following Example 1 of Section 9.1C.

8.4F LINEARITY

A first-order system is **linear** if for $i = 1, \ldots, n$ the ith equation is of the form

$$y_i' = a_{i1}(t)y_1 + a_{i2}(t)y_2 + \cdots + a_{in}(t)y_n + F_i(t) \tag{25a}$$

In matrix notation, a linear system is of the form

$$\mathbf{y}' = A(t)\mathbf{y} + \mathbf{F}(t), \quad \text{where } A(t) = (a_{ij}(t))_{n \times n} \text{ and } \mathbf{F}(t) = [F_1(t) \cdots F_n(t)]^T \tag{25b}$$

Such a system is **homogeneous** if $\mathbf{F}(t) \equiv \mathbf{0}$, and **nonhomogeneous** otherwise. For example, in the example in Section 8.4B we considered a nonhomogeneous linear system whose matrix form is

$$\underbrace{\begin{bmatrix} y_1' \\ y_2' \end{bmatrix}}_{\mathbf{y}'} = \underbrace{\begin{bmatrix} 0 & 1 \\ 1 & 0 \end{bmatrix}}_{A(t)} \underbrace{\begin{bmatrix} y_1 \\ y_2 \end{bmatrix}}_{\mathbf{y}} + \underbrace{\begin{bmatrix} 0 \\ t \end{bmatrix}}_{\mathbf{F}(t)} \quad [A(t) \equiv \text{constant}] \tag{26}$$

An nth-order differential equation is **linear** if it is of the form

$$y^{(n)} = \phi_1(t)y + \phi_2(t)y' + \cdots + \phi_n(t)y^{(n-1)} + F(t) \tag{27}$$

It is **homogeneous** if $F(t) \equiv 0$ as well. The second-order IVP of Example 2 in Section 8.4C is not linear. (Why?) It is easy to see that the procedure in (10) of Section 8.4C yields a linear (homogeneous) nth-order system when applied to a linear (homogeneous) nth-order differential equation (Exercise 8-17).

If the entries of $A(t)$ and $\mathbf{F}(t)$ are continuous, then one can introduce the **antiderivative matrix**

$$M(t) = \int A(t)\, dt = \left(\int a_{ij}(t)\, dt \right)_{n \times n} \tag{28}$$

(where $\int dt$ is performed entrywise, ignoring constants of integration), and the $n \times n$ **exponential matrices** $e^{M(t)}$ and $e^{-M(t)}$, where

$$e^{\pm M(t)} = I \pm M(t) + \frac{1}{2!} M(t)^2 \pm \frac{1}{3!} M(t)^3 + \cdots = \sum_{n=0}^{\infty} \frac{(\pm 1)^n}{n!} M(t)^n \tag{29}$$

Both $e^{M(t)}$ and $e^{-M(t)}$ are defined and continuous whenever $M(t)$ is, in which case $e^{-M(t)}$ can be used as an integrating factor to show that the solution of the nonhomogeneous linear $(\text{IVP})_n$

$$\mathbf{y}' = A(t)\mathbf{y} + \mathbf{F}(t), \quad \mathbf{y}(t_0) = \mathbf{y}_0 \tag{30}$$

is given by the matrix formula

$$\mathbf{y}(t) = e^{M(t)} e^{-M(t_0)} \mathbf{y}_0 + e^{M(t)} \int_{t_0}^{t} e^{-M(\tau)} \mathbf{F}(\tau)\, d\tau \tag{31}$$

Formulas (28)–(31) are pursued in more detail in Exercises 8-18 through 8-20. Although generally awkward to use computationally, they are of considerable theoretical importance. For example, it follows from formula (31) that *the linear* (IVP)$_n$ (30) *has a unique solution over every interval on which all entries of* $\mathbf{F}(t)$ *and* $A(t)$ *are continuous.*

Formula (31) is but one indication of the fact that when trying to solve an IVP *analytically,* it is important to know whether it is linear or nonlinear. On the other hand, the *numerical procedures* described in this chapter apply equally well whether the IVP is linear or nonlinear! The *boundary* value problems described next, on the other hand, are easier to solve numerically when they are linear.

Boundary Value Problems   8.5

Consider the problem of solving the nth-order differential equation

$$y^{(n)} = f(t, y, y', y'', \ldots, y^{(n-1)}) \tag{1a}$$

subject to n constraints on y and/or its derivatives of the form

$$y^{(k_1)}(t_1) = \beta_1, \quad y^{(k_2)}(t_2) = \beta_2, \quad \ldots, \quad y^{(k_n)}(t_n) = \beta_n \tag{1b}$$

If all t_j's are the same, say t_0, then (1) is an nth-order IVP. However, if the **boundary conditions** (1b) involve m distinct t_i's, where $m > 1$, then (1) is an nth-order, m-point **boundary value problem** (abbreviated **BVP**). These arise naturally in the study of beam deflections, heat flow, and various dynamic systems.

An analysis of the general nth-order BVP is beyond the scope of this book. We shall focus our attention on the second-order, two-point BVP

$$\boxed{\text{(BVP)}_2 \quad y'' = f(t, y, y'), \qquad y(a) = \alpha, \qquad y(b) = \beta} \tag{2}$$

In (BVP)$_2$, the boundary conditions "nail down" the solution at (a, α) and (b, β).

8.5A   THE SHOOTING METHOD

We wish to use our ability to solve a second-order IVP as a tool for solving (BVP)$_2$. Toward this end, consider the associated IVP

$$\boxed{\text{(IVP)}_x \quad y'' = f(t, y, y'), \qquad y(a) = \alpha, \qquad y'(a) = x} \tag{3}$$

If we denote the solution of (IVP)$_x$ by $y_x(t)$, then

$$x = \text{the initial slope (at } t = a) \text{ of } y_x(t) \tag{4}$$

Our objective is to find that value $\bar{x}$ for which

$$y_{\bar{x}}(b) = \beta = \text{desired boundary value at } t = b \tag{5}$$

If the solution curve $y = y_{\bar{x}}(t)$ is thought of as a "trajectory," then the condition $y_{\bar{x}}(b) = \beta$ corresponds to hitting the "target value" β at $t = b$. When this occurs,

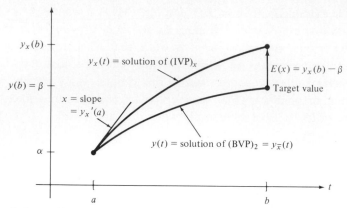

FIGURE 8.5-1   GRAPHICAL REPRESENTATION OF x, $y_x(t)$, $y(t)$, AND $E(x)$.

$y_{\bar{x}}(t)$ satisfies (BVP)₂, and hence is the desired $y(t)$ (see Figure 8.5-1). This is why the strategy of searching for an $\bar{x}$ for which $y_{\bar{x}}(t)$ satisfies (5) is called the **Shooting Method** for solving (BVP)₂.

To carry out the Shooting Method, we introduce the error function

$$E(x) = y_x(b) - \beta \tag{6}$$

The value of $E(x)$ is the amount by which $y_x(b)$ misses the "target value" β. So *the problem of solving* (BVP)₂ *can be viewed as that of finding a root $\bar{x}$ of $E(x)$*, that is, solving

$$E(x) = 0$$

Once $\bar{x} = y'(a)$ has been found, the desired $y(t)$ is $y_{\bar{x}}(t)$.

Since each evaluation of $E(x)$ requires a lot of work, namely integrating (IVP)$_x$ from $t_0 = a$ to $t_F = b$, it is important to find the desired root of $E(x)$ using a method that converges rapidly. Although the Newton–Raphson (NR) method was the most rapidly convergent of Chapter 2, it is not suitable for this application because we generally have no analytic expression for $E(x)$ to differentiate. On the other hand, *the Secant (SEC) Method of Section 2.2F is ideally suited.* For this application, the iterative equation for the Secant Method becomes

$$x_{k+1} = x_k - \frac{E(x_k)(x_k - x_{k-1})}{E(x_k) - E(x_{k-1})} \tag{7}$$

EXAMPLE. Use the Shooting Method to solve the following nonlinear two-point BVP to about 5s accuracy.

$$y'' = y'\left[\frac{1}{t} + \frac{2y'}{y}\right], \qquad y(1) = 4, \qquad y(2) = 8 \tag{8}$$

Solution. We wish to find a root $\bar{x}$ of

$$E(x) = y_x(b) - \beta = y_x(2) - 8 \tag{9a}$$

where $y_x(t)$ is the solution of the associated initial value problem

$$(\text{IVP})_x \quad y'' = y'\left[\frac{1}{t} + \frac{2y'}{y}\right], \qquad y(1) = 4, \qquad y'(1) = x \tag{9b}$$

The "natural" candidate for an initial guess of $y'(1)$ is

$$\frac{\beta - \alpha}{b - a} = \frac{8 - 4}{2 - 1} = 4 \qquad [\text{slope of the line from } (a, \alpha) \text{ to } (b, \beta)]$$

However, an attempt to solve $(\text{IVP})_x$ with $x = 4$ reveals that $y_x(t)$ has a singularity between $a = 1$ and $b = 2$. Consequently, we "aim low," taking say half this slope, namely $x = 2$, as an initial guess. This time

$$x = 2 \quad \Rightarrow \quad y_x(2) = 16 \quad \Rightarrow \quad E(x) = y_x(2) - 8 = 8 \tag{9c}$$

Since SEC requires two initial guesses and $E(2) > 0$, we try a smaller (more negative) slope, say $x = 1$. Using an accurate solver to solve $(\text{IVP})_x$ with $x = 1$, we find that

$$x = 1 \quad \Rightarrow \quad y_x(2) = 6.4 \quad \Rightarrow \quad E(x) = y_x(2) - 8 = -1.6$$

We can now begin the iteration. Taking $x_{-1} = 2$, $x_0 = 1$, and then

$$x_{k+1} = x_k + \Delta x_k, \qquad \text{where } \Delta x_k = \frac{-E(x_k)(x_k - x_{k-1})}{E(x_k) - E(x_{k-1})} \tag{10}$$

for $k = 0, 1, \ldots$, we get the results shown in Table 8.5-1. The $y_x(2)$ values were obtained using an accurate $(\text{IVP})_n$ solver.

TABLE 8.5-1   SHOOTING METHOD ITERATIONS WHEN $(\text{BVP})_2$ IS NONLINEAR.

k	$x_k = x$	$y_x(2)$	$E(x) = y_x(2) - 8$	Δx_k	$x_{k+1} = x_k + \Delta x_k$
-1	2	16	8		
0	1	6.4	-1.6	0.1666667	1.1666667
1	1.1666667	7.1111111	-0.8888889	0.2083333	1.3750000
2	1.3750000	8.2580645	0.2580645	-0.0468750	1.3281250
3	1.3281250	7.9688716	-0.03112840	0.00504557	1.3331706
4	1.3331706	7.9902356	-0.00976443	0.00016339	1.3333334

A look at the Δx_k column of Table 8.5-1 reveals that

$$x_5 \doteq 1.333333 \text{ should approximate } \bar{x} = y'(1) \text{ to about } 6s \tag{11}$$

So the desired $y(t)$ can be obtained to about $5s$ by solving $(\text{IVP})_x$ to about $6s$ on $[1, 2]$ with $x = 1.333333$.

As it turns out, this (IVP)$_x$ can be solved analytically. In fact,

$$y_x(t) = \frac{32}{8 + x(1 - t^2)} \qquad \text{so that } y_x(2) = \frac{32}{8 - 3x} \tag{12}$$

This formula for $y_x(2)$ makes it possible to find $\bar{x}$ analytically. We simply impose the boundary condition at $b = 2$:

$$y_{\bar{x}}(2) = \beta \iff \frac{32}{8 - 3\bar{x}} = 8 \iff \bar{x} = \frac{4}{3} \Rightarrow y(t) = y_{\bar{x}}(t) = \frac{24}{7 - t^2} \tag{13}$$

So the Shooting Method did indeed find $\bar{x}$ to 6s.

In practice, when we do not have an analytic expression for $y_x(b)$, the Shooting Method must rely on an accurate (IVP)$_n$-solver such as that given in Section 8.4D to find $y_x(b)$ for a particular initial slope x.

A pseudoprogram for solving a nonlinear (BVP)$_2$ by the Shooting Method is shown in Figure 8.5-2. Note that the initial *Xprev* is obtained by "aiming low" as we did in (9c), and the initial X is constrained to be close to *Xprev*.

8.5B THE IMPORTANCE OF LINEARITY FOR THE SHOOTING METHOD

The following example illustrates how the Shooting Method is particularly effective when (BVP)$_2$ is *linear*, that is, of the form

$$y'' = \phi_1(t)y + \phi_2(t)y' + F(t), \qquad y(a) = \alpha, \qquad y(b) = \beta \tag{14}$$

EXAMPLE. Use the Shooting Method to solve the linear BVP

$$y'' = -\frac{2}{t}(y' - 2), \qquad y\left(\frac{1}{2}\right) = 3, \qquad y(1) = 3 \tag{15}$$

Solution. We wish to find a root $\bar{x}$ of

$$E(x) = y_x(b) - \beta = y_x(1) - 3 \tag{16a}$$

where $y_x(t)$ is the solution of the associated initial value problem

$$\text{(IVP)} \quad y'' = -\frac{2}{t}(y' - 2), \qquad y\left(\frac{1}{2}\right) = 3, \qquad y'\left(\frac{1}{2}\right) = x \tag{16b}$$

Since $\alpha = \beta$ (both are 3), a reasonable initial guess for $y'\left(\frac{1}{2}\right)$ is $x = 0$. Using an accurate (IVP)$_n$ solver to solve (IVP)$_x$ with $x = 0$ gives

$$x = 0 \Rightarrow y_x(1) = 3.5 \Rightarrow E(x) = 3.5 - 3 = \tfrac{1}{2}, \qquad \text{that is, } E(0) = \tfrac{1}{2} \tag{17a}$$

Since $E(0)$ is positive, we try a more negative initial slope, say $x = -1$, as our second initial guess. Solving (IVP)$_x$ accurately gives

$$x = -1 \Rightarrow y_x(1) = 3.25 \Rightarrow E(x) = 3.25 - 3 = \tfrac{1}{4}, \qquad \text{that is, } E(-1) = \tfrac{1}{4} \tag{17b}$$

Algorithm: Shooting Method

Purpose: To solve, to *NumSig* significant digits, the second-order BVP

$$y'' = f(t, y, y') \qquad y(a) = \alpha, \quad y(b) = \beta$$

The method requires solving the associated (IVP)$_x$, namely

$$y'' = f(t, y, y') \qquad y(a) = \alpha, \quad y'(a) = x$$

for $y_x(t)$ in order to evaluate $E(x) = y_x(b) - \beta$. The Secant Method is used to get $\bar{x}$ (= slope of $y(t)$ at $t = a$) as a root of $E(x)$.

{*initialize*}
GET a, b, α, β,   {parameters of BVP}
     NumSig, *MaxIt*   {termination parameters}
$RelTol \leftarrow 0.5 * 10^{-NumSig}$
$Xprev \leftarrow \frac{1}{4}(\beta - \alpha)/(b - a)$ {$\frac{1}{4}$*slope from (a, α) to (b, β)}

Solve (IVP)$_x$ with $x = Xprev$ to get $y_x(b)$ to at least *NumSig* digits

$Eprev \leftarrow y_x(b) - \beta$
$X \leftarrow Xprev - 0.2 * \text{sign}(Eprev)$ {second initial guess of $\bar{x}$}

{*iterate:* Secant Method}
DO FOR $k = 1$ TO *MaxIt* UNTIL **termination test** is satisfied
  BEGIN
  Solve (IVP)$_x$ with $x = X$ to get $y_x(b)$ to at least *NumSig* digits
  $E \leftarrow y_x(b) - \beta$
  $DeltaX \leftarrow -E*(X - Xprev)/(E - Eprev)$
  {update} $Xprev \leftarrow X$; $Eprev \leftarrow E$; $X \leftarrow X + DeltaX$
  {**termination test:** $|DeltaX| \leqslant RelTol* |X|$}
  END

IF **termination text** succeeded {$\bar{x} \doteq X$ to at least *NumSig* digits}
  THEN BEGIN
        Solve (IVP)$_x$ with $x = X$ to get $y_x(t) \approx y(t)$ on $[a, b]$
        OUTPUT (Solution: $(t_j, y_x(t_j))$ for $t_j = a$ to b)
        END
  ELSE OUTPUT (Convergence did not occur in *MaxIt* iterations)

FIGURE 8.5-2   PSEUDOPROGRAM FOR THE SHOOTING METHOD.

The two points

$$(x_{-1}, E(x_{-1})) = (0, \tfrac{1}{2}) \qquad \text{and} \qquad (x_0, E(x_0)) = (-1, \tfrac{1}{4})$$

are plotted on a set of $x, E(x)$-axes in Figure 8.5-3. The x-intercept of their secant line is

$$x_1 = x_0 - \frac{E(x_0)\,(x_0 - x_{-1})}{E(x_0) - E(x_{-1})} = -1 - \frac{\frac{1}{4}(-1 - 0)}{\frac{1}{4} - \frac{1}{2}} = -2$$

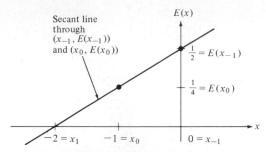

FIGURE 8.5-3   USING SEC TO GET x_1 FROM $x_{-1} = 0$ AND $x_0 = -1$.

Remarkably, upon solving (IVP)$_x$ with $x = x_1 = -2$, we find that

$$x = -2 \quad \Rightarrow \quad y_x(1) = 3 \quad \Rightarrow \quad E(-2) = 0, \qquad \text{that is, } \bar{x} = -2 \qquad \textbf{(17c)}$$

We have thus found the desired root $\bar{x} = y'(\frac{1}{2})$ in one iteration! The desired solution is obtained by integrating (IVP)$_x$ in (16b) from $a = \frac{1}{2}$ to $b = 1$ with $x = \bar{x} = -2$.

An analytic expression for the solution of (IVP)$_x$ in (16b) is

$$y_x(t) = 2t + \frac{1}{t}\left(\frac{2-x}{4}\right) + \left(\frac{2+x}{2}\right) \qquad \textbf{(18)}$$

as the reader can verify. Putting $t = b = 1$ gives

$$y_x(1) = 2 + \left(\frac{2-x}{4}\right) + \left(\frac{2+x}{2}\right) = \frac{7}{2} + \frac{x}{4} \qquad \textbf{(19)}$$

Notice that $y_x(1)$ varies *linearly* with x. As a result, the graph of

$$E(x) = y_x(1) - 3 = \frac{1}{2} + \frac{x}{4} \qquad \textbf{(20)}$$

is precisely the secant line drawn in Figure 8.5-3! This explains why the Secant Method found $\bar{x}$ in only one iteration.

In fact, $E(x)$ *will vary linearly with x whenever* (BVP)$_2$ *is linear.* In this case the first iterate x_1 determined by *any* two initial values

$$(x_{-1}, E(x_{-1})) \qquad \text{and} \qquad (x_0, E(x_0))$$

will be exactly $\bar{x} = y'(a)$ if $E(x_{-1})$ and $E(x_0)$ are exact. A proof of this important result is outlined in Exercise 8-27.

8.5C   THE FINITE DIFFERENCE METHOD

An alternative strategy for solving

$$\text{(BVP)}_2 \qquad y'' = f(t, y, y'), \qquad y(a) = \alpha, \qquad y(b) = \beta \tag{21}$$

is to partition $[a, b]$ into n subintervals using $n + 1$ h-spaced t_j's

and then replace $y'(t)$ and $y'(t_j)$ by finite difference approximations such as the $O(h^2)$ central difference approximations

$$\boxed{y''(t_j) \approx \frac{y_{j+1} - 2y_j + y_{j-1}}{h^2} \qquad \text{and} \qquad y'(t_j) \approx \frac{y_{j+1} - y_{j-1}}{2h}} \tag{22}$$

for $j = 1, 2, \ldots, n - 1$ [see (19) of Section 7.2B]. This strategy is called the **Finite Difference Method.** It converts the *analytic* problem of solving (BVP)_2 to an approximating *algebraic* problem of solving $n - 1$ equations in the $n - 1$ unknowns

$$y_1, \ldots, y_{n-1}, \qquad \text{where } y_j \approx y(t_j) \quad \text{for } j = 1, 2, \ldots, n - 1 \tag{23}$$

Note that $y_0 = y(a) = \alpha$ and $y_n = y(b) = \beta$ are known from (BVP)_2.

EXAMPLE. Use the Finite Difference Method to solve the nonlinear (BVP)_2

$$y'' = y' \left[\frac{1}{t} + \frac{2y'}{y} \right], \qquad y(1) = 4, \qquad y(2) = 8 \tag{24}$$

Solution. We first replace y'' and y' by their $O(h^2)$ central difference approximations at t_j for $j = 1, 2, \ldots, n - 1$. The result is

$$\frac{y_{j+1} - 2y_j + y_{j-1}}{h^2} = \frac{y_{j+1} - y_{j-1}}{2h} \left[\frac{1}{t_j} + \frac{2(y_{j+1} - y_{j-1})}{2hy_j} \right], \qquad y_0 = 4, \qquad y_n = 8$$

Upon multiplying by $2h^2 t_j$ and collecting the *linear* terms in y_{j-1}, y_j, and y_{j+1} on the left-hand side, this becomes

$$(2t_j + h)y_{j-1} - 4t_j y_j + (2t_j - h)y_{j+1} = d_j \tag{25a}$$

where $y_0 = 4$, $y_n = 8$, and

$$d_j = \frac{t_j}{y_j} (y_{j+1} - y_{j-1})^2, \qquad j = 1, 2, \ldots, n - 1 \tag{25b}$$

The dominance (although not strict) of the $-4t_j y_j$ term on the left side of (25a) suggests that we can solve the jth equation for

$$y_j^{(\text{new})} = \frac{1}{4t_j} \{(2t_j + h)y_{j-1} + (2t_j - h)y_{j+1} - d_j\}, \qquad j = 1, 2, \ldots, n-1 \qquad (26)$$

and then use Gauss–Seidel iteration (Section 4.5A). Initially, we take the y_j's to be on the straight-line trajectory from (a, α) to (b, β), that is,

$$y_j = \alpha + \frac{\beta - \alpha}{b - a}(t_j - a), \qquad j = 0, 1, \ldots, n \qquad (27)$$

The preceding approach, that is, applying Gauss–Seidel iteration to an approximating **discretized system,** is called the **Liebmann Process.** It is implemented in the FORTRAN program shown in Figure 8.5-4. The FUNCTION subprogram shown in Figure 8.5-5 calculates

$$\text{DELTAY} = y_j^{(\text{new})} - y_j$$

for use in the Gauss–Seidel iteration (lines 3600–4500 of Figure 8.5-4).†

Two runs of the resulting program are shown in Figure 8.5-6. Since TOLER = 0.5E-6, the y_j's shown approximate the solution of the discretized system (25) to about $6s$. It can be shown that *if $O(h^n)$ formulas are used to get the approximating discretized system, then the approximation $y(t_j) \approx y_j$ is also $O(h^n)$.* To illustrate, since the exact $y(t)$ is $24/(7 - t^2)$ [see (13)], we see from Figure 8.5-6 that the truncation errors $\tau[h]$ at $t_j = 1.4$ are

$$\tau[0.2] = y(1.4) - y_j[0.2] = 4.76190 - 4.74349 \doteq 0.0184$$

$$\tau[0.1] = y(1.4) - y_j[0.1] = 4.76190 - 4.75752 \doteq 0.0044$$

So $\tau[0.1] \approx \frac{1}{4}\tau[0.2]$. We can thus use Richardson's formula with $n = 2$ and $r = (0.2)/(0.1) = 2$ to get the improved estimate

$$y(1.4) \approx \frac{2^2(4.75752) - 4.74349}{4 - 1} = 4.76220 \qquad (28)$$

This is accurate to almost $5s$.

8.5D THE FINITE DIFFERENCE METHOD WHEN (BVP)₂ IS LINEAR

Let us see what happens when (BVP)₂ is linear, that is, of the form

$$y'' = \phi_1(t)y + \phi_2(t)y' + F(t), \qquad y(a) = \alpha, \qquad y(b) = \beta \qquad (29)$$

† The program uses subscripts $1, \ldots, \text{NP1} (= n + 1)$ rather than $0, \ldots, n$ because ANSI FORTRAN does not allow zero subscripts.

```
00100    C  * * * * * * * * *    LIEBMANN    PROCESS   * * * * * * * * * * *  C
00200    C                                                                   C
00300    C  THIS PROGRAM SOLVES THE SECOND ORDER BOUNDARY VALUE PROBLEM      C
00400    C        Y" = F(T,Y,Y'),  Y(A) = ALPHA,  Y(B) = BETA               C
00500    C  BY REPLACING  Y'  AND  Y"  BY THEIR O(H*H) CENTRAL DIFFERENCE    C
00600    C  APPROXIMATIONS AT TJ = A + J*H (J = 1, ... , N-1), THEN SOLVING  C
00700    C  THE RESULTING SYSTEM BY GAUSS-SEIDEL ITERATION.  THE USER MUST   C
00800    C  PROVIDE THE FUNCTION DELTAY(J, N, NP1, H, T, Y) TO FORM          C
00900    C            DELTAY = YJ(NEW) - YJ(CURRENT)                         C
01000    C                                                                   C
01100    C  * * * * * * * * * * * * * * * * * * *  VERSION 1:  5/1/81        C
01200
01300          DIMENSION T(101), Y(101)
01400          LOGICAL CONVGD
01500          DATA IW, IR, MAXIT, TOLER /5, 5, 500, 1.E-6/
01600
01700          WRITE(IW,1)
01800      1   FORMAT('0ENTER N, A, B, ALPHA, BETA')
01900          READ(IR,*) N, A, B, ALPHA, BETA
02000          NP1 = N+1
02100
02200    C  FORM H AND THE NP1 POINTS (TJ,YJ) ON THE STRAIGHT
02300    C  LINE FROM (A,ALPHA) [J=1] TO (B,BETA) [J=NP1]
02400
02500          H = (B - A)/N
02600          SLOPE = (BETA - ALPHA)/(B - A)
02700          DO 10 J=1, NP1
02800              DELTJ = (J-1)*H
02900              T(J) = A + DELTJ
03000              Y(J) = ALPHA + SLOPE*DELTJ
03100      10   CONTINUE
03200
03300    C  NOW T(1) = A, T(NP1) = B, Y(1) = ALPHA, AND Y(NP1) = BETA.
03400    C  ITERATE UNTIL Y(J) APPEARS TO APPROXIMATE Y AT A+(J-1)*H
03500
03600          DO 100 K = 1, MAXIT
03700              CONVGD = .TRUE.
03800              DO 50 J = 2, N
03900                  DYJ = DELTAY(J, N, NP1, H, T, Y)
04000                  IF (ABS(DYJ).GT.TOLER*ABS(Y(J))) CONVGD = .FALSE.
04100                  Y(J) = Y(J) + DYJ
04200      50       CONTINUE
04300              ITER = K
04400              IF (CONVGD) GOTO 200
04500     100   CONTINUE
04600
04700          WRITE(IW,2) MAXIT
04800      2   FORMAT(' CONVERGENCE NOT APPARENT IN',I5,' ITERATIONS')
04900          STOP
05000
05100     200   WRITE(IW,3), ITER, (T(J), Y(J), J=1,NP1)
05200      3   FORMAT(' AFTER',I4,'  ITERATIONS:',//,5X,'TJ',11X,'YJ',
05300      &          101(/,F10.5,E16.6))
05400          STOP
05500          END
```

FIGURE 8.5-4 A FORTRAN PROGRAM FOR THE LIEBMANN PROCESS.

Using the $O(h^2)$ approximations of $y''(t_j)$ and $y'(t_j)$ gives

$$\frac{y_{j+1} - 2y_j + y_{j-1}}{h^2} = \phi_1(t_j)y_j + \phi_2(t_j)\left(\frac{y_{j+1} - y_{j-1}}{2h}\right) + F(t_j)$$

```
00100            FUNCTION DELTAY(J, N, NP1, H, T, Y)
00200            DIMENSION T(NP1), Y(NP1)
00300
00400   C  THIS SUBPROGRAM RETURNS DELTAY = YJ(NEW) - YJ(CURRENT)
00500   C  FOR THE BVP DESCRIBED IN EXAMPLE 8.5C OF THE TEXT.
00600
00700            DJ = T(J)*(Y(J+1) - Y(J-1))**2/Y(J)
00800            RESID = (2*T(J)+H)*Y(J-1) + (2*T(J)-H)*Y(J+1) - DJ
00900            DELTAY = RESID/(4*T(J)) - Y(J)
01000
01100            RETURN
01200            END
```

FIGURE 8.5-5   USER PROVIDED CODE FOR THE PROGRAM IN FIGURE 8.5-4.

Multiplying by $2h^2$ and collecting y_{j-1}, y_j, and y_{j+1} terms on the left gives for $j = 1$, $2, \ldots, n - 1$

$$\underbrace{[2 + h\phi_2(t_j)]}_{a_j} y_{j-1} - \underbrace{[4 + 2h^2\phi_1(t_j)]}_{b_j} y_j + \underbrace{[2 - h\phi_2(t_j)]}_{c_j} y_{j+1} = \underbrace{2h^2F(t_j)}_{d_j} \tag{30}$$

Since $y_0 = y(t_0) = y(a) = \alpha$ and $y_n = y(t_n) = y(b) = \beta$, the matrix form of this *linear, tridiagonal* system is

$$\begin{bmatrix} b_1 & c_1 & & & & \\ a_2 & b_2 & c_2 & & & \\ & & \ddots & & & \\ & & & a_{n-2} & b_{n-2} & c_{n-2} \\ & & & & a_{n-1} & b_{n-1} \end{bmatrix} \begin{bmatrix} y_1 \\ y_2 \\ \vdots \\ y_{n-2} \\ y_{n-1} \end{bmatrix} = \begin{bmatrix} d_1 - a_1\alpha \\ d_2 \\ \vdots \\ d_{n-2} \\ d_{n-1} - c_{n-1}\beta \end{bmatrix} \tag{31}$$

where a_j, b_j, c_j, and d_j are defined in (30), and

$$y_j \text{ approximates } y(t_j) = y(a + jh) \qquad \text{for } j = 1, 2, \ldots, n-1 \tag{32}$$

EXAMPLE. Use the Finite Difference Method to solve the linear $(BVP)_2$

$$y'' = \frac{-2}{t}(y' - 2) = 0, \qquad y(0.5) = 3, \qquad y(1) = 3 \tag{33}$$

```
ENTER N, A, B, ALPHA, BETA          ENTER N, A, B, ALPHA, BETA
5, 1, 2, 4, 8                       10, 1, 2, 4, 8

AFTER  28  ITERATIONS:              AFTER  96  ITERATIONS:
```

TJ	YJ		TJ	YJ
1.00000	0.400000E+01		1.00000	0.400000E+01
1.20000	0.430869E+01		1.10000	0.414421E+01
1.40000	0.474349E+01		1.20000	0.431467E+01
1.60000	0.537399E+01		1.30000	0.451672E+01
1.80000	0.634223E+01		1.40000	0.475752E+01
2.00000	0.800000E+01		1.50000	0.504676E+01
			1.60000	0.539800E+01
			1.70000	0.583064E+01
			1.80000	0.637359E+01
			1.90000	0.707188E+01
			2.00000	0.800000E+01

FIGURE 8.5-6   RUNS OF THE PROGRAM WITH $h = 0.2$ ($n = 5$) AND $h = 0.1$ ($n = 10$).

Solution. Here $\phi_1(t) = 0$, $\phi_2(t) = -2/t$, and $F(t) = 4/t$; so (30) becomes

$$\left[2 - 2\frac{h}{t_j}\right] y_{j-1} - [4 + 2h^2 \cdot 0] y_j + \left[2 + 2\frac{h}{t_j}\right] y_{j+1} = \frac{8h^2}{t_j} \tag{34}$$

Multiplying both sides by $t_j/2$ and replacing $t_j \pm h$ by $t_{j\pm 1}$ gives

$$(E_j) \quad t_{j-1} y_{j-1} - 2t_j y_j + t_{j+1} y_{j+1} = 4h^2, \qquad j = 1, \ldots, n-1 \tag{35a}$$

Imposing the boundary conditions in (E_1) and (E_{n-1}), we get

$$t_0 y_0 = a\,\alpha = \tfrac{3}{2} \quad \text{and} \quad t_n y_n = b\,\beta = 3 \tag{35b}$$

For example, $n = 5$ $[h = (1 - \tfrac{1}{2})/5 = 0.1]$ gives the tridiagonal system

$$\begin{bmatrix} -1.2 & 0.7 & & \\ 0.6 & -1.4 & 0.8 & \\ & 0.7 & -1.6 & 0.9 \\ & & 0.8 & -1.8 \end{bmatrix} \begin{bmatrix} y_1 \\ y_2 \\ y_3 \\ y_4 \end{bmatrix} = \begin{bmatrix} 0.04 - \tfrac{3}{2} \\ 0.04 \\ 0.04 \\ 0.04 - 3 \end{bmatrix} = \begin{bmatrix} -1.46 \\ 0.04 \\ 0.04 \\ -2.96 \end{bmatrix} \tag{36}$$

Solving this tridiagonal system by Gaussian elimination shows that

$$y_1 = 2.8666667, \qquad y_2 = 2.8285714, \qquad y_3 = 2.8500000, \qquad y_4 = 2.9111111 \tag{37a}$$

For this particular equation these values approximate

$$y(t_1) = y(0.6), \qquad y(t_2) = y(0.7), \qquad y(t_3) = y(0.8), \qquad y(t_4) = y(0.9) \tag{37b}$$

accurately to $8s$. In general, one should double n to check the accuracy and, if necessary, use Richardson's formula with $n = r = 2$ as we did in Section 8.5C.

8.5E COMPARISON OF THE SHOOTING METHOD AND FINITE DIFFERENCE METHOD

Effect of Linearity. If $(BVP)_2$ is linear, the Shooting Method requires only two integrations of $(IVP)_x$ on $[a, b]$, whereas the Finite Difference Method yields a *linear* system with a diagonally dominant, banded coefficient matrix that can be solved quickly and accurately by Gaussian elimination even for large n. If $(BVP)_2$ is nonlinear, the Shooting Method becomes an iterative method (namely SEC), whereas the Finite Difference Method yields a nonlinear system that can be solved by Gauss–Seidel iteration (the Leibmann process).

Sources of Error. Whether $(BVP)_2$ is linear or nonlinear, the solution obtained by the Finite Difference Method reflects the truncation error of the finite difference approximations of y'' and y'; the accuracy should therefore be assessed by comparing the calculated y_j values to those obtained with n doubled. The accuracy obtained by the Shooting Method is limited only by the accuracy of the calculated $y_x(b)$ values.

Use of a Program. Whether $(BVP)_2$ is linear or nonlinear, the Shooting Method requires code for only $f(t, y, y')$. So this method should be tried whenever an $(\text{IVP})_n$ solver (or a program for the Shooting Method itself) is available. However, the code for the Finite Difference Method is much easier to write; it is therefore recommended if a reliable solver is not around or if the BVP appears to be stiff.

More extensive comparisons can be found in [23 and 24].

Exercises

In Exercises 8-1 through 8-12, (A)–(H) will refer to the following IVPs. The exact solutions are provided for reference to help confirm the order of the methods used. It is hoped that this confirmation will help the reader to use the methods intelligently when $y(t)$ is not known.

A. $y' = \dfrac{y}{t} - 2,\ y(1) = 2;\ h = 0.1$ $[y(t) = 2t(1 - \ln t)]$

B. $y' = \dfrac{1}{2}\left(\dfrac{y}{t} + \dfrac{t}{y}\right),\ y(1) = 3;\ h = 0.2$ $[y(t) = \sqrt{t^2 + 8t}]$

C. $y' = \sqrt{y},\ y(0) = 1;\ h = 0.2$ $[y(t) = \tfrac{1}{4}(t + 2)^2]$

D. $y' = -(t + 1)y,\ y(-1) = 1;\ h = 0.1$ $[y(t) = \sqrt{e^{-(t+1)^2}}]$

E. $y' = \dfrac{-t}{y},\ y(0) = 2;\ h = 0.1$ $[y(t) = \sqrt{4 - t^2}\text{ for } -2 \leqslant t \leqslant 2]$

F. $y' = t + 3\dfrac{y}{t},\ y(1) = 0;\ h = 0.5$ $[y(t) = t^3 - t^2]$

G. $y' = 2(y + 1),\ y(0) = 0;\ h = 0.1$ $[y(t) = e^{2t} - 1]$

H. $y' = 2(y - 1)^2,\ y(0) = 2;\ h = 0.05$ $[y(t) = 2(1 - t)/(1 - 2t)]$

Section 8.1

8-1. Verify that the $y(t)$s shown in (A)–(H) are solutions of the given IVPs.

8-2. Verify that $y(t)$ in (8) of Section 8.1A is a solution of the linear IVP in (6) for any choice of C. Is $y(t)$ differentiable at $t = 1$? Explain.

8-3. (a) For (A)–(H) of your choice, use Euler's method to take
   (i) two h-steps to get to $t = t_0 + 2h$
   (ii) four $(h/2)$-steps to get to $t = t_0 + 2h$
   (b) Do the two estimates of $y(t_0 + h)$ and $y(t_0 + 2h)$ obtained in part (a) confirm that Euler's method is first-order, that is, that $E[\tfrac{1}{2}h] \approx \tfrac{1}{2}E[h]$? If not, try to explain; if so, use Richardson's formula to get an improved estimate of $y(t_0 + 2h)$ and discuss the accuracy achieved.

Section 8.2

8-4. (a) For (A)–(H) of your choice, use the second-order Taylor's method to take
(i) one h-step to get to $t = t_0 + h$
(ii) two $(h/2)$-steps to get to $t = t_0 + h$
(b) Do the two approximations of $y(t_0 + h)$ obtained in part (a) confirm that the method is second-order, that is, that $E[\frac{1}{2}h] \approx \frac{1}{4}E[h]$? If not, try to explain; if so, use Richardson's formula to get an improved estimate of $y(t_0 + h)$ and discuss the accuracy achieved.

8-5. For (A)–(H) of your choice, repeat (a) and (b) of Exercise 8-4 for the Modified Euler method. Compare the accuracy to that of Exercise 8-4.

8-6. Same as Exercise 8-5 but with Huen's method.

8-7. For (A)–(H) of your choice, take two h-steps of RK4. Compare the accuracy at $t_0 + h$ to that obtained by other methods.

8-8. For (A)–(H) of your choice, take two steps of RKF4 using $Rmax = h^4$ where h is given in (A)–(H). Compare the accuracy at $t_0 + h$ to that of other methods.

Section 8.3

8-9. Explain how the Huen's method formula [(20) of Section 8.2B] can be viewed as a "corrector" formula. What is the "predictor"?

8-10. For (A)–(H) of your choice, use APC4 to find y_4, y_5, and y_6. Use the exact values $y(t_j) = y_j$ and $y'(t_j) = f_j$, $j = 0, 1, 2, 3$, to start the method. If the p_j's come out to be exact, try to explain why.

8-11. For those of (A)–(H) you considered in Exercise 8-10, use the $y_0, \ldots, y_6$ values obtained to get y_7 and y_8 with the step size (a) halved [see (9) of Section 8.3E]; (b) doubled.

8-12. Show that numerical methods can be used to integrate backward by replacing h by $-h$ to get to $y_j \approx y(t_0 - jh)$ as indicated.
(a) Use Euler's method for (A) to get to $t_4 = 0.6$.
(b) Use the second-order Taylor's method for (E) to get to $t_3 = 0.4$
(c) Use the modified Euler method for (B) to get to $t_3 = 0.4$
(d) Use Huen's method for (D) to get to $t_3 = -1.3$.
(e) Use RK4 for (E) to get to $t_2 = -0.2$.
(f) Use APC4 for (G) to get to $t_5 = -0.5$ (Use exact values at t_1, t_2, and t_3 to start the method.)

Section 8.4

8-13. In this exercise, (I) and (J) refer to the following (IVP)$_2$s

(I) $y_1' = y_2 + t,\ y_1(0) = 1$
$y_2' = -4y_1 + 3,\ y_2(0) = 2$ $\quad \left(\mathbf{y}(t) = \begin{bmatrix} \sin 2t + 1 \\ 2 \cos 2t - t \end{bmatrix} \right)$

(J) $y_1' = 1 + 2e^{-y_2},\ y_1(1) = -1$
$y_2' = t - y_1,\ y_2(1) = 0$ $\quad \left(\mathbf{y}(t) = \begin{bmatrix} t - 2/t \\ 2 \ln t \end{bmatrix} \right)$

For (I), (J) of your choice, state whether the (IVP)$_2$ is linear and verify that the given $\mathbf{y}(t)$ is a solution. Then:

(a) (i) Use Euler's method $[\mathbf{y}_{j+1} = \mathbf{y}_j + h\mathbf{f}(t_j, \mathbf{y}_j) \approx \mathbf{y}(t_j + h)]$ with $h = 0.2$ to find $\mathbf{y}_1$ and $\mathbf{y}_2$.

(ii) Repeat (i) with h halved, i.e. $h = 0.1$.

(iii) Use Richardson's formula to get an improved approximation of $\mathbf{y}(t_0 + 0.2)$; discuss the improvement in accuracy.

(b) Do (i)–(iii) of part (a) but for the modified Euler method:

$$\mathbf{y}_{j+1} = \mathbf{y}_j + h\mathbf{f}(t_j + \tfrac{1}{2}h, \mathbf{y}_j + \tfrac{1}{2}h\mathbf{f}(t_j, \mathbf{y}_j)) \approx \mathbf{y}(t_j + h)$$

(c) Use RK4$_n$ with $h = 0.2$ to get $\mathbf{y}_1$ and $\mathbf{y}_2$. Compare the accuracy of $\mathbf{y}_1$ to that of the approximations of $\mathbf{y}(t_0 + 0.2)$ found in parts (a) and (b).

8-14. Do (a)–(c) of Exercise 8-13 for the (IVP)$_3$ in (2) of Section 8.4A.

8-15. In (a)–(d), change to a first-order system in matrix form. If the given nth-order IVP is linear, write the system as $\mathbf{y}' = A\mathbf{y} + \mathbf{F}(t)$.

(a) $y''' - \dfrac{y''}{y^2} - 2ty' = 0$, $y(0) = 1$, $y'(0) = -1$, $y''(0) = 2$

(b) $e^{-t}y^{(iv)} + e^t y'' + 2ty = 4$, $y(0) = y''(0) = 1$, $y'''(0) = y'(0) = 0$

(c) $ty'' + t^2 y' - \dfrac{y}{t} = e^t$, $y(1) = 3$, $y'(1) = 0$

(d) $y'' - y'e^y + ty = t^2$, $y(1) = 0$, $y'(1) = 1$

8-16. (Satellite Motion). The equation of motion of a satellite fired from an orbiting space station are

$$x'' = -G\frac{x}{r^3}, \quad x(0) = x_0, \quad x'(0) = v_{0x}$$

$$y'' = -G\frac{y}{r^3}, \quad y(0) = 0, \quad y'(0) = v_{0y}$$

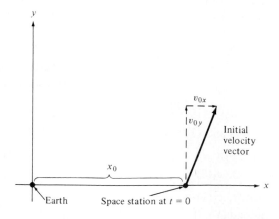

where $r = \sqrt{x^2 + y^2}$ is the distance to the earth as shown. Convert this second-order system to an equivalent (IVP)$_4$ using

$$y_1 = x, \quad y_2 = x', \quad y_3 = y, \quad y_4 = y'$$

8-17. Show that the (IVP)$_n$ equivalent to the linear nth-order IVP in (27) of Section 8.4E can be written as $\mathbf{y}' = A(t)\mathbf{y}$, $\mathbf{y}(t_0) = \mathbf{y}_0$, hence is linear.

8-18. For $A = \begin{bmatrix} 0 & 1 \\ 1 & 0 \end{bmatrix}$ and $At = \begin{bmatrix} 0 & t \\ t & 0 \end{bmatrix}$, show the following.

(a) If n is even, then $A^n = I$; if n is odd, then $A^n = A$.

(b) Deduce from part (a) and (29) of Section 8.4F that

$$e^{At} = (\cosh t)I_2 + (\sinh t)A = \begin{bmatrix} \cosh t & \sinh t \\ \sinh t & \cosh t \end{bmatrix}$$

(c) Deduce from part (b) that $de^{At}/dt = Ae^{At}$ and $e^{-At} = e^{A(-t)} = [e^{At}]^{-1}$

(d) Use formula (31) of Section 8.4F with $M(t) = At$ to show that $y(t) = \cosh t - t$ is the solution of $y'' = y + t$, $y(0) = 1$, $y'(0) = -1$.
(**NOTE:** You must solve $\mathbf{y}' = A\mathbf{y} + [0 \quad t]^T$, $\mathbf{y}(0) = [1 \quad -1]^T$. Why?)

8-19. In (a)–(d), consider the constant matrix

$$A = \begin{bmatrix} 0 & 1 & 0 \\ 0 & 0 & 1 \\ 0 & 0 & 0 \end{bmatrix}, \quad \text{for which } At = \begin{bmatrix} 0 & t & 0 \\ 0 & 0 & t \\ 0 & 0 & 0 \end{bmatrix}$$

(a) A square matrix A for which $A^k = 0$ for some k is called **idempotent.** Show that A is idempotent.

(b) Deduce from your matrices A, A^2, A^3, . . . in part (a) that

$$e^{At} = \begin{bmatrix} 1 & t & \frac{1}{2}t^2 \\ 0 & 1 & t \\ 0 & 0 & 1 \end{bmatrix}, \quad \text{hence that } \frac{d}{dt}e^{At} = Ae^{At} = \begin{bmatrix} 0 & 1 & t \\ 0 & 0 & 1 \\ 0 & 0 & 0 \end{bmatrix}$$

(c) Verify that $e^{-At} = e^{A(-t)}$ is $[e^{At}]^{-1}$ (i.e., $e^{-At}e^{At} = I_3$).

(d) Use formula (31) of Section 8.4F, with $M(t) = At$, to solve the (IVP)$_3$

$$\begin{array}{ll} y_1' = y_2, & y_1(0) = 1 \\ y_2' = y_3, & y_2(0) = 0 \\ y_3' = 6, & y_3(0) = 0 \end{array} \quad \left(\text{Exact solution: } \mathbf{y}(t) = \begin{bmatrix} t^3 + 1 \\ 3t^2 \\ 6t \end{bmatrix} \right)$$

8-20. Let $\int A(t)\,dt$ and $e^{\pm M(t)}$ be defined as in (28) and (29) of Section 8.4F, and perform differentiation and series summation of matrices componentwise. Prove (a)–(d) for any differentiable $n \times n$ matrices $A(t)$ and $B(t)$.

(a) Product Rule: $\dfrac{d}{dt} A(t)B(t) = A(t)\dfrac{dB(t)}{dt} + B(t)\dfrac{dA(t)}{dt}$.

(b) Chain Rule: $\dfrac{d}{dt} e^{A(t)} = A'(t)e^{A(t)}$, hence $\dfrac{d}{dt}\left(e^{\int A(t)\,dt}\right) = A(t)e^{\int A(t)\,dt}$.

(c) Exponent Rule: $e^{A(t)+B(t)} = e^{A(t)}e^{B(t)}$.
HINT: Show that both sides have the same derivative, hence must differ by a constant matrix C. Take $t = 0$ to show that $C = 0$.)

(d) Inverse Rule: $e^{-A(t)} = [e^{A(t)}]^{-1}$.

(e) Using (a)–(d), verify that formula (31) of Section 8.4F does indeed give a solution of $\mathbf{y}' = A(t)\mathbf{y} + \mathbf{F}(t)$, $\mathbf{y}(t_0) = \mathbf{y}_0$.

Section 8.5

8-21. (a) Verify that $y_x(t)$ in (11) is the solution of (9b) in Section 8.5A.

(b) Verify that $y_x(t)$ in (20) is the solution of (17) in Section 8.5B.

8-22. Suppose you know that $y_x(t) = e^{tx} - 2$ is the solution of

$$(IVP)_x \quad y'' = f(t, y, y'), \qquad y(0) = -1, \quad y'(0) = x$$

(a) Is the differential equation $y'' = f(t, y, y')$ linear? Explain.

(b) Find $y(t)$ for the BVP: $y'' = f(t, y, y')$, $y(0) = -1$, $y(1) = 0$

8-23. In (a) and (b), verify that the given $y_x(t)$ is the solution of the associated $(IVP)_x$. Then use the Shooting Method with

$$x_{-1} = \frac{1}{4} \frac{\beta - \alpha}{b - a} \quad \text{and} \quad x_0 = x_{-1} - 0.2*\text{sign}(E(x_{-1}))$$

[and with the given $y_x(t)$ used to evaluate $y_x(b)$] to find $\bar{x}$ to 6s. Verify your answer by using $y_x(t)$ to find $\bar{x}$ analytically.

(a) $y'' = \dfrac{-2y'}{t}$, $y(1) = -1$, $y(2) = 0$ $\quad \left[y_x(t) = \dfrac{t - x}{t} \right]$

(b) $y'' = (y')^2$, $y(1) = 0$, $y(2) = \ln \dfrac{1}{2}$ $\quad \left[y_x(t) = -\ln \left(t - 1 - \dfrac{1}{x} \right) \right]$

In Exercises 8-24 through 8-26, (K)–(N) refer to the following BVPs:

(K) $y'' = 2y' - y - 3$, $y(0) = -3$, $y(2) = 1$ $\quad [y(t) = 2te^{t-2} - 3]$

(L) $y'' = 3ty' - 9y + 3t^2 + 2$, $y(1) = 1$, $y(2) = -2$ $\quad [y(t) = t + t^2 - t^3]$

(M) $y'' = \dfrac{2}{y' + 1}$, $y(1) = \dfrac{1}{3}$, $y(4) = \dfrac{20}{3}$ $\quad \left[y(t) = \dfrac{4}{3} t^{3/2} - t \right]$

(N) $y'' = t(y')^2$, $y(0) = \dfrac{\pi}{2}$, $y(2) = \dfrac{\pi}{4}$ $\quad \left[y(t) = \cot^{-1} \left(\dfrac{t}{2} \right) \right]$

8-24. Apply the Finite Difference Method with n subintervals to (K)–(N) of your choice. If linear, find the jth equation of the tridiagonal system $T\mathbf{x} = \mathbf{d}$ [see (31) of Section 8.5D]; if nonlinear, solve the jth equation for y_j (to use the Liebmann Process).

8-25. For (K)–(N) of your choice, use the Finite Difference Method with $n = 3$ subintervals to get y_1 [$\approx y(a + h)$] and y_2 [$\approx y(a + 2h)$] to 4s.

8-26. For (K)–(N) of your choice, use the Finite Difference Method, first with $n = 2$ and then with $n = 4$ subintervals. If nonlinear, get 4s accuracy. Apply Richardson's formula to your values at $t = \frac{1}{2}(a + b)$.

8-27. (a) (**Superposition Principle**). Show that if $y_1(t)$ and $y_2(t)$ satisfy

$$y'' = \phi_1(t)y + \phi_2(t)y' + F(t)$$

then so does $ry_1(t) + sy_2(t)$ for any r and s such that $r + s = 1$.

(b) Deduce from part (a) that for any x_0, x_1, and x, the solution of (IVP)$_x$ is

$$\circledast \quad y_x(t) = y_{x_0}(t)\, L_0(x) + y_{x_{-1}}(t)\, L_{-1}(x)$$

where $L_0(x)$ and $L_{-1}(x)$ are the Lagrange polynomials

$$L_0(x) = \frac{x - x_{-1}}{x_0 - x_{-1}} \quad \text{and} \quad L_{-1}(x) = \frac{x - x_0}{x_{-1} - x_0}$$

(See Exercise 6-5.) Clearly, $\circledast$ is linear in x.

Computer and Programming Exercises

8-28. **(a)** Write a pseudoprogram for a subroutine TAYLOR (f, t_0, t_F, y_0, $Nsteps$, n) which integrates (IVP): $y' = f(t, y)$, $y(t_0) = y_0$ from t_0 to t_F in $Nsteps$ steps using the nth-order Taylor's method where n can be 1, 2, or 3.

   (b) Implement your pseudoprogram in a subroutine. Test it using the examples in Sections 8.1B and 8.2A.

8-29. **(a)** Write a pseudoprogram for a subroutine HUEN(f, t_0, t_F, y_0, $Nsteps$), which integrates (IVP) from t_0 to t_F in $Nsteps$ steps using Huen's method [(20) of Section 8.2B].

   (b) Implement your pseudoprogram in a subroutine. Test it using part (b) of the example in Section 8.2B.

   NOTE: In Exercises 8-30, 8-33, and 8-34, (A)–(H) are as defined at the beginning of this exercise set.

8-30. For (A)–(H) of your choice and any available *fixed-stepsize* IVP-solver:

   (a) Estimate $y(t_0 + 10\,h)$ using 10 h-steps, then 20 $(h/2)$-steps.

   (b) If $E[h]$ and $E[h/2]$ confirm the order of the method, discuss the improvement that results from Richardson's formula; if not, try to explain what went wrong.

8-31. Assuming you did not know that $y(t)$ for (H) had a singularity at $t_s = \frac{1}{2}$, use any available computer program to try to estimate t_s to 4s.

8-32. Write a calling program for SUBROUTINE RKF4 (Figure 8.4-1).

8-33. Describe the necessary input data and write a subprogram EVALF to solve the IVPs in (A)–(H) using SUBROUTINE RKF4 of Figure 8.4-1.

8-34. Repeat Exercise 8-33 for the (IVP)$_3$ in (2) of Section 8.4A.

8-35. Use any (IVP)$_n$ solver available to solve to 6s:

   (a) The (IVP)$_3$ in (2) of Section 8.4A on [0, 2].

   (b) The second-order IVP in Exercise 8-15(c).

   (c) The second-order IVP in Exercise 8-15(d).

   (d) The (IVP)$_4$ obtained in Exercise 8-16 on $[0, \pi/2]$. Use the "normalized" values $G = 1$, $x_0 = 1$, $y_0 = 0$, $v_{0x} = 0$, $v_{0y} = 1$. (The exact solution is $x = \cos t$, $y = \sin t$.)

8-36. Use any available (IVP)$_n$ or (BVP)$_2$ solver to solve (K)–(N) of Exercise 8-24 to 6s.

9

Eigenvalues

In this final chapter we present the basic properties of *eigenvalues* λ and *eigenvectors* $\mathbf{v}$ of an $n \times n$ matrix A, and we show how they help us gain a geometric understanding of the effect of multiplying $\mathbf{x}$ by A. We also show how they can be used to describe the solution of the linear first-order system

$$\frac{d\mathbf{y}}{dt} = A\mathbf{y}, \qquad \mathbf{y}(t_0) = \mathbf{y}_0, \qquad (A_{n \times n} = \text{constant})$$

and how they can help us find the *characteristic values* λ for which there exist nontrivial solutions of boundary value problems such as

$$\frac{d^2 y}{dt^2} + \lambda y = 0, \qquad y(0) = y(L) = 0$$

which arise in studying axially loaded beams.

It will be assumed that all entries of matrices A are real numbers. However, eigenvalues λ may be complex.

The reader is expected to be thoroughly familiar with the basic algebraic properties of matrices (Section 3.1) and determinants (Section 3.5). In addition, the reader will need to know the following basic results about linear independence in n-space [2]:

1. The vectors $\mathbf{v}_1, \ldots, \mathbf{v}_k$ are called **linearly independent** if

$$\alpha_1 \mathbf{v}_1 + \alpha_2 \mathbf{v}_2 + \cdots + \alpha_k \mathbf{v}_k = \mathbf{0}$$

can hold only if $\alpha_1 = \cdots = \alpha_k = 0$; otherwise, they are **linearly dependent**.

2. Any n linearly independent vectors $\mathbf{v}_1, \ldots, \mathbf{v}_n$ are a **basis** for n-space, by which we mean that every $\mathbf{x}$ in n-space can be expressed in only *one way* as the linear combination

$$\mathbf{x} = \alpha_1 \mathbf{v}_1 + \alpha_2 \mathbf{v}_2 + \cdots + \alpha_n \mathbf{v}_n$$

These *unique scalars* $\alpha_1, \alpha_2, \ldots, \alpha_n$ are called the **components of x** with respect to the basis $\{\mathbf{v}_1, \ldots, \mathbf{v}_n\}$.

3. An $n \times n$ matrix V is nonsingular if and only if its columns $\mathbf{v}_1, \ldots, \mathbf{v}_n$ are linearly independent hence form a basis for n-space.

9.1 Basic Properties of Eigenvalues and Eigenvectors

9.1A THE CHARACTERISTIC POLYNOMIAL $p_A(\lambda)$

We wish to find scalars λ for which there exist *nonzero* vectors $\mathbf{v}$ such that

$$\boxed{A\mathbf{v} = \lambda\mathbf{v} \qquad (A \text{ multiplies } \mathbf{v} \text{ into a multiple of itself})} \qquad (1)$$

When this occurs, we call λ an **eigenvalue**† for A, $\mathbf{v}$ an **eigenvector** for λ, and $(\lambda, \mathbf{v})$ an **eigenpair** for A. It is immediate from (1) that

if $\mathbf{v}$ is an eigenvector for λ, so is $\alpha\mathbf{v}$ for any $\alpha \neq 0$

Eigenpairs $(\lambda, \mathbf{v})$ and $(\lambda, \alpha\mathbf{v})$ will not be considered as different.

Clearly, $O\mathbf{x} = 0\mathbf{x}$ and $I_n\mathbf{x} = 1\mathbf{x}$ for *any* $\mathbf{x}$; so $(0, \mathbf{x})$ is an eigenpair for $O_{n \times n}$ and $(1, \mathbf{x})$ is an eigenpair for I_n for *any* nonzero $\mathbf{x}$. To see that eigenpairs must exist for any $n \times n$ matrix A, note that

$$A\mathbf{v} = \lambda\mathbf{v}, \quad \mathbf{v} \neq \mathbf{0} \qquad \Longleftrightarrow \qquad (A - \lambda I_n)\mathbf{v} = \mathbf{0}, \quad \mathbf{v} \neq \mathbf{0} \qquad (2a)$$

So *eigenpairs are possible if and only if* $(A - \lambda I_n)$ *is singular*, that is,

$$\boxed{p_A(\lambda) = \det(A - \lambda I_n) = 0} \qquad (2b)$$

---

† The prefix "eigen" is German for "self." Some authors use **characteristic value** for eigenvalue, and **characteristic vector** for eigenvector.

It is immediate from the definition of det that $p_A(\lambda)$ is a polynomial in λ whose leading term, $(-1)^n\lambda^n$, comes from the diagonal product $\prod_{k=1}^{n}(a_{kk} - \lambda)$ [see (1) of Section 3.5A]. We call $p_A(\lambda)$ the **characteristic polynomial** of A. Since $p_A(\lambda)$ has degree n, it follows from (2b) and the Fundamental Theorem of Algebra that *every* $n \times n$ *matrix* A *has exactly* n (*possibly repeated and possibly complex*) *eigenvalues, namely the roots of* $p_A(\lambda)$. If we denote them by $\lambda_1, \ldots, \lambda_n$, then $p_A(\lambda)$ can be factored as

$$p_A(\lambda) = (-1)^n(\lambda - \lambda_1)(\lambda - \lambda_2)\cdots(\lambda - \lambda_n) = \prod_{j=1}^{n}(\lambda_j - \lambda) \qquad \text{(3a)}$$

Upon taking $\lambda = 0$ in (2b) and (3a) we see that

$$\det A = \lambda_1\lambda_2\cdots\lambda_n = \text{constant term of } p_A(\lambda) \qquad \text{(3b)}$$

So *A is invertible if and only if all eigenvalues are nonzero*, in which case multiplying (1) by $\lambda^{-1}A^{-1}$ gives $A^{-1}\mathbf{v} = (1/\lambda)\mathbf{v}$. Thus

$$\boxed{(\lambda, \mathbf{v}) \text{ is an eigenpair for } A \quad \Longleftrightarrow \quad \left(\frac{1}{\lambda}, \mathbf{v}\right) \text{ is an eigenpair for } A^{-1}} \qquad \text{(4)}$$

In theory, all eigenpairs for A can be found by first solving $p_A(\lambda) = 0$ and then finding nontrivial solutions of $(A - \lambda I_n)\mathbf{v} = \mathbf{0}$.

EXAMPLE. Find all eigenpairs for

a. $A = \begin{bmatrix} 3 & 0 & 1 \\ 0 & -3 & 0 \\ 1 & 0 & 3 \end{bmatrix}$ **b.** $A^{-1} = \begin{bmatrix} \frac{3}{8} & 0 & -\frac{1}{8} \\ 0 & -\frac{1}{3} & 0 \\ -\frac{1}{8} & 0 & \frac{3}{8} \end{bmatrix}$ $\qquad$ (5)

Solution
a. We first use the "arrow rule" to get

$$p_A(\lambda) = \det(A - \lambda I) = \begin{vmatrix} 3-\lambda & 0 & 1 \\ 0 & -3-\lambda & 0 \\ 1 & 0 & 3-\lambda \end{vmatrix}$$

$$= (3-\lambda)^2(-3-\lambda) + (3+\lambda) = -(3+\lambda)[(3-\lambda)^2 - 1]$$

$$= -(3+\lambda)[\lambda^2 - 6\lambda + 8] = -(\lambda+3)(\lambda-2)(\lambda-4)$$

So the eigenvalues of A, in order of decreasing magnitude, are

$$\lambda_1 = 4, \qquad \lambda_2 = -3, \qquad \lambda_3 = 2 \qquad \text{(6a)}$$

To find an eigenvector for $\lambda_1 = 4$ we must solve $(A - 4I)\mathbf{v} = \mathbf{0}$ for a *nonzero* $\mathbf{v} = [v_1 \ v_2 \ v_3]^T$. Using Gaussian elimination, we get

$$[A - 4I : 0] = \begin{bmatrix} -1 & 0 & 1 & : & 0 \\ 0 & -7 & 0 & : & 0 \\ 1 & 0 & -1 & : & 0 \end{bmatrix} \longrightarrow \begin{bmatrix} -1 & 0 & 1 & : & 0 \\ 0 & -7 & 0 & : & 0 \\ 0 & 0 & 0 & : & 0 \end{bmatrix} \Longleftrightarrow \begin{matrix} v_1 = v_3 \\ v_2 = 0 \end{matrix}$$

Solutions of $A\mathbf{v} = 4\mathbf{v}$ are therefore of the form $[\alpha \quad 0 \quad \alpha]^T = \alpha[1 \quad 0 \quad 1]^T$, where $\alpha \neq 0$ is arbitrary. Similarly, the eigenvectors for $\lambda_2 = -3$ and $\lambda_3 = 2$ are scalar multiples of $\mathbf{v}_2 = [0 \quad 1 \quad 0]^T$ and $\mathbf{v}_3 = [1 \quad 0 \quad -1]^T$, respectively. So a set of eigenvectors for the eigenvalues in (6a) are, respectively,

$$\mathbf{v}_1 = \begin{bmatrix} 1 \\ 0 \\ 1 \end{bmatrix}, \quad \mathbf{v}_2 = \begin{bmatrix} 0 \\ 1 \\ 0 \end{bmatrix}, \quad \mathbf{v}_3 = \begin{bmatrix} 1 \\ 0 \\ -1 \end{bmatrix} \tag{6b}$$

b. Rather than proceed as in part (a), we simply use (4) and (6) to get *by inspection*:

$$(\tfrac{1}{4}, \mathbf{v}_1), \quad (-\tfrac{1}{3}, \mathbf{v}_2), \quad \text{and} \quad (\tfrac{1}{2}, \mathbf{v}_3) \quad \text{are the eigenpairs of } A^{-1}$$

The reader is urged to verify that $A^{-1}\mathbf{v}_i = (1/\lambda_i)\mathbf{v}_i$ for $i = 1, 2, 3$.

The method of finding eigenvalues directly as roots of $p_A(\lambda)$ is impractical for large n because of the combined effects of the ill-conditioned nature of root finding (Section 2.1E) and the roundoff error that is inevitable in calculating $p_A(\lambda)$. Alternative methods will be described in Sections 9.2 and 9.3. To help understand these methods, we first describe the role of *similarity transformations* in finding eigenpairs.

9.1B SIMILAR MATRICES AND DIAGONALIZABILITY

Of special importance for the study of eigenvalues are **diagonal matrices.** These will be denoted by

$$D = \text{diag}(\lambda_1, \lambda_2, \ldots, \lambda_n) = \begin{bmatrix} \lambda_1 & & & \\ & \lambda_2 & & \\ & & \ddots & \\ & & & \lambda_n \end{bmatrix} \quad \begin{pmatrix} \text{off-diagonal} \\ \text{entries are 0} \end{pmatrix} \tag{7a}$$

It is easy to see that for $j = 1, 2, \ldots, n$,

$$D\mathbf{e}_j = \lambda_j \mathbf{e}_j, \quad \text{where } \mathbf{e}_j = \text{col}_j I_n = [0 \quad \cdots \quad 0 \quad \underset{j\text{th component}}{1} \quad 0 \quad \cdots \quad 0]^T \tag{7b}$$

Thus, *by inspection,* the eigenpairs of $D = \text{diag}(\lambda_1, \ldots, \lambda_n)$ are $(\lambda_1, \mathbf{e}_1), \ldots (\lambda_n, \mathbf{e}_n)$. This simple but useful result makes it desirable to find ways to transform a general $n \times n$ matrix A into a diagonal matrix having the same eigenvalues. Unfortunately, the elementary operations that can be used to reduce $A \to D$ are *not* suitable because the SCALE and SUBTRACT operations alter eigenvalues (Exercise 9-5). What is needed are *similarity transformations* $A \to V^{-1}AV$ described next.

Two $n \times n$ matrices A and B are called **similar** if there exists a nonsingular matrix V such that $B = V^{-1}AV$ (or, equivalently, $A = VBV^{-1}$). In this case,

$$A\mathbf{v} = \lambda\mathbf{v} \quad \Longleftrightarrow \quad VBV^{-1}\mathbf{v} = \lambda\mathbf{v} \quad \Longleftrightarrow \quad B(V^{-1}\mathbf{v}) = \lambda(V^{-1}\mathbf{v})$$

So *similar matrices have identical eigenvalues;* in fact,

$$\boxed{(\lambda,\, \mathbf{v})\text{ is an eigenpair for } A \quad \Longleftrightarrow \quad (\lambda,\, V^{-1}\mathbf{v})\text{ is an eigenpair for } V^{-1}AV} \qquad \text{(8)}$$

An $n \times n$ matrix A is called **diagonalizable** if it is similar to a diagonal matrix. The fundamental diagonalizability result is the following:

Diagonalization Theorem. *Let A be an $n \times n$ matrix. Then*

$$V^{-1}AV = D = \mathrm{diag}\,(\lambda_1, \ldots, \lambda_n), \qquad \text{where } V = [\mathbf{v}_1 \,\vdots\, \mathbf{v}_2 \,\vdots\, \cdots \,\vdots\, \mathbf{v}_n] \qquad \text{(9a)}$$

can hold if and only if the columns $\mathbf{v}_1, \ldots, \mathbf{v}_n$ of V are eigenvectors (for $\lambda_1, \ldots, \lambda_n$, respectively) which form a basis for n-space. This means that every n-vector $\mathbf{x}$ can be expressed uniquely as the linear combination

$$\mathbf{x} = \alpha_1\mathbf{v}_1 + \alpha_2\mathbf{v}_2 + \cdots + \alpha_n\mathbf{v}_n, \qquad \text{where } A\mathbf{v}_j = \lambda_j\mathbf{v}_j \quad \text{for } j = 1, \ldots, n \qquad \text{(9b)}$$

If (9a) holds, then we know from linear algebra that the columns of the nonsingular matrix V are linearly independent, and hence are a basis. Also, since $VDV^{-1} = A$ and $D\mathbf{e}_j = \lambda_j\mathbf{e}_j$, we know from (8) that

$$A(V\mathbf{e}_j) = \lambda_j(V\mathbf{e}_j)$$

But $V\mathbf{e}_j = \mathrm{col}_j V = \mathbf{v}_j$; so (9b) $\Rightarrow$ (9a). Conversely, if (9b) holds, we use $\mathbf{v}_1, \ldots, \mathbf{v}_n$ to form $V = [\mathbf{v}_1 \,\vdots\, \cdots \,\vdots\, \mathbf{v}_n]$; then

$$V^{-1}AV\mathbf{e}_j = V^{-1}A\mathbf{v}_j = V^{-1}(\lambda_j\mathbf{v}_j) = \lambda_j V^{-1}(V\mathbf{e}_j) = \lambda_j\mathbf{e}_j = \mathrm{col}_j D$$

Since $V^{-1}AV\mathbf{e}_j = \mathrm{col}_j(V^{-1}AV)$, we see that (9b) implies (9a), completing the proof of the Diagonalization Theorem.

It follows from the Diagonalization Theorem that *every matrix having distinct, real eigenvalues is diagonalizable* [Exercise 9-7(b)]. However, there are matrices with repeated eigenvalues that nevertheless are diagonalizable (Exercise 9-8).

To illustrate, let us use the eigenvectors (6b) to form

$$V = [\mathbf{v}_1 \,\vdots\, \mathbf{v}_2 \,\vdots\, \mathbf{v}_3] = \begin{bmatrix} 1 & 0 & 1 \\ 0 & 1 & 0 \\ 1 & 0 & -1 \end{bmatrix} \qquad \text{for which } V^{-1} = \begin{bmatrix} \frac{1}{2} & 0 & \frac{1}{2} \\ 0 & 1 & 0 \\ \frac{1}{2} & 0 & -\frac{1}{2} \end{bmatrix} \qquad \text{(10a)}$$

The reader should verify that $VV^{-1} = I_3$ and that

$$\underbrace{\begin{bmatrix} \frac{1}{2} & 0 & \frac{1}{2} \\ 0 & 1 & 0 \\ \frac{1}{2} & 0 & -\frac{1}{2} \end{bmatrix}}_{V^{-1}} \underbrace{\begin{bmatrix} 3 & 0 & 1 \\ 0 & -3 & 0 \\ 1 & 0 & 3 \end{bmatrix}}_{A} \underbrace{\begin{bmatrix} 1 & 0 & 1 \\ 0 & 1 & 0 \\ 1 & 0 & -1 \end{bmatrix}}_{V} = \underbrace{\begin{bmatrix} 4 & 0 & 0 \\ 0 & -3 & 0 \\ 0 & 0 & 2 \end{bmatrix}}_{\mathrm{diag}\,(4,\,-3,\,2)} \qquad \text{(10b)}$$

Had we arrived at (10b) without a priori knowledge of the eigenpairs of A, we could have used the Diagonalization Theorem to deduce that

$$Av_1 = 4v_1, \quad Av_2 = -3v_2, \quad \text{and} \quad Av_3 = 2v_3 \tag{10c}$$

EXAMPLE. Show that the matrix $A = \begin{bmatrix} 5 & 4 \\ -1 & 1 \end{bmatrix}$ is not diagonalizable.

Solution. We first get $p_A(\lambda) = \det (A - \lambda I_2)$.

$$p_A(\lambda) = \begin{bmatrix} 5 - \lambda & 4 \\ -1 & 1 - \lambda \end{bmatrix} = (5 - \lambda)(1 - \lambda) + 4 = \lambda^2 - 6\lambda + 9 = (\lambda - 3)^2$$

So $v = [v_1 \quad v_2]^T \neq 0$ is an eigenvector of A only if $(A - 3I_2)v = 0$, i.e.

$$\begin{bmatrix} 2 & 4 \\ -1 & -2 \end{bmatrix} \begin{bmatrix} v_1 \\ v_2 \end{bmatrix} = \begin{bmatrix} 0 \\ 0 \end{bmatrix} \quad \Leftrightarrow \quad v_1 = -2v_2 \quad \Leftrightarrow \quad v = \alpha \begin{bmatrix} 2 \\ -1 \end{bmatrix}$$

Thus all eigenvectors for A are nonzero scalar multiples of $[2 \quad -1]^T$. Since *two* linearly independent vectors are needed for a basis, there cannot be a basis of eigenvectors for A. By the Diagonalization Theorem, A is not diagonalizable.

9.1C USING EIGENVECTORS TO UNCOUPLE LINEAR IVPs

Of all (IVP)$_n$'s, the most frequently encountered is the *linear* first-order system

$$\frac{dy_1}{dt} = a_{11}y_1 + a_{12}y_2 + \cdots + a_{1n}y_n, \qquad y_1(t_0) = y_{01}$$

$$\vdots \qquad\qquad\qquad\qquad\qquad \vdots \tag{11a}$$

$$\frac{dy_n}{dt} = a_{n1}y_1 + a_{n2}y_2 + \cdots + a_{nn}y_n, \qquad y_n(t_0) = y_{0n}$$

in which the a_{ij}'s are constant. By letting

$$y = \begin{bmatrix} y_1 \\ \vdots \\ y_n \end{bmatrix}, \quad y' = \frac{dy}{dt} = \begin{bmatrix} y_1' \\ \vdots \\ y_n' \end{bmatrix}, \quad \text{and} \quad y_0 = \begin{bmatrix} y_{01} \\ \vdots \\ y_{0n} \end{bmatrix} \tag{11b}$$

this system can be expressed in matrix form as

$$\frac{dy}{dt} = Ay, \quad y(t_0) = y_0, \qquad \text{where } A = (a_{ij})_{n \times n} \text{ is constant} \tag{11c}$$

Suppose that $V^{-1}AV = D = \text{diag}(\lambda_1, \ldots, \lambda_n)$. Then the change of variables

$$y = Vz \qquad \text{satisfies} \qquad \frac{dy}{dt} = V \frac{dz}{dt} \tag{12}$$

because the V entries are constant. Hence (11c) can be written as

$$V \frac{dz}{dt} = A(Vz), \qquad Vz(t_0) = y_0$$

But $V^{-1}AV = D$; so upon premultiplying by V^{-1}, we get

$$\frac{d\mathbf{z}}{dt} = D\mathbf{z}, \quad \mathbf{z}(t_0) = \mathbf{z}_0, \quad \text{where } \mathbf{z}_0 = V^{-1}\mathbf{y}_0 = [z_{01} \cdots z_{0n}]^T \quad (13a)$$

The equations represented by this *diagonal* system are

$$\frac{dz_1}{dt} = \lambda_1 z_1, \qquad z_1(t_0) = z_{01}$$

$$\vdots \qquad\qquad \vdots \qquad\qquad\qquad (13b)$$

$$\frac{dz_n}{dt} = \lambda_n z_n, \qquad z_n(t_0) = z_{0n}$$

Since dz_i/dt depends *only* on z_i, the solution of this "uncoupled" system is

$$z_1(t) = z_{01}e^{\lambda_1(t-t_0)} \qquad\qquad\qquad \begin{bmatrix} z_{01}e^{\lambda_1(t-t_0)} \\ \vdots \\ z_{0n}e^{\lambda_n(t-t_0)} \end{bmatrix} \quad (14)$$

$$\vdots \qquad\qquad \text{that is, } \mathbf{z}(t) = $$

$$z_n(t) = z_{0n}e^{\lambda_n(t-t_0)}$$

It follows from this and (12) that the solution of (11) can be expressed in terms of the columns $\mathbf{v}_1, \ldots, \mathbf{v}_n$ of V. Specifically,

$$\boxed{\mathbf{y}(t) = V\mathbf{z}(t) = z_{01}e^{\lambda_1(t-t_0)}\mathbf{v}_1 + \cdots + z_{0n}e^{\lambda_n(t-t_0)}\mathbf{v}_n, \quad \text{where } \mathbf{z}_0 = V^{-1}\mathbf{y}_0} \quad (15)$$

[see (6b) of Section 3.1D]. In words, if A in (11) is diagonalizable, then the solution of (11) is a weighted sum of the eigenvectors of A in which the "weight" of $\mathbf{v}_i$ is the exponential $z_{0i}e^{\lambda_i t}$, where $A\mathbf{v}_i = \lambda_i \mathbf{v}_i$ and $\mathbf{z}_0 = V^{-1}\mathbf{y}_0$.

EXAMPLE 1. Find the solution of the linear $(IVP)_3$

$$\frac{d}{dt}\begin{bmatrix} y_1 \\ y_2 \\ y_3 \end{bmatrix} = \underbrace{\begin{bmatrix} 3 & 0 & 1 \\ 0 & -3 & 0 \\ 1 & 0 & 3 \end{bmatrix}}_{A}\begin{bmatrix} y_1 \\ y_2 \\ y_3 \end{bmatrix}, \quad \mathbf{y}(0) = \begin{bmatrix} 0 \\ -2 \\ 2 \end{bmatrix} = \mathbf{y}_0 \quad (16a)$$

Solution. We saw in (10b) that $V^{-1}AV = \text{diag}(4, -3, 2)$, where

$$V = [\mathbf{v}_1 \vdots \mathbf{v}_2 \vdots \mathbf{v}_3] = \begin{bmatrix} 1 & 0 & 1 \\ 0 & 1 & 0 \\ 1 & 0 & -1 \end{bmatrix} \quad \text{and} \quad V^{-1} = \begin{bmatrix} \frac{1}{2} & 0 & \frac{1}{2} \\ 0 & 1 & 0 \\ \frac{1}{2} & 0 & -\frac{1}{2} \end{bmatrix} \quad (16b)$$

Since $V^{-1}\mathbf{y}_0 = V^{-1}[0 \ -2 \ 2]^T = [1 \ -2 \ -1]^T$, we can use (15) with $t_0 = 0$ to express the solution of (16a) as

$$\mathbf{y}(t) = (1)e^{4t}\begin{bmatrix} 1 \\ 0 \\ 1 \end{bmatrix} + (-2)e^{-3t}\begin{bmatrix} 0 \\ 1 \\ 0 \end{bmatrix} + (-1)e^{2t}\begin{bmatrix} 1 \\ 0 \\ -1 \end{bmatrix} = \begin{bmatrix} e^{4t} - e^{2t} \\ -2e^{-3t} \\ e^{4t} + e^{2t} \end{bmatrix} \quad (16c)$$

Notice that for large t, $\mathbf{y}(t) \approx e^{4t}\mathbf{v}_1$. More generally, we see from (15) that if $|\lambda_1| > |\lambda_i|$ for $i > 1$, then $\mathbf{y}(t) \approx z_{01}e^{\lambda_1 t}\mathbf{v}_1$ for large t provided that $z_{01} \neq 0$. This is why it is often important to know only the *dominant* eigenvalue of A (i.e., the one of largest magnitude) and an associated eigenvector.

Note: Recall that a differential equation is *stiff* if its solution has terms $e^{\lambda_1 t}$ and $e^{\lambda_n t}$, where $|\lambda_1| \gg |\lambda_n|$ [see Section 8.4E]. In view of (15), we see that the *linear* (IVP)$_n$

$$\mathbf{y}' = A\mathbf{y}, \qquad \mathbf{y}(t_0) = \mathbf{y}_0$$

will be stiff whenever it has eigenvalues of *both* large *and* small magnitude. Thus (16a) is *not* stiff. For the general nonlinear (IVP)$_n$,

$$\mathbf{y}' = \mathbf{f}(t, \mathbf{y}), \qquad \mathbf{y}(t_0) = \mathbf{y}_0$$

stiffness can be determined by examining the Jacobian matrix $\partial \mathbf{f}(t, \mathbf{y})/\partial \mathbf{y} = (\partial f_i(t, \mathbf{y})/\partial y_j)_{n \times n}$. Further details can be found in [17].

It should be apparent from (15) that the eigenvalues and eigenvectors of A are intimately related to the "natural responses" of linear systems described by $\mathbf{y}' = A\mathbf{y}$, where A is constant. A specific illustration is given next.

EXAMPLE 2. For $t \geq 0$, the current i in the "lumped parameter" RLC circuit shown in Figure 9.1-1 satisfies the second-order linear IVP

$$L\frac{d^2i}{dt^2} + R\frac{di}{dt} + \frac{1}{C}i = 0, \qquad i(0) = \frac{E}{R}, \quad i'(0) = 0 \qquad \text{(17a)}$$

Dividing by L, we can rewrite the equation as

$$\frac{d^2i}{dt^2} + 2\beta\frac{di}{dt} + \gamma i = 0 \qquad \text{when } \beta = \frac{R}{2L} \quad \text{and} \quad \gamma = \frac{1}{LC} \qquad \text{(17b)}$$

If we introduce the variables y_1 and y_2, where

$$y_1 = i(t), \qquad y_2 = \frac{di}{dt}, \qquad \text{that is, } \mathbf{y} = \begin{bmatrix} i \\ \dfrac{di}{dt} \end{bmatrix} \qquad \text{(18a)}$$

then the equation (17b) can be written as the linear (IVP)$_2$

$$\left. \begin{array}{ll} \dfrac{dy_1}{dt} = y_2, & y_1(0) = \dfrac{E}{R} \\ \dfrac{dy_2}{dt} = -\gamma y_1 - 2\beta y_2, & y_2(0) = 0 \end{array} \right\} \Leftrightarrow \frac{d\mathbf{y}}{dt} = \begin{bmatrix} 0 & 1 \\ -\gamma & -2\beta \end{bmatrix}\mathbf{y}, \qquad \mathbf{y}(0) = \begin{bmatrix} \dfrac{E}{R} \\ 0 \end{bmatrix} \qquad \text{(18b)}$$

The characteristic polynomial of the coefficient matrix A is

$$p_A(\lambda) = \begin{vmatrix} -\lambda & 1 \\ -\gamma & -2\beta - \lambda \end{vmatrix} = \lambda(\lambda + 2\beta) + \gamma = \lambda^2 + 2\beta\lambda + \gamma \qquad \text{(19)}$$

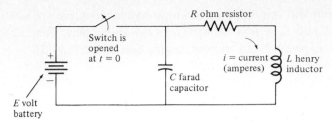

FIGURE 9.1-1 AN *RLC*-CIRCUIT.

Hence by the quadratic formula, the eigenvalues of A are

$$\lambda_1 = -\beta + \sqrt{\beta^2 - \gamma} = \frac{-R}{2L} + \sqrt{\left(\frac{R}{2L}\right)^2 - \frac{1}{LC}} \qquad \textbf{(20a)}$$

$$\lambda_2 = -\beta - \sqrt{\beta^2 - \gamma} = \frac{-R}{2L} - \sqrt{\left(\frac{R}{2L}\right)^2 - \frac{1}{LC}} \qquad \textbf{(20b)}$$

These will be real if what is under the radical in nonnegative, that is, if

$$\beta^2 - \gamma \geqslant 0 \qquad \Leftrightarrow \qquad \left(\frac{R}{2L}\right)^2 \geqslant \frac{1}{RC} \qquad \textbf{(21)}$$

and a complex-conjugate pair otherwise. The circuit is called **overdamped, critically damped,** or **underdamped** according as $\beta^2 > \gamma$, $\beta^2 = \gamma$, or $\beta^2 > \gamma$, as shown in Table 9.1-1.

When the circuit is underdamped, $i(t)$ will "ring" (i.e., oscillate) with a **natural frequency** of $\omega = \sqrt{\gamma - \beta^2}$ hertz while decaying like $e^{-\beta t}$. In the limiting case when $R = 0$,

$$i(t) = \frac{E}{R} \cos \frac{t}{\sqrt{LC}}$$

TABLE 9.1-1 POSSIBLE RESPONSES OF CURRENT IN AN *RLC* CIRCUIT.

Condition on $\beta = \dfrac{R}{2L}$ *and* $\gamma = \dfrac{1}{LC}$	*Eigenvalues* λ_1 *and* λ_2	*Solution* $i(t) = $ *current in circuit*
$\beta^2 > \gamma$ (overdamped)	$\lambda_1 = -\beta + \sqrt{\beta^2 - \gamma}$ $\lambda_2 = -\beta - \sqrt{\beta^2 - \gamma}$ (real, distinct, negative)	$i(t) = \dfrac{E}{R}\left(\dfrac{\lambda_1 e^{\lambda_2 t} - \lambda_2 e^{\lambda_1 t}}{\lambda_1 - \lambda_2}\right)$
$\beta^2 = \gamma$ (critically damped)	$\lambda_1 = \lambda_2 = -\beta$ (real, equal, negative)	$i(t) = \dfrac{E}{R}(1 + \beta t)e^{-\beta t}$
$\beta^2 < \gamma$ (underdamped)	$\lambda_1 = -\beta + i\omega$ $\lambda_2 = -\beta - i\omega,\ \omega = \sqrt{\beta - \beta^2}$ [complex conjugates, $Re(\lambda) < 0$]	$i(t) = \dfrac{E}{R} e^{-\beta t}\left(\cos \omega t + \dfrac{\beta}{\omega} \sin \omega t\right)$

that is, the circuit will ring indefinitely with a natural frequency of $\omega = 1/\sqrt{LC}$ hertz. Finally, given L and C, if R is adjusted for critical damping, then $|i(t)|$ will shrink to zero as rapidly as possible and without ringing (see Exercise 9-12).

9.2   The Power Method

The **dominant** member of a set of numbers (e.g., eigenvalues of A, or components of $\mathbf{x}$) is the one of largest magnitude. For example, both $+4$ and -4 are dominant components of the vector $\mathbf{x} = [2 \quad -4 \quad 4 \quad -\frac{1}{2}]^T$; and $-\frac{1}{2}$ is the **least dominant.**

For the remainder of this chapter, eigenvalues will be indexed in order of decreasing magnitude, that is,

$$|\lambda_1| \geq |\lambda_2| \geq \cdots \geq |\lambda_n| \tag{1}$$

so that λ_1 will be dominant. We now describe a procedure for obtaining the **dominant eigenpair** $(\lambda_1, \mathbf{v}_1)$ when the following assumptions hold:

Assumption 1. $|\lambda_1|$ *is strictly greater than* $|\lambda_i|$ *for* $i = 2, \ldots, n$.

Assumption 2. A *has* n *eigenvectors* $\mathbf{v}_1, \ldots, \mathbf{v}_n$ *(where* $A\mathbf{v}_i = \lambda_i\mathbf{v}_i$ *for all* i*), which are a basis for n-space.*

9.2A   THE POWER METHOD FOR FINDING DOMINANT EIGENVALUES

In its simplest form, the **Power Method** is the iterative algorithm defined by multiplying an initial guess $\mathbf{x}_0$ by successively higher powers of A:

$$\boxed{\text{Choose } \mathbf{x}_0, \text{ then take } \mathbf{x}_{k+1} = A\mathbf{x}_k \text{ for } k = 0, 1, 2, \cdots} \tag{2a}$$

Thus $\mathbf{x}_1 = A\mathbf{x}_0$, $\mathbf{x}_2 = A\mathbf{x}_1 = A^2\mathbf{x}_0$, $\mathbf{x}_3 = A\mathbf{x}_2 = A^3\mathbf{x}_0, \ldots$, so that

$$\boxed{\mathbf{x}_k = A^k\mathbf{x}_0 \qquad \text{for } k = 1, 2, 3, \cdots} \tag{2b}$$

In view of Assumption 2, $\mathbf{x}_0$ can be represented uniquely as

$$\mathbf{x}_0 = \alpha_1\mathbf{v}_1 + \alpha_2\mathbf{v}_2 + \cdots + \alpha_n\mathbf{v}_n$$

But $A\mathbf{v}_i = \lambda_i\mathbf{v}_i$, hence $A^k\mathbf{v}_i = \lambda_i^k\mathbf{v}_i$ for $k \geq 1$. So in view of Assumption 1,

$$A^k\mathbf{x}_0 = \alpha_1\lambda_1^k\mathbf{v}_1 + \alpha_2\lambda_2^k\mathbf{v}_2 + \cdots + \alpha_n\lambda_n^k\mathbf{v}_n \tag{3a}$$

$$= \lambda_1^k \left[\alpha_1 \mathbf{v}_1 + \alpha_2 \left(\frac{\lambda_2}{\lambda_1} \right)^k \mathbf{v}_2 + \cdots + \alpha_n \left(\frac{\lambda_n}{\lambda_1} \right)^k \mathbf{v}_n \right] \qquad \textbf{(3b)}$$

$$\approx \lambda_1^k \alpha_1 \mathbf{v}_1 \qquad \text{for large } k, \text{ provided that } \alpha_1 \neq 0 \qquad \textbf{(3c)}$$

Since $\lambda_1^k \alpha_1 \mathbf{v}_1$ is a scalar multiple of $\mathbf{v}_1$, $\mathbf{x}_k = A^k \mathbf{x}_0$ *will approach an eigenvector for the dominant eigenvalue* λ_1 (i.e., $A\mathbf{x}_k \approx \lambda_1 \mathbf{x}_k$); so if $\mathbf{x}_k$ is scaled so that its dominant component is 1, then

$$(\text{dominant component of } A\mathbf{x}_k) \approx \lambda_1 \cdot (\text{dominant component of } \mathbf{x}_k) = \lambda_1 \qquad \textbf{(3d)}$$

The **Scaled Power Method** described in Figure 9.2-1 is based on (3).

The **scale** step sets the dominant component of the current $\mathbf{x}$ to 1. So when **termination test** is satisfied, it follows from (3d) that the current *BigXi* approximates the dominant eigenvalue λ_1, and from (3c) that the current $\mathbf{x}$ approximates an eigenvector for λ_1.

Algorithm: Scaled Power Method

Purpose: To find the dominant eigenpair $(\lambda_1, \mathbf{v}_1)$ of a given $n \times n$ matrix A to *NumSig* significant digits.

$\{initialize\}$
GET n, A, $\mathbf{x}_0$, $\{$initial nonzero guess of $\mathbf{v}_1\}$
        NumSig, MaxIt $\{$termination parameters$\}$
$Tol \leftarrow 10^{-NumSig}$; $\mathbf{x} \leftarrow \mathbf{x}_0$ $\{\mathbf{x} = [x_1 \quad x_2 \quad \cdots \quad x_n]^T$ is the current $\mathbf{x}_k\}$

$\{iterate\}$
DO FOR $k = 1$ TO *MaxIt* UNTIL **termination test** is satisfied
  BEGIN

  $\mathbf{x}_{new} \leftarrow A\mathbf{x}$; $BigXi \leftarrow \max_{1 \leq i \leq n} (|i\text{th component of } \mathbf{x}_{new}|)$

  $\{scale\}$ $\mathbf{x}_{new} \leftarrow \dfrac{1}{BigXi} \mathbf{x}_{new}$ $\{$dominant component of $\mathbf{x}_{new}$ is now 1$\}$

  $d\mathbf{x} \leftarrow \mathbf{x}_{new} - \mathbf{x}$
  $\{update\}$ $\mathbf{x} \leftarrow \mathbf{x}_{new}$
  $\{$termination test: $|dx_i| \leq Tol*\max(1, |x_i|)$, $i = 1, 2, \ldots, n\}$
  END

IF **termination test** succeeded
  THEN OUTPUT (Dominant eigenpair, to *NumSig* digits, is $(BigXi, \mathbf{x})$)
  ELSE OUTPUT (Convergence did not occur in *MaxIt* iterations)

FIGURE **9.2-1**   PSEUDOPROGRAM FOR THE SCALED POWER METHOD.

Notice how the **scale** step makes it easy to see if $x_{new} \approx x$. More important, it avoids the possibility of overflow (if $|\lambda_1| > 1$) or underflow (if $|\lambda_1| < 1$) in calculating the components of x_{new} when k is large [see the λ_1^{k+1} scalar in (3c)]. Consequently, the Power Method should always be carried out "scaled" as in Figure 9.2-1.

EXAMPLE. Perform four iterations of the scaled Power Method for the matrix A in (5) of Section 9.1A. Start with $x_0 = [0 \quad 1 \quad 2]^T$.

Solution. Using the notation $Ax_k = BigXi x_{k+1}$ we get

$$k=0: \quad Ax_0 = \begin{bmatrix} 3 & 0 & 1 \\ 0 & -3 & 0 \\ 1 & 0 & 3 \end{bmatrix} \begin{bmatrix} 0 \\ 1 \\ 2 \end{bmatrix} = \begin{bmatrix} 2 \\ -3 \\ 6 \end{bmatrix} = 6 \begin{bmatrix} \frac{1}{3} \\ -\frac{1}{2} \\ 1 \end{bmatrix} (= BigXi\, x_1)$$

$$k=1: \quad Ax_1 = \begin{bmatrix} 3 & 0 & 1 \\ 0 & -3 & 0 \\ 1 & 0 & 3 \end{bmatrix} \begin{bmatrix} \frac{1}{3} \\ -\frac{1}{2} \\ 1 \end{bmatrix} = \begin{bmatrix} 2 \\ \frac{3}{2} \\ \frac{10}{3} \end{bmatrix} = \frac{10}{3} \begin{bmatrix} \frac{3}{5} \\ \frac{9}{20} \\ 1 \end{bmatrix} (= BigXi\, x_2)$$

Two more iterations give $Ax_2 = BigXi\, x_3$ and $Ax_3 = BigXi\, x_4$:

$$Ax_2 = \begin{bmatrix} \frac{14}{5} \\ -\frac{27}{20} \\ \frac{18}{5} \end{bmatrix} = \frac{18}{5} \begin{bmatrix} \frac{7}{9} \\ -\frac{3}{8} \\ 1 \end{bmatrix}, \quad Ax_3 = \begin{bmatrix} \frac{10}{3} \\ \frac{9}{8} \\ \frac{34}{9} \end{bmatrix} = \frac{34}{9} \begin{bmatrix} \frac{15}{17} \\ \frac{81}{272} \\ 1 \end{bmatrix}$$

Evidently, $BigXi \to 4 = \lambda_1$ and $x_k \to [1 \quad 0 \quad 1]^T = v_1$ [see (6) of Section 9.1].

Notice that the second component of x_k alternates sign while decreasing in magnitude; *this indicates convergence to zero.* A component that alternates sign with *constant* magnitude indicates that (1) fails (i.e., $|\lambda_1| = |\lambda_2|$); in this case the method may still yield λ_1 but will not yield v_1.

9.2B CONVERGENCE CONSIDERATIONS

It follows from (3b) that the convergence of x_k to a scalar multiple of v_1 is most rapid when $|\lambda_1| \gg |\lambda_i|$ (i.e., $\lambda_i/\lambda_1 \approx 0$) for $i > 1$. The slow convergence of the second component of the preceding example results from the fact that $\lambda_2/\lambda_1 = (-3)/4 = 0.75 \approx 0$.

If an approximation of v_1 is not known, $x_0 = [1 \quad 1 \quad \cdots \quad 1]^T$ is usually tried. It may turn out that the x_0 chosen has $\alpha_1 = 0$. When this occurs, the Power Method (in the absence of roundoff error) should yield λ_2 and v_2 [see (2a) and Exercise 9-17]. If there is any doubt that the dominant eigenvalue has been obtained, try a different x_0.

If $|\lambda_1| = |\lambda_2|$ (i.e., either $\lambda_1 = \pm\lambda_2$ or λ_1 and λ_2 are a complex-conjugate pair), then the Power Method will fail whether Scaled or not. This will be indicated by irregular behavior of some component of x_k (see Exercise 9-15). In such situations the method must be modified (see [38]), or a more sophisticated method such as the QR algorithm (Section 9.3E) can be used.

9.2C THE INVERSE POWER METHOD FOR FINDING SMALLEST EIGENVALUES

We saw in (4) of Section 9.1A that for a nonsingular matrix A,

$$(\lambda, \mathbf{v}) \text{ is an eigenpair for } A \quad \Longleftrightarrow \quad \left(\frac{1}{\lambda}, \mathbf{v}\right) \text{ is an eigenpair for } A^{-1} \qquad (4)$$

If follows that *the dominant eigenvalue of A^{-1} is λ_n^{-1}, that is, the reciprocal of the least dominant eigenvalue of A.* Hence if $\lambda_n \neq 0$ and $|\lambda_n| < |\lambda_i|$ for $i \neq n$, we can find $1/\lambda_n$ and an associated eigenvector $\mathbf{v}_n$ by applying the Scaled Power Method to A^{-1}, that is, by repeating the iterative step

$$\mathbf{x}_{k+1} = \frac{1}{BigXi} A^{-1}\mathbf{x}_k \qquad (BigXi = \text{dominant component of } A^{-1}x_k) \qquad (5)$$

until $\mathbf{x}_{k+1} \approx \mathbf{v}_n$ and $BigXi \approx 1/\lambda_n$. If A is singular, we shall be unable to find A^{-1}, indicating that $\lambda_n = 0$.

The application of the Scaled Power Method to A^{-1} is called the **Inverse Power Method** for finding the least dominant eigenpair $(\lambda_n, \mathbf{v}_n)$ for A.

EXAMPLE. Find the least dominant eigenpair for A if

$$A = \begin{bmatrix} 3 & 0 & 1 \\ 0 & -3 & 0 \\ 1 & 0 & 3 \end{bmatrix} \quad \text{for which } A^{-1} = \begin{bmatrix} \frac{3}{8} & 0 & -\frac{1}{8} \\ 0 & -\frac{1}{3} & 0 \\ -\frac{1}{8} & 0 & \frac{3}{8} \end{bmatrix} \qquad (6)$$

using the Inverse Power Method with $\mathbf{x}_0 = \begin{bmatrix} 0 & 1 & 2 \end{bmatrix}^T$.

Solution. Using the notation $A^{-1}\mathbf{x}_k = BigXi\,\mathbf{x}_{k+1}$ for $k = 0, 1, 2$, we get

$$A^{-1}\mathbf{x}_0 = \begin{bmatrix} \frac{3}{8} & 0 & -\frac{1}{8} \\ 0 & -\frac{1}{3} & 0 \\ -\frac{1}{8} & \frac{3}{8} & \frac{3}{8} \end{bmatrix}\begin{bmatrix} 0 \\ 1 \\ 2 \end{bmatrix} = \begin{bmatrix} -\frac{1}{4} \\ -\frac{1}{3} \\ \frac{3}{4} \end{bmatrix} = \left(\frac{3}{4}\right)\begin{bmatrix} -\frac{1}{3} \\ -\frac{4}{9} \\ 1 \end{bmatrix} = BigXi\,\mathbf{x}_1$$

$$A^{-1}\mathbf{x}_1 = \begin{bmatrix} \frac{3}{8} & 0 & -\frac{1}{8} \\ 0 & -\frac{1}{3} & 0 \\ -\frac{1}{8} & 0 & \frac{3}{8} \end{bmatrix}\begin{bmatrix} -\frac{1}{3} \\ -\frac{4}{9} \\ 1 \end{bmatrix} = \begin{bmatrix} -\frac{1}{4} \\ \frac{4}{27} \\ \frac{5}{12} \end{bmatrix} = \left(\frac{5}{12}\right)\begin{bmatrix} -\frac{3}{5} \\ \frac{16}{45} \\ 1 \end{bmatrix} = BigXi\,\mathbf{x}_2$$

$$A^{-1}\mathbf{x}_2 = \begin{bmatrix} \frac{3}{8} & 0 & -\frac{1}{8} \\ 0 & -\frac{1}{3} & 0 \\ -\frac{1}{8} & 0 & \frac{3}{8} \end{bmatrix}\begin{bmatrix} -\frac{3}{5} \\ \frac{16}{45} \\ 1 \end{bmatrix} = \begin{bmatrix} -\frac{7}{20} \\ -\frac{16}{135} \\ \frac{9}{20} \end{bmatrix} = \left(\frac{9}{20}\right)\begin{bmatrix} -\frac{7}{9} \\ -\frac{64}{243} \\ 1 \end{bmatrix} = BigXi\,\mathbf{x}_3$$

The *BigXi*'s $\frac{3}{4}, \frac{5}{12}, \frac{9}{20}$, are approaching $\frac{1}{2}$ (the reciprocal if $\lambda_3 = 2$), and $\mathbf{x}_k$ is approaching a scalar multiple of the eigenvector $\mathbf{v}_3 = [1 \quad 0 \quad -1]^T$ [see (6) of Section 9.1A].

9.2D   SHIFTING EIGENVALUES

For any scalar s,

$$A\mathbf{v} = \lambda\mathbf{v} \quad \Longleftrightarrow \quad (A - sI)\mathbf{v} = (\lambda - s)\mathbf{v} \tag{7a}$$

Thus, as illustrated graphically in Figure 9.9-2,

$$\boxed{(\lambda, \mathbf{v}) \text{ is an eigenpair for } A \quad \Longleftrightarrow \quad (\lambda - s, \mathbf{v}) \text{ is an eigenpair for } A - sI} \tag{7b}$$

Let λ_s be the eigenvalue of A nearest s and let $\mathbf{v}_s$ be an associated eigenvector. Then $(\lambda_s - s, \mathbf{v}_s)$ will be the least dominant eigenpair for $A - sI$, hence $((\lambda_s - s)^{-1}, \mathbf{v}_s)$ is the dominant eigenpair of $(A - sI)^{-1}$. Solving for λ_s, we get

$$\boxed{\lambda_s = \frac{1}{\text{dominant eigenvalue of } (A - sI)^{-1}} + s} \tag{8}$$

This strategy for finding $(\lambda_s, \mathbf{v}_s)$ will be referred to as the **Shifted Inverse Power Method.**

EXAMPLE. Use the Shifted Inverse Power Method with $\mathbf{x}_0 = [1 \quad 1 \quad 1]^T$ to find the eigenvalue nearest $s = -\frac{5}{2}$ of

$$A = \begin{bmatrix} 3 & 0 & 1 \\ 0 & -3 & 0 \\ 1 & 0 & 3 \end{bmatrix} \quad \text{for which } A - sI = A + \frac{5}{2}I = \begin{bmatrix} \frac{11}{2} & 0 & 1 \\ 0 & -\frac{1}{2} & 0 \\ 0 & 0 & \frac{11}{2} \end{bmatrix} \tag{9}$$

Solution. Applying the Scaled Inverse Power Method to $A - sI$ gives

$$(A + \tfrac{5}{2}I)^{-1}\mathbf{x}_0 = (-2)[-7.69231\text{E}-2 \quad 1 \quad -7.69231\text{E}-2]^T = BigXi\,\mathbf{x}_1$$

$$(A + \tfrac{5}{2}I)^{-1}\mathbf{x}_1 = (-2)[-5.91716\text{E}-3 \quad 1 \quad 5.91716\text{E}-3]^T = BigXi\,\mathbf{x}_2$$

$$(A + \tfrac{5}{2}I)^{-1}\mathbf{x}_2 = (-2)[-4.55166\text{E}-4 \quad 1 \quad -4.55166\text{E}-4]^T = BigXi\,\mathbf{x}_3$$

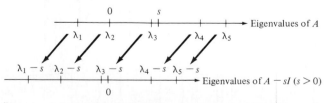

FIGURE 9.2-2   EIGENVALUES OF A AND $A - sI$ ($s > 0$).

In view of the alternating signs of the (shrinking) first and last components of $\mathbf{x}_k$, we see that $\mathbf{v}_s = [0 \quad 1 \quad 0]^T$; and -2 is the dominant eigenvalue of $(A + \frac{5}{2}I)^{-1}$. So, by (8), the eigenvalue of A nearest $s = -\frac{5}{2}$ is

$$\lambda_s = \frac{1}{(-2)} + \left(-\frac{5}{2}\right) = -3$$

9.2E   PRACTICAL CONSIDERATIONS WHEN USING THE POWER METHOD

The following result shows that *the diagonal entries of A are reasonable values to try for s in using the Shifted Inverse Power Method.*

Gerschgorin's Disk Theorem. *For $A = (a_{ij})_{n \times n}$ and $i = 1, \ldots, n$, let D_i denote the circular disk consisting of all points z in the complex plane such that $|z - a_{ii}| \leq r_i$, where*

$$r_i = \sum_{j \neq i} |a_{ij}| \quad \left(\begin{matrix} \text{the sum of the magnitudes of the} \\ \text{off-diagonal entries of } \text{row}_i \, A \end{matrix} \right)$$

Then each D_i contains at least one eigenvalue of A, and each eigenvalue of A lies in at least one D_i.

A proof of this theorem is given in [26]. For the matrix A in (9), it assures us that two eigenvalues satisfy $|\lambda - 3| \leq 1$ (rows 1 and 3) and the other satisfies $|\lambda - (-3)| \leq 0$ (row 2).

The Shifted Inverse Power Method can be used to find any eigenpair $(\lambda_i, \mathbf{v}_i)$ for which we can find an s such that

$$|\lambda_i - s| < |\lambda_j - s| \qquad \text{for all } j \neq i \tag{10}$$

(i.e., s is closer to λ_i than any other λ_j). When this cannot be done, the method must be modified [38] or another method used (see Section 9.3E.)

When $(A - sI)^{-1}$ is easy to find accurately (e.g., when $n = 2$ or perhaps 3), the iteration

$$\mathbf{x}_{\text{new}} \leftarrow \frac{1}{BigXi} \overline{\mathbf{x}}, \qquad \text{where } \overline{\mathbf{x}} = (A - sI)^{-1} \mathbf{x}_{\text{current}} \tag{11}$$

can be carried out using $(A - sI)^{-1}$ as we have done here. Otherwise, one should find an LU-Decomposition for $A - sI$ and then find $\overline{\mathbf{x}}$ in (11) by completing the forback matrix

$$[\hat{L} \backslash \hat{U} : \hat{\mathbf{x}}_{\text{current}} : \overline{\mathbf{c}} : \overline{\mathbf{x}}] \qquad \text{(see Section 3.3C)} \tag{12}$$

at each iteration. This procedure requires essentially the same number of arithmetic operations as multiplying $\mathbf{x}_{\text{current}}$ by $(A - sI)^{-1}$ but without the extra roundoff introduced by actually finding this inverse.

In most situations the Power Method and/or Shifted Inverse Power Method will find any desired eigenpairs of a given matrix A. However, if there is frequent need for *all* eigenpairs of A, then the methods of the next section should be used.

9.3   Methods for Finding All Eigenpairs of a Matrix

For any $m \times n$ matrix A, the **transpose** of A, written A^T, is the $n \times m$ matrix whose ith row is $(\text{col}_i\ A)^T$ for $i = 1, \ldots, n$. A straightforward verification shows that for any A and B we have $(A^T)^T = A$, and

$$(AB)^T = B^T A^T \tag{1}$$

that is, *the transpose of a product is the product of the transposes in the reverse order.*

9.3A   SYMMETRIC MATRICES

A square matrix is **symmetric** if $a_{ij} = a_{ji}$ for all $i \neq j$. This can be expressed succinctly as

$$A \text{ is symmetric} \quad \Longleftrightarrow \quad A^T = A \quad (A \text{ is its own transpose}) \tag{2}$$

The simplest symmetric matrices are diagonal matrices. In particular, I_n and $O_{n \times n}$ are symmetric. The matrix A in (9) of Section 9.2D is a symmetric matrix that is not diagonal. It follows from (1) that $(A^T A)^T = A^T (A^T)^T = A^T A$, and similarly that $(AA^T)^T = AA^T$; thus

$$A^T A \quad \text{and} \quad AA^T \quad \text{are symmetric for any } m \times n \text{ matrix } A \tag{3}$$

Most numerical procedures for finding eigenvalues of a *symmetric* matrix A rely on the ability to diagonalize A as $U^{-1}AU$, where U^{-1} is especially easy to get, as described next.

9.3B   ORTHOGONAL MATRICES

A real $n \times n$ matrix U is called **orthogonal** if its transpose is its inverse, that is,

$$UU^T = U^T U = I_n \tag{4a}$$

In view of the definition of matrix multiplication, this means that

$$\text{row}_i\ U (\text{row}_j\ U)^T = (\text{col}_i\ U)^T \text{col}_j\ U = \begin{cases} 0 & \text{if } i \neq j \\ 1 & \text{if } i = j \end{cases} \tag{4b}$$

Notice that if U and V are orthogonal, then by (1) and (4a),

$$(UV)^T(UV) = (V^TU^T)(UV) = V^T(U^TU)V = V^TV = I_n$$

This shows that *the product of orthogonal matrices is orthogonal.*

Orthogonal matrices have certain desirable geometric properties. Specifically, if $\mathbf{x} = [x_1 \cdots x_n]^T$ and $\mathbf{y} = [y_1 \cdots y_n]^T$ are viewed as points in n-space and we define

$$\mathbf{x} \cdot \mathbf{y} = \mathbf{x}^T\mathbf{y} = x_1y_1 + \cdots + x_ny_n, \qquad \text{the \textbf{dot product} of } \mathbf{x} \text{ and } \mathbf{y} \qquad \textbf{(5a)}$$

$$\|\mathbf{x}\| = \sqrt{\mathbf{x} \cdot \mathbf{x}} = \sqrt{x_1^2 + \cdots + x_n^2}, \qquad \text{the \textbf{Euclidean length} of } \mathbf{x} \qquad \textbf{(5b)}$$

$$\angle(\mathbf{x}, \mathbf{y}) = \cos^{-1}\left(\frac{\mathbf{x} \cdot \mathbf{y}}{\|\mathbf{x}\|\ \|\mathbf{y}\|}\right), \qquad \text{the \textbf{angle between} } \mathbf{x} \text{ \textbf{and} } \mathbf{y} \quad (\text{if } \mathbf{x}, \mathbf{y} \neq \mathbf{0}) \qquad \textbf{(5c)}$$

then *an orthogonal matrix U preserves dot products, lengths, and angles*, that is,

$$U\mathbf{x} \cdot U\mathbf{y} = \mathbf{x} \cdot \mathbf{y} \qquad \text{for all } \mathbf{x}, \mathbf{y} \qquad \textbf{(6a)}$$

$$\|U\mathbf{x}\| = \|\mathbf{x}\| \qquad \text{for all } \mathbf{x} \qquad \textbf{(6b)}$$

$$\angle(U\mathbf{x}, U\mathbf{y}) = \angle(\mathbf{x}, \mathbf{y}) \qquad \text{for all nonzero } \mathbf{x} \text{ and } \mathbf{y} \qquad \textbf{(6c)}$$

Indeed, using (5a), (1) and (4a), we see that for any $\mathbf{x}$ and $\mathbf{y}$,

$$U\mathbf{x} \cdot U\mathbf{y} = (U\mathbf{x})^TU\mathbf{y} = \mathbf{x}^TU^TU\mathbf{y} = \mathbf{x}^T\mathbf{y} = \mathbf{x} \cdot \mathbf{y}$$

proving (6a); (6b) and (6c) now follow directly from (5b) and (5c).

In view of the definitions (5), (4b) asserts that *the rows (or columns) of an orthogonal matrix are* **unit vectors** *(i.e., of length 1) that are mutually perpendicular.*

EXAMPLE (ROTATION MATRICES). The **rotation matrix** R_θ defined by

$$R_\theta = \begin{bmatrix} \cos\theta & -\sin\theta \\ \sin\theta & \cos\theta \end{bmatrix} \qquad \textbf{(7)}$$

satisfies $R_{(-\theta)} = R_\theta^T = R_\theta^{-1}$, and hence is orthogonal for any angle θ [see (12) of Section 3.1H]. Geometrically, multiplying $\mathbf{x}$ by R_θ has the effect of rotating $\mathbf{x}$ counterclockwise by θ radians about the origin in 2-space, as shown in Figure 9.3-1. More generally, the *i, j*-**rotation matrix** defined for $i < j$ as the $n \times n$ matrix

$$R_{ij}(\theta) = \begin{bmatrix} 1 & 0 & \cdots & 0 & \cdots & 0 & \cdots & 0 \\ \vdots & \vdots & & \vdots & & \vdots & & \vdots \\ 0 & 0 & \cdots & \cos\theta & & -\sin\theta & \cdots & 0 \\ \vdots & \vdots & & \vdots & & \vdots & & \vdots \\ 0 & 0 & \cdots & \sin\theta & & \cos\theta & \cdots & 0 \\ \vdots & \vdots & & \vdots & & \vdots & & \vdots \\ 0 & 0 & \cdots & 0 & \cdots & 0 & \cdots & 1 \end{bmatrix} \begin{matrix} \\ \\ \leftarrow \text{row}_i \\ \\ \leftarrow \text{row}_j \\ \\ \\ \end{matrix} \qquad \textbf{(8)}$$

$$\underbrace{\qquad}_{\text{col}_i} \quad \underbrace{\qquad}_{\text{col}_j}$$

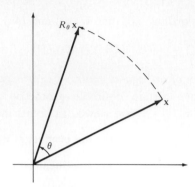

FIGURE 9.3-1   MULTIPLYING x BY R_θ IN 2-SPACE.

(in which the entries not shown are the same as I_n) is orthogonal for any real θ and any $i < j$. An example when $n = 3$ is

$$R_{13}\left(\frac{\pi}{6}\right) = \begin{bmatrix} \cos\dfrac{\pi}{6} & 0 & -\sin\dfrac{\pi}{6} \\ 0 & 1 & 0 \\ \sin\dfrac{\pi}{6} & 0 & \cos\dfrac{\pi}{6} \end{bmatrix} = \begin{bmatrix} \dfrac{\sqrt{3}}{2} & 0 & \dfrac{-1}{2} \\ 0 & 1 & 0 \\ \dfrac{1}{2} & 0 & \dfrac{\sqrt{3}}{2} \end{bmatrix} \tag{9}$$

Multiplying $\mathbf{x} = [x \quad y \quad z]^T$ by $R_{13}(\pi/6)$ has the effect of rotating $\mathbf{x}$ counterclockwise by $\pi/6$ radians about the y-axis in 3-space.

The inverse of an orthogonal matrix U is U^T; so it can be found *by inspection* for *any n.* When such matrices appear in a similarity transformation, $B = \mathrm{U}^{-1}AU$ becomes

$$B = U^TAU \tag{10}$$

in which case B is said to be **orthogonally similar** to A.

The following important result, which is proved in linear algebra, assures us that *every symmetric matrix is orthogonally similar to a diagonal matrix.*

Symmetric Diagonalization Theorem. *If A is symmetric, then there is an orthogonal matrix U such that* $U^TAU = $ diag $(\lambda_1, \ldots, \lambda_n)$. *Hence the eigenvalues of A are all real, and the columns* $\mathbf{u}_1, \ldots, \mathbf{u}_n$ *of U form a basis of mutually perpendicular unit eigenvectors (often referred to as an* **orthonormal** *basis of eigenvectors*).

For example, the reader can verify that for the symmetric 3×3 matrix A in the example of Section 9.2D, $U = R_{13}(\pi/4)$ satisfies

$$\begin{bmatrix} \dfrac{1}{\sqrt{2}} & 0 & \dfrac{1}{\sqrt{2}} \\ 0 & 1 & 0 \\ -\dfrac{1}{\sqrt{2}} & 0 & \dfrac{1}{\sqrt{2}} \end{bmatrix} \begin{bmatrix} 3 & 0 & 1 \\ 0 & -3 & 0 \\ 1 & 0 & 3 \end{bmatrix} \begin{bmatrix} \dfrac{1}{\sqrt{2}} & 0 & -\dfrac{1}{\sqrt{2}} \\ 0 & 1 & 0 \\ \dfrac{1}{\sqrt{2}} & 0 & \dfrac{1}{\sqrt{2}} \end{bmatrix} = \begin{bmatrix} 4 & 0 & 0 \\ 0 & -3 & 0 \\ 0 & 0 & 2 \end{bmatrix}$$

$$\underbrace{}_{U^T = U^{-1}} \qquad \underbrace{}_{A = A^T} \qquad \underbrace{}_{U = R_{13}\left(\dfrac{\pi}{4}\right)} \qquad \underbrace{}_{\text{diag}(4, -3, 2)}$$

If A is symmetric, U is orthogonal, and $B = U^T A U$, then

$$B^T = U^T A^T (U^T)^T = U^T A U = B$$

So *any matrix orthogonally similar to a symmetric matrix is also symmetric*. In particular, if $A = (a_{ij})$ is symmetric and

$$B = R_{ij}(\theta)^T A R_{ij}(\theta) \tag{11a}$$

then B is symmetric, and a straightforward multiplication shows that

$$b_{ij} = b_{ji} = a_{ij}[\cos^2 \theta - \sin^2 \theta] + (a_{jj} - a_{ii}) \sin \theta \cos \theta \tag{11b}$$

$$b_{ik} = b_{ki} = a_{ik} \cos \theta + a_{jk} \sin \theta \qquad \text{for } k \neq i, j \quad (\text{in row}_i \ B, \text{col}_i \ B) \tag{11c}$$

$$b_{jk} = b_{kj} = -a_{ik} \sin \theta + a_{jk} \cos \theta \qquad \text{for } k \neq i, j \quad (\text{in row}_j \ B, \text{col}_j \ B) \tag{11d}$$

$$b_{ii} = a_{ii} \cos^2 \theta + a_{jj} \sin^2 \theta + 2a_{ij} \sin \theta \cos \theta \tag{11e}$$

$$b_{jj} = a_{ii} \sin^2 \theta + a_{jj} \cos^2 \theta - 2a_{ij} \sin \theta \cos \theta \tag{11f}$$

with the remaining entries of B identical to those of A.

9.3C JACOBI'S METHOD FOR SYMMETRIC MATRICES

If θ is chosen so that

$$a_{ij} \cos(2\theta) + \tfrac{1}{2}(a_{jj} - a_{ii}) \sin(2\theta) = 0 \tag{12a}$$

then, in view of (11b), the matrix $B = R_{ij}(\theta)^T A R_{ij}(\theta)$ will satisfy

$$b_{ij} = b_{ji} = 0 \tag{12b}$$

The θ (in radians) that satisfies (12a) can be expressed as

$$\theta = \begin{cases} \dfrac{1}{2} \tan^{-1}\left(\dfrac{2a_{ij}}{a_{ii} - a_{jj}}\right) & \text{if } a_{ii} \neq a_{jj} \tag{13a} \\[2ex] \dfrac{\pi}{4} & \text{if } a_{ii} = a_{jj} \tag{13b} \end{cases}$$

If A is symmetric and i and j are the indices of the dominant superdiagonal entry of A, then in view of (12b), the matrix B should be "closer" to being diagonal than A. The iterative procedure incorporating this strategy is called **Jacobi's method**. If we start with $A_0 = A$, the method generates rotation matrices

$$R_k = R_{ij}(\theta_k), \qquad k = 1, 2, \ldots \tag{14}$$

such that $A_k = R_k^T A_{k-1} R_k$ has zeros where A_{k-1} had its dominant off-diagonal entries. It can be shown [38] that this selection of i, j, and θ_k for each k ensures that

---

Algorithm: Jacobi's Method

Purpose: To find all eigenpairs of a given $n \times n$ matrix A to a prescribed accuracy. The method uses the rotation matrix $R_{ij}(\theta)$ defined in (8) iteratively to form an orthogonal matrix U such that $U^T A U = \text{diag } (\lambda_1, \ldots, \lambda_n)$ to the desired accuracy.

{initialize}
GET n, A,   {matrix parameters}
    MaxIt, *NumDec*   {termination parameters}
$U \leftarrow I_n$; $AbsTol \leftarrow 10^{-NumDec}$

{iterate}
DO FOR $k = 1$ TO *MaxIt* UNTIL **termination test** is satisfied
  BEGIN
  Get i, j of the dominant superdiagonal entry, a_{ij} {$i < j$}
  MaxOffDiag $\leftarrow |a_{ij}|$
  {rotate i, j}
    BEGIN
    {get θ} IF $a_{ii} = a_{ij}$ THEN *Theta* $\leftarrow \tan^{-1}(1)$ {$= \pi/4$}
                       ELSE *Theta* $\leftarrow \frac{1}{2}\tan^{-1}[2a_{ij}/(a_{ii} - a_{jj})]$
    $R \leftarrow R_{ij}(Theta)$ {R is R_k}
    $A \leftarrow R^T A R$ {A is A_k; a_{ij} is now zero}
    $U \leftarrow UR$ {U is U_k}
    END
  {termination test: *MaxOffDiag* $<$ *AbsTol*}
  END

IF **termination test** succeeded
  THEN OUTPUT (The eigenpairs of A are $(a_{jj}, \text{col}_j U)$, $j = 1, \ldots, n$)
  ELSE OUTPUT (Convergence did not occur in *MaxIt* iterations)

FIGURE 9.3-2   PSEUDOPROGRAM FOR JACOBI'S METHOD.

$$A_k = R_k^T A_{k-1} R_k \to D = \text{diag}\,(\lambda_1, \ldots, \lambda_n) \quad \text{as } k \to \infty \tag{15}$$

Since $A_0 = A$, we can express A_k in terms of A as follows:

$$\boxed{A_k = (U_k)^T A U_k, \qquad \text{where } U_k = R_1 R_2 \cdots R_k = U_{k-1} R_k} \tag{16}$$

The matrix U_k in (16) is a product of orthogonal matrices, and hence is orthogonal. As $k \to \infty$ it will approach the U guaranteed by the Symmetric Diagonalization Theorem above. Notice that Jacobi's method yields approximations of *all* eigenvalues (the diagonal entries of A_k) and *all* eigenvectors (the corresponding columns of U_k).

A pseudoprogram for Jacobi's method is given in Figure 9.3-2. If A is 2×2, then only one rotation is needed to diagonalize A. This might also be the case for $n > 2$ [see (10)]. In general, however, A_k in (15) never actually equals D.

In discussing $R_k = R_{ij}(\theta_k)$, it will be convenient to use the abbreviations

$$S_k = \sin\theta_k \quad \text{and} \quad C_k = \cos\theta_k, \qquad k = 1, 2, \ldots \tag{17}$$

EXAMPLE. Perform two iterations of Jacobi's method for the symmetric matrix

$$A = \begin{bmatrix} 3 & 0.01 & 0.02 \\ 0.01 & 2 & 0.1 \\ 0.02 & 0.1 & 1 \end{bmatrix} \tag{18}$$

Solution. The largest superdiagonal entry of A is $0.1 = a_{23}$. By (13a)

$$\theta_1 = \frac{1}{2}\tan^{-1}\left(\frac{2a_{23}}{a_{22} - a_{33}}\right) = \frac{1}{2}\tan^{-1}\left(\frac{2(0.1)}{2-1}\right) = 0.0986978 \quad \text{(radians)}$$

$$C_1 = \cos\theta_1 = 0.995133 \qquad \text{and} \qquad S_1 = \sin\theta_1 = 0.0985376$$

Putting these values in $R_1 = R_{23}(\theta_1)$, we get A_1 as

$$A_1 = R_1^T A_0 R_1 = \begin{bmatrix} 1 & 0 & 0 \\ 0 & C_1 & S_1 \\ 0 & -S_1 & C_1 \end{bmatrix} \begin{bmatrix} 3 & 0.01 & 0.02 \\ 0.01 & 2 & 0.1 \\ 0.02 & 0.1 & 1 \end{bmatrix} \begin{bmatrix} 1 & 0 & 0 \\ 0 & C_1 & -S_1 \\ 0 & S_1 & C_1 \end{bmatrix}$$

$$= \begin{bmatrix} 3 & 0.011922 & 0.018917 \\ 0.011922 & 2.009902 & 0 \\ 0.018917 & 0 & 0.990098 \end{bmatrix} \tag{19}$$

For this first rotation, U_1 is simply R_1 itself.

Notice that the rotation which "zeros" the 2, 3-entry makes the 1, 2-entry slightly larger. However, the dominant superdiagonal entry of A_1 (namely $a_{13} = 0.018917$) is much smaller than that of A_0 (namely $a_{23} = 0.1$). Continuing, we obtain

$$\theta_2 = \frac{1}{2}\tan^{-1}\left(\frac{2a_{13}}{a_{11} - a_{33}}\right) = \frac{1}{2}\tan^{-1}\left(\frac{2(0.018917)}{3 - 0.990098}\right) \doteq 0.00941079$$

$$C_2 = \cos\theta_2 = 0.999956 \qquad \text{and} \qquad S_2 = \sin\theta_2 = 0.00941065$$

Putting these values in $R_2 = R_{13}(\theta_2)$, we get A_2 as $R_2^T A_1 R_2$, that is as

$$A_2 = \begin{bmatrix} C_2 & 0 & S_2 \\ 0 & 1 & 0 \\ -S_2 & 0 & C_2 \end{bmatrix} \begin{bmatrix} 3 & 0.011922 & 0.018917 \\ 0.011922 & 2.009902 & 0 \\ 0.018917 & 0 & 0.990098 \end{bmatrix} \begin{bmatrix} C_2 & 0 & -S_2 \\ 0 & 1 & 0 \\ S_2 & 0 & C_2 \end{bmatrix}$$

$$\doteq \begin{bmatrix} 3.000178 & 0.011922 & 0 \\ 0.011922 & 2.009902 & -0.000112 \\ 0 & -0.000112 & -0.989920 \end{bmatrix} \tag{20a}$$

and we get U_2 as $U_1 R_2 = R_{23}(\theta_1) R_{13}(\theta_2)$, that is as

$$U_2 = \begin{bmatrix} 1 & 0 & 0 \\ 0 & 0.995133 & -0.098538 \\ 0 & 0.098538 & 0.995133 \end{bmatrix} \begin{bmatrix} 0.999956 & 0 & -0.009411 \\ 0 & 1 & 0 \\ 0.009411 & 0 & 0.999956 \end{bmatrix}$$

$$\doteq \begin{bmatrix} 0.999956 & 0 & -0.009411 \\ -0.000927 & 0.995133 & -0.098533 \\ 0.009365 & 0.098538 & 0.995089 \end{bmatrix} \tag{20b}$$

A third iteration, using $R_3 = R_{12}(\theta_3)$, where $\theta_3 = 0.012035$ (radians), yields the following values of $A_3 = R_3^T A_2 R_3$ and $U_3 = U_2 R_3$.

$$A_3 \doteq \begin{bmatrix} 3.00032 & 0 & -1.35\text{E}-6 \\ 0 & 2.00976 & -1.122\text{E}-4 \\ -1.35\text{E}-6 & -1.122\text{E}-4 & 0.989920 \end{bmatrix} \tag{21a}$$

$$U_3 \doteq \begin{bmatrix} 0.999883 & -0.0120355 & -0.0094108 \\ 0.0110502 & 0.995072 & -0.0985332 \\ 0.0105503 & 0.0984177 & 0.995089 \end{bmatrix} \tag{21b}$$

The underlined digits are those that would be wrong *after* rounding. Even had we not known the exact eigenvalues, we would have known from Gerschgorin's disk theorem and inspection of A_3 that

$$|\lambda_1 - 3.00032| < 1.4\text{E}-6; \quad |\lambda_2 - 2.00976| < 1.13\text{E}-4; \quad |\lambda_3 - 0.98992| < 1.14\text{E}-4$$

The FORTRAN subroutine ROTATE shown in Figure 9.3-3 performs one rotation of Jacobi's method. After selecting THETA in lines 900 to 1100 [see (13)], it uses (11) to replace A by $R^T A R$ and U by UR [without actually forming $R = R_{ij}$(THETA)] in lines 1700 to 3100. Then NROTAT, which counts the number of rotations performed, is incremented in line 3300.

```
00100              SUBROUTINE ROTATE(I,J)
00200              DIMENSION A(6,6), U(6,6)
00300              COMMON N, NROTAT, A, U
00400    C - - - - - - - - - - - - - - - - - - - - - - - - - - - C
00500    C THIS SUBROUTINE PERFORMS THE ROTATION REPLACEMENTS   C
00600    C      A <-- RTRANSPOSE*A*R    AND    U <-- U*R        C
00700    C WHERE R = R[I,J](THETA) MAKES A(I,J) = A(J,I) = 0    C
00800    C - - - - - - - - - - - - - - -  VERSION 1:  5/1/81  C
00900              THETA = ATAN(1.0)
01000              IF (ABS(A(I,I)-A(J,J)) .GT. 1.E-6*ABS(A(I,I)))
01100          &      THETA = .5*ATAN(2.*A(I,J)/(A(I,I)-A(J,J)))
01200              SIN = SIN(THETA)
01300              COS = COS(THETA)
01400    C
01500    C ROTATE:  A <-- RTRANS*A*R   AND   U <-- U*R
01600    C
01700              DO 10 K=1,N
01800                 UKI = U(K,I)
01900                 U(K,I) =  UKI*COS + U(K,J)*SIN
02000                 U(K,J) = -UKI*SIN + U(K,J)*COS
02100                 IF (K.EQ.I .OR. K.EQ.J) GOTO 10
02200                    A(K,I) =  A(I,K)*COS + A(J,K)*SIN
02300                    A(K,J) = -A(I,K)*SIN + A(J,K)*COS
02400                    A(J,K) = A(K,J)
02500                    A(I,K) = A(K,I)
02600       10     CONTINUE
02700              AII = A(I,I)
02800              A(I,I) = AII*COS**2 + A(J,J)*SIN**2 + 2.*A(I,J)*SIN*COS
02900              A(J,J) = AII*SIN**2 + A(J,J)*COS**2 - 2.*A(I,J)*SIN*COS
03000              A(I,J) = 0.
03100              A(J,I) = 0.
03200    C
03300              NROTAT = NROTAT + 1
03400    C
03500              RETURN
03600              END
```

FIGURE 9.3-3 ROTATE: A FORTRAN SUBROUTINE FOR ONE ROTATION OF JACOBI'S METHOD.

9.3D PRACTICAL CONSIDERATIONS FOR JACOBI'S METHOD

As long as the programming language used has an inverse tangent function (e.g., ATAN in FORTRAN, Arctan in Pascal, or ATN in BASIC), (13) can be used to get θ, hence $\sin \theta$ and $\cos \theta$. Otherwise, the following procedure can be used.

IF $a_{ii} = a_{jj}$

$\qquad$ THEN $\sin \theta = \cos \theta = \dfrac{1}{\sqrt{2}}$ $\qquad \left\{ \theta = \dfrac{\pi}{4} \right\}$ $\hfill$ (22a)

ELSE BEGIN

$\qquad \tan 2\theta = \dfrac{2a_{ij}}{(a_{ii} - a_{jj})}$ $\qquad \left\{ \dfrac{-\pi}{2} < 2\theta < \dfrac{\pi}{2} \right\}$ $\hfill$ (22b)

$\qquad \cos 2\theta = \dfrac{+1}{\sqrt{1 + \tan^2 2\theta}}$ $\qquad \{ \cos 2\theta > 0 \}$ $\hfill$ (22c)

$\qquad \cos \theta = \dfrac{+1}{\sqrt{\frac{1}{2}(1 + \cos 2\theta)}}$ $\qquad \{ \cos \theta > 0 \}$ $\hfill$ (22d)

$$\sin \theta = \frac{\frac{1}{2}(\tan 2\theta \cos 2\theta)}{\cos \theta} \qquad \{\text{same sign as } \tan 2\theta\} \qquad (22e)$$

END

For large n, it is time consuming (i.e., expensive) to have a computer scan the $n(n-1)1/2$ superdiagonal (or subdiagonal) entries of the current A to find the maximum off-diagonal $|a_{ij}|$. What is often done in practice is to set a "threshold" magnitude *Thresh* for a scan, and perform a rotation whenever $|a_{ij}| \geqslant$ *Thresh*, as shown in Figure 9.3-4. The value of *Thresh* for any scan is set to

---

Algorithm: Jacobi's Method with Thresholds

Purpose: To perform Jacobi's method more efficiently by using fewer superdiagonal scans and more rotations per scan. The parameter *Fraction* (between 0 and 1) controls the frequency of rotations, with the number of rotations per scan increasing as *Fraction* $\to$ 0.

{*initialize*}
GET n, A, *NumDec*, *MaxIt*,   {as in Jacobi's method algorithm}
    Fraction   {$0 <$ *Fraction* < 1}
$U \leftarrow I_n$;   *AbsTol* $\leftarrow 10^{-NumDec}$
MaxOffDiag $\leftarrow$ (largest superdiagonal $|a_{ij}|$)   {$i < j$}

{*iterate*}
DO FOR $k = 1$ TO *MaxIt* UNTIL **termination test** is satisfied
  BEGIN
   Thresh $\leftarrow$ *Fraction* * *MaxOffDiag*;   *MaxOffDiag* $\leftarrow$ 0
   DO FOR $i = 1$ TO $n - 1$ {scan ith row of A}
    DO FOR $j = i + 1$ TO n
     BEGIN
     If $|a_{ij}| >$ *Thresh* THEN **rotate** i, j {as in Jacobi's method}
     IF $|a_{ij}| >$ *MaxOffDiag* THEN *MaxOffDiag* $\leftarrow |a_{ij}|$
     END
   {Now *MaxOffDiag* = largest unrotated $|a_{ij}|$ scanned}
   {**termination test**: *MaxOffDiag* $<$ *AbsTol*}
   END

IF **termination test** succeeded
  THEN OUTPUT (The eigenpairs of A are $(a_{jj}, \text{col}_j U)$, $j = 1, \ldots , n$)
  ELSE OUTPUT (Convergence did not occur in *MaxIt* iterations)

FIGURE 9.3-4 PSEUDOPROGRAM FOR JACOBI'S METHOD WITH THRESHOLDS.

*Fraction * MaxOffdiag*

where *Fraction* is a number between 0 and 1 and *MaxOffdiag* is the magnitude of the largest off-diagonal term that was *not* "zeroed" during the preceding scan. The **rotate i, j** step is performed in a subroutine such as that given in Figure 9.3-3.

If this strategy is applied to $A_{3\times3}$ of the example in Section 9.3C with *Fraction* set to 0.3, we get the results shown in Figure 9.3-5. All eigenpairs appear to be accurate to 6*s*.

It should be noted that Jacobi-type methods have been developed for nonsymmetric matrices. These are discussed in [29].

9.3E FACTORIZATION METHODS

If all eigenpairs of a nonsymmetric matrix A are needed, then Jacobi's method cannot be used. The methods developed for this situation utilize a factorization much like the LU-factorization of Section 3.3C.

One of the more effective methods for finding all eigenpairs of any matrix A is the **QR-method.** It is usually performed in two steps.

STEP 1: Replace A by a similar matrix $P^{-1}AP$ whose entries more than one row below the main diagonal are all zero. Such matrices are said to be in **upper-Hessenberg** form. A nonsingular matrix P that does this is usually obtained in one of two ways:

a. Householder's method. This method uses $n - 2$ **Householder transformations**

$$A_k = P_k^T A_{k-1} P_k, \qquad \text{where } P_k = I - 2\mathbf{u}_k\mathbf{u}_k^T \tag{23}$$

```
JACOBI'S METHOD WITH THRESHOLDS (FRACT= 0.300) FOR THE MATRIX

            3.00000     0.01000     0.02000
            0.01000     2.00000     0.10000
            0.02000     0.10000     1.00000

SCAN # 1 (THRESH = 0.030000):  1 ROTATIONS.  [ A : U ] IS:

   3.0000000  0.0119221  0.0189173    1.0000000  0.0000000  0.0000000
   0.0119221  2.0099019  0.0000000    0.0000000  0.9951333 -0.0985376
   0.0189173  0.0000000  0.9900980    0.0000000  0.0985376  0.9951333

SCAN # 2 (THRESH = 0.006000):  2 ROTATIONS.  [ A : U ] IS:

   3.0003215 -0.0000021  0.0000000    0.9998833 -0.0120387 -0.0094088
  -0.0000021  2.0097583 -0.0002277    0.0110524  0.9950612 -0.0986460
   0.0000000 -0.0002277  0.9899200    0.0105499  0.0985305  0.9950781

SCAN # 3 (THRESH = 0.000068):  1 ROTATIONS.  [ A : U ] IS:

   3.0003215 -0.0000021 -0.0000000    0.9998833 -0.0120366 -0.0094114
  -0.0000021  2.0097583  0.0000000    0.0110524  0.9950832 -0.0984238
  -0.0000000  0.0000000  0.9899200    0.0105499  0.0983083  0.9951001
```

FIGURE 9.3-5 THREE SCANS OF JACOBI'S METHOD WITH THRESHOLDS.

for some suitably chosen unit vector $\mathbf{u}_k$, $k = 1, \ldots, n - 2$. The P_k's are easily seen to be orthogonal *and* symmetric. If $A = A_0$ is symmetric, A_{n-2} will be tridiagonal and symmetric.

b. Elementary Transformation Method. This method uses Gaussian elimination in the form of $n - 2$ transformations

$$A_k = E_k A_{k-1} E_k^{-1}, \qquad \text{where } E_k \text{ is an elementary matrix} \tag{24}$$

that is, E_k is a matrix such that $E_k A$ has the effect of one of the elementary row operations.

The Elementary Transformation Method does not yield a tridiagonal matrix if A is symmetric; and unlike the Householder transformations (for which $P = P_1 P_2 \cdots P_{n-2}$ is orthogonal, hence well conditioned), the use of $P = (E_{n-1} \cdots E_2 E_1)^{-1}$ may cause $P^{-1}AP$ to be more ill conditioned than A (although this possibility can be minimized by the use of a suitable pivoting strategy). However, it requires only about half as many arithmetic operations as Householder's method.

STEP 2: Starting with $A_0 = A$, form a sequence of decompositions

$$A_k - s_k I = Q_k R_k, \qquad A_{k+1} = R_k Q_k + s_k I \tag{25}$$

where Q_k is orthogonal, R_k is upper (i.e., right)-triangular, and s_k is a shifting scalar [see (7) of Section 9.2C] chosen so that

$$A_{k+1} \to \text{diag}(\lambda_1, \ldots, \lambda_n) \text{ rapidly as } k \to \infty \tag{26}$$

Although step 2 can be performed without step 1, the substantial savings in iterations needed for convergence makes step 1 worth incorporating. Details of the *QR*-method and of a related factorization method called the **LR-method** can be found in [29 and 38].

Well-tested software implementing these methods can be found in the EISPAK package developed at the Argonne National Laboratories.

9.4 Characteristic Values and Solutions of Homogeneous BVPs

A linear, second-order BVP is called **homogeneous** if both the differential equation and the boundary conditions are homogeneous, that is, if it is of the form

$$\phi_2(t)y'' + \phi_1(t)y' + \phi_0(t)y = 0, \qquad y(a) = y(b) = 0 \tag{1}$$

Such BVPs always have the **trivial solution** $y(t) \equiv 0$.

Our attention will be confined to homogeneous equations of the form

$$\boxed{a_2(t)y'' + a_1(t)y' + [a_0(t) - \lambda]y = 0, \qquad y(a) = y(b) = 0} \tag{2}$$

Physical systems governed by (2) are found to have nontrivial solutions $y(t)$ (called **characteristic solutions**) for *certain* values of the parameter λ (called **characteristic values** or **eigenvalues**). The terminology follows from the fact that these $(\lambda, y(t))$ pairs satisfy

$$\mathscr{D}y = \lambda y, \qquad \text{where } \mathscr{D} = a_2(t)\frac{d^2}{dt^2} + a_1(t)\frac{d}{dt} + a_0(t)$$

As with eigenvectors of matrices, *if $y(t)$ is a characteristic solution of a BVP, so is $\alpha y(t)$ for any $\alpha \neq 0$.*

The following example illustrates the importance of knowing the characteristic values and solutions of homogeneous BVPs.

9.4A   BUCKLING OF AXIALLY LOADED BEAMS

Suppose that a thin, uniform beam L units long is subjected to a constant compressing force P along its axis. Such a force is called an **axial load.** Let $y = y(x)$ denote the horizontal deflection x units up from the base, as shown in Figure 9.4-1.

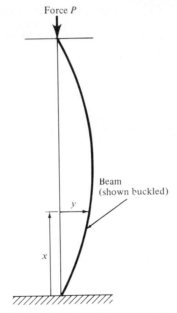

FIGURE 9.4-1   AN AXIALLY LOADED BEAM.

It can be shown that the shape of the beam is governed by the linear, homogeneous BVP

$$\frac{d^2y}{dx^2} + \frac{P}{EI}y = 0, \qquad y(0) = y(L) = 0 \tag{3a}$$

where E and I are constants that reflect the elasticity of the beam's material and the geometry of its cross section, respectively. Since the load P is assumed fixed, we can rewrite this as

$$y'' - \lambda y = 0, \qquad y(0) = y(L) = 0 \tag{3b}$$

where $\lambda = -P/EI$ is negative. It is easy to see that

$$y'' = \lambda y, \qquad \text{where } \lambda < 0 \quad \Leftrightarrow \quad y(x) = A \cos \sqrt{-\lambda}\, x + B \sin \sqrt{-\lambda}\, x \qquad (4)$$

Since $y(0) = 0$, A must be zero; hence the homogeneous boundary condition at the right endpoint can be written as

$$B \sin \sqrt{-\lambda}\, L = 0, \qquad \text{where } -\lambda = \frac{P}{EI} \qquad (5)$$

As long as $\sqrt{-\lambda}\, L$ is not a multiple of π, (5) forces B to be zero, and the trivial solution $y(x) \equiv 0$ is the only possible one. However, if

$$\sqrt{-\lambda}\, L = k\pi, \qquad \text{that is, } \lambda = -\left(\frac{k\pi}{L}\right)^2 \qquad (6a)$$

then $\sin \sqrt{-\lambda}\, L = 0$, leaving B unrestricted. For such λ's, $y(x)$ can be nonzero for $0 < x < L$ (i.e., *the beam can buckle*). Axial loads

$$P = -EI\lambda, \qquad \lambda \text{ an eigenvalue of the BVP} \qquad (6b)$$

are called **buckling loads** or **critical loads** and should be avoided. The buckling load of primary interest is the *smallest* one because this load can cause the beam to break before larger loads can be applied!

9.4B NUMERICAL PROCEDURE FOR ESTIMATING CHARACTERISTIC VALUES

When E and or I are not constant but vary with x, we may not be able to find an analytic solution to use to obtain formulas like (6). The critical loads for such beams must therefore be found from a numerical solution.

The general procedure when

$$a_2(x)y'' + a_1(x)y' + a_0(x)y = \lambda y, \qquad y(a) = y(b) = 0 \qquad (7)$$

is to subdivide $[a,\ b]$ using the $n + 1$ h-spaced points

$$a = x_0 < x_1 < \cdots < x_j = a + jh < \cdots < x_{n-1} < x_n = b \qquad (8)$$

and then use central difference approximations such as the $O(h^2)$ formulas

$$y'(x_j) \approx \frac{y_{j+1} - y_j}{2h} \quad \text{and} \quad y''(x_j) \approx \frac{y_{j+1} - 2y_j + y_{j-1}}{h^2}, \qquad h = \frac{b-a}{n} \qquad (9)$$

as we did in Section 8.5D. Putting (9) in (7) with $y_0 = y_n = 0$ gives

$$\boxed{\frac{1}{h^2}\{\alpha_j y_{j-1} + \beta_j y_j + \gamma_j y_{j+1}\} = \lambda y_j} \qquad (10a)$$

where

$$\alpha_j = a_2(x_j) - \frac{h}{2} a_1(x_j), \quad \beta_j = -2a_2(x_j) + h^2 a_0(x_j), \quad \gamma_j = a_2(x_j) + \frac{h}{2} a_1(x_j) \quad \textbf{(10b)}$$

for $j = 1, \ldots, n - 1$. In matrix form this tridiagonal system is

$$Ty = \lambda y \quad \text{where } T = \frac{1}{h^2} \begin{bmatrix} \beta_1 & \gamma_1 & & & & \\ \alpha_2 & \beta_2 & \gamma_2 & & & \\ & & \ddots & & & \\ & & & \alpha_{n-2} & \beta_{n-2} & \gamma_{n-2} \\ & & & & \alpha_{n-1} & \beta_{n-1} \end{bmatrix} \quad \textbf{(10c)}$$

Since $Ty = \lambda y$ approximates the BVP in (7), the eigenpairs (λ, y) of T should approximate the eigenpairs $(\lambda, y(x))$ of the BVP, with $y = [y_1 \cdots y_{n-1}]^T$ and $y(x)$ related as follows

$$y_j \approx y(x_j), \quad \text{where } x_j = a + jh \quad \text{for } j = 1, \ldots, n - 1 \quad \textbf{(11)}$$

EXAMPLE. Set up and solve the matrix equation $Ty = \lambda y$ that approximates

$$y'' = \lambda y \quad (\lambda < 0), \quad y(0) = y(L) = 0 \quad \textbf{(12)}$$

using $n = 2, 3, 4, 5$, and discuss how well the eigenvalues of T approximate the characteristic values $\lambda = -(k\pi/L)^2$ obtained in (6a).

Solution. For this simple BVP, $a_0(x) = a_1(x) \equiv 0$ and $a_2(x) \equiv 1$; hence

$$\alpha_j = 1, \quad \beta_j = -2, \quad \text{and} \quad \gamma_j = 1 \quad \text{for } j = 1, \ldots, n - 1 \quad \textbf{(13)}$$

[see (10a)]. Thus for any n, the $(n - 1) \times (n - 1)$ matrix T in (10c) is

$$T = \frac{1}{h^2} \begin{bmatrix} -2 & 1 & & & \\ 1 & -2 & 1 & & \\ & & \ddots & & \\ & & 1 & -2 & 1 \\ & & & 1 & -2 \end{bmatrix}, \text{ where } h = \frac{L}{n} \quad \textbf{(14)}$$

For small values of n the eigenvalues of this simple, symmetric T can be found analytically as roots of its characteristic polynomial. This is done for $n = 2, 3, 4, 5$ in Table 9.4-1.

Notice that reasonable estimates of the *least* dominant eigenvalue $\lambda_{min} = -(\pi/L)^2$ (corresponding to the smallest buckling load P) can be obtained with smaller values of n than is required to get comparable estimates of the larger λ's. Even for more complicated differential equations, the Inverse Power Method can be applied to T to

TABLE 9.4-1 APPROXIMATING CHARACTERISTIC VALUES BY EIGENVALUES OF T.

n	h	Characteristic Polynomial of T $p_T(\lambda) = \det(T - \lambda I_{n-1})$	Eigenvalues of T (roots of $p_T(\lambda)$)	Characteristic Values $\lambda = -\left(\dfrac{k\pi}{L}\right)^2$
2	$\dfrac{L}{2}$	$\dfrac{1}{h^2}\{-2-\lambda h^2\}$	$-\dfrac{2}{h^2} = -\dfrac{8}{L^2}$	$-\left(\dfrac{\pi}{L}\right)^2 \doteq -\dfrac{9.87}{L^2}$
3	$\dfrac{L}{3}$	$\dfrac{1}{h^2}\{(-2-\lambda h^2)^2 - 1\}$	$-\dfrac{1}{h^2} = -\dfrac{9}{L^2}$ $-\dfrac{3}{h^2} = -\dfrac{27}{L^2}$	$-\left(\dfrac{\pi}{L}\right)^2 \doteq -\dfrac{9.87}{L^2}$ $-\left(\dfrac{2\pi}{L}\right)^2 \doteq -\dfrac{39.48}{L^2}$
4	$\dfrac{L}{4}$	$\dfrac{1}{h^2}\{(-2-\lambda h^2)[(-2-\lambda h^2)^2 - 2]\}$	$\dfrac{1}{h^2}(-2+\sqrt{2}) \doteq -\dfrac{9.37}{L^2}$ $-\dfrac{2}{h^2} = -\dfrac{32}{L^2}$ $\dfrac{1}{h^2}(-2-\sqrt{2}) = -\dfrac{54.63}{L^2}$	$-\left(\dfrac{\pi}{L}\right)^2 \doteq -\dfrac{9.87}{L^2}$ $-\left(\dfrac{2\pi}{L}\right)^2 \doteq -\dfrac{39.48}{L^2}$ $-\left(\dfrac{3\pi}{L}\right)^2 \doteq -\dfrac{88.83}{L^2}$
5	$\dfrac{L}{5}$	$\dfrac{1}{h^2}\{(-2-\lambda h^2)^4 - 3(-2-\lambda h^2)^2 + 1\}$	$\dfrac{1}{h^2}\left(-2+\sqrt{\dfrac{1}{2}(3+\sqrt{5})}\right) \doteq -\dfrac{9.55}{L^2}$ $\dfrac{1}{h^2}\left(-2+\sqrt{\dfrac{1}{2}(3-\sqrt{5})}\right) \doteq -\dfrac{34.55}{L^2}$ $\dfrac{1}{h^2}\left(-2-\sqrt{\dfrac{1}{2}(3-\sqrt{5})}\right) \doteq -\dfrac{65.45}{L^2}$ $\dfrac{1}{h^2}\left(-2-\sqrt{\dfrac{1}{2}(3+\sqrt{5})}\right) \doteq -\dfrac{90.45}{L^2}$	$-\left(\dfrac{\pi}{L}\right)^2 \doteq -\dfrac{9.87}{L^2}$ $-\left(\dfrac{2\pi}{L}\right)^2 \doteq -\dfrac{39.48}{L^2}$ $-\left(\dfrac{3\pi}{L}\right)^2 \doteq -\dfrac{88.83}{L^2}$ $-\left(\dfrac{4\pi}{L}\right)^2 \doteq -\dfrac{157.91}{L^2}$

obtain reasonable approximations of λ_{min} and an associated characteristic solution $y(x)$ using small n's, especially if the following discussion is utilized.

9.4C IMPROVING ACCURACY OF ESTIMATES OF λ

Let $E[h]$ denote the error of approximating $\lambda_{min} = -(\pi/L)^2$ by the least dominant eigenvalue of T. From Table 9.4-1,

$$h = \frac{L}{2} \quad \Rightarrow \quad E\left[\frac{L}{2}\right] = \lambda_{min} - \left(-\frac{8}{L^2}\right) \doteq -\frac{1.87}{L^2}$$

$$h = \frac{L}{4} \quad \Rightarrow \quad E\left[\frac{L}{4}\right] = \lambda_{min} - \left(-\frac{9.37}{L^2}\right) \doteq -\frac{0.50}{L^2} \approx \left(\frac{L/4}{L/2}\right)^2 E\left[\frac{L}{2}\right]$$

$$h = \frac{L}{5} \quad \Rightarrow \quad E\left[\frac{L}{5}\right] = \lambda_{min} - \left(-\frac{9.55}{L^2}\right) \doteq -\frac{0.27}{L^2} \approx \left(\frac{L/5}{L/2}\right)^2 E\left[\frac{L}{2}\right]$$

Evidently, $E[L/n] \approx (2/n)^2 E[L/2]$, suggesting that the least dominant eigenvalue of T is an $O(h^2)$ approximation of λ_{min}. In fact, the following more general result can be proved.

If $O(h^m)$ approximations are used to get the system $T\mathbf{y} = \lambda\mathbf{y}$ from the linear, homogeneous BVP

$$a_2(x)y'' + a_1(x)y' + [a_0(x) - \lambda]y = 0, \qquad y(a) = y(b) = 0 \tag{15}$$

then the eigenvalues and eigenvectors of T are $O(h^m)$ approximations of the corresponding characteristic values and solutions of the BVP.

We can therefore use Richardson's improvement formula of Section 7.1D. From the $h = L/4$ and $h = L/5$ estimates of $\lambda_{min} = -(\pi/L)^2$, we get

$$(\lambda_{min})_{improved} = \frac{(\frac{5}{4})^2(-9.55/L^2) - (-9.36/L^2)}{(\frac{5}{4})^2 - 1} = -\frac{9.87}{L^2} \tag{16}$$

This is accurate to the $2d$ carried in the intermediate computations.

The reader is urged to use Richardson's formula whenever more than one approximation of λ and $y(t)$ are obtained.

9.4D THE STURM–LIOUVILLE EQUATION

A frequently occurring linear BVP is

$$\boxed{\frac{d}{dx}[f(x)y'] + [r(x) - \lambda w(x)]\,y = 0, \qquad y(a) = y(b) = 0} \tag{17}$$

in which $f(x)$, $r(x)$, and $w(x)$ are continuous on $[a, b]$ and $w(x) > 0$ on (a, b). This BVP, called the **Sturm–Liouville equation,** has some very desirable theoretical properties [5], and lends itself to the following numerical procedure. First, replace $d[f(x)y']/dx$ at x_j by the $O(h^2)$ central difference formula but *using a step size $h/2$,* getting

$$\frac{f\left(x_j+\frac{h}{2}\right)y'\left(x_j+\frac{h}{2}\right)-f\left(x_j-\frac{h}{2}\right)y'\left(x_j-\frac{h}{2}\right)}{2(h/2)} + [r(x_j)-\lambda w(x_j)]y_j=0$$

Then replace $y'(x_j \pm h/2)$ in the same way, getting

$$\frac{1}{h}\left\{f\left(x_j+\frac{h}{2}\right)\left(\frac{y_{j+1}-y_j}{h}\right)-f\left(x_j-\frac{h}{2}\right)\left(\frac{y_j-y_{j-1}}{h}\right)\right\} + r(x_j)y_j=\lambda w(x_j)y_j$$

Finally, divide by $w(x_j)$ and collect y_{j-1}, y_j, and y_{j+1} terms to get

$$\alpha_j y_{j-1}+\beta_j y_j+\gamma_j y_{j+1}=\lambda y_j \tag{18a}$$

where $y_0 = y_n = 0$, and for $j = 1, \ldots, n-1$ $\left(\text{with } h=\dfrac{b-a}{n}\right)$

$$\boxed{\alpha_j=\frac{f\left(x_j-\dfrac{h}{2}\right)}{h^2 w(x_j)}, \quad \gamma_j=\frac{f\left(x_j+\dfrac{h}{2}\right)}{h^2 w(x_j)}, \quad \text{and} \quad \beta_j=\frac{r(x_j)}{w(x_j)}-\alpha_j-\gamma_j} \tag{18b}$$

In matrix form, the $(n-1) \times (n-1)$ tridiagonal system (18a) is

$$\boxed{Ty=\lambda y \qquad \text{where } y=[y_1 \quad \cdots \quad y_{n-1}]^T \text{and } T=\text{trid}\,(\alpha, \beta, \gamma)} \tag{18c}$$

If $w(x) \equiv$ constant, then it is immediate from (18b) that $\alpha_{j+1} = \gamma_j$, $j = 1, \ldots, n-2$, and hence that the tridiagonal matrix T is symmetric. Its n eigenpairs can therefore be found simultaneously using Jacobi's method.

EXAMPLE. Use (18) with $n = 3$, 5, and 7 to get an accurate approximation of the least dominant eigenvalue of

$$\frac{d}{dx}[(1+x^2)y']+2\lambda y=0, \qquad y(0)=y(2)=0 \tag{19}$$

Solution. This is a Sturm–Liouville equation with

$$f(x)=1+x^2, \quad r(x)\equiv 0, \quad \text{and} \quad w(x)\equiv w=-2$$

Hence by (18),

$$\alpha_j=\frac{1+\left(x_j-\dfrac{h}{2}\right)^2}{-2h^2}, \quad \gamma_j=\frac{1+\left(x_j+\dfrac{h}{2}\right)^2}{-2h^2}, \quad \beta_j=-(\alpha_j+\gamma_j) \tag{20}$$

Since $w(x) = $ constant, T will be symmetric. We can therefore use either the Power Method or Jacobi's method to get the following results:

$n = 3$ $(h = \frac{2}{3})$:

By (20),

$$T = \begin{bmatrix} \beta_1 & \gamma_1 \\ \alpha_2 & \beta_2 \end{bmatrix} = \begin{bmatrix} \frac{9}{8}(\frac{10}{9} + 2) & -\frac{9}{8}(2) \\ -\frac{9}{8}(2) & \frac{9}{8}(2 + \frac{34}{9}) \end{bmatrix} = \begin{bmatrix} 3.5 & -2.25 \\ -2.25 & 6.5 \end{bmatrix}$$

The eigenpairs of this T are (to $5d$):

$$\left(2.29584, \begin{bmatrix} 0.88167 \\ 0.47186 \end{bmatrix} \right), \quad \left(7.70416, \begin{bmatrix} -0.47186 \\ 0.88167 \end{bmatrix} \right)$$

$n = 5$ $(h = \frac{2}{5})$:

By (20),

$$T = \begin{bmatrix} 7.5 & -4.25 & & \\ -4.25 & 10.5 & -6.25 & \\ & -6.25 & 15.5 & -9.25 \\ & & -9.25 & 22.5 \end{bmatrix}$$

The two least dominant eigenpairs of this $T_{4\times4}$ are

$$(2.46098, [\ 0.55283 \quad 0.65547 \quad 0.46716 \quad 0.21564]^T)$$
$$(8.17772, [-0.74538 \quad 0.11886 \quad 0.55102 \quad 0.35588]^T)$$

$n = 7$ $(h = \frac{2}{7})$: The two least dominant eigenpairs of the $T_{6\times6}$ are

$$(2.51448, [0.36022 \quad 0.54583 \quad 0.54293 \quad 0.42929 \quad 0.27720 \quad 0.12810]^T)$$
$$(8.89002, [-0.61134 \quad -0.38873 \quad 0.15935 \quad 0.45757 \quad 0.43205 \quad 0.23179]^T)$$

Since large values of h were used, we should use Richardson's formula to improve the three available estimates of $\lambda_{\min}$ (see Table 9.4-2).

TABLE 9.4-2   RICHARDSON TABLE FOR $\lambda_{\min}$ VALUES.

	h	$F[h], O(h^2)$	$F_1[h], O(h^4)$	$F_2[h]$
$r = \frac{5}{3}$ $\begin{cases} \\ \\ \end{cases}$	$\frac{2}{3}$	2.29584		
	$\frac{2}{5}$	2.46098	2.55387	
$r = \frac{7}{5}$ $\begin{cases} \\ \end{cases}$	$\frac{2}{7}$	2.51448	2.57021	2.57902

It appears from this Richardson table that

$$\lambda_{\min} \doteq F_2[\tfrac{2}{7}] = 2.579$$

That $F_1[h]$ is $O(h^4)$ follows from the fact that the truncation error of the approximation $f'(x) \approx \delta f(x)/2h$ is of the form $Ch^2 + Dh^4 + \cdots$ [see (24) of Section 7.1E].

9.5 Using Eigenvalues to Uncover the Structure of A

In this final section we use the eigenpairs of A to help provide insight into the effect of multiplying $\mathbf{x}$ by A and to get computable formulas for $\|A\|$ and cond A (see Section 4.2C).

9.5A THE PRINCIPAL AXIS THEOREM

Let A be a symmetric $n \times n$ matrix. In this case $\|\cdot\|$ will denote the Euclidean norm $\|\cdot\|_2$. The Symmetric Diagonalization Theorem of Section 9.3B assures us of the existence of vectors $\mathbf{u}_1, \ldots, \mathbf{u}_n$ such that

$$A\mathbf{u}_i = \lambda_i \mathbf{u}_i, \quad i = 1, \ldots, n \quad \text{(the } \mathbf{u}_i\text{'s are eigenvectors } A) \tag{1a}$$
$$\mathbf{u}_i^T \mathbf{u}_j = 1 \quad \text{if } i = j, \quad \text{and} \quad = 0 \quad \text{if } i \neq j \quad \text{(the } \mathbf{u}_i\text{'s are orthonormal)} \tag{1b}$$

It follows that every $\mathbf{x}$ can be represented uniquely as

$$\mathbf{x} = \alpha_1 \mathbf{u}_1 + \alpha_2 \mathbf{u}_2 + \cdots + \alpha_n \mathbf{u}_n = \sum_{i=1}^{n} \alpha_i \mathbf{u}_i \tag{1c}$$

Such orthonormal bases of eigenvectors are often called **principal axes** for A, and the components $\alpha_1, \ldots, \alpha_n$ along these axes the **principal components** of $\mathbf{x}$. It is immediate from (1) that

$$\|\mathbf{x}\|^2 = \mathbf{x}^T\mathbf{x} = \left(\sum_i \alpha_i \mathbf{u}_i\right)^T \left(\sum_j \alpha_j \mathbf{u}_j\right) = \sum_{i,j} \alpha_i \alpha_j \mathbf{u}_i^T \mathbf{u}_j = \sum_i \alpha_i^2 \tag{2}$$

Thus $\|\mathbf{x}\|^2$ *can be obtained as the sum of the squares of the principal components of* $\mathbf{x}$. And since $\mathbf{u}_i$ is an eigenvector for λ_i for each i,

$$A\mathbf{x} = \lambda_1 \alpha_1 \mathbf{u}_1 + \lambda_2 \alpha_2 \mathbf{u}_2 + \cdots + \lambda_n \alpha_n \mathbf{u}_n = \sum_i \lambda_i \alpha_i \mathbf{u}_i \tag{3}$$

In words, *the effect of multiplying* $\mathbf{x}$ *by* A *is to multiply the ith principal component of* $\mathbf{x}$ *by* λ_i. Hence, if we denote the ith principal component of $A\mathbf{x}$ by β_i, then by (3) and (2),

$$\left(\frac{\beta_1}{\lambda_1}\right)^2 + \left(\frac{\beta_2}{\lambda_2}\right)^2 + \cdots + \left(\frac{\beta_n}{\lambda_n}\right)^2 = \sum_{i=1}^{n} \left(\frac{\beta_i}{\lambda_i}\right)^2 = \sum_{i=1}^{n} \alpha_i^2 = \|\mathbf{x}\|^2$$

provided that all λ_i's are nonzero. Otherwise, $\Sigma_{i=1}^n$ should be replaced by $\Sigma_{\lambda_i \neq 0}$, that is, the summation over all i for which $\lambda_i \neq 0$. This proves:

The Principal Axis Theorem. *Let A be a symmetric matrix with principal axes* $\mathbf{u}_1, \ldots,$ $\mathbf{u}_n$ *and let* $\mathbf{y}$ *be a vector with principal components* $\beta_1, \ldots, \beta_n$. *Then*

$$\mathbf{y} = A\mathbf{x}, \text{ where } \|\mathbf{x}\| = 1 \quad \Longleftrightarrow \quad \sum_{\lambda_i \neq 0} \left(\frac{\beta_i}{\lambda_i}\right)^2 = 1 \qquad \textbf{(4)}$$

In words, A multiplies the unit ball onto the hyperellipsoid with semiaxes of length $|\lambda_1|$, $\ldots, |\lambda_n|$ *directed along the principal axes.*

EXAMPLE. If

$$A = \begin{bmatrix} 0 & \sqrt{3} \\ \sqrt{3} & 2 \end{bmatrix}$$

sketch the set of all $A\mathbf{x}$, where $\|\mathbf{x}\| = 1$.

Solution. It is easy to verify that

$$\begin{bmatrix} 0 & \sqrt{3} \\ \sqrt{3} & 2 \end{bmatrix}\begin{bmatrix} 1 \\ \sqrt{3} \end{bmatrix} = 3\begin{bmatrix} 1 \\ \sqrt{3} \end{bmatrix} \quad \text{and} \quad \begin{bmatrix} 0 & \sqrt{3} \\ \sqrt{3} & 2 \end{bmatrix}\begin{bmatrix} \sqrt{3} \\ -1 \end{bmatrix} = -1\begin{bmatrix} \sqrt{3} \\ -1 \end{bmatrix} \qquad \textbf{(5)}$$

It follows that a pair of principal axes for A is

$$\mathbf{u}_1 = \begin{bmatrix} \frac{1}{2} \\ \sqrt{\frac{3}{2}} \end{bmatrix} \quad \text{and} \quad \mathbf{u}_2 = \begin{bmatrix} \sqrt{\frac{3}{2}} \\ -\frac{1}{2} \end{bmatrix}$$

So if $\mathbf{x} = \alpha_1\mathbf{u}_1 + \alpha_2\mathbf{u}_2$ and $A\mathbf{x} = \beta_1\mathbf{u}_1 + \beta_2\mathbf{u}_2$, then by (4),

$$\|\mathbf{x}\| = \alpha_1^2 + \alpha_2^2 = 1 \quad \Longleftrightarrow \quad \left(\frac{\beta_1}{3}\right)^2 + \left(\frac{\beta_2}{-1}\right)^2 = 1 \qquad \textbf{(6)}$$

Hence $A\mathbf{x}$ lies on the ellipse sketched in Figure 9.5-1.

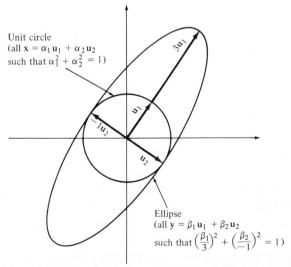

Unit circle
(all $\mathbf{x} = \alpha_1\mathbf{u}_1 + \alpha_2\mathbf{u}_2$
such that $\alpha_1^2 + \alpha_2^2 = 1$)

$3\mathbf{u}_1$

$\mathbf{u}_1$

$-\mathbf{u}_2$

$\mathbf{u}_2$

Ellipse
(all $\mathbf{y} = \beta_1\mathbf{u}_1 + \beta_2\mathbf{u}_2$
such that $\left(\frac{\beta_1}{3}\right)^2 + \left(\frac{\beta_2}{-1}\right)^2 = 1$)

FIGURE 9.5-1   THE PRINCIPAL AXIS THEOREM WHEN $\lambda_1 = 3$, $\lambda_2 = -1$.

9.5B DESCRIBING $||A||$ AND cond A WHEN A IS SYMMETRIC

Let λ_1 be the dominant eigenvalue of a symmetric matrix A. The Principal Axis Theorem suggests that $A\mathbf{x}$ is at most $|\lambda_1|$ times as long as $\mathbf{x}$, that is, that $||A|| = |\lambda_1|$. To prove this, note from (2) and (3) that

$$||A\mathbf{x}||^2 = \sum \alpha_i^2 \lambda_i^2 \leqslant \lambda_1^2 \sum \alpha_i^2 = \lambda_1^2 ||\mathbf{x}||^2$$

So by the definition of matrix norm [see (13) of Section 4.2C],

$$||A|| = \max_{\mathbf{x} \neq 0} \frac{||A\mathbf{x}||}{||\mathbf{x}||} \leqslant \sqrt{\lambda_1^2} = |\lambda_1| \tag{7a}$$

Equality holds when $\mathbf{x} = \mathbf{u}_1$ (the eigenvector for λ_1) because

$$\mathbf{x} = \mathbf{u}_1 \;\Rightarrow\; ||A\mathbf{x}|| = ||\lambda_1 \mathbf{x}|| = |\lambda_1|\, ||\mathbf{x}|| \tag{7b}$$

It follows that $||A|| = |\lambda_1|$. Since A^{-1} is symmetric whenever A is (Exercise 9-22), we have the following important result.

Spectral Radius Theorem. *Let A be symmetric. Then with $||\cdot|| = ||\cdot||_2$:*
a. $||A|| = \max \{|\lambda_1|, \ldots, |\lambda_n|\}$, *the* **spectral radius** *of A.*
b. *If A is also invertible, then* $||A^{-1}|| = 1/\min \{|\lambda_1|, \ldots, |\lambda_n|\}$

c.
$$\text{cond } A = \frac{\text{largest } |\lambda_i|}{\text{smallest } |\lambda_i|} \tag{8}$$

Thus, *for a symmetric matrix A, ill conditioning corresponds to A having eigenvalues of both large and small magnitude* (see Section 4.2C). Geometrically, this corresponds to the hyperellipsoid (4) being very eccentric in at least one cross section.

For example, the 2×2 matrix A in (5) satisfies

$$||A|| = |3| = 3, \quad ||A^{-1}|| = \frac{1}{|-1|} = 1, \quad \text{and} \quad \text{cond } A = 3 \cdot 1 = 3$$

Since 3 is of the order of magnitude of 1, A is well conditioned.

9.5C POSITIVE DEFINITE MATRICES

We have just seen how multiplication by a symmetric matrix A can "distort" the Euclidean unit sphere by stretching the components along its principal axes $\mathbf{u}_i$ by different amounts λ_i. One way to compensate for this distortion is to use

$$||\mathbf{x}||_A = \sqrt{\mathbf{x}^T A \mathbf{x}}, \qquad \text{the } \textbf{norm induced by } A \tag{9}$$

rather than $\|\mathbf{x}\|$ to measure distance from $\mathbf{0}$. In order for $\|\mathbf{x}\|_A$ to be defined for all $\mathbf{x}$ and nonzero if $\mathbf{x} \neq \mathbf{0}$, A must have the property that

$$\boxed{\mathbf{x}^T A \mathbf{x} > 0 \qquad \text{for all } \mathbf{x} \neq \mathbf{0}} \tag{10}$$

Symmetric matrices having this property are called **positive definite.**

If $\mathbf{u}_1, \ldots, \mathbf{u}_n$ is a set of principal axes for the symmetric matrix A and $\alpha_1, \ldots, \alpha_n$ are the principal components of $\mathbf{x}$, then by (1) and (3),

$$\mathbf{x}^T A \mathbf{x} = \left(\sum_i \alpha_i \mathbf{u}_i \right)^T \left(\sum_j \lambda_j \alpha_j \mathbf{u}_j \right) = \sum_i \alpha_i^2 \lambda_i \tag{11}$$

Since $\alpha_i^2 > 0$, (10) is possible if and only if $\lambda_i > 0$ for all i. Thus

$$\boxed{\begin{array}{l} \text{A symmetric matrix is positive definite if and} \\ \text{only if all of its eigenvalues are positive.} \end{array}} \tag{12}$$

The determination of whether a symmetric matrix A is positive definite can therefore be made *by inspection* whenever all its eigenvalues are known. Otherwise, this determination can be made by carrying out the algorithm for the *Choleski factorization*:

$$A = LL^T, \qquad \text{where } L \text{ is lower triangular and invertible} \tag{13}$$

[See Table 3.3-2]. This factorization is possible if and only if A is positive definite.

Suppose that A is a nonsingular but not necessarily symmetric matrix. Then A^TA is symmetric [see (3) of Section 9.3A], and with $\|\cdot\|$ still $\|\cdot\|_2$,

$$\mathbf{x}^T (A^T A)\mathbf{x} = (\mathbf{x}^T A^T)(A\mathbf{x}) = (A\mathbf{x})^T (A\mathbf{x}) = \|A\mathbf{x}\|^2 \geqslant 0 \tag{14}$$

But $\|A\mathbf{x}\|^2 = 0 \iff A\mathbf{x} = \mathbf{0} \iff \mathbf{x} = \mathbf{0}$ because A is nonsingular. Similarly, $\mathbf{x}^T (AA^T)\mathbf{x} > 0$ all for $\mathbf{x} \neq \mathbf{0}$. Thus

$$A^T A \text{ and } AA^T \text{ are positive definite for any nonsingular } A \tag{15}$$

This result can be generalized to any $m \times n$ matrix A for which A^TA (or AA^T) turns out to be nonsingular. In this more general form, (15) plays an important role in statistics and optimization theory.

9.5D   RELATING cond A TO EIGENVALUES WHEN A IS NOT SYMMETRIC

Let A be an invertible matrix that is not symmetric. If λ_1 is its dominant eigenvalue and $\mathbf{v}_1$ is an associated eigenvector, then

$$\|A\| = \max_{\mathbf{x} \neq 0} \frac{\|A\mathbf{x}\|}{\|\mathbf{x}\|} \geqslant \frac{\|A\mathbf{v}_1\|}{\|\mathbf{v}_1\|} = \frac{\|\lambda_1 \mathbf{v}_1\|}{\|\mathbf{v}_1\|} = |\lambda_1| \tag{16}$$

no matter what $||\cdot||$ is used on n-space. However, $||A||$ *may be strictly larger than* $|\lambda_1|$. To get a more precise formula, note from (14) that when $||\cdot||$ is $||\cdot||_2$,

$$||A||^2 = \max_{x \neq 0} \frac{||Ax||^2}{||x||^2} = \max_{x \neq 0} \frac{x^T(A^TA)x}{||x||^2}$$

Since A^TA is positive definite, the expression on the right gives the largest eigenvalue of A^TA (Exercise 9-42). So for a nonsymmetric matrix A (a), (b), and (c) of the Spectral Radius Theorem of Section 9.5B get replaced by

$$||A|| = \sqrt{\text{largest eigenvalue of } A^TA} \qquad \textbf{(17a)}$$

$$||A^{-1}|| = \sqrt{\text{smallest eigenvalue of } A^TA} \qquad \textbf{(17b)}$$

$$\text{cond } A = \left(\frac{\text{largest eigenvalue of } A^TA}{\text{smallest eigenvalue of } A^TA} \right)^{1/2} \qquad \textbf{(17c)}$$

where $||A||$ and $||A^{-1}||$ are with respect to $||\cdot||_2$ on n-space.

9.5E THE GENERALIZED EIGENVALUE PROBLEM

There are times when it is necessary to find λ and x such that

$$Bx = \lambda Cx, \qquad \text{where } B \text{ and } C \text{ are given } n \times n \text{ matrices} \qquad \textbf{(18)}$$

If C is nonsingular, this can be rewritten as

$$(C^{-1}B)\,x = \lambda x \qquad \text{(find an eigenvalue of } C^{-1}B) \qquad \textbf{(19)}$$

If B and C are both symmetric, then $C^{-1}B$ need not be symmetric (see Exercise 9-23); in this case the use of (19) destroys some of the geometric structure of (18). However, if C is positive definite, then the *Choleski decomposition* can be used to write C as

$$C = LL^T, \qquad \text{where } L \text{ is lower triangular and invertible} \qquad \textbf{(20a)}$$

This in turn can be used to transform (18) as follows:

$$Bx = \lambda Cx \qquad \Longleftrightarrow \qquad B(L^T)^{-1}\,L^Tx = \lambda LL^Tx$$
$$\Longleftrightarrow \qquad L^{-1}B(L^T)^{-1}\,L^Tx = \lambda L^Tx \qquad \textbf{(20b)}$$

This last equality can be written as

$$Av = \lambda v, \qquad \text{where } A = L^{-1}B(L^T)^{-1} \quad \text{and} \quad v = L^Tx \qquad \textbf{(21)}$$

The desired λ's and x's in (18) can now be obtained from the eigenpairs (λ, v) of this matrix A. Specifically,

$$Av_i = \lambda_iv_i \qquad \Longleftrightarrow \qquad Bx_i = \lambda_iCx_i, \qquad \text{where } x_i = (L^T)^{-1}v_i \qquad \textbf{(22)}$$

Since $(L^T)^{-1} = (L^{-1})^T$ (Exercise 9-22), we see from (21) that $A^T = L^{-1}B^T(L^T)^{-1}$, and hence that A is symmetric whenever B is.

Exercises

Section 9.1

9-1. In part (a) of the example in Section 9.1A, use Gaussian elimination to show that the *only* eigenvectors for $\lambda_2 = -3$ and $\lambda_3 = 2$ are scalar multiples of $v_2 = \begin{bmatrix} 0 & 1 & 0 \end{bmatrix}^T$ and $v_3 = \begin{bmatrix} 1 & 0 & -1 \end{bmatrix}^T$, respectively.

9-2. In (a)–(d), find the characteristic polynomial and all eigenpairs of A; then deduce the eigenpairs of A^{-1}.

$$\text{(a) } A = \begin{bmatrix} 0 & 1 \\ 1 & 0 \end{bmatrix} \quad \text{(b) } A = \begin{bmatrix} 4 & 5 \\ 3 & 2 \end{bmatrix} \quad \text{(c) } A = \begin{bmatrix} 0 & 1 \\ -1 & 2 \end{bmatrix} \quad \text{(d) } \begin{bmatrix} 0 & -1 \\ 1 & 0 \end{bmatrix}$$

9-3. How are the eigenpairs of αA related to those of A? Justify.

9-4. In (a) and (b), find all eigenpairs of D and state whether D is invertible; justify your answers.

(a) $D = \text{diag}\,(8, -1, 3)$ (b) $D = \text{diag}\,(-2, 3, 0)$

9-5. Which elementary operations are needed to reduce $A \rightarrow B \rightarrow C$ where

$$A = \begin{bmatrix} 1 & 1 \\ 3 & 1 \end{bmatrix}, \quad B = \begin{bmatrix} 1 & 0 \\ 0 & -2 \end{bmatrix}, \quad \text{and} \quad C = \begin{bmatrix} 2 & 0 \\ 0 & -2 \end{bmatrix}$$

Do the SUBTRACT and SCALE operations alter eigenvalues? Explain.

9-6. Prove:

(a) If A is similar to B, then $\det A = \det B$ and $p_A(\lambda) = p_B(\lambda)$.

(b) If A and B are diagonalizable and $p_A(\lambda) = p_B(\lambda)$, then A is similar to B.

9-7. (a) *Prove:* If $(\lambda_1, \ldots, \lambda_n$ are distinct eigenvalues of A (i.e., $\lambda_i \neq \lambda_j$ for $i \neq j$) with corresponding eigenvectors $v_1, \ldots, v_n$, then $v_1, \ldots, v_n$ are linearly independent. (OUTLINE: Assume $v_j = \Sigma_{i \neq j}\, \alpha_i v_i$ where $\alpha_i \neq 0$ for all i, and reach a contradiction.)

(b) Use the result in part (a) to prove that every matrix having n distinct eigenvalues is diagonalizable.

9-8. Let $D = \text{diag}\,(1, 1, 3)$. Show that for *any* nonsingular matrix V, $A = VDV^{-1}$ is diagonalizable although $\lambda = 1$ is a repeated eigenvalue.

9-9. For A in (a)–(d) of Exercise 9-2, find a matrix V such that $V^{-1}AV = \text{diag}\,(\lambda_1, \lambda_2)$ *if* such a V exists. If not, explain why not.

9-10. Use your answers to (a) and (b) of Exercise 9-9 and (15) of Section 9.1C to solve

(a) $y_1' = y_2$, $y_1(1) = 2$ (b) $y_1' = 4y_1 + 5y_2$, $y_1(0) = 1$
   $y_2' = y_1$, $y_2(1) = -1$ $y_2' = 3y_1 + 2y_2$, $y_2(0) = 0$

Describe the approximate behavior of $y(t)$ for large t.

9-11. (a) Apply (15) of Section 9.1C and your answer to Exercise 9-9(c) to the $(IVP)_2$

$$y_1' = y_2, \qquad\qquad y_1(0) = 1$$

$$y_2' = -y_1 + 2y_2, \qquad y_2(0) = 0$$

Can you explain why the formula does not work?

(b) Verify that $y(t) = e^t[\alpha_1 + \beta_1 t \quad \alpha_2 + \beta_2 t]^T$. Find $\alpha_1, \alpha_2, \beta_1, \beta_2$.

9-12. Suppose that $L = 50 \cdot 10^{-3}$ henries and $C = 0.5 \cdot 10^{-6}$ farads in the *RLC* circuit of Figure 9.1-1.

(a) What is the natural frequency when $R = 0$?

(b) Find R_{crit} (in ohms) needed for critical damping.

(c) Find $i(t)$ when (i) $R = \frac{1}{2}R_{crit}$; (ii) $R = R_{crit}$; (iii) $R = 2R_{crit}$.

(d) Sketch $i(t)$ for your answers to (i)–(iii) of part (c).

Section 9.2

For the matrices A and the initial guesses x_0 given in Exercises 9-13 through 9-16, do (a)–(d) (if possible).

(a) Find x_1, x_2, x_3, x_4 by the Scaled Power Method.

(b) Find x_1, x_2, x_3, x_4 by the Inverse Power Method. (Use the formula for A^{-1}.)

(c) Find x_1, x_2, x_3, x_4 using the Shifted Inverse Power Method, shifting by the given scalar s. (Use the formula for $(A - sI)^{-1}$.)

(d) Determine whether the iterations in parts (a)–(c) appear to be converging to the desired eigenpair (λ, v). If not, try to explain why.

9-13. $A = \begin{bmatrix} 4 & -2 \\ -3 & 5 \end{bmatrix}$, $x_0 = \begin{bmatrix} 1 \\ -1 \end{bmatrix}$, $s = 3$ Eigenpairs: $\left(2, \begin{bmatrix} 1 \\ 1 \end{bmatrix}\right), \left(7, \begin{bmatrix} -2 \\ 3 \end{bmatrix}\right)$

9-14. $A = \begin{bmatrix} 4 & -2 \\ -3 & 5 \end{bmatrix}$, $x_0 = \begin{bmatrix} 1 \\ 1 \end{bmatrix}$, $s = 5$ Eigenpairs: $\left(2, \begin{bmatrix} 1 \\ 1 \end{bmatrix}\right), \left(7, \begin{bmatrix} -2 \\ 3 \end{bmatrix}\right)$

9-15. $A = \begin{bmatrix} 4 & -1 \\ 1 & 2 \end{bmatrix}$, $x_0 = \begin{bmatrix} -1 \\ 1 \end{bmatrix}$, $s = -1$ Eigenpair: $\left(3, \begin{bmatrix} 1 \\ 1 \end{bmatrix}\right)$

9-16. $A = \begin{bmatrix} 4 & 5 \\ 3 & 2 \end{bmatrix}$, $x_0 = \begin{bmatrix} 2 \\ 1 \end{bmatrix}$, $s = 3$ Eigenpairs: $\left(-1, \begin{bmatrix} 1 \\ -1 \end{bmatrix}\right), \left(7, \begin{bmatrix} 5 \\ 3 \end{bmatrix}\right)$

9-17. Consider the example in Section 9.2C. Do three iterations of the Inverse Power Method using $x_0 = [1 \quad 1 \quad 1]^T$. Explain why it is converging to (λ_2, v_2) and not (λ_3, v_3) as intended. (See Exercise 9-29.)

9-18. Prove: $Av = \lambda v \Rightarrow A^k v = \lambda^k v$ for $k = 1, 2, \ldots$.

9-19. Use Gerschgorin's disk theorem to describe the regions of the complex plane that contain the eigenvalues of A:

$$\text{(a)} \quad A = \begin{bmatrix} 2 & 0.1 & -0.5 \\ 0.2 & -4 & 0.6 \\ 0.1 & 0.1 & 3 \end{bmatrix} \qquad \text{(b)} \quad A = \begin{bmatrix} 0 & 0.1 & -0.1 \\ -2 & 8 & 1 \\ 1 & 3 & 10 \end{bmatrix}$$

9-20. Use the methods of Section 9.2 to find all eigenpairs of the matrices in (a) and (b) of Exercise 9-19 to 3s.

Section 9.3

9-21. Verify that $(AB)^T = B^T A^T$ when $A = \begin{bmatrix} 1 & 2 \\ 3 & 4 \end{bmatrix}$ and $B = \begin{bmatrix} 5 & 6 & 7 \\ 8 & 9 & 0 \end{bmatrix}$.

9-22. Prove: If A is invertible, so is A^T; in fact, $(A^T)^{-1} = (A^{-1})^T$. Deduce that A^{-1} is symmetric if A is.

9-23. (a) Let $A = \begin{bmatrix} a & b \\ b & c \end{bmatrix}$ and $B = \begin{bmatrix} d & e \\ e & f \end{bmatrix}$ be symmetric 2×2 matrices. Find a condition on a, b, c, d, e, f which assures that both AB and BA are symmetric.

(b) Find symmetric 2×2 matrices A and B such that AB is *not* symmetric.

9-24. If $A_{n \times n}$ is symmetric and B is similar to A, is B symmetric? Justify.

9-25. For any $A_{n \times n}$, show that $\mathbf{e}_j = \mathrm{col}_j\, I_n$ satisfies $A\mathbf{e}_j = \mathrm{col}_j\, A$ for $j = 1, \ldots, n$.

9-26. (**Polar Decomposition**) Show that any nonzero vector $\mathbf{x}$ in n-space can be written as $\rho\mathbf{u}$, where $\rho = \|\mathbf{x}\| > 0$ and $\mathbf{u}$ is a unit vector.

9-27. For $\mathbf{x} = \begin{bmatrix} 1 & -1 & 1 \end{bmatrix}^T$ and $\mathbf{y} = \begin{bmatrix} 2 & 3 & -1 \end{bmatrix}^T$, find $\cos \angle(\mathbf{x}, \mathbf{y})$.

9-28. Prove:

(a) If A preserves length (e.g., if A is orthogonal), then all eigenvalues of A satisfy $|\lambda| = 1$.

(b) For any unit vector $\mathbf{u}$, $P = I - 2\mathbf{u}\mathbf{u}^T$ is symmetric and orthogonal.

9-29. (**Formula for Components Relative to an Orthogonal Basis**) Suppose that $\mathbf{v}_1, \ldots,$ $\mathbf{v}_n$ are nonzero and orthogonal (i.e., $\mathbf{v}_i^T \mathbf{v}_j = 0$ for $i \neq j$). Then for any $\mathbf{x}$,

$$\mathbf{x} = \sum_{j=1}^{n} \alpha_j \mathbf{v}_j \;\Rightarrow\; \alpha_j = \frac{\mathbf{x}^T \mathbf{v}_j}{\|\mathbf{v}_j\|^2}, \qquad j = 1, \ldots, n$$

Deduce that $\mathbf{v}_1, \ldots, \mathbf{v}_n$ are linearly independent.

9-30. Let R_θ be the 2×2 rotation matrix in (7) of Section 9.3B.

(a) Prove geometrically that multiplying $\mathbf{x} = \begin{bmatrix} x_1 & x_2 \end{bmatrix}^T$ by R_θ rotates $\mathbf{x}$ by θ radians counterclockwise (Figure 9.3-1).

(b) Using trigonometric identities, show that $R_\theta R_\phi = R_{(\theta+\phi)}$. Interpret this result geometrically.

(c) Find a 2×2 orthogonal matrix that is *not* a rotation matrix.

9-31. In (a)–(c), use Jacobi's method to find a rotation matrix U and a diagonal matrix $D = \mathrm{diag}\,(\lambda_1, \lambda_2)$ such that $U^T A U = D$.

$$\text{(a)} \quad A = \begin{bmatrix} 5 & -2 \\ -2 & 8 \end{bmatrix} \qquad \text{(b)} \quad A = \begin{bmatrix} 2 & 1 \\ 1 & 2 \end{bmatrix} \qquad \text{(c)} \quad A = \begin{bmatrix} -23 & 36 \\ 36 & -2 \end{bmatrix}$$

9-32. For the matrices A in (a) and (b), perform two iterations of Jacobi's method.

$$\text{(a)} \quad A = \begin{bmatrix} 1 & -1 & 2 \\ -1 & 1 & 0 \\ 2 & 0 & 2 \end{bmatrix} \qquad \text{(b)} \quad A = \begin{bmatrix} 0 & 3 & 2 \\ 3 & 0 & 1 \\ 2 & 1 & 0 \end{bmatrix}$$

9-33. Repeat Exercise 9-32 using Jacobi's method with thresholds (Figure 9.3-4) with *Fraction* = 0.6.

Section 9.4

9-34. Suppose that $E = 30 \cdot 10^6$ psi, $I = 100$ in.^{3}, and $L = 100$ in. for the beam considered in the example in Section 9.4B. Find the smallest critical load P_{min} and the approximation of P_{min} using $n = 4$ subintervals (see Table 9.4-1).

9-35. Consider the homogeneous BVP $xy'' + y' + [x^2 - \lambda]y = 0$, $y(0) = y(1) = 0$.
   (a) Approximate this BVP by the linear system $Ty = \lambda y$ as in Section 9.4B using
   (i) $n = 2$; (ii) $n = 3$; (iii) $n = 4$ subintervals.
   (b) Using any method, find to $6s$ the least dominant eigenvalue of the matrices T obtained in (i)–(iii) of part (a).
   (c) For the eigenvalues $\lambda_{(i)}$, $\lambda_{(ii)}$, and $\lambda_{(iii)}$ obtained in part (b), use Richardson's formula first to use $\lambda_{(i)}$ to improve $\lambda_{(ii)}$, and then to use $\lambda_{(ii)}$ to improve $\lambda_{(iii)}$. Assuming that these improved approximations are $O(h^4)$, use $\lambda_{(ii),improved}$ to improve $\lambda_{(iii),improved}$.

9-36. Do (a)–(c) of Exercise 9-35 for the BVP

$$(1 + x^2)y'' + 2xy' - \lambda y = 0, \qquad y(-1) = y(1) = 0$$

9-37. (a) Find conditions on $a_2(x)$ and $a_1(x)$ that imply that

$$\circledast \quad a_2(x)y'' + a_1(x)y' + [a_0(x) - \lambda]y = 0, \qquad y(a) = y(b) = 0$$

   is a Sturm–Liouville equation [see (17) of Section 9.4C].
   (b) Find an integrating factor $\mu(x)$ such that multiplying $\circledast$ by $\mu(x)$ converts it to the Sturm–Liouville equation

$$\frac{d}{dx}[a_2(x)\mu(x)y'] + \mu(x)[a_0(x) - \lambda]y = 0, \qquad y(a) = y(b) = 0$$

9-38. Consider the BVP $y'' - \lambda y = 0$, $y(0) = y(L) = 0$.
   (a) Show that it is a Sturm–Liouville equation.
   (b) Set up the T matrix in (18c) of Section 9.4C. How does it compare to that given in (14) of Section 9.4B?

9-39. Show that the BVP in Exercise 9-35 is a Sturm–Liouville equation. Then do (a)–(c) of Exercise 9-35 using the matrix T in (18c) of Section 9.4C. Compare the accuracy obtained to that of Exercise 9-35.

9-40. Repeat Exercise 9-39 for the BVP given in Exercise 9-36.

Section 9.5

9-41. Use the definition of $\|A\|$ given in (13) of Section 4.2C to prove that:
   (a) $\|\cdot\|$ satisfies the norm conditions given in (12) of Section 4.2C.
   (b) If $D = \text{diag}(\lambda_1, \lambda_2, \ldots, \lambda_n)$, then $\|D\| = \max\{|\lambda_1|, \ldots, |\lambda_n|\}$.
   (c) If $\|\cdot\| = \|\cdot\|_2$ on n-space, then $\|U\| = 1$ for any orthogonal matrix U.

9-42. Prove: If A is positive definite, then [see (11) of Section 9.5C]

$$\frac{\mathbf{x}^T A \mathbf{x}}{\|\mathbf{x}\|^2} = \text{largest (most positive) eigenvalue of } A$$

9-43. For the matrices A in (a)–(c) of Exercise 9-31, and with $\| \cdot \| = \| \cdot \|_2$, sketch the set of all $A\mathbf{x}$ ($\|\mathbf{x}\| = 1$), and use the Spectral Radius Theorem to find $\|A\|$, $\|A^{-1}\|$, and cond A.

9-44. In (a) and (b), find $p_{AA^T}(\lambda)$, then use the results of Section 9.5D to find cond A.

(a) $A = \begin{bmatrix} 2 & 0 \\ -1 & \sqrt{3} \end{bmatrix}$ (b) $A = \begin{bmatrix} 100 & 1 \\ 0.1 & 0 \end{bmatrix}$

9-45. Which of the matrices in Exercise 9-31 are positive definite? Justify.

9-46. It can be shown [26] that $A_{n \times n}$ is positive definite if and only if the determinants of all upper left-hand submatrices are positive, that is,

$$\det(a_{ij})_{k \times k} > 0 \qquad \text{for } k = 1, \ldots, n$$

Use this result to show that A of Exercise 4-14 is positive definite, but B of Exercise 4-14 is not.

9-47. Suppose that $B = \begin{bmatrix} 2 & 4 \\ 4 & 14 \end{bmatrix}$, $C = \begin{bmatrix} 1 & 3 \\ 3 & 13 \end{bmatrix}$, and $L = \begin{bmatrix} 1 & 0 \\ 3 & 2 \end{bmatrix}$.

(a) Verify that $C = LL^T$ and use this to transform $B\mathbf{x} = \lambda C\mathbf{x}$ into $A\mathbf{v} = \lambda \mathbf{v}$.

(b) Find the eigenpairs of A in part (a) and use them to get all solutions of $B\mathbf{x} = \lambda C\mathbf{x}$.

Computer and Programming Exercises

9-48. (a) Write a subprogram MULT(n, A, $\mathbf{x}$, $\mathbf{y}$) that forms $\mathbf{y} = A\mathbf{x}$, where A is $n \times n$ and $\mathbf{x} = [x_1 \cdots x_n]^T$.

(b) Write a subprogram SCALE(n, $\mathbf{x}$, *BigXi*, $\mathbf{x}_{\text{scaled}}$) that finds *BigXi*, the dominant component of $\mathbf{x}$, and forms $\mathbf{x}_{\text{scaled}} = (1/BigXi)\mathbf{x}$.

(c) Use MULT and SCALE in a subprogram POWER(n, A, X, *BigXi*, *MaxIt*, termination test parameters) that implements the **iterate** steps of the Scaled Power Method Algorithm described in Figure 9.2-1. Test it using the example in Section 9.2A. Be sure that the subprogram returns A unchanged to the calling program.

9-49. Modify POWER of Exercise 9-48(c) by adding the parameters *Shift* and s to the parameter list. The modified program should be as in Exercise 9-48(c) if *Shift* = FALSE but should do the Shifted Inverse Power Method of Section 9.2D if *Shift* = TRUE. Test it using the examples in Sections 9.2C ($s = 0$) and 9.2D ($s = -\frac{5}{2}$).

9-50. Use any computer program(s) available to find to $5s$ all eigenpairs of the following matrices.

(a) Exercise 9-19(a)   (b) Exercise 9-19(b)   (c) Exercise 9-33(a)

(d) Exercise 9-33(b)   (e) A of Exercise 4-14   (f) B of Exercise 4-14

Using Pseudoprograms to Describe Algorithms

Pseudoprograms for numerical algorithms will be preceded by a heading and prologue of the following form:

Algorithm: Name (Comments about **Name**)
Purpose: (General description, introducing important variables)

This will be followed by the pseudocode itself, using the following structures and conventions.

Identifiers (Names of Variables) **I.1**

A SCALARS (NUMBERS)

These will be in *italics,* usually starting with an uppercase letter, for example,

$$Value, \ NumSig, \ DxMax, \ Tolerance$$

with no limit on the number of characters used. However, integer variables used as subscripts (indices) will generally be single, lowercase letters such as i, j, k, m, n.

B VECTORS (ONE-DIMENSIONAL ARRAYS)

These will be in **lowercase boldface**:

$$\mathbf{b}, \mathbf{c}, \mathbf{x}_0$$

Their components will be denoted by b_i, c_i, x_{0i} (or $x_{0,i}$), respectively.

C MATRICES (TWO-DIMENSIONAL ARRAYS)

These will be in *UPPERCASE ITALICS*:

$$A, B, DD$$

Their entries will be denoted by a_{ij}, b_{ij}, and $DD(i, j)$ respectively.

D FUNCTIONS

These will be denoted in the customary way, that is,

$$f(x), g(x), f(t, y)$$

The user is presumed to have the means of evaluating all functions.

I.2 Input

The values needed for the execution of an algorithm will be described using one or more statements of the form

GET (data list)

For example, an algorithm to scale an m by n array A by a scalar λ would begin with the statement

GET *Lamda, m, n, A*

NOTE: No attempt will be made to describe exactly how the entries of the data list are to be made available to an actual computer program implementing the algorithm. The user must decide if the data are to be read from a file, entered interactively from a terminal, passed as parameters (or in common) to a subroutine, or simply defined as constants within the program itself.

I.3 Output

Intermediate and final values that may be of interest to the user are indicated by statements of one of the forms:

OUTPUT (list of identifiers whose values are to be noted)
OUTPUT (message about the values of certain relevant identifiers)

For example, to indicate that **u** was created from **x**, we would use a statement of the form

$$\text{OUTPUT (original array: } \mathbf{x}\text{; new array: } \mathbf{u}\text{)}$$

OUTPUT messages will not be formatted. In particular, headings designed to improve the understandability of printed output will not be indicated in pseudoprograms.

NOTE: OUTPUT statements are included only to indicate where in the program certain numerical values are available. The reader implementing an algorithm should feel free to omit or augment these statements, depending on the nature of the implementation.

Assign Statements **I.4**

The back-arrow ($\leftarrow$) will be used to assign values to variables. For example, the effect of the statement

$$Det \leftarrow Det * a_{jj}$$

is to multiply the current value of *Det* by the current value of a_{jj} and store the result as the new current value of *Det*.

Statement Format **I.5**

A SIMPLE STATEMENTS

Generally, each line of pseudocode contains one statement. Statements will be written beginning at the left margin except if indented as described below. If several statements appear on one line, semicolons (;) will be used to separate them.

B COMPOUND STATEMENTS (BEGIN . . . END)

When several statements are to be executed either as a single block or not at all, we will "bracket" them between BEGIN and END (usually indented) either on one line as, for example,

$$\text{BEGIN} \quad a \leftarrow x; \quad L \leftarrow Y \quad \text{END}$$

or on several lines as, for example,

$$\begin{aligned} &\text{BEGIN} \\ &a \leftarrow x \\ &L \leftarrow Y \\ &\text{END} \end{aligned}$$

It is important to think of a compound statement as a *single* statement.

I.6 Flow of Control (IF Statements)

There are times when the next action to be taken depends on whether or not a certain condition holds, that is, whether a logical expression describing the condition is true or false.

A IF . . . THEN

The structure to be used to ensure that an action is taken only if a certain condition holds is

IF (logical expression) THEN (statement)

Here (statement) can be a compound statement, in which case we shall use the indented format

IF (logical expression) THEN
  (statement)

For example, the conditional statement

IF $Val > MaxVal$ THEN $Val \leftarrow MaxVal$

ensures that *Val* never exceeds *MaxVal*. If we also wanted to use the integer variable n to count the number of times $Val \leftarrow MaxVal$ was executed, we would replace this statement by

IF $Val \leftarrow MaxVal$ THEN
  BEGIN $Val \leftarrow MaxVal;$ $n \leftarrow n + 1$ END

after initializing n to 0 earlier in the program.

B IF . . . THEN . . . ELSE

This structure is used to ensure that one action is taken if a condition holds, and a *different* action is taken if it fails. Its format is

> IF (logical expression)
>   THEN [statement to be executed if (logical expression) is true]
>   ELSE (different statement to be executed if it is false)

Thus, for example, the statement

> IF $L*Y > 0$
>   THEN $Y \leftarrow -Y$
>   ELSE BEGIN $L \leftarrow 2*L$; $Y \leftarrow 0.5*Y$ END

will change the sign of Y if L and Y have the same sign, and will double L and halve Y otherwise.

Repetition Statements (Iteration)   **I.7**

A   COUNT CONTROLLED LOOPS

If a statement (possibly compound) is to be repeated a specified number of times, we shall use the structure

> DO FOR $Index = Istart$ TO $Istop$
>   (statement)

This will cause (statement) to be executed, with $Index = Istart$, then $Istart + 1, \ldots$, then $Istop$. *It will not be executed at all if Istart $>$ Istop.*†

Occasionally, we shall use the more complex structure

> DO FOR $Index = Istart$ TO $Istop$ STEP k
>   (statement)

where k can be negative. This structure will execute (statement) for $Index = Istart$, $Istart + k, \ldots$, until $Index$ "passes" $Istop$. Thus, for example, the program fragments

$Sum1 \leftarrow 0$; $Sign \leftarrow +1$ $Sum2 \leftarrow 0$; $Sign \leftarrow +1$
DO FOR $i = 2$ TO 5   DO FOR $i = 7$ TO 2 STEP -2
   BEGIN   BEGIN
   $Sum1 \leftarrow Sum1 + Sign*a_i$ $Sum2 \leftarrow Sum2 + Sign*a_i$
   $Sign \leftarrow -Sign$ $Sign \leftarrow -Sign$
   END   END

will form $Sum1 = a_2 - a_3 + a_4 - a_5$ and $Sum2 = a_7 - a_5 + a_3$, respectively.

† In FORTRAN, DO-loops are executed at least once, even if $Istart > Istop$. If it is important to avoid this, a statement of the form "IF (ISTART.GT.ISTOP) GO TO 100" must be inserted before the loop to branch around it.

B CONDITIONALLY CONTROLLED LOOPS

When the number of iterations is not known in advance, we must use a condition (as described by a logical expression) to control the repetition. This will be done in one of two ways:

DO WHILE (logical expression)   DO UNTIL (logical expression)
    (statement)   (statement)

These structures will cause the following to be repeated indefinitely:

IF (logical expression) is true   Execute (statement)
    THEN execute (statement)   IF (logical expression) is true
    ELSE exit loop   THEN exit loop

The DO WHILE structure will thus perform *no* iterations if (logical expression) is false upon entering the loop. On the other hand, the DO UNTIL structure always executes (statement) *at least once*. To illustrate this difference, suppose that we wanted *GreatInt* to be the greatest integer that is less than or equal to ($\leqslant$) a given positive real number x. Both program fragments

$GreatInt \leftarrow 0$ $GreatInt \leftarrow 0$
DO WHILE $GreatInt \leqslant x - 1$ DO UNTIL $GreatInt > x - 1$
    $GreatInt \leftarrow GreatInt + 1$ $GreatInt \leftarrow GreatInt + 1$

will calculate *GreatInt* correctly for $x \geqslant 1$. However, if $0 < x < 1$, then the DO WHILE fragment will (correctly) yield *GreatInt* $= 0$, whereas the DO UNTIL fragment will (incorrectly) yield *GreatInt* $= 1$.

C COUNT AND CONDITIONALLY CONTROLLED LOOPS

Most numerical methods require performing a calculation repeatedly until a desired accuracy is achieved. However, to prevent the unexpected (and possibly expensive) occurrence of "infinite loops," it is prudent to put an upper limit, say *MaxIt*, on the number of iterations that can be performed. This will be done using the following structure:

DO $k = 1$ TO *MaxIt* UNTIL **termination test** is satisfied
    BEGIN
    (statements describing the repeated calculation)
    {**termination test:** (logical expression)}
    END

Exit from such a loop will occur after *MaxIt* iterations, or sooner if **termination test** is satisfied, that is, if (logical expression) becomes true during the execution of the loop.

Descriptive (Informal) Statements and Phrases   **I.8**

Phrases given in English prose (rather than the formal structures described above) will be set in ordinary type. For example,

$$\text{GET termination test parameters}$$

will be used if the precise nature of the termination test parameters are to be left to the user or described in detail later. Similarly, the statement

$$\text{Solve } A\mathbf{x} = \mathbf{b} \text{ for } \overline{\mathbf{x}} = A^{-1}\mathbf{b}$$

leaves the precise method of solution up to the user.

Comments and Labels   **I.9**

Clarifying comments will be inserted in braces ($\{. \ . \ .\}$). For example,

$$\text{IF } L*Y > 0 \qquad \{L \text{ and } Y \text{ have the same sign}\}$$

leaves no doubt about the purpose of the logical expression $L*Y > 0$.

Also enclosed in braces will be **labels**. These are brief phrases, set in ***boldface italic*** or **boldface type**, placed immediately before the statements they describe. They are intended to serve as an outline of the major steps of the algorithm. For example, most numerical methods are *iterative* algorithms of the form:

> {*initialize*}
> (Statements preparing for the iteration)
> {*iterate*}
> DO FOR $k = 1$ TO *MaxIt* UNTIL **termination test** is satisfied
>   BEGIN
>   (Iterative step of the method, possibly using other **labels**)
>   {**termination test:** (logical expression)}
>   END
> OUTPUT (results of the iteration)

With the one exception of the **termination test** (which is actually executed at the end of each iteration, as in the preceding pseudoprogram outline), comments and labels in braces are *external* to the pseudoprogram. They are included only to help readability and can be removed without affecting the execution of the algorithm.

I.10 The STOP Statement (Algorithm Failure)

The word STOP will be used in a pseudoprogram if it becomes evident during the execution of an algorithm that the algorithm will fail. It is left to the reader implementing the STOP statement to record this occurrence (e.g., set a flag and/or print an error message) and terminate the execution in an appropriate way.

Review of the Basic Results of Calculus

Continuity II.1

A DEFINITION

Let f be a function that is defined in a neighborhood of the point a.
Then f is **continuous at** a if

$$\lim_{x \to a} f(x) = f(a)$$

Geometrically, the graph of f "unbroken" at $(a, f(a))$. Thus if f is continuous on a whole interval I, its graph is an unbroken curve over I. Two important results that say this more precisely are

B EXTREME VALUE THEOREM (EVT)

If f is continuous on a closed interval $[a, b]$, then f assumes a maximum value M and a minimum value m, that is, there exist points x_M and x_m in $[a, b]$ such that

$$m = f(x_m) \leqslant f(x) \leqslant f(x_M) = M \qquad \text{for any } x \text{ in } [a, b]$$

C INTERMEDIATE VALUE THEOREM (IVT)

If f is continuous on a closed interval $[a, b]$ and $m < c < M$, where m and M are as in the preceding theorem, then there exists at least one point ξ_c in $[a, b]$ such that

$$f(\xi_c) = c.$$

443

It follows from IVT that if f is continuous on $[a, b]$ and $f(a)$ and $f(b)$ have opposite sign, then f has at least one root between a and b.

Taken together, EVT and IVT say that *if f is continuous on a closed interval $[a, b]$, then its range is also a closed interval,* namely $[m, M]$; moreover if $\xi_1, \ldots, \xi_n$ lie in $[a, b]$ then, since $nm \leq \sum_{k=1}^{n} f(\xi_k) \leq nM$, there must be a point ξ in $[a, b]$ such that

$$f(\xi) = \frac{1}{n}\{f(\xi_1) + \cdots + f(\xi_n)\}$$

II.2 Derivatives

A DEFINITION

Let f be defined in a neighborhood of the point a.

The **derivative of f at a** is the number

$$f'(a) = \lim_{x \to a} \frac{\Delta f(x)}{\Delta x}, \qquad \text{where } \frac{\Delta f(x)}{\Delta x} = \frac{f(x) - f(a)}{x - a}$$

Recall that *differentiability at a guarantees continuity at a.*

Geometrically, $f'(a)$ gives the slope of the *tangent line* at $(a, f(a))$ on the graph of f. The number $\Delta f(x)/\Delta x$, called the **difference quotient of f** at $x = a$, gives the slope of the *secant line* from $(a, f(a))$ to the nearby point $(x, f(x))$ on the graph of f. Similarly,

$$f''(a) = \lim_{x \to a} \frac{\Delta f'(x)}{\Delta x} = \frac{d}{dx} f'(x)\Big|_{x=a}$$

indicates the *concavity* of the graph of f near $(a, f(a))$.

It is intuitively evident that the more derivatives of f we know *at $x = a$,* the better we can describe the behavior of the graph of f *near $(a, f(a))$.* This is made precise in the following important result.

B TAYLOR'S THEOREM WITH LAGRANGE'S FORM OF THE REMAINDER

If $f(a), f'(a), \ldots, f^{(n)}(a)$ exist and x is near a, then the nth **Taylor polynomial** (based at $x = a$), namely

$$P_n(x) = f(a) + \frac{f'(a)}{1!}(x - a) + \cdots + \frac{f^{(n)}(a)}{n!}(x - a)^n$$

can be used to approximate $f(x)$. Define the nth **remainder** $R_n(x)$ by

$$R_n(x) = f(x) - P_n(x) = \text{the error of approximating } f(x) \text{ by } P_n(x)$$

If $f^{(n)}$ is continuous on $[a, x]$ and $f^{(n+1)}$ exists on (a, x), then there exists at least one point ξ between a and x such that

$$R_n(x) = \frac{f^{(n+1)}(\xi)}{(n+1)!}(x-a)^{n+1}$$

This theorem generalizes the following familiar result (take $n = 0$ and $x = b$):

C   MEAN VALUE THEOREM (MVT)

If f is continuous on $[a, b]$ and differentiable on (a, b), then there exists at least one point ξ between a and b such that

$$f(b) = f(a) + f'(\xi)(b-a)$$

Suppose that f is continuous on $[a, b]$ and $f^{(n)}$ exists on (a, b) and it is known that f has $n + 1$ distinct roots, say $x_0, x_1, \ldots, x_n$, on $[a, b]$. Since $f(x_i) = 0$ for $i = 0$, $1, \ldots, n$, applying MVT to the n subintervals

$$[x_0, x_1], \quad [x_1, x_2], \quad \ldots, \quad [x_{n-1}, x_n]$$

shows that there are points ξ_i in (x_{i-1}, x_i) such that $f'(\xi_i) = 0$ for $i = 1, 2, \ldots, n$. In other words, f' has n distinct roots on (a, b). Continuing inductively, we see that $f'', f''', \ldots, f^{(n)}$ have respectively $n - 1, n - 2, \ldots, 1$ roots. This proves the following result.

D   GENERALIZED ROLLE'S THEOREM

If f is continuous and has $n + 1$ distinct roots on $[a, b]$ and $f^{(n)}$ exists on (a, b), then there exists a point ξ in (a, b) such that $f^{(n)}(\xi) = 0$.

E   TAYLOR SERIES REPRESENTATION

If f has a Taylor series representation

$$\circledast \quad f(x) = \sum_{n=0}^{\infty} \frac{f^{(n)}(a)}{n!}(x-a)^n = f(a) + \frac{f'(a)}{1!}(x-a) + \frac{f''(a)}{2!}(x-a)^2 + \cdots$$

with radius of convergence R, then f has continuous derivatives of all orders for $|x - a| < R$; in fact, on the interval of convergence, $f^{(k)}(x)$ is represented by the series obtained by differentiating the Taylor series $\circledast$ termwise k times, for $k = 1, 2, \ldots$.

II.3 *h*-Increment Notation

If we fix x instead of a, then a point near x will be denoted by $x + h$, where h is a small, nonzero increment. In this notation,

$$f \text{ is continuous at } x \quad \Longleftrightarrow \quad \lim_{h \to 0} f(x + h) = f(x)$$

and the definition of the derivative of f at x can be written as

$$f'(x) = \lim_{h \to 0} \frac{\Delta f(x)}{h}, \qquad \text{where } \frac{\Delta f(x)}{h} = \frac{f(x + h) - f(x)}{h}$$

Finally, the nth Taylor approximation (based at x) can be described as

$$f(x + h) \approx P_n(x + h) = f(x) + \frac{f'(x)}{1!} h + \cdots + \frac{f^{(n)}(x)}{n!} h^n$$

$$R_n(x + h) = f(x + h) - P_n(x + h) = \frac{f^{(n+1)}(x + \theta h)}{(n + 1)!} h^{n+1}, \qquad \text{where } 0 < \theta < 1$$

II.4 Definite Integrals

A DEFINITIONS

If f is defined on $[a, b]$ $(a < b)$, let

$$a = x_0 < x_1 < \cdots < x_k < \cdots < x_{n-1} < x_n = b$$

be a partition of $[a, b]$. A **Riemann sum** for this partition is

$$f(c_1) \Delta x_1 + f(c_2) \Delta x_2 + \cdots + f(c_n) \Delta x_n = \sum_{k=1}^{n} f(c_k) \Delta x_k$$

where

$$\Delta x_k = x_k - x_{k-1} \text{ (the length of } [x_{k-1}, x_k]) \qquad \text{and} \qquad x_{k-1} \leqslant c_k \leqslant x_k$$

The **definite integral of f on $[a, b]$** is defined as

$$\int_a^b f(x)\, dx = \lim_{\max \Delta x_k \to 0} \left(\sum_{k=1}^{n} f(c_k) \Delta x_k \right)$$

provided the limit exists, that is, provided that for any $\epsilon > 0$ you can find a $\delta > 0$ such that

$$\max \Delta x_k < \delta \quad \Rightarrow \quad \left| \int_a^b f(x)\, dx - \sum_{k=1}^n f(c_k)\, \Delta x_k \right| < \epsilon$$

no matter what values are used for c_k, $k = 1, 2, \ldots, n$. When this limit exists, f is **(Riemann) integrable** over $[a, b]$.

B   FUNDAMENTAL THEOREM OF CALCULUS

If f is continuous on $[a, b]$, then f is integrable on $[a, b]$ and

$$\int_a^b f(x)\, dx = F(x) \Big]_a^b = F(b) - F(a)$$

where $F(x)$ is any antiderivative of $f(x)$, that is, $F'(x) = f(x)$ on $[a, b]$.

C   GENERALIZED MEAN VALUE THEOREM FOR INTEGRALS

If f is continuous on $[a, b]$ and g is a nonnegative integrable function on $[a, b]$, then there exists a point c in (a, b) such that

$$\int_a^b f(x) g(x)\, dx = f(c) \int_a^b g(x)\, dx$$

When $\int_a^b f(x)\, dx$ is defined as in A above (i.e., as a limit of approximating Riemann sums), $\int_a^b f(x)\, dx$ is called a **proper** integral. It is easy to see that $\int_a^b f(x)\, dx$ *cannot* be proper if either $a = -\infty$ or $b = +\infty$, of if f is unbounded on $[a, b]$; **improper** integrals, defined for these situations, are described in Section 7.6.

Partial Derivatives II.5

Suppose that f is a function of several variables, say $x_1, x_2, \ldots, x_n$. It will be convenient to use the vector $\mathbf{x}$ to denote the n-tuple $(x_1, \ldots, x_n)$. Then

$$f(x_1, x_2, \ldots, x_n) \text{ will be abbreviated as } f(\mathbf{x})$$

A   DEFINITION

The **partial derivative of f with respect to x_j** at $\mathbf{x} = (x_1, \ldots, x_n)$ is the number

$$\frac{\partial f}{\partial x_j}(\mathbf{x}) = \lim_{h \to 0} \frac{f(\mathbf{x} + h e_j) - f(\mathbf{x})}{h}$$

where

$$\mathbf{x} + h\mathbf{e}_j = (x_1, \ldots, x_{j-1}, x_j + h, x_{j+1}, \ldots, x_n)$$

The number $\partial f(\mathbf{x})/\partial x_j$ is also denoted by $f_{x_j}(\mathbf{x})$

B THEOREM

If the second partials

$$f_{x_i x_j} = \frac{\partial}{\partial x_j}(f_{x_i}) \qquad \text{and} \qquad f_{x_j x_i} = \frac{\partial}{\partial x_i}(f_{x_j})$$

both exist in an open region (of n-space) on which one of them is continuous, then $f_{x_i x_j}(\mathbf{x}) = f_{x_j x_i}(\mathbf{x})$ for all $\mathbf{x}$ in this region.

This result allows us to find higher-order partials of f in any convenient order as long as the result is continuous.

C DEFINITION

If $f_{x_1}(\mathbf{x}), \ldots, f_{x_n}(\mathbf{x})$ all exist, then the **total differential of f at x** is defined by

$$df(\mathbf{x}) = f_{x_1}(\mathbf{x})\, dx_1 + f_{x_2}(\mathbf{x})\, dx_2 + \cdots + f_{x_n}(\mathbf{x})\, dx_n$$

where $dx_1, \ldots, dx_n$ can be viewed as increments from $x_1, \ldots, x_n$, respectively.

The following result justifies the use of the **linear approximation**

$$f(\mathbf{x} + \mathbf{dx}) = f(x_1 + dx_1, \ldots, x_n + dx_n) \approx f(\mathbf{x}) + df(\mathbf{x})$$

when the increment $\mathbf{dx} = (dx_1, \ldots, dx_n)$ is "small" in the sense that

$$\|\mathbf{dx}\| = \max\{|dx_1|, \ldots, |dx_n|\} \approx 0$$

D THEOREM

If all second partials of f are continuous in a neighborhood of $\mathbf{x}$, then the error of approximating $f(\mathbf{x} + \mathbf{dx})$ by $f(\mathbf{x}) + df(\mathbf{x})$ goes to zero faster than $d\mathbf{x}$ in the sense that

$$\lim_{\|\mathbf{dx}\| \to 0} \frac{f(\mathbf{x} + \mathbf{dx}) - [f(\mathbf{x}) + df(\mathbf{x})]}{\|d\mathbf{x}\|} = 0$$

An important consequence of this result is the following.

E   THEOREM (CHAIN RULE)

If f is a differentiable function of $x_1, x_2, \ldots, x_n$ and each of these is a function of $u_1, u_2, \ldots, u_m$, then for any $j = 1, 2, \ldots, m$,

$$\frac{\partial f}{\partial u_j} = \frac{\partial f}{\partial x_1} \cdot \frac{\partial x_1}{\partial u_j} + \frac{\partial f}{\partial x_2} \cdot \frac{\partial x_2}{\partial u_j} + \cdots + \frac{\partial f}{\partial x_n} \cdot \frac{\partial x_n}{\partial u_j}$$

where the partials with respect to u_j are at a fixed $\mathbf{u} = (u_1, \ldots, u_m)$ and the partials with respect to $x_1, \ldots, x_n$ are at the $\mathbf{x} = (x_1, \ldots x_n)$ corresponding to this fixed $\mathbf{u}$.

The proof of any results not included here can be found in [4].

Bibliography

1. Acton, F. S. (1970), *Numerical Methods That (Usually) Work.* Harper & Row, Publishers, New York.
2. Anton, H. (1977), *Elementary linear algebra,* 2nd ed. John Wiley & Sons, Inc., New York.
3. Bailey, P. B., L. F. Shampine, and P. E. Waltman (1968), *Nonlinear Two-Point Boundary-Value Problems.* Academic Press, Inc., New York.
4. Bartle, R. G. (1976), *The Elements of Real Analysis,* 2nd ed. John Wiley & Sons, Inc., New York.
5. Birkhoff, G., and G. Rota (1962), *Ordinary Differential Equations.* John Wiley & Sons, Inc., New York.
6. Brent, R. (1973), *Algorithms for Minimization Without Derivatives.* Prentice-Hall, Inc., Englewood Cliffs, N.J.
7. Broyden, C. G. (1965), "A class of methods for solving nonlinear simultaneous equations." *Mathematics of Computation,* **19,** 577–593.
8. Childs, S. B., and M. J. Maron (1976), "An efficient method for optimization under equality constraints," *Applied Mathematics and Computation,* **2,** 272–282.
9. Dahlquist, G., and Å. Björk (1974), *Numerical Methods.* Prentice-Hall, Inc., Englewood Cliffs, N.J.
10. De Boor, C. (1978), *A Practical Guide to Splines.* Springer Verlag New York, Inc., New York.
11. Draper, N. R., and H. Smith (1966), *Applied Regression Analysis.* John Wiley & Sons, Inc., New York.
12. Enright, W. H. (1974), "Optimal second derivative methods for stiff systems," R. A. Willoushby, ed., *Stiff Differential Equations,* Plenum Publishing Corporation, New York.
13. Enright, W. H., T. E. Hull, and B. Lindberg (1975), "Comparing numerical methods for stiff systems of O.D.E.'s." *BIT,* **15,** 10–48.
14. Fehlberg, E. (1970), "Klassiche Runge-Kutta Formeln vierter und niedrigerer Ordnung mit Schrittweiten-Kontrolle und ihre Anwendung auf Wärmeleitungs-probleme." *Computing,* **6,** 61–71.
15. Forsythe, G. E., M. A. Malcum, and C. B. Moler (1977), *Computer Methods for Mathematical Computation.* Prentice-Hall, Inc., Englewood Cliffs, N.J.

16. Forsythe, G. E., and C. B. Moler (1967), *Computer Solution of Linear Algebraic Systems.* Prentice-Hall, Inc., Englewood Cliffs, N.J.

17. Gear, C. W. (1971), *Numerical Initial-Value Problems in Ordinary Differential Equations.* Prentice-Hall, Inc., Englewood Cliffs, N.J.

18. Hamming, R. W. (1973), *Numerical Methods for Engineers and Scientists,* 2nd ed. McGraw-Hill Book Company, New York.

19. Henrici, P. (1963), *Error Propagation for Difference Methods.* John Wiley & Sons, Inc., New York.

20. Hildebrand, F. B. (1974), *Introduction to Numerical Analysis,* 2nd ed. McGraw-Hill Book Company, New York.

21. Hull, T. E., and W. H. Enright (1976), "Test results on initial-value methods for nonstiff ordinary differential equations." *SIAM Journal of Numerical Analysis,* **13,** No. 6, 944–961.

22. Hull, T. E., W. H. Enright, B. M. Fellen, and A. E. Sedgewick (1972), "Comparing numerical methods for ordinary differential equations." *SIAM Journal of Numerical Analysis,* **9,** No. 4, 603–637.

23. Isaacson, E., and H. B. Keller (1966), *Analysis of Numerical Methods.* John Wiley & Sons, Inc., New York.

24. Keller, H. B. (1968), *Numerical Methods for Two-Point Boundary-Value Problems.* John Wiley & Sons, Inc., New York.

25. Luke, Y. L. (1975), *Mathematical Functions and Their Approximations.* Academic Press, Inc., New York.

26. Noble, B., and J. W. Daniel (1977), *Applied Linear Algebra,* 2nd ed. Prentice-Hall, Inc., Englewood Cliffs, N.J.

27. Ortega, J. M. (1972), *Numerical Analysis—A Second Course.* Academic Press, Inc., New York.

28. Ortega, J. M., and W. C. Rheinboldt (1970), *Iterative Solution of Nonlinear Equations in Several Variables.* Academic Press, Inc., New York.

29. Ralston, A., and P. Rabinowitz (1978), *A First Course in Numerical Analysis,* 2nd ed. McGraw-Hill Book Company, New York.

30. Ralston, A., and H. S. Wilf, ed. (1967), *Numerical Methods for Digital Computers,* Vols. 1 and 2. John Wiley & Sons, Inc., New York.

31. Rorres, C., and H. Anton (1977), *Applications of Linear Algebra.* John Wiley & Sons, Inc., New York.

32. Schultz, M. H. (1966), *Spline Analysis.* Prentice-Hall, Inc., Englewood Cliffs, N.J.

33. Shampine, L. F., and C. W. Gear (1979), "A user's view of solving stiff ordinary differential equations." *SIAM Review,* **21,** No. 1, 1–17.

34. Stroud, A. H., and D. Secrest (1966), *Gaussian Quadrature Formulas.* Prentice-Hall, Inc., Englewood Cliffs, N.J.

35. Varga, R. S. (1962), *Matrix Iterative Analysis.* Prentice-Hall, Inc., Englewood Cliffs, N.J.

36. Wendroff, B. (1966), *Theoretical Numerical Analysis.* Academic Press, Inc., New York.

37. Wilkinson, J. H. (1963), *Rounding Errors in Algebraic Processes.* H. M. Stationery Office, London.

38. Wilkinson, J. H. (1965), *The Algebraic Eigenvalue Problem.* Clarendon Press, Oxford, England.

39. Wilkinson, J. H., and C. Reinsch (1971), *Handbook for Automatic Computation,* Vols. 1 and 2. Springer-Verlag New York, Inc., New York.

40. Young, D. M., and R. T. Gregory (1973), *A Survey of Numerical Mathematics,* Vols. 1 and 2. Addison-Wesley Publishing Co., Inc., Reading, Mass.

Answers to Selected Exercises

Chapter 1

1.

	$DQ[h]$	$DQ[h/r]$	$DQ[h/r^2]$	$DQ[h/r^3]$	$DQ[h/r^4]$
(a)	-0.951626	-0.990066	-0.998003	-0.999600	-0.999920
(b)	0.692778	0.703559	0.706222	0.706886	0.707052

3. $\frac{1}{8}, \ldots , \frac{7}{8}$. Those $\geq \frac{1}{2}$ are normalized.

4. **(b)** $-(10110.11)_2 = -(0.1011011)_2 \cdot 2^5$,   **(d)**, **(e)**, and **(f)**
$+(0.1)_2 = +(0.1)_2 \cdot 2^0$

5. **(a)** $5\frac{13}{16}$ **(b)** $-28\frac{3}{16}$ **(c)** 1.5 **(d)** -0.25

6. $M \cdot 2^c$, where $c = 0, -1$, or $+1$, and $M = \frac{1}{2}, \frac{5}{8}, \frac{3}{4}$, or $\frac{7}{8}$; $s = \frac{1}{4}$; $L = \frac{7}{4}$

7. **(d)** $S = e^6 \sum_{k=1}^{50} (e^{-0.2})^k = e^6 e^{-0.2} \sum_{k=0}^{49} (e^{-0.2})^k$. Now use (GS).

8. **(a)** (i) $1 + 2^2 + 2^3 + 2^{24}(1 + 2^2 + 2^3 + 2^6) = 13 + 2^{24}(77) = 1{,}291{,}845{,}645$;
(ii) $77/8192$
(b) (i) $2^1 + 2^3 + \cdots + 2^{29} = 2(1 + 4 + \cdots + 4^{14}) = 2(4^{15} - 1)/3 = 715{,}827{,}882$;
(ii) not normalized

10. **(a)** $-14.28, -14.3$ **(d)** $-0.00, -0.00300$ **(e)** $4394.95, 4390$

12. **(a)** $0.7426 \neq 0.7424$ **(b)** $1.932 \neq 1.933$

14. **(a)** $A \to d(\ln x)/dx$ as $h \to 0$
(c) negligible addition, loss of significance, and error magnification

16. **(a)** $A = (1 - \cos x)/\sin x$, or $\tan(\frac{1}{2}x)$; $B = 1/(\sqrt{x^2 + 1} + x)$; $C = -x/(1 + x)$

18. **(b)** $((-2x^2 + 1)x - 5)x^2 - 10, -9.4375$

19. $[\ln(x + h) - \ln x]/h = \ln(1 + u)/(ux) \approx [1 - u/2 + u^2/3 - \cdots + (-u)^{n-1}/n]/x$

20. **(a)** $\epsilon \doteq -0.0091$, $\rho = 11\epsilon$, $\% = 100\rho$ **(b)** $\epsilon \doteq 0.00091$, $\rho \doteq 0.01$, $\% \doteq 1.00$

21. **(a)** X's satisfy $x - \epsilon < X < x + \epsilon$, where $\epsilon = \frac{1}{2} \cdot 10^{-3} |x|$

22.

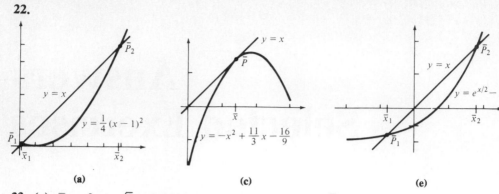

(a)   (c)   (e)

23. (a) $\bar{x}_1 = 3 - \sqrt{8} \doteq 0.1716$; cannot get $\bar{x}_2 = 3 + \sqrt{8} \doteq 5.828$ by Repeated Substitution.

(c) Can get $\bar{x} = \frac{4}{3}$ (slowly) if $x_0 > \bar{x}$; but not if $x_0 < \bar{x}$.

(e) Can get $\bar{x}_1 = -1.5361$; cannot get $\bar{x}_2 = 3.3567$ by Repeated Substitution.

24. (a) Linear (to $\bar{x}_1$)   (b) quadratic (to $\bar{x}_2$)   (c) neither (to $\bar{x}^+$)
(d) linear (to $\bar{x}_1$).

25. (a) 1.78   (b) 1.732

Chapter 2

1. (a) $x^5 - c$ (b) $\tan x - 2x$ (c) $\tan x - c$

2. (a) $e^x = 2 - x^2$ (b) $x^5 = 9 - x^2$ (c) $\cot x = x^2$ (d) $e^{-x} = \frac{1}{2}x - \frac{1}{2}$

4. (a) -1.3160 and 0.53727 (b) 1.4690 (c) 0.89521 (d) 1.4631

8. (a) (i) -1.2248, 1.4702, -12.336; (ii) -27, -18.058, -12.125

9. (b) $\bar{x} \doteq 0.729402\ [F'(\bar{x}) = 0]$ (c) $F(x)_{\max} = F(0) = 1$, $F(x)_{\min} = F(\bar{x}) \doteq -3.9988$

10. 0.65453

11. (a) 5.82842 (b) 1.25000 (c) 1.33333 (d) 1.29586 (e) 3.35669

12. (a) 1.05, 0.925, 0.9875, 1.01875 (b) 1.1122, 1.0328, 1.0087, 1.0022
(c) Neither

13. (a) 0.98634 (b) 1.6453

14. The smallest integer greater than $\ln[(b - a)/\epsilon]/\ln 2$

15. Both formulas suffer from loss of significance and error magnification when both x_{k-1} and x_k are near $\bar{x}$. But the effect on $x_k + \Delta x_{\sec}$ is less likely to be serious. (Why?)

19. 0.99980; one additional significant digit

20. $(x_2)_{\text{improved}} = 8.8769375$ approximates $\bar{x} \doteq 8.8769364$ to about $7s$!

	x_1	x_2	x_3	x_4	$(x_4)_{\text{improved}}$
21. (a)	-0.205714	-0.139956	-0.094650	-0.063731	0.002717
(b)	-0.234046	-0.178752	-0.136971	-0.104386	-0.011075
22. (a)	3.03086	3.01566	3.00789	3.00396	2.99994
(b)	3.03882	3.02410	3.01508	3.00936	2.99945

24. (a) $m = 3$ **(b)** $\Delta x_k / \Delta x_{k-1} \approx \frac{2}{3}$ **(c)** yes
25. (a) $m = 2$ **(b)** $\Delta x_k / \Delta x_{k-1} \approx \frac{1}{2}$ **(c)** yes
27. The function $f(x) = x^{1/3}$ has no Taylor series based at $\bar{x} = 0$.

29.

	r_1	s_1	r_2	s_2
(a)	$\frac{4}{3}$	$-\frac{1}{3}$	-1.12397	-0.332415
(c)	1.93099	-1.29774	1.84501	-0.937337

34. (a) $0.113343, 0.329130$
36. (a) $2, 2, \frac{1}{2} \pm \frac{1}{2}i$ **(c)** $-\frac{1}{2}, 1, 2, \frac{1}{2}(1 \pm \sqrt{\frac{1}{5}})$

Chapter 3

1. (c) (i) $\frac{1}{-1}\begin{bmatrix} 3 & 2 \\ 2 & 1 \end{bmatrix}$; **(ii)** $\frac{1}{-3}\begin{bmatrix} 1 & -1 \\ -1 & -2 \end{bmatrix}$; $A^{-1}B^{-1} = \frac{1}{3}\begin{bmatrix} 1 & -7 \\ 1 & -4 \end{bmatrix}$

(iii) $(AB)^{-1} = \begin{bmatrix} -4 & -1 \\ 7 & 1 \end{bmatrix}^{-1} = \frac{1}{3}\begin{bmatrix} 1 & 1 \\ -7 & -4 \end{bmatrix} = B^{-1}A^{-1} \neq A^{-1}B^{-1}$

2. (a) $AB^{-1} - BA^{-1}$ **(d)** $B^{-1} + A^{-1}$ **(e)** $B + B^{-1}$

8. (a) $[A \ : \ \mathbf{b}] = \begin{bmatrix} 1 & 2 & : & -3 \\ 4 & 3 & : & 18 \end{bmatrix}$, $\mathbf{x} = \begin{bmatrix} x \\ y \end{bmatrix}$

(b) $A^{-1} = \frac{-1}{5}\begin{bmatrix} 3 & -2 \\ -4 & 1 \end{bmatrix}$, $A^{-1}\mathbf{b} = \begin{bmatrix} 9 \\ -6 \end{bmatrix}$

10. (a) $\bar{\mathbf{c}} = \begin{bmatrix} 3 & -2 & \frac{1}{3} \end{bmatrix}^T$ **(c)** $\bar{\mathbf{c}} = \begin{bmatrix} -1 & -1 & 0 & 0 \end{bmatrix}^T$
11. (a) $\bar{\mathbf{x}} = \begin{bmatrix} \frac{1}{3} & -2 & 3 \end{bmatrix}^T$ **(c)** $\bar{\mathbf{x}} = \begin{bmatrix} 3 & 0 & 2 & -1 \end{bmatrix}^T$
12. (a) $4, 9, 25, 100, 10{,}000$ **(b)** $2, 6, 20, 90, 9900$
13. (a) $ad = 4, ae = 3, bd = 2, be + cf = 2$

(b) (i) $\begin{bmatrix} 4 & 0 \\ 2 & \frac{1}{2} \end{bmatrix}\begin{bmatrix} 1 & \frac{3}{4} \\ 0 & 1 \end{bmatrix}$; **(ii)** $\begin{bmatrix} 1 & 0 \\ \frac{1}{2} & 1 \end{bmatrix}\begin{bmatrix} 4 & 3 \\ 0 & \frac{1}{2} \end{bmatrix}$; **(iii)** $\begin{bmatrix} 2 & 0 \\ 1 & \sqrt{\frac{1}{2}} \end{bmatrix}\begin{bmatrix} 2 & \frac{3}{2} \\ 0 & \sqrt{\frac{1}{2}} \end{bmatrix}$

14. (b) (i) $\begin{bmatrix} 2 & 0 \\ 1 & -\frac{1}{2} \end{bmatrix}\begin{bmatrix} 1 & \frac{1}{2} \\ 0 & 1 \end{bmatrix}$; **(ii)** $\begin{bmatrix} 1 & 0 \\ \frac{1}{2} & 1 \end{bmatrix}\begin{bmatrix} 2 & 1 \\ 0 & -\frac{1}{2} \end{bmatrix}$; **(iii)** not possible

15. (b) (i) $\begin{bmatrix} 4 & 0 \\ -2 & 1 \end{bmatrix}\begin{bmatrix} 1 & -\frac{1}{2} \\ 0 & 1 \end{bmatrix}$; **(ii)** $\begin{bmatrix} 1 & 0 \\ -\frac{1}{2} & 1 \end{bmatrix}\begin{bmatrix} 4 & -2 \\ 0 & 1 \end{bmatrix}$; **(iii)** $\begin{bmatrix} 2 & 0 \\ -1 & 1 \end{bmatrix}\begin{bmatrix} 2 & -1 \\ 0 & 1 \end{bmatrix}$
18. *Note:* To get A from $\hat{A}\ (=\hat{L}\hat{U})$, perform row interchanges in *reverse* order. For example, in (b), perform $\rho_2 \rightleftarrows \rho_3$ *then* $\rho_1 \rightleftarrows \rho_3$ on $\hat{A}$ to get A.
19. (a) Partial Pivoting   **(b)** neither   **(c)** both   **(d)** Basic Pivoting
(e) neither
20. (a) $\begin{bmatrix} -2 & 1 & 0 \end{bmatrix}^T$ **(b)** $\begin{bmatrix} -5 & -1 & 1 \end{bmatrix}^T$ **(c)** $\begin{bmatrix} 2 & 0 & 1 & 0 \end{bmatrix}^T$
(d) $\begin{bmatrix} 2 & -1 & -1 & 1 \end{bmatrix}^T$ **(e)** $\begin{bmatrix} 3 & 1 & -1 \end{bmatrix}^T$ **(f)** $\begin{bmatrix} 2 & -2 & 3 & 3 \end{bmatrix}^T$
23. (a) $\begin{bmatrix} 0 & 2 & -1 \end{bmatrix}^T$ **(b)** $\begin{bmatrix} -1 & 1 & 0 \end{bmatrix}^T$ **(c)** $\begin{bmatrix} 2 & 0 & 1 & -1 \end{bmatrix}^T$
(d) $\begin{bmatrix} 0 & -1 & -3 & 2 \end{bmatrix}^T$
29. (a) $\begin{bmatrix} 1 & 1 & -1 \end{bmatrix}^T$ **(b)** $\begin{bmatrix} 2 & -2 & 2 & -1 \end{bmatrix}^T$

31. (a) $(-1)^n\alpha$ **(b)** $\alpha\beta$ **(c)** $3^n\alpha\beta^2$ **(d)** α/β **(e)** $2^n\alpha$ **(f)** α^6/β^3

36. (a) 5   **(b)** -15 **(c)** 20   **(d)** 14

39. (a) $\bar{\mathbf{x}}_1 = [-2 \quad 1 \quad 0]^T, \bar{\mathbf{x}}_2 = [0 \quad 1 \quad -2]^T$

    (c) $\bar{\mathbf{x}}_1 = [\frac{5}{4} \quad -\frac{1}{4} \quad \frac{1}{2}]^T, \bar{\mathbf{x}}_2 = [-1 \quad \frac{1}{2} \quad -\frac{1}{2}]^T, \bar{\mathbf{x}}_3 = [-\frac{1}{2} \quad \frac{1}{2} \quad 0]^T$

    (d) $\bar{\mathbf{x}}_1 = [2 \quad 1 \quad 0 \quad 0]^T, \bar{\mathbf{x}}_2 = [1 \quad -1 \quad -1 \quad 1]^T$

40. (a) $\begin{bmatrix} 3 & -1 & -\frac{1}{2} \\ -1 & \frac{1}{2} & 0 \\ 1 & -\frac{1}{2} & \frac{1}{2} \end{bmatrix}$ **(b)** $\begin{bmatrix} \frac{9}{2} & -2 & 5 \\ \frac{9}{2} & -2 & 4 \\ -2 & 1 & -2 \end{bmatrix}$ **(c)** $\frac{1}{4}\begin{bmatrix} 5 & -4 & -2 \\ -1 & 2 & 2 \\ 2 & -2 & 0 \end{bmatrix}$

    (d) $\frac{1}{2}\begin{bmatrix} 17 & -4 & -1 & -1 \\ 23 & -6 & -1 & -2 \\ -11 & 2 & 1 & 1 \\ 8 & -2 & 0 & -1 \end{bmatrix}$ **(e)** $\frac{1}{4}\begin{bmatrix} 16 & -23 & -2 & 10 \\ 8 & -16 & 0 & 6 \\ -4 & 3 & 2 & -2 \\ 4 & -6 & 0 & 2 \end{bmatrix}$

Chapter 4

1. Using either BP or PP, the "forback matrix" $[\hat{L}\backslash\hat{U} : \hat{\mathbf{b}} : \bar{\mathbf{c}} : \bar{\mathbf{x}}]$ is

    (a) $\begin{bmatrix} \boxed{1.34} & -3.99 & : & -3.98 & : & -2.97 & : & 0.220 \\ -0.252 & \boxed{-0.01} & : & 0.74 & : & 0.8 & : & 0.800 \end{bmatrix}$

    (b) $\begin{bmatrix} \boxed{1.34} & -3.99 & : & -3.98 & : & -2.97 & : & 3.17 \\ -0.252 & \boxed{-0.00548} & : & 0.74 & : & 1.54 & : & 1.54 \end{bmatrix}$

$\bar{\mathbf{x}}_{SPP}$ is $[5.00 \quad 2.00]^T$ either with or without PEP.

2. $\bar{\mathbf{x}}_{BP} = [-0.1 \quad -1.98]^T$ in part (a); $[-0.0282 \quad -1.99]^T$ in part (b); $\bar{\mathbf{x}}_{PP} = \bar{\mathbf{x}}_{SPP} = [-0.01 \quad -2]^T$ in parts (a) and (b)

3. (b) and **(c)** [*Hint:* Augment $\hat{A}$ with a row-scale column $\hat{\mathbf{s}}$.]

4. (a) Same as that for Basic Pivoting [Exercise 3-17(a) (i)]

    (b) $\begin{bmatrix} \boxed{2} & -\frac{1}{2} & 1 \\ 1 & \boxed{\frac{5}{2}} & 0 \\ 0 & 1 & \boxed{3} \end{bmatrix}$ $(\rho_1 \rightleftarrows \rho_2)$ **(c)** $\begin{bmatrix} \boxed{1} & -1 & -2 & 0 \\ -1 & \boxed{2} & 0 & 0 \\ 2 & 2 & \boxed{4} & \frac{3}{2} \\ 0 & 2 & 1 & \frac{5}{2} \end{bmatrix}$ $\begin{matrix}(\rho_1 \rightleftarrows \rho_2)\\(\rho_2 \rightleftarrows \rho_4)\end{matrix}$

    (d) $\begin{bmatrix} \boxed{3} & 0 & -\frac{1}{3} & 0 \\ 0 & \boxed{-1} & 1 & 0 \\ 1 & 0 & \boxed{-\frac{5}{3}} & -\frac{3}{5} \\ 0 & 2 & -2 & \boxed{\frac{14}{5}} \end{bmatrix}$ $\begin{matrix}(\rho_1 \rightleftarrows \rho_3)\\(\rho_2 \rightleftarrows \rho_4)\end{matrix}$

5. (a) $\frac{1}{3}$ **(b)** $\frac{1}{9}$ **(c)** $\frac{1}{2}$ **(d)** $\frac{1}{2}$ **(e)** $\frac{1}{2}$

6. $C_p(A) \doteq 0.02/5.34 \doteq 0.0037$; A is ill conditioned.

7. $C_p(A) \doteq 1.15/2.32 \doteq 0.500$; A is not ill conditioned.

10. $A_1 \doteq \begin{bmatrix} -2.28 & 0.96 \\ 1.56 & -0.48 \end{bmatrix}$, $A_2 \doteq \begin{bmatrix} -2.0688 & 0.9984 \\ 1.5216 & -0.4992 \end{bmatrix}$,

$$A_3 \doteq \begin{bmatrix} -2.0020 & 1 \\ 1.5006 & -0.5 \end{bmatrix}, \qquad A_4 = A^{-1} \ (5s)$$

11. (a) $[3 \quad 1 \quad 2]^T$ **(b)** $[2 \quad 3 \quad 1]^T$ **(c)** $[1 \quad 3 \quad 2]^T$ **(d)** $[1 \quad 2 \quad 3 \quad 4]^T$
   (e) $[4 \quad 1 \quad 3 \quad 2]^T$

13. (a) Solving (E_1) for x_2, then (E_2) for x_1, then (E_3) for x_3 gives:
   $x_1 = [\frac{11}{16} \quad \frac{1}{2} \quad -\frac{61}{48}]^T$, $x_2 = [0.69401 \quad 0.94097 \quad -1.1217]^T$
   (b) Solving (E_1) for x_4, (E_2) for x_1, (E_3) for x_2, (E_4) for x_3, then (E_5) for x_5
   gives: $x_1 = [\frac{3}{5} \quad -\frac{1}{6} \quad -\frac{13}{9} \quad \frac{1}{3} \quad \frac{103}{120}]^T$;
   $x_2 = [1.0606 \quad 0.13056 \quad -1.0731 \quad 0.077778 \quad 1.0478]^T$

14. (b) For $Ax = [0 \quad -1 \quad 5]^T$: $x_1 = [0 \quad -\frac{1}{2} \quad \frac{4}{5}]^T$, $x_2 = [0.62 \quad -0.63 \quad 0.996]^T$;
   for $Bx = [-2 \quad -3 \quad 2]^T$: $x_1 = [-1 \quad 0 \quad 1]^T$, $x_2 = [-\frac{1}{2} \quad \frac{1}{8} \quad \frac{7}{4}]^T$

15. (a) Sketch $y = e^{x/2}$ and $y = 1/(x - 1)$; one root
   (b) Sketch $x = 9 - y^2$ and $y = \ln x$; two roots
   (c) Sketch $(\frac{1}{2}x)^2 - (\frac{1}{2}y)^2 = 1$ and $y = 2 \sin x - 1$; two roots

16. (a) $\bar{x}_1 \doteq [1.4777 \quad 2.0935]^T$
   (b) $\bar{x}_1 \doteq [5.8685 \quad 1.7696]^T$, $\bar{x}_2 \doteq [0.050206 \quad -2.9916]^T$
   (c) $\bar{x}_1 \doteq [2.1207 \quad 0.70517]^T$, $\bar{x}_2 \doteq [-2.7124 \quad -1.8323]^T$

17. (a) $\begin{bmatrix} 2x & -3\cos y & -2z \\ -2y & -2x & 1 \\ e^{x+y} & e^{x+y} & 2z \end{bmatrix}$ **(b)** $\begin{bmatrix} 0 & -3 & 0 \\ 0 & 0 & 1 \\ 1 & 1 & 0 \end{bmatrix} \begin{bmatrix} dx \\ dy \\ dz \end{bmatrix} = \begin{bmatrix} 0 \\ -1 \\ -1 \end{bmatrix}$; $x_1 = x_0 + dx = \begin{bmatrix} -1 \\ 0 \\ -1 \end{bmatrix}$

18. (a) See where circle radius a meets hyperbola $y = 1/x$. (i) $a > \sqrt{2}$; (ii) $a = \sqrt{2}$;
   (iii) $a < \sqrt{2}$
   (c) $x_1 = [2 \quad \frac{1}{2}]^T$, $x_2 = [\frac{29}{15} \quad \frac{31}{60}]^T$, $x_3 \doteq [1.93185 \quad 0.517637]^T$ (quadratic)
   (d) $x_1 = [\frac{3}{2} \quad 1]^T$, $x_2 = [1.15 \quad 0.9]^T$, $x_3 \doteq [1.0628 \quad 0.937805]^T$ (linear)

19. (a) $[0.86639 \quad -2.5776]^T$ **(b)** $[-0.61062 \quad 2.1483]^T$

20. $[0.58930 \quad 0.69455]^T$

Chapter 5

1. (a) $\hat{L}(x) = 2.85 - 1.5x$; $E(\hat{L}) = 0.09$ **(b)** $\hat{L}(x) = -14.7 + 9.5x$; $E(\hat{L}) = 1.1$

3. (a) $\alpha(\Sigma x_k^{2\beta}) - \Sigma y_k x_k^\beta = 0$; $\alpha(\Sigma x_k^{2\beta} \ln x_k) - \Sigma y_k x_k^\beta \ln x_k = 0$
   (c) $\alpha\Sigma e^{-2x_k} + \beta\Sigma e^{-5x_k} = \Sigma y_k e^{-x_k}$; $\alpha\Sigma e^{-5x_k} + \beta\Sigma e^{-8x_k} = \Sigma y_k e^{-4x_k}$ (linear)

4.

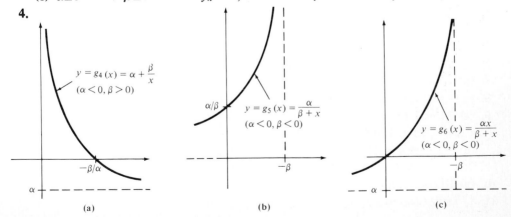

(a)   (b)   (c)

5. (b) $g(x) \doteq 1.9942e^{0.47962x}$; $h(x) \doteq 2.3032x^{1.3995}$

6. (b) $g(x) \doteq -4.5772/(-6.2710 + x)$; $h(x) \doteq -3.1829x/(-7.4254 + x)$

7. (b) $g(x) \doteq 0.21887 + 2.2075 \ln x$; $h(x) \doteq 5.0403 - 5.2902/x$

8. (b) $g(x) \doteq -17.499/(-6.1252 + x)$; $h(x) \doteq 0.36979e^{0.89295x}$

9. On semilog paper: $\alpha e^{\beta x}$ and $\alpha + \beta \ln x$; on log-log paper: αx^β

12. (a) $\hat{g}(x) = 0.15x^2 - 1.95x + 3$; $E(\hat{g}) = 0$; $R(\hat{g}) = 1$ (exact fit)

   (b) $\hat{g}(x) = 5.3571x^2 - 5.5x - 4.6286$; $E(\hat{g}) \doteq 0.4571$; $R(\hat{g}) \doteq 0.9877$

13. (a) $\hat{g}_2(x) \doteq 4.6226x - 23.614$; $R(\hat{g}_2) \doteq 0.57198$

   (b) $\hat{g}_3(x) \doteq 1.9994x^2 - 13.372x + 6.3768$; $R(\hat{g}_3) \doteq 1.0000$

14. (a) $\hat{g}_3(x) \doteq -0.00095906x^2 - 0.38566x + 4.3244$; $R(\hat{g}_3) \doteq 0.5815$

   (b) $\hat{g}_4(x) \doteq 0.013661x^3 - 0.39056x^2 + 2.4262x + 0.95133$; $R(\hat{g}_4) \doteq 0.9924$

15. $\hat{g}(x) \doteq 0.50078 + 4.8668 \sin (\pi x/10)$; $R(\hat{g}) = 0.9673$

16. $\hat{g}(x) \doteq 0.43973 + 4.8724 \sin (\pi x/10) + 0.76033 \cos (\pi x/10)$; $R(\hat{g}) = 0.9985$

17. $\hat{g}(x) \doteq 0.50132 + 4.8503 \sin (\pi x/10) + 0.19626 \sin (2\pi x/10)$; $R(\hat{g}) = 0.9693$

18. $\hat{g}(x) \doteq 0.0375x^2 - 109.75x + 92125$

19. $X_1 = -2$, $X_2 = -1.2$, $X_3 = 0$, $X_4 = +1.2$, $X_5 = +2$; $C_p(A) \doteq 0.1036$

20. (a) $r(x) = (1 - x/2 + x^2/12)/(1 + x/2 + x^2/12)$

   (b) $r(x) = (x - 7x^3/60)/(1 + x^2/20)$

21. (a) (i) $p_{econ}(x) = 191/192 - x + 13x^2/24 - x^3/6$;

   (ii) $p_{econ}(x) = 191/192 - 9x/8 + 13x^2/24$

   (b) (i) and (ii): $p_{econ}(x) = (383x - 60x^3)/384$

22. (a) (i) $p_{econ}(x) = -\frac{1}{2} - x + 2x^2/3 - x^3/6$; (ii) $p_{econ}(x) = -\frac{1}{2} - 3x/2 + 2x^2/3$

   (b) (i) and (ii): $p_{econ}(x) = (23x - 3x^3)/24$

23. (a) $R_4(x) = -e^{-c}x^5/5!$ (i) $|R_4(x)| \leq e^{1/2}(\frac{1}{2})^5/5!$; (ii) $|R_4(x)| \leq e^1(1)^5/5!$

   (b) $R_6(x) = x^7(\cos c)/7!$ (i) $|R_6(x)| \leq 1(\frac{1}{2})^7/7!$ (ii) $|R_6(x)| \leq 1(1)^7/7!$

Chapter 6

1. $p_{1,3}(x) = 6x^2 - 11x + 6$

2. (a) $1\dfrac{(x-2)}{(0-2)} + 1\dfrac{(x-0)}{(2-0)}$

   (b) $1\dfrac{(x-2)(x-3)}{(0-2)(0-3)} + 1\dfrac{(x-0)(x-3)}{(2-0)(2-3)} + 10\dfrac{(x-0)(x-2)}{(3-0)(3-2)}$

4. (a) (i) 0; (ii) 1; (iii) 0; (iv) 1; (v) 0

6. $P_2, \ldots , P_5$ lie on a parabola or straight line; P_3, P_4, P_5 lie on a straight line.

7. (b) $-20, -1, -\frac{1}{4}, 2, -4$

8. $y_0 = 20$, $y_1 = 31$, $y_2 = -2$, $y_3 = -1$, $y_4 = 146$

9. (a) $21 - 14(x + 2) + 4(x + 2)(x + 1) - 1(x + 2)(x + 1)x +$
   $1(x + 2)(x + 1)x(x - 1)(x - 2)$

   (d) $-3 - 4(x - 1) + 1(x - 1)x - 1(x - 1)x(x + 1) +$
   $1(x - 1)x(x + 1)(x - 2)(x + 2)$

10. (a) $[[[1(x - 2)(x - 1) - 1]x + 4](x + 1) - 14](x + 2) + 21$; -71

11. 1, 19, 0 (degree $p_{0,4}(x) \leq 3$)

13. (c) $[[[2(x-2)-3]x+18](x+2)-40](x+1)+6$; 4

17. (a) $\hat{p}_0 = 0.5$, $\hat{p}_1 \doteq 0.53965$, $\hat{p}_2 \doteq 0.54005$, $\hat{p}_3 \doteq 0.53989$, $\hat{p}_4 \doteq 0.53987$, $\hat{p}_5 \doteq 0.53988$

18. (a) $\hat{p}_4(-0.5) \doteq 0.30932$ **(b)** $1 - \hat{p}_5(0.5) \doteq 0.30858$

19. (a) $\hat{p}_5(0.52) \doteq 0.69848$ **(b)** $\hat{p}_4(0.22) \doteq 0.58675$ **(c)** $\hat{p}_3(1.4) \doteq 0.92000$

21. (a) $\hat{p}_4(0.55) \doteq -0.597$ **(b)** $\hat{p}_3(0.86) \doteq -0.152$ **(c)** $\hat{p}_2(1.3) \doteq 0.21$

23. (a) $\hat{p}_2(13) = 3.629$. Only $2s$ accuracy is evident from the $\hat{p}_m(13)$ values.

25. (a) $\hat{x}_0 = 0.861572$, $\hat{x}_1 = 3.432254$, $\hat{x}_2 = 7.067746$, $\hat{x}_3 = 9.638428$

27. Yes. The Δ^2 column is about constant (≈ 2.0).

29. (a) For (I), (III), and (IV), $s(x) = x^3$ is the unique interpolating spline.

    (b) (I) $\begin{bmatrix} 6 & 1 \\ 1 & 4 \end{bmatrix}\begin{bmatrix} \sigma_1 \\ \sigma_2 \end{bmatrix} = \begin{bmatrix} 6 \\ 24 \end{bmatrix}$; (II) $\begin{bmatrix} 8 & 1 \\ 1 & 5 \end{bmatrix}\begin{bmatrix} \sigma_1 \\ \sigma_2 \end{bmatrix} = \begin{bmatrix} -18 \\ 36 \end{bmatrix}$;

    (III) $\begin{bmatrix} 4 & -1 \\ 0 & 3 \end{bmatrix}\begin{bmatrix} \sigma_1 \\ \sigma_2 \end{bmatrix} = \begin{bmatrix} -6 \\ 18 \end{bmatrix}$; (IV) $\begin{bmatrix} 5 & 1 \\ 1 & \frac{7}{2} \end{bmatrix}\begin{bmatrix} \sigma_1 \\ \sigma_2 \end{bmatrix} = \begin{bmatrix} 6 \\ 21 \end{bmatrix}$

    (c) For (I), (III), and (IV) $\sigma_k = d^2(x^3)/dx^2$ at x_k for $k = 0, 1, 2, 3$; that is, $\sigma_0 = -12$, $\sigma_1 = 0$, $\sigma_2 = 6$, $\sigma_3 = 12$. For (II), $\sigma_0 = \sigma_1 \doteq -3.2308$, $\sigma_2 = \sigma_3 \doteq 7.8462$

30. (a) $\sigma_0 = \sigma_4 = 0$, $\sigma_1 \doteq -0.52091$, $\sigma_2 \doteq 0.055766$, $\sigma_3 \doteq -0.025904$

    (b) $x_2 < z = 7 < x_3$ ($k = 2$); $s(7) = q_2(7) \doteq 2.5634 \approx \sqrt{7}$

32. (a) $\sigma_0 = -0.59838$, $\sigma_1 = -0.43935$, $\sigma_2 = 0.037737$, $\sigma_3 = -0.017147 = \sigma_4$

    (b) $s(7) = q_2(7) \doteq 2.5746 \approx \sqrt{7}$

33. (a) $c_{11} = c_{21} = 0$, $c_{31} = 1$ **(c)** $c_{12} \doteq 0.12864$, $c_{22} \doteq 0.027883$, $c_{32} \doteq -0.0027223$

Chapter 7

1. (a) $h - h^2/2 + h^3/3$ **(b)** $1 - h^2/2 + h^4/24$

2. $\Delta f(x)/h = 0.70298$; $\delta f(x)/2h = 1.9282$ ($\delta f(x)/2h$ will $\approx f'(x)$ better as $h \to 0$)

4. Note from (12) of Section 7.1B that $F[h] = \Delta f(x)/h$ is $O(h^2)$ if $f''(x) = 0$.

5. $F_1[0.1] = 0.95833$, $F_1[0.05] = 0.2$, $F_2[0.05] = 0.17554$

6. $F[0.6] = -1.4$, $F[0.2] = -1.8$, $F_1[0.2] = -2$ (exact). See (12) of Section 7.1B.

7. $F[0.2] = -1.0205$, $F[0.05] = -1.0013$, $F_1[0.05] = -0.99997$

9. $F[0.2] = 1.5811$, $F[0.1] = 1.1575$, $F_1[0.1] = 1.0163$ (worse!)

10. $F[1] = 8$, $F[0.5] = 5$, $F_1[0.5] = 4$ (exact)

$F[0.5]$	$F[0.1]$	$F[0.05]$	$F_1[0.1]$	$F_1[0.05]$	$F_2[0.05]$
12. 1.2974	1.0517	1.0254	0.99028	0.99913	1.0021
13. 1.0422	1.0017	1.0004	0.99998	1.0000	1.0000
14. 0.70711	0.31623	0.22361	0.21851	0.13099	0.10181

15. (a) Using (18a): $F[0.5] = -8.62$, $F[1] = -6.46$, $F[2] = -1.08$; $F_1[0.5] = -9.34$, $F_1[1] = -8.2533$; $F_2[0.5] = -9.495$

    (b) Using (20b) [or (19b) and Richardson]: $F[0.5] = 2.56$

(c) Using (20a): $F[0.5] = 2.567$
(d) Using (18b): $F[-0.5] = -5.12$, $F[-1] = -5.36$; $F_1[-0.5] = -5.04$

16. (a) Using (18b): $F[2] = 0$ (b) Using (20a): $F[2] = -6$
(c) Using (18c): $F[-2] = -0.75$
(d) Using (18a): $F[-2] = 1$, $F[-4] = -5$; $F_1[-2] = 3$

19. (a) (i) 0.26965; (ii) 0.43279 (Exact is 0.28868.)

26. (a) 9   (b) 10.47   (c) 9.49   (d) 9.49   (e) 17.773
(f) $3.6 + 9.90375 \doteq 13.50$

27. (a) 888   (b) 307   (c) 299.5   (d) 246.5

28. (a)

h	$T_0 = T$	$T_1 = S$	T_2
4	-2048		
2	-1088	-768	
1	-788	-688	$-682\frac{2}{3}$

(b)

h	$T_0 = T$	$T_1 = S$	T_2
$\frac{1}{2}$	0.645235		
$\frac{1}{4}$	0.635409	0.632134	
$\frac{1}{8}$	0.632943	0.632121	0.632121

(c) 0.922507 ($h = \frac{1}{4}$, i.e., 4 panels)   (d) Exactly 12.8 ($h = 1$, i.e., 4 panels)

30. With 32 panels, $T_5[\frac{1}{8}] = 5.3303$ (only 3s accuracy)

35. (a) 20.25 (exact)   (b) 1.3307   (c) 0 (exact)

36. (a) $-682\frac{2}{3}$ (b) 0.632121   (c) 0.46128   (d) 12.8   (e) 0.346549
(f) 1.70711

37. (a) 6.3534   (b) 5.3384

39. (a) (i) [0, 2], $f(0^+) = 1$; (ii) $I \doteq 3.684$ (4 panels)
(b) (i) [0, 1], [1, 2]; (ii) $I = \frac{3}{4} + \frac{11}{4} = 7.5$ (exactly)
(c) (i) [0, 1], $f(0^+) = 0.5$; (ii) $I \doteq 0.4864$ (4 panels)
(d) (i) [0, 4], [4, 50]; (ii) $I \doteq 0.8862$
(e) (i) [-1, 0], [0, 1]; (ii) $I = (-1.25) + (-3.25) = -4.5$ (exactly)
(f) (i) $f(x) = x^3 - x^2 + x - 1$ ($x \neq -1$); (ii) $I = -\frac{25}{12}$ (exactly)

40. Singularities at $x = 0$ in (a)–(d); also at $x = 1$ in (c). Aside from isolating the singularities, one could change variables to get:

(a) $2 \int_0^{\sqrt{\pi}} \frac{\sin u^2}{u^2} \, du$ (removable singularity at $u = 0$); $u = \sqrt{x}$

(b) $\int_1^{\infty} e^{1/u} \, du$ (diverges because $e^{1/u} \to 1 \neq 0$ as $u \to \infty$); $u = 1/x$

(c) $\int_0^{\pi/2} \ln (\sin \theta) \, d\theta$ (singularity only at $\theta = 0$); $x = \sin \theta$

(d) $\int_0^1 3ue^u \, du$ (proper); $u = x^{1/3}$

41. All of (a)–(d) are on unbounded intervals; and (c) has a singularity at $x = 0$. Aside from isolating $\pm \infty$ [and the singularity in (c)], one can let $u = e^x$ in (a) and $u = \sqrt{x}$ in (b).

42. (b) $(e^{1/\sqrt{3}} + e^{-1/\sqrt{3}}) (\pi/3) \tan (\pi/6) \doteq 1.41639$
(c) $[g(2.42265) + g(3.57735)] \approx [2.631785 + 5.951549] \doteq 8.58333$ (exact)
(d) $x_1 = 2 - 2\sqrt{0.6}$, $x_2 = 2$, $x_3 = 2 + 2\sqrt{0.6}$;
$I \approx 2/9 \, [5(0.85437) + 8(8.77811) + 5(22.46949)] \doteq 41.5209$

Chapter 8

Approx. of	(a) (i) Using h	(ii) Using $h/2$	(b) Improved
3. (A) $y(1.1)$	2.00000	1.99524	1.99048
$y(1.2)$	1.98182	1.97228	1.96274
(B) $y(1.2)$	3.33333	3.32797	3.32261
$y(1.4)$	3.64711	3.63735	3.62759
(C) $y(0.2)$	1.20000	1.20488	1.20976
$y(0.4)$	1.41909	1.42931	1.42953
5. (A) $y(1.1)$	1.99048	1.99036	1.99032
(B) $y(1.2)$	3.32262	3.32264	3.32263
(C) $y(0.2)$	1.20976	1.20994	1.21000
6. (A) $y(1.1)$	1.99091	1.99047	1.99032
(B) $y(1.2)$	3.32356	3.32288	3.32265
(C) $y(0.2)$	1.20955	1.20988	1.20999

7. $y_1 = 1.99032$ for (A); 3.32265 for (B); 1.21000 for (C).
$y_2 = 1.96243$ for (A); 3.62767 for (B); 1.44000 for (C)

8. (a) $y_1 = 1.99032 \approx y(1.1)$; $y_2 = 1.83806 \approx y(1.42858)$ $[h = 0.32858]$.
(b) $y_1 = 3.32265 \approx y(1.2)$; $y_2 = 4.47216 \approx y(2.0)$ $[h = 0.8]$.
(c) $y_1 = 1.21000 \approx y(0.2)$; $y_2 = 2.25001 \approx y(1.0)$ $[h = 0.8]$

10. y_4 is $1.85788 \approx y(1.4)$ for (A); $4.20001 \approx y(1.8)$ for (B); $1.96 = y(0.8)$ for (C).
y_5 is $1.78361 \approx y(1.5)$ for (A); $4.47215 \approx y(2.0)$ for (B); $2.25 = y(1.0)$ for (C)

12. (a) 1.85476 **(c)** 1.83386 **(e)** 1.98997

13. For (I) **(a)** $\mathbf{y}(0.2) \approx$ (i) $\mathbf{y}_1 = [1.4 \quad 1.8]^T$; (ii) $\mathbf{y}_2 = [1.4 \quad 1.72]^T$
(b) $\mathbf{y}(0.2) \approx$ (i) $\mathbf{y}_1 = [1.4 \quad 1.64]^T$; (ii) $\mathbf{y}_2 = [1.39 \quad 1.6408]^T$
For (J) **(a)** $\mathbf{y}(1.2) \approx$ (i) $\mathbf{y}_1 = [-0.4 \quad 0.4]^T$; (ii) $\mathbf{y}_2 = [-0.43625 \quad 0.38]^T$
(b) $\mathbf{y}(1.2) \approx$ (i) $\mathbf{y}_1 = [-0.43251 \quad 0.36]^T$; (ii) $\mathbf{y}_2 = [-0.46802 \quad 0.36363]^T$
(c) Using RK4 for (I): $\mathbf{y}(0.2) \approx [1.38933 \quad 1.64213]^T$; for (J): $\mathbf{y}(1.2) \approx [-0.46662 \quad 0.36461]^T$

15. (a) $\dfrac{d}{dt} \begin{bmatrix} y_1 \\ y_2 \\ y_3 \end{bmatrix} = \begin{bmatrix} y_2 \\ y_3 \\ \dfrac{y_3}{y_1^2} + 2ty_2 \end{bmatrix}$, $\qquad \mathbf{y}(0) = \begin{bmatrix} 1 \\ -1 \\ 2 \end{bmatrix}$

(c) $\dfrac{d}{dt} \begin{bmatrix} y_1 \\ y_2 \end{bmatrix} = \begin{bmatrix} 0 & 1 \\ \dfrac{1}{t^2} & -t \end{bmatrix} \begin{bmatrix} y_1 \\ y_2 \end{bmatrix} + \begin{bmatrix} 0 \\ \dfrac{e^t}{t} \end{bmatrix}$, $\qquad \mathbf{y}(1) = \begin{bmatrix} 3 \\ 0 \end{bmatrix}$

16. $y_1' = y_2$, $y_2' = Gy_1/r^3$; $y_3' = y_4$, $y_4' = -Gy_3/r^3$; $r = \sqrt{y_1^2 + y_3^2}$;
$\mathbf{y}_0 = [x_0 \quad v_{0x} \quad 0 \quad v_{0y}]^T$

22. (a) No   **(b)** $\bar{x} = \ln 2$, so $y(t) = 2^t - 2$

23. The exact $\bar{x}$'s are **(a)** 2 **(b)** $-\frac{1}{2}$.

24. (a) $(1 + h)y_{j-1} + (-2 + h^2)y_j + (1 - h)y_{j+1} = -3h^2$, $y_0 = -3$, $y_n = 1$
(b) $(1 + 1.5t_j h)y_{j-1} + (-2 + 9h^2)y_j + (1 - 1.5t_j h)y_{j+1} = (3t_j^2 + 2)h^2$,
$y_0 = 1$, $y_n = -2$

(c) $y_j = \frac{1}{2}\{y_{j-1} + y_{j+1} - 4h^3/(y_{j+1} - y_{j-1} + 2h)\}$, $y_0 = \frac{1}{3}$, $y_n = \frac{20}{3}$

(d) $y_j = \frac{1}{2}\{y_{j-1} + y_{j+1} - \frac{1}{4} t_j(y_{j-1})^2\}$, $y_0 = \pi/2$, $y_n = \pi/4$

25. Approx. of

	(K)	(L)	(M)	(N)
$y(a+h)$	-2.762	0.9206	1.775	1.247
$y(a+2h)$	-1.887	0.2063	3.930	0.9806

26. (M) $y_1 = 2.777$ $(n = 2)$; $y_2 = 2.772$ $(n = 4)$; $(4y_2 - y_1)/3 = 2.770$

(N) $y_1 = 1.101$ $(n = 2)$; $y_2 = 1.106$ $(n = 4)$; $(4y_2 - y_1)/3 \doteq 1.106$

Chapter 9

2. (a) $p_A(\lambda) = \lambda^2 - 1$; eigenpairs are $(1, [1 \quad 1]^T)$ and $(-1, [1 \quad -1]^T)$.

(b) $p_A(\lambda) = \lambda^2 - 6\lambda - 7$; eigenpairs are $(7, [5 \quad 3]^T)$ and $(-1, [1 \quad -1]^T)$

9. (a) $V = \begin{bmatrix} 1 & 1 \\ 1 & -1 \end{bmatrix}$, $V^{-1}AV = \text{diag}(1, \ -1)$

(b) $V = \begin{bmatrix} 5 & 1 \\ 3 & 1 \end{bmatrix}$, $V^{-1}AV = \text{diag}(7, \ -1)$

10. (a) $\mathbf{y}(t) = [y_1(t) \quad y_2(t)]^T = [\frac{1}{2}e^{t-1} + \frac{3}{2}e^{1-t} \quad \frac{1}{2}e^{t-1} - \frac{3}{2}e^{1-t}]^T$

	$\mathbf{x}_1^T$	$\mathbf{x}_2^T$	$\mathbf{x}_3^T$	$\mathbf{x}_4^T$	$\lim_k \mathbf{x}_k^T$
13. (a)	$[-0.7500 \quad 1]$	$[-0.6897 \quad 1]$	$[-0.6732 \quad 1]$	$[-0.6685 \quad 1]$	$[-\frac{2}{3} \quad 1]$
(b)	$[1 \quad -0.3333]$	$[1 \quad 0.3846]$	$[1 \quad 0.7867]$	$[1 \quad 0.9351]$	$[1 \quad 1]$
(c)	$[0 \quad 1]$	$[1 \quad \frac{1}{2}]$	$[0.8572 \quad 1]$	$[1 \quad 0.9615]$	$[1 \quad 1]$
16. (a)	$[1 \quad 0.6154]$	$[1 \quad 0.5978]$	$[1 \quad 0.6003]$	$[1 \quad 0.6000]$	$[0 \quad 0.6]$
(b)	$[\frac{1}{2} \quad 1]$	$[1 \quad -0.6250]$	$[-0.9318 \quad 1]$	$[1 \quad -0.9901]$	$\pm[1 \quad -1]$
(c)	$[1 \quad 0.7143]$	$[1 \quad 0.5]$	$[1 \quad 0.7143]$	$[1 \quad 0.5]$	None

17. Notice that $\mathbf{x}_0 = [1 \quad 1 \quad 1]^T = 1\mathbf{v}_1 + 1\mathbf{v}_2 + 0\mathbf{v}_3$

19. (a) $|\lambda_1 - (-4)| < 0.6$; $|\lambda_2 - 3| < 0.1$; $|\lambda_3 - 2| < 0.5$

20. (a) $\lambda_1 = -4.01$, $\mathbf{v}_1 = [-0.0178 \quad 1 \quad -0.0140]^T$

$\lambda_2 = 2.96$, $\mathbf{v}_2 = [-0.515 \quad 0.0714 \quad 1]^T$

$\lambda_3 = 2.06$, $\mathbf{v}_3 = [1 \quad 0.223 \quad -0.108]^T$

23. (a) $ae + bf = bd + ce$

27. $\cos \angle \mathbf{x}, \mathbf{y} = \mathbf{x}^T\mathbf{y}/(\|\mathbf{x}\| \, \|\mathbf{y}\|) = (-2)/(\sqrt{3} \, \sqrt{14}) = -2/\sqrt{42}$

31. (b) $U = \dfrac{1}{\sqrt{2}} \begin{bmatrix} 1 & -1 \\ 1 & 1 \end{bmatrix}$, $D = \begin{bmatrix} 3 & 0 \\ 0 & 1 \end{bmatrix}$ (c) $U = \dfrac{1}{5} \begin{bmatrix} 4 & 3 \\ -3 & 4 \end{bmatrix}$, $D = \begin{bmatrix} -50 & 0 \\ 0 & 25 \end{bmatrix}$

32. (a) Using first $R_1 = R_{13}(-0.662909)$ then $R_2 = R_{12}(0.395664)$

$$A_1 = \begin{bmatrix} -0.561553 & -0.788205 & 0 \\ -0.788205 & 1 & -0.615412 \\ 0 & -0.615412 & 3.561553 \end{bmatrix}$$

$$A_2 = \begin{bmatrix} -0.890226 & 0 & -0.236853 \\ 0 & 1.328674 & -0.568008 \\ -10.236853 & -0.568008 & 3.561553 \end{bmatrix}$$

35. (a) $\alpha_j = x_j - h/2$, $\beta_j = x_j(-2 - h^2 x_j)$, $\gamma_j = x_j + h/2$

(c)

	n	h	$F[h] = \lambda_{min}$	$F_1[h]$	$F_2[h]$
$r = \frac{3}{2}$	2	$\frac{1}{2}$	-3.75		
$r = \frac{4}{3}$	3	$\frac{1}{3}$	-3.40453	3.12815	
	4	$\frac{1}{4}$	-3.20341	2.94483	2.85998

37. (a) $a_1(x) = d(a_2(x))/dx$ **(b)** $\mu(x) = \exp(\int(a_1 - a_2') \, dx)$
38. (a) $f(x) \equiv 1$, $r(x) \equiv 0$, $w(x) \equiv 1$ **(b)** The T matrix is the same.
39. (a) $f(x) = x$, $r(x) = x^2$, $w(x) = 1$ **(b)** and **(c)**: Same as Exercise 9-35.
43. (b) $\|A\| = 3$, $\|A^{-1}\| = 1$, cond $A = 3$. Not ill-conditioned.
(c) $\|A\| = 50$, $\|A^{-1}\| = \frac{1}{25}$, cond $A = 2$. Not ill-conditioned.
44. (a) $p_{AA^T}(\lambda) = (\lambda - 4)^2 - 4$; cond $A = 3$
47. (a) $A = \begin{bmatrix} 2 & 4 \\ 4 & 14 \end{bmatrix}$ **(b)** $\lambda = 3$, $\mathbf{x} = \alpha \begin{bmatrix} 5 \\ -1 \end{bmatrix}$ and $\lambda = 1$, $\mathbf{x} = \alpha \begin{bmatrix} -1 \\ 1 \end{bmatrix}$
50. (a) $\lambda_1 = -4.01196$, $\mathbf{v}_1 = [-0.017798 \quad 1 \quad -0.014008]^T$
$\lambda_2 = 2.95557$, $\mathbf{v}_2 = [-0.51577 \quad 0.071431 \quad 1]^T$
$\lambda_3 = 2.05640$, $\mathbf{v}_3 = [1 \quad 0.022290 \quad -0.10834]^T$
(c) $\lambda_1 = 3.7093$, $\mathbf{v}_1 = [0.63178 \quad -0.23319 \quad 0.73924]^T$
$\lambda_2 = 1.1939$, $\mathbf{v}_2 = [-0.17215 \quad 0.88765 \quad 0.42713]^T$
$\lambda_3 = -0.90321$, $\mathbf{v}_3 = [-0.75579 \quad 0.39711 \quad -0.52066]^T$
(e) $\lambda_1 = 8.8483$, $\mathbf{v}_1 = [0.66521 \quad 0.46257 \quad -0.58611]^T$
$\lambda_2 = 3.1154$, $\mathbf{v}_2 = [0.58795 \quad 0.15935 \quad 0.79305]^T$
$\lambda_3 = 0.03628$, $\mathbf{v}_3 = [-0.46024 \quad 0.87214 \quad 0.16597]^T$

Index